INTERNATIONAL CHEMICAL SERIES

Louis P. Hammett, Ph.D., *Consulting Editor*

DIELECTRIC BEHAVIOR AND STRUCTURE

INTERNATIONAL CHEMICAL SERIES

LOUIS P. HAMMETT, PH.D., *Consulting Editor*

Amsden—
  Physical Chemistry for Premedical Students
Anderson—
  Chemical Calculations
Arthur and Smith—
  Semimicro Qualitative Analysis
Bachman—
  Organic Chemistry
Daniels—
  Mathematical Preparation for Physical Chemistry
Daniels, Mathews, Williams, and Staff—
  Experimental Physical Chemistry
Dole—
  Experimental and Theoretical Electrochemistry
Eastman and Rollefson—
  Physical Chemistry
Gibb—
  Optical Methods of Chemical Analysis
Glasstone, Laidler, and Eyring—
  The Theory of Rate Processes
Griffin—
  Technical Methods of Analysis
Gurney—
  Ionic Processes in Solution
Hamilton and Simpson—
  Calculations of Analytical Chemistry
Hammett—
  Introduction to the Study of Physical Chemistry
  Physical Organic Chemistry
  Solutions of Electrolytes

Laidler—
  Chemical Kinetics
Leighou—
  Chemistry of Engineering Materials
Mellon—
  Chemical Publications
Millard—
  Physical Chemistry for Colleges
Moore—
  History of Chemistry
Morton—
  Laboratory Technique in Organic Chemistry
  The Chemistry of Heterocyclic Compounds
Paul—
  Principles of Chemical Thermodynamics
Reedy—
  Elementary Qualitative Analysis
  Theoretical Qualitative Analysis
Rieman, Neuss, and Naiman—
  Quantitative Analysis
Smyth—
  Dielectric Behavior and Structure
Snell and Biffen—
  Commercial Methods of Analysis
Soule—
  Library Guide for the Chemist
Stone and McCullough—
  Experiments, Theory, and Problems in General Chemistry
Wetmore and LeRoy—
  Principles of Phase Equilibria
Woodman—
  Food Analysis

DIELECTRIC BEHAVIOR AND STRUCTURE

Dielectric Constant and Loss, Dipole Moment and Molecular Structure

CHARLES PHELPS SMYTH

Professor of Chemistry, Princeton University

McGRAW-HILL BOOK COMPANY, INC.

New York   Toronto   London

1955

DIELECTRIC BEHAVIOR AND STRUCTURE

Library of Congress Catalog Card Number 54-10646

II

THE MAPLE PRESS COMPANY, YORK, PA.

PREFACE

Some twenty-five years ago the writer prepared the manuscript of a book which was published under the title "Dielectric Constant and Molecular Structure." "Dipole Moment" would have been used instead of "Dielectric Constant" had it not been for the unfamiliarity of the term to the scientific public. At that time it was possible to collect, correlate, and interpret virtually all the data on the subject available in the literature. Since then knowledge of the field has grown to such an extent that a completely new book is necessary. The number of dipole moment measurements now in the literature is too great to permit the complete and detailed discussion attempted twenty-five years ago. Moreover, the extensive work which has been carried out on the relations of dielectric constant and loss to structure and intermolecular forces can profitably be considered in connection with the relations between dipole moment and molecular structure.

The material is so arranged that the reader interested primarily in dielectric behavior as exemplified in dielectric constant and loss may obtain the theory in the first two chapters, the experimental information and interpretation in the next three, and the methods of measurement in Chap. VI. The reader interested primarily in dipole moments will find the information needed for their determination in Chaps. VI and VII, a general account of their relations to molecular structure in Chap. VIII, and a detailed tabulation and interpretation of the moments of the principal types of compound in Chaps. IX to XII. Amino acids, peptides, and proteins are treated in Chap. XIII, and induced polarization, particularly optical refraction, in the last chapter. Although other arrangements would have been possible and, for some purposes, preferable, it is believed that the order employed preserves a logical continuity, while grouping together material of special interest to certain readers.

It was originally intended to include in the book an appendix listing all dipole moment values in the literature up to the time of publication, but it became apparent that such a list would add too much to the size of the book and would soon be rendered obsolete by the rapid addition of new data to the literature. It is hoped that the full tabulation of moment values according to compound type may serve a more useful though somewhat different purpose. If a moment value is not to be found in this book, the reader is referred to the following:

"Tables of Electric Dipole Moments," L. G. Wesson, The Technology Press, Cambridge, Mass., 1948.

"Table of Dielectric Constants and Electric Dipole Moments of Substances in the Gaseous State," A. A. Maryott and F. Buckley, *National Bureau of Standards Circular* 537, June 25, 1953.

Tables in the annual "Digest of the Literature on Dielectrics," National Academy of Sciences, National Research Council, Washington, D.C.

Much of the theoretical material in the first two chapters has been far more fully treated in "Theory of Dielectrics," by H. Fröhlich, Oxford University Press, London, 1949, and in "Theory of Electric Polarisation," by C. J. F. Böttcher, Elsevier Publishing Company, Houston, 1952.

The writer wishes to express his indebtedness to several authors for their permission to reproduce diagrams from their papers, to Dr. J. L. Oncley for a number of literature references for Chap. XIII, to Dr. J. G. Powles and Dr. G. N. Roberts, who read and helpfully criticized several of the chapters of the book, and, above all, to his students and coworkers whose experimental work has done much to make this book possible.

CHARLES P. SMYTH

CONTENTS

CHAPTER I

STATIC DIELECTRIC CONSTANT AND DIPOLE MOMENT

1. Introduction. The investigation of dielectric properties has provided an important approach to an understanding of the structure of matter, and, without some understanding of the relation of these properties to matter, our extensive knowledge of dielectric behavior loses much of its significance. The present accepted interpretation of the dielectric constant and loss of un-ionized materials is based upon the theory of Debye[1] and subsequent refinements, but equations for the representation of dielectric behavior can be derived without reference to any structural model. The so-called static or low-frequency dielectric constant will be examined first, since it has thus far proved most useful in investigating structure and since understanding of the static constant is necessary for the treatment of the high-frequency constant.

2. Dielectric Constant. The dielectric constant is familiar in the expression for the force between two point charges e and e' separated by a distance r in a homogeneous unbounded dielectric, where force $= ee'/\epsilon r^2$, in which ϵ is the dielectric constant, a constant characteristic of the medium between the two charges. The dielectric constant of a material may also be defined as the ratio of the field strength in vacuum to that in the material for the same distribution of charge. In the m.k.s. system the dielectric constant of free space is 8.854×10^{-12} farad per m. An electric conductor charged with a quantity of electricity q at a potential V is said to have a capacity $C = q/V$. A simple electric condenser much used in the discussion of dielectric behavior consists of two parallel conducting plates, each of area A cm.², at a distance apart r cm. The capacity of this condenser is

$$C = \frac{\epsilon A}{4\pi r} \qquad \text{electrostatic units}$$

$$= 0.08854 \frac{\epsilon A}{r} \qquad \mu\mu\text{f} \tag{2.1}$$

[1] P. Debye, *Physik. Z.*, **13**, 97 (1912); "Handbuch der Radiologie" (Marx), Akademische Verlagsgesellschaft m.b.H., Leipzig, 1925, VI, pp. 597–653; "Polar Molecules," Chemical Catalog, New York, 1929.

in which ϵ is the ratio of the dielectric constant of the medium between the plates to that of free space. It is this ratio ϵ which is used as the dielectric constant. It may be determined by taking the capacitance of a condenser with vacuum between the plates as C_0 and the capacitance C of the condenser with a material between the plates as ϵC_0; that is, $C = \epsilon C_0$, and

$$\epsilon = \frac{C}{C_0} \tag{2.2}$$

The dielectric constant thus defined is evidently dimensionless.

3. Electric Moment. Let the condenser consist of two parallel plates in vacuum whose distance apart is small in comparison with their dimensions, and let one plate have a charge $+A$ and the other a charge $-A$, where σ is the surface density of charge. Inside the condenser the intensity of the electric field perpendicular to the plates is

$$E_0 = 4\pi\sigma \tag{3.1}$$

If the space between the condenser plates is now filled with a homogeneous dielectric material of dielectric constant ϵ while the charges on the plates remain unchanged, the field strength decreases to

$$E = \frac{4\pi\sigma}{\epsilon} \tag{3.2}$$

The decrease in field strength is

$$E_0 - E = 4\pi\sigma \left(1 - \frac{1}{\epsilon}\right) = 4\pi\sigma \frac{\epsilon - 1}{\epsilon} \tag{3.3}$$

This same decrease could be effected by reducing σ by an amount

$$\frac{\sigma(\epsilon - 1)}{\epsilon} = P \tag{3.4}$$

by charging the surface of the dielectric opposite each plate with a charge of opposite sign to that on the plate. The surface density of this charge is P. It is produced by an induced charge shift throughout the dielectric, which gives an electric moment per unit volume, and is called the polarization. It is not to be confused with the molar polarization used in later sections.

A quantity called the electric displacement is defined as

$$D = 4\pi\sigma \tag{3.5}$$

From Eq. (3.2), it is evident that

$$D = \epsilon E \tag{3.6}$$

and, from Eqs. (3.4) to (3.6), it follows that

$$D = E + 4\pi P \tag{3.7}$$

Substituting for D the value given by Eq. (3.6) gives

$$\epsilon - 1 = \frac{4\pi P}{E} \tag{3.8}$$

The charges $+PA$ on one surface of the dielectric material and $-PA$ on the opposite surface, resulting from a displacement of charge throughout the dielectric, give an electric moment PAr to the dielectric slab, r being its thickness. As $Ar = V$, the volume of the slab, the total electric moment is PV, and P is evidently the electric moment per unit volume of dielectric. The polarized slab behaves like an assembly of electric dipoles parallel to one another. Each dipole is a pair of electric charges, equal in size, opposite in sign, and very close together. The size of the dipole moment is the product of either charge e by the distance r between them, that is,

$$\mu = er \tag{3.9}$$

4. Permanent and Induced Dipole Moments. We know that matter contains positive and negative charges, and we shall explore the manner in which displacement of these charges can give rise to the polarization which we have just discussed. If a charge e is bound elastically to a position of equilibrium, any displacement from this position will be opposed by a restoring force fr, which may be assumed to be proportional to the distance r of the displacement. An electric field F acting on the charge e exerts on it a force Fe, which displaces it in the direction of the field until the restoring force fr is just equal to it, that is,

$$Fe = fr \tag{4.1}$$

f is a proportionality constant. An electric moment $m = er$ is created by this displacement. Substituting $r = m/e$ in (4.1) gives

$$m = \frac{Fe^2}{f} \tag{4.2}$$

For the particular case of a molecule containing several electrons, each of charge e, the total moment induced in the molecule in the direction of the field is

$$\sum m = F \sum \frac{e^2}{f} \tag{4.3}$$

Molecular polarizability is defined by means of Eq. (4.3) as the dipole moment induced in a molecule by unit electric field

$$F = 1 \text{ e.s.u.} = 300 \text{ volts per cm.}$$

that is,

$$\alpha_0 = \sum \frac{e^2}{f} \tag{4.4}$$

f is evidently the force constant for the binding of the electrons. A more exact quantum-mechanical treatment leads to an expression similar in form.[1]

A different situation results if, instead of being elastically bound to a single equilibrium position, the charge has several possible equilibrium positions, the probability of which depends upon the strength of the external field. This may be examined according to Fröhlich[2] by assuming a single particle with charge e and two equilibrium positions A and B separated by a distance b. If the particle is in thermal equilibrium with its surroundings, it will oscillate about one of the two equilibrium positions with an energy of the order of kT, where k is the Boltzmann constant, the gas constant per molecule, and T is the absolute temperature. Occasionally, through a fluctuation, the particle will gain enough energy to jump over the potential energy barrier separating A and B. Since the energies of A and B are equal, the probability of its being in either A or B is $\frac{1}{2}$. If an electric field is applied, the two equilibrium positions are shifted through small distances which, for convenience, are taken to be the same for each and represented by r. There is now a difference between the potential energies U_A and U_B because of difference in the interaction energy with the external field F, which makes an angle θ with the direction AB, so that

$$U_A - U_B = ebF \cos \theta \qquad (4.5)$$

The probabilities p_A and p_B of the particles being in A or B are no longer $\frac{1}{2}$, but

$$p_A = \frac{e^{-U_A/kT}}{e^{-U_A/kT} + e^{-U_B/kT}} \qquad p_B = \frac{e^{-U_B/kT}}{e^{-U_A/kT} + e^{-U_B/kT}} \qquad (4.6)$$

in which e is the natural logarithmic base and not the charge. From Eqs. (4.5) and (4.6), it follows that

$$p_A - p_B = \frac{e^{ebF(\cos \theta)/kT} - 1}{e^{ebF(\cos \theta)/kT} + 1} \qquad (4.7)$$

On an average, the effect of the field is to displace the particle by a distance $(p_B - p_A)b/2$ and thereby induce an average moment

$$\frac{1}{2} eb(p_B - p_A) \qquad (4.8)$$

In the direction of the field F, the moment is

$$\frac{1}{2} eb(\cos \theta)(p_B - p_A) \qquad (4.9)$$

[1] N. F. Mott and I. N. Sneddon, "Wave Mechanics and Its Applications," Oxford, London, 1948, p. 169.

[2] H. Fröhlich, "Theory of Dielectrics," Oxford, London, 1949, pp. 17–20.

and substitution from (4.7) gives

$$\tfrac{1}{2}\ eb\ \cos\ \theta\ \frac{e^{ebF(\cos\ \theta)/kT}\ -\ 1}{e^{ebF(\cos\ \theta)/kT}\ +\ 1} \tag{4.10}$$

As ebF is normally very small in comparison to kT, this expression can be developed in terms of ebF/kT to obtain

$$\frac{(\tfrac{1}{2}\ eb)^2 F\ \cos^2\ \theta}{kT} \tag{4.11}$$

Since the displacement r gives rise to an additional moment er, the total moment in the direction of the field is

$$\frac{(\tfrac{1}{2}\ eb)^2 F\ \cos^2\ \theta}{kT} + er \tag{4.12}$$

If a charge $-e$ is fixed midway between the equilibrium positions A and B, two equal charges of opposite sign form a dipole of length $\tfrac{1}{2}b$ and moment

$$\mu\ =\ \tfrac{1}{2}\ eb \tag{4.13}$$

The shift of the particle of charge e from A to B, or vice versa, is then equivalent to rotating the dipole about one end through an angle of 180° from one position of equilibrium to another. The average moment thus produced in the direction of the field is given by the first term of (4.12), and the total average moment in the direction of the field is

$$\bar{m}\ =\ \frac{\mu^2\ \cos^2\ \theta}{kT}\ F + er \tag{4.14}$$

It is evident that the contribution of a permanent dipole moment to polarization and, hence, dielectric constant is temperature-dependent, while that of the moment induced by the displacement of elastically bound charges is independent of temperature. The elastically bound charge is directly displaced by the field, but, although it may be convenient to picture the dipole as turned directly by the field, the treatment employed in obtaining Eq. (4.14) involves dipole orientation as the result of a slight alteration in the probability of the jump of a dipole from one equilibrium position to another and not through direct turning by the field.

5. Clausius-Mosotti Equation. A long-used relationship known as the Clausius-Mosotti formula[1] may be derived[2] macroscopically without reference to any molecular theory. Let a constant field F be applied to

---

[1] O. F. Mosotti, *Mem. Soc. Ital. Sc.* (*Modena*), **14**, 49 (1850); R. Clausius, "Die Mechanische Wärmetheorie," Vieweg-Verlag, Brunswick, Germany, 1879, vol. II, p. 94.

[2] H. Fröhlich, "Theory of Dielectrics," Oxford, London, 1949, p. 170.

a sphere of a continuous isotropic dielectric. The field produced inside the sphere is then given by

$$E = \frac{3}{\epsilon + 2} F \tag{5.1}$$

The electric moment induced in the sphere is

$$m_s = \alpha_s F \tag{5.2}$$

where α_s is the polarizability of the sphere, a macroscopic quantity. Since the electric moment per unit volume of the dielectric is, according to (3.8),

$$P = \frac{(\epsilon - 1)E}{4\pi} \tag{5.3}$$

and the volume of the sphere is

$$V = \frac{4\pi a_s{}^3}{3} \tag{5.4}$$

it is evident that

$$m_s = PV = \frac{(\epsilon - 1)a_s{}^3}{3} E = \alpha_s F \tag{5.5}$$

Substitution of expression (5.1) for E and rearrangement gives

$$\frac{\epsilon - 1}{\epsilon + 2} = \frac{\alpha_s}{a_s{}^3} \tag{5.6}$$

a macroscopic Clausius-Mosotti expression for a sphere of dielectric, which is of no direct use. For a conducting sphere, ϵ is infinite and α_s is equal to $a_s{}^3$, a relation sometimes employed to obtain an approximate molecular radius, the volume of the sphere being taken as that of a molecule.

The molecular Clausius-Mosotti formula may be obtained by substituting in (5.6) the values of α_s and $a_s{}^3$ given by

$$\alpha_s = N_s \alpha_0 \tag{5.7}$$

and $$\frac{4\pi a^3}{3} = \frac{V}{N_s} = \frac{4\pi a_s{}^3}{3 N_s} \tag{5.8}$$

in which α_0 is the polarizability per molecule, a is the approximate molecular radius, and N_s is the number of molecules in the sphere. The expression obtained is

$$\frac{\epsilon - 1}{\epsilon + 2} = \frac{\alpha_0}{a^3} \tag{5.9}$$

a is not a true molecular radius, but only the radius of a sphere equal in volume to that occupied per molecule by the dielectric substance. A more useful form of the equation is obtained by substituting for a^3 the value obtained from the equation

$$\frac{4\pi a^3}{3} = \frac{M}{dN} \tag{5.10}$$

in which M is the molecular weight of the substance, d its density, and N the number of molecules per mole. Equation (5.9) then becomes

$$\frac{\epsilon - 1}{\epsilon + 2} \frac{M}{d} = \frac{4\pi N}{3} \alpha_0 \tag{5.11}$$

Substitution in (5.11) of the Maxwell relation[3] $\epsilon = n^2$, where n is the refractive index, gives

$$\frac{n^2 - 1}{n^2 + 2} \frac{M}{d} = \frac{4\pi N}{3} \alpha_0 \tag{5.12}$$

the Lorentz-Lorenz expression[4,5] for the molar refraction.

The Clausius-Mosotti equation can be derived[6] in somewhat similar fashion in terms of a molecular picture by the selection of a sphere of suitable size. The molecules of a dielectric are pictured as placed between conducting plates which are large in comparison with the distance between them. A homogeneous field is established in the dielectric when the plates are uniformly charged with a surface density σ. If the actual electric intensity acting upon a single molecule is F, the molecule should have induced upon it a moment which, analogously to Eq. (5.2), may be written

$$m = \alpha_0 F \tag{5.13}$$

where α_0 is the polarizability of the molecule. α_0 is a constant, characteristic of the substance in an isotropic condition, but in anisotropic bodies it may have different values in different directions, so that the value in Eq. (5.13) may be a mean.

F may be conveniently considered by supposing a unit positive charge in the medium to be enclosed by a small sphere, which is large compared to molecular dimensions but small compared to the distance between the plates. The force acting on this unit charge may now be treated as consisting of three components: that is,

$$F = F_1 + F_2 + F_3 \tag{5.14}$$

F_1 is the force due to the charges of surface density σ on the plates, so that,

[3] J. C. Maxwell, "Treatise on Electricity," Oxford, London, 1881, vol. II.

[4] H. A. Lorentz, *Ann. Physik*, **9**, 641 (1880).

[5] L. Lorenz, *Ann. Physik*, **11**, 70 (1880).

[6] P. Debye, "Polar Molecules," Chemical Catalog, New York, 1929, chap. I. See also C. P. Smyth, "Dielectric Constant and Molecular Structure," Chemical Catalog, New York, 1931, chap. I.

as in (3.1),

$$F_1 = 4\pi\sigma \tag{5.15}$$

F_2, which is due to the polarization of the material outside of the small sphere, may be obtained by imagining all matter to be removed from the sphere. It consists of the force due to the layers of induced charge on the material facing the plates plus the force exerted by the charge on the surface of the small spherical cavity and may be shown to be

$$F_2 = -4\pi P + \frac{4\pi}{3} P \tag{5.16}$$

F_3, the force due to the material contained within the small sphere, is dependent upon the structure of the particular material and cannot be obtained in a generally valid expression. It may be shown[7] that in a cubic crystal F_3 is zero, and the same is true in gases and, as an approximation, in liquids in which the molecules are oriented at random in the absence of an externally applied field. Bearing in mind that we are placing a necessary limitation upon the generality of our conclusions and that we can expect to find our equations applicable accurately only to gases and, as an approximation, to liquids, let us assume $F_3 = 0$. Then

$$F = 4\pi\sigma - 4\pi P + \frac{4\pi}{3} P$$

From Eqs. (3.5) and (3.7), the field strength acting upon a single molecule is

$$F = E + \frac{4\pi}{3} P \tag{5.17}$$

The electric moment per unit volume P is simply $N_1 m$, where N_1 is the number of molecules per cubic centimeter, that is,

$$P = N_1 m = N_1 \alpha_0 F = N_1 \alpha_0 \left(E + \frac{4\pi}{3} P \right) \tag{5.18}$$

If we substitute for P its value $(\epsilon - 1)E/4\pi$ given by (3.8), we obtain the relation

$$\frac{\epsilon - 1}{\epsilon + 2} = \frac{4\pi N_1}{3} \alpha_0 \tag{5.19}$$

Since in a pure substance $N_1 = Nd/M$, substitution and rearrangement gives

$$\frac{\epsilon - 1}{\epsilon + 2} \frac{M}{d} = \frac{4\pi N}{3} \alpha_0 \tag{5.20}$$

[7] H. A. Lorentz, "Theory of Electrons," Teubner Verlagsgesellschaft, Leipzig, 1909, 306, note 55.

which is identical with (5.11) and is called the molar polarization P, a quantity obviously different from the P used to denote the electric moment of unit volume. Since ϵ is a pure number and M/d is the molar volume, P and α_0 have the dimensions of volume. It is apparent that, if α_0 is constant, P is constant if the expression for P is complete.

The approximate constancy of P for many substances is illustrated by the values in Table 5.1, which extend over a wide range of temperature and, at some temperatures, are obtained by interpolation. The constancy of octane and benzene is due to the absence of any factors which may cause appreciable deviation from (5.20), while that of liquid ethyl bromide is due to the approximate cancellation of one another by strong opposing influences, which will be discussed later. Constancy in such cases is rare. The vapor of ethyl bromide has a much higher polarization, which decreases as a linear function of the reciprocal of the absolute temperature. Equations (5.11) and (5.12) indicate identity between the

TABLE 5.1. MOLAR POLARIZATION OF 2,2,4-TRIMETHYLPENTANE,[8] ETHYL BROMIDE,[9,10] AND BENZENE[11,12]

t, °C.	C_8H_{18} liq.	C_2H_5Br liq.	t, °C.	C_8H_{18} liq.	C_2H_5Br gas	C_6H_6 liq.	C_6H_6 gas
−90	39.19	54.24	10			26.73	
−70	39.27	54.38	30		104.2	26.80	
−50	39.32	54.54	50	39.46	99.1	26.82	26.9
−30	39.37	54.67	70	39.58	94.5	26.80	27.0
−10	39.40	54.84	90	39.76	90.5		27.1
10	39.43	54.98	150		80.8		27.0
30	39.44	55.07					

polarization P and the molar refraction, and the values found agree fairly closely for many substances, even when P is determined for long electric waves and n for visible light. It is for these same substances that P is approximately independent of temperature. Thus, MR_D, the molar refraction for the sodium D line, is 39.25 for 2,2,4-trimethylpentane at 20°, differing by only 0.19 from the value of P at that temperature (Table 5.1), and, for benzene, the value 26.18 is but slightly lower than that of P. On the other hand, ethyl bromide has a value of 19.10 for MR_D, much lower than that of P. It may be said in general that the polarization is approximately independent of temperature for those substances for which the values of the polarization and the molar refraction are close together,

[8] C. P. Smyth and W. N. Stoops, *J. Am. Chem. Soc.*, **50**, 1883 (1928).

[9] C. P. Smyth and S. O. Morgan, *J. Am. Chem. Soc.*, **50**, 1547 (1928).

[10] C. P. Smyth and K. B. McAlpine, *J. Chem. Phys.*, **2**, 499 (1934).

[11] C. P. Smyth and W. N. Stoops, *J. Am. Chem. Soc.*, **51**, 3312 (1929).

[12] K. B. McAlpine and C. P. Smyth, *J. Am. Chem. Soc.*, **55**, 453 (1933).

while, for other substances, it varies markedly. The reason for this variation is apparent in the relation given by (4.14).

6. Debye Equation.[1] For convenience in considering the effect of the permanent moment μ, indicated by Eq. (4.14) as a possible major source of the polarization, we shall treat the molecule as a rigid system of charges and disregard, for the time being, the moment induced in the molecule by a field of intensity F. If the molecule were oriented with the axis of its dipole in the direction of F, the potential energy of the molecule would be $u = -\mu F$, but the axis will ordinarily make an angle θ with the direction of F, so that

$$u = -\mu F \cos \theta \tag{6.1}$$

and the preceding equation is merely the special case when $\theta = 0°$. According to Boltzmann's law, the number of molecules distributed with the axes of their dipoles pointing in the directions within a solid angle $d\Omega$ is $Ae^{-u/kT}\,d\Omega$, where A is a constant depending on the number of molecules considered, k is the molecular gas constant equal to 1.38×10^{-16}, and T is the absolute temperature. Substituting the value of u given by Eq. (6.1), we have the number pointing within the angle $d\Omega$, $Ae^{(\mu F/kT)\,\cos\theta}\,d\Omega$. The total number of molecules obtained by integration over all possible directions is then $\int Ae^{(\mu F/kT)\,\cos\theta}\,d\Omega$, and the total moment in the direction of the field is $\int Ae^{(\mu F/kT)\,\cos\theta}\mu \cos\theta\,d\Omega$. The average moment per molecule in the direction of the field is, therefore,

$$\bar{m} = \frac{\int Ae^{(\mu F/kT)\,\cos\theta}\mu \cos\theta\,d\Omega}{\int Ae^{(\mu F/kT)\,\cos\theta}\,d\Omega} \tag{6.2}$$

Substituting
$$X = \frac{\mu F}{kT} \tag{6.3}$$

and
$$\xi = \cos\theta \tag{6.4}$$

and making use of the relation $d\Omega = 2\pi \sin\theta\,d\theta$, it is found that

$$\frac{\bar{m}}{\mu} = \frac{\int_{-1}^{+1} e^{x\xi}\xi\,d\xi}{\int_{-1}^{+1} e^{x\xi}\,d\xi} \tag{6.5}$$

Integrating numerator and denominator and simplifying, we obtain

$$\frac{\bar{m}}{\mu} = \frac{e^x + e^{-x}}{e^x - e^{-x}} - \frac{1}{X} \tag{6.6}$$

Since
$$\frac{e^x + e^{-x}}{e^x - e^{-x}} = \coth X$$

$$\frac{\bar{m}}{\mu} = \coth X - \frac{1}{X} = L(X) \tag{6.7}$$

[1] See footnote 1, Sec. 1.

$L(X)$ was derived by Langevin[2] in calculating the mean magnetic moment of gas molecules carrying a permanent magnetic moment and is, consequently, called the Langevin function. When $L(X)$ is plotted against X, that is, $\bar{m}/\mu$ against $\mu F/kT$, the curve is practically linear for very small values of $\mu F/kT$, while, for large values, $\bar{m}/\mu$ approaches 1. The physical significance of this is that for small field intensities—the field strengths used in ordinary dielectric-constant measurements are well within this range—the average moment in the direction of the field is proportional to the field, while for large field intensities saturation effects occur.   For very high voltages, practically all the molecules should be oriented with their dipole axes in the direction of the field so that further increase in the field strength would have little influence upon the mean effect of the permanent moment.   In actual dielectric-constant measurements, the dielectric would normally break down long before such voltages were reached.

For small values of X, $L(X)$ can be expanded in the series

$$L(X) = \frac{X}{3} - \frac{X^3}{45} + \cdots \qquad (6.8)$$

When X is very small, as under normal experimental conditions, only the first term need be considered, so that

$$L(X) = \frac{X}{3} \qquad (6.9)$$

and

$$\bar{m} = \frac{\mu X}{3} = \frac{\mu^2 F}{3kT} \qquad (6.10)$$

The effect of this mean moment produced by orientation of the dipoles in the field is added to the induced moment, which has been temporarily disregarded, so that the total mean moment in the direction of the field is given by

$$\bar{m} = \alpha_0 F + \frac{\mu^2 F}{3kT} = \left(\alpha_0 + \frac{\mu^2}{3kT} \right) F \qquad (6.11)$$

where α_0 is the polarizability by distortion and $\mu^2/3kT$ the polarizability by orientation.   Evidently, the total polarizability is

$$\alpha = \alpha_0 + \frac{\mu^2}{3kT} \qquad (6.12)$$

It is evident that a more general expression than Eq. (5.20) is obtained by replacing α_0 in that equation by α as given by (6.12), so that

$$\frac{\epsilon - 1}{\epsilon + 2} \frac{M}{d} = P = \frac{4\pi N}{3} \alpha = \frac{4\pi N}{3} \left(\alpha_0 + \frac{\mu^2}{3kT} \right) \qquad (6.13)$$

Debye[1] has given a somewhat more general derivation of the equation,

[2] P. Langevin, *J. phys.*, [4]**4**, 678 (1905); *Ann. chim. et phys.*, [8]**5**, 70 (1905).

in which α_0 is expressed as the average of the three polarizabilities along the three axes of the molecule treated as an ellipsoid of polarization.

7. Quantum-mechanical Correction of Debye Equation. Early attempts[1,2] to apply the quantum theory to the problem of the mean moment in an electric field led to an equation of the same general form as (6.13) but with a different coefficient for the second term. However, applications of quantum mechanics[3-6] to simple polyatomic molecules gave equations from which results practically identical with those of the classical Debye equation might be obtained.

Van Vleck[7] derived a general equation valid for all types of molecules in the gaseous state:

$$\frac{\epsilon - 1}{\epsilon + 2}\frac{M}{d} = \frac{4\pi N}{3}\alpha_0 + \frac{4\pi N}{3}\frac{\mu^2}{3kT}[1 - f(T)] \tag{7.1}$$

where

$$f(T) = \frac{h^2}{48\pi^2 kT\mu^2}\left[\mu_x{}^2\left(\frac{1}{B} + \frac{1}{C}\right) + \mu_y{}^2\left(\frac{1}{C} + \frac{1}{A}\right) + \mu_z{}^2\left(\frac{1}{A} + \frac{1}{B}\right)\right] \tag{7.2}$$

in which h is the Planck constant (6.624×10^{-27} erg sec.), μ_x, μ_y, and μ_z are the components of μ along three axes x, y, and z, and A, B, and C are the moments of inertia of the molecule about these axes. $f(T)$ is so small for most molecules, because of the sizes of their moments of inertia, that it is experimentally indistinguishable from zero. However, for the molecules of a few hydrides, the moments of inertia are so small as to make the effect of $f(T)$ appreciable in accurate measurements. Bell and Coop[8] have found it necessary to use $f(T)$ in calculating the dipole moments of hydrogen chloride and deuterium chloride from measurements of the dielectric constants of the gases and have found that its use in the calculation reduces the difference between the moment values[9] of ammonia and deuteroammonia from 2 to 1 per cent. The largest effect observed for the correction factor is in the case of the small hydrogen fluoride molecule,[10,11] for which the classical theory gives a dipole moment value 1.91 $\times$

[1] W. Pauli, *Z. Physik*, **6**, 319 (1921).

[2] L. Pauling, *Proc. Nat. Acad. Sci. U.S.*, **12**, 32 (1926); *Phys. Rev.*, **27**, 568 (1926).

[3] R. deL. Kronig, *Proc. Nat. Acad. Sci. U.S.*, **12**, 488 (1926).

[4] L. Mensing and W. Pauli, Jr., *Physik. Z.*, **27**, 509 (1926).

[5] C. Manneback, *Physik. Z.*, **27**, 563 (1926).

[6] P. Debye, "Polar Molecules," Chemical Catalog, New York, 1929, chap. IX.

[7] J. H. Van Vleck, *Phys. Rev.*, **29**, 727 (1927); *ibid.*, **30**, 31 (1927); "The Theory of Electric and Magnetic Susceptibilities," Oxford, London, 1932, chap. VII.

[8] R. P. Bell and I. E. Coop, *Trans. Faraday Soc.*, **34**, 1209 (1938).

[9] J. M. A. deBruyne and C. P. Smyth, *J. Am. Chem. Soc.*, **57**, 1203 (1935).

[10] N. B. Hannay and C. P. Smyth, *J. Am. Chem. Soc.*, **68**, 171 (1946).

[11] R. A. Oriani and C. P. Smyth, *J. Am. Chem. Soc.*, **70**, 125 (1948); *J. Chem. Phys.*, **16**, 1167 (1948).

10^{-18}, while the quantum theory gives 1.94×10^{-18}, corrected from the previously published values. Decrease of temperature evidently increases the size of $f(T)$, thereby increasing the difference between the results of the classical and the quantum-mechanical treatments, but solidification normally alters or eliminates the orientation polarization so that the difference between the two treatments cannot be detected. It is evident that, except for a very few, extremely small molecules, the factor $f(T)$ is so small that the equation obtained by quantum-mechanical treatment is indistinguishable from the classical equation. Even for these few small molecules, the difference is apparent with the experimental techniques now used only in accurate gas measurements.

8. Physical Significance and Magnitudes of the Quantities in the Debye Equation.[1]   The part of the polarization due to distortion of the molecule by the field may be called the "induced polarization" and that due to orientation of the molecular dipole in the field, the "orientation polarization." α_0 may be regarded as a measure of the ease of displacement of the charges, inversely proportional to what might be called a mean binding force acting upon the charges.   Equation (5.12) indicates that the first term of (6.13), the induced polarization, is equal to the molar refraction.   The refractive index is ordinarily measured for visible light, the refraction of which is due primarily to the displacement of electrons.   This part of the polarization may therefore be called P_E. The dielectric constant, on the other hand, is measured in an alternating electric field, the frequency of which is very low in comparison to that of the light.   In this slowly alternating field atoms and groups of atoms in the molecule may undergo displacement and thus make a small contribution to the polarization, which will be called P_A.   As the refraction varies with frequency, P_E may be extrapolated to infinite wavelength (see Sec. XIV.1), which is practically equivalent to the frequency used in measuring ϵ, by the use of a simple dispersion formula such as

$$P_E = \left(1 - \frac{\lambda_0^2}{\lambda^2}\right) \frac{n^2 - 1}{n^2 + 2} \frac{M}{d} \qquad (8.1)$$

in which n is the refractive index for light of wavelength λ, and λ_0 is the wavelength corresponding to a characteristic vibration frequency related to but not identical with the frequency of the maximum light absorption.[2] This does not take care of P_A, which cannot be determined directly but is fortunately small and often negligible.   The induced polarization is thus seen to be the sum of P_E and P_A, both of which will be further discussed later.

---

[1] C. P. Smyth, "Dielectric Constant and Molecular Structure," Chemical Catalog, New York, 1931, chap. I.
[2] C. P. Smyth, *Phil. Mag.*, **45**, 849 (1923).

The second part of Eq. (6.13), the orientation polarization, will be called P_M. If all the molecules were oriented with the axes of their dipoles in the direction of the field F, the permanent moment μ would be added to the induced moment $\alpha_0 F$, but orientation of the molecules is opposed by their thermal motion, which, of course, varies with temperature. For very large values of T, P_M evidently becomes negligibly small: that is, at very high temperatures thermal motion practically prevents orientation of the molecules in the field and the polarization should consist only of that due to distortion of the molecule. The total polarization

$$P = P_E + P_A + P_M \tag{8.2}$$

is plotted in Fig. 8.1 against the logarithm of the frequency.

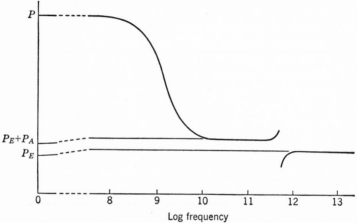

FIG. 8.1. Total polarization $P = P_E + P_A + P_M$ against log frequency.

The classical theory appears to indicate that thermal agitation increasing with increasing temperature decreases orientation of the molecules in the field and thus decreases the polarization. Debye's derivation of P_M by wave mechanics[3] indicates that only molecules of zero rotational energy contribute to P_M and that the number of these molecules decreases with increasing temperature, thus decreasing the polarization. Debye reconciles this with the classical result by showing in terms of the classical theory that only those molecules which if left to themselves would oscillate between two extreme positions contribute to P_M. Obviously, the number of such molecules decreases with increasing temperature, and the polarization, therefore, decreases.

In the derivation of the expression for P_M on the basis of either classical or quantum mechanics, it has been assumed that neighboring molecules do not interfere with one another's motion in such a way as to cause

[3] P. Debye, "Polar Molecules," Chemical Catalog, New York, 1929, chap. IX.

orientation in the absence of an externally applied field.   In other words, when the field is applied, the molecules are free to orient in it except in so far as their orientation is opposed by their thermal motion.   When molecules with strong fields of force around them are brought close together, this condition cannot be expected to hold.   When the molecules are fixed by solidification, they are usually unable to orient in a rapidly alternating applied field so that their dipoles may contribute to the polarization.   With $P_M = 0$, only the induced polarization $P_E + P_A$ is left. The determination of the polarization in the solid state has occasionally been used as a means of obtaining the value of P_A as the difference between P for the solid and P_E, which is readily secured.   If the frequency of the alternating field used in the measurement is sufficiently high, dipole molecules are unable to orient in it and the orientation drops out, that is, $P_M = 0$, but at least a trace of orientation may often contribute to the polarization of the solid.   The reduction of the polarization by high frequency and viscosity of the medium will be treated in Chap. II.

It is desirable to obtain an idea of the magnitudes of the quantities which have been under discussion.   If in the expression for molar refraction [Eq. (5.12)] we substitute reasonable values for the quantities involved, $n = 1.5$, $M = 100$, $d = 1$, $N = 6.023 \times 10^{23}$,   we obtain approximately 10^{-23} for the molecular polarizability α_0.   The permanent dipole moment of a molecule might be expected to have a magnitude not far from that of the product of an electronic charge, 4.80×10^{-10} e.s.u., by an intramolecular distance, perhaps 1 A. or 10^{-8} cm., that is, 4.8×10^{-18}.   We shall see presently that the experimentally determined values of the permanent moment are so generally of the order of 10^{-18} that this quantity is often taken as the unit of dipole moment and called a "debye." By setting $F = 1$ in Eq. (6.11) we find that $\alpha_0 + \mu^2/3kT$ is the total mean moment per molecule in the direction of a field of unit intensity, that is, 1 e.s.u. or 300 volts per cm., a field of the order of magnitude used in dielectric-constant measurements.   We have just found that α_0 has a magnitude of 10^{-23} and μ a magnitude of 10^{-18}.   As $k = 1.38 \times 10^{-16}$ and T is about 300 at room temperature, $\mu^2/3kT$ is found to be about 10^{-23}. The total average contribution of each molecule to the electric moment of the dielectric in the direction of the field is therefore of the order of magnitude of 10^{-23}.   The contribution of the permanent dipole of the molecule, if it possesses one, to the polarization of the material is of the same magnitude as that of the induced dipole, although the moment of the permanent dipole is commonly about 100,000 times the moment induced in the molecule by unit electric field.   The amount of molecular orientation produced in the material by a field of 300 volts per cm. is evidently so small that the complete orientation of only one molecular dipole in every hundred thousand plus the very small charge shift responsible for the induced moment in each molecule would produce the observed dielectric constant. In actual fact, it is found that, if the molecule has a permanent dipole moment, its contribution to the polarization is generally larger than that of the induced moment, although still of the same order of magnitude.

9. Experimental Verification of the Debye Equation. The polarization values in Table 5.1 show that the Clausius-Mosotti expression, which accounts for polarization only in terms of dipole moment resulting from induced charge shift in the molecule, represents the behavior of 2,2,4-trimethylpentane and benzene satisfactorily, but is inadequate in the case of ethyl bromide. We shall now examine the validity of the Debye equation, which takes account of both induced and permanent moments in the molecule. The equation can conveniently be written

$$P = \frac{\epsilon - 1}{\epsilon + 2} \frac{M}{d} = a + \frac{b}{T} \tag{9.1}$$

where the constants are

$$a = \frac{4\pi N}{3} \alpha_0 = P_E + P_A \tag{9.2}$$

and

$$b = \frac{4\pi N \mu^2}{9k} = P_M T \tag{9.3}$$

The polarization P, when plotted against the reciprocal of the absolute temperature, should evidently give a straight line of slope b and intercept a at $1/T = 0$. It may be convenient to write

$$PT = aT + b \tag{9.4}$$

and plot PT against T. Then the slope of the straight line is the induced polarization, and the intercept obtained by extrapolation to absolute zero is b. The curves[1] in Fig. 9.1 show the linearity required by the Debye theory. The extrapolations of the lines for benzene and propane pass through the origin at $T = 0$, showing that the molecules of these two substances have no permanent moments. For these two substances, the Debye equation reduces to the Clausius-Mosotti expression, which has been shown in Table 5.1 to be adequate for benzene in both the liquid and gaseous states. The intercepts on the ordinate axis for toluene and propylene, which have less symmetrical molecules, show that the molecules of these substances have small permanent dipole moments, which may be calculated from the values of b given by the intercepts.

For gases the dielectric constant is so close to 1 that $\epsilon + 2$ may be set equal to 3 as a good approximation. This substitution in Eq. (6.13), together with that of $M/d = V$, the molar volume, gives

$$(\epsilon - 1)V = 4\pi N \left(\alpha_0 + \frac{\mu^2}{3kT} \right) \tag{9.5}$$

[1] K. B. McAlpine and C. P. Smyth, *J. Am. Chem. Soc.*, **55**, 453 (1933).

The dielectric constants of a wide variety of gases and vapors have been investigated, but no deviation from the linear relation required by the Debye equation has been found at ordinary pressures except in a few cases where association, dissociation, or changing intramolecular energy invalidates the results as a test for the equation.

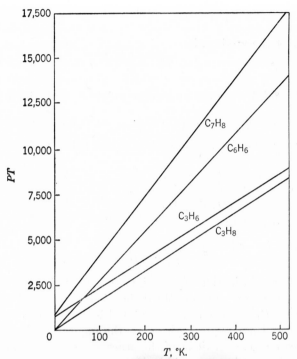

Fig. 9.1. PT-T curves for propane, propylene, benzene, and toluene. [K. B. *McAlpine and C. P. Smyth, J. Am. Chem. Soc.,* **55**, 453 (1933).]

10. Dipole Moment in Solution. In liquids, the molecules are so close together that interaction between their permanent dipoles, if any, becomes important. If, however, the dipoles are sufficiently separated from one another by nonpolar molecules, they should behave much as if in the gaseous condition.

In a mixture of two substances 1 and 2, since $P = (4\pi N/3)\alpha$ [cf. Eq. (6.13)], we may write

$$\frac{\epsilon - 1}{\epsilon + 2} = \frac{4\pi}{3} n_1 \alpha_1 + \frac{4\pi}{3} n_2 \alpha_2 \tag{10.1}$$

where α_1 is the polarizability of a molecule of component 1 and α_2 is that of a molecule of 2, and n_1 and n_2 are the numbers of molecules per cc. of components 1 and 2. The mole fractions of 1 and 2 in the mixtures are

$$c_1 = \frac{n_1}{n_1 + n_2} \quad \text{and} \quad c_2 = \frac{n_2}{n_1 + n_2} \tag{10.2}$$

and the molar polarizations are

$$P_1 = \frac{4\pi N}{3}\, \alpha_1 \quad \text{and} \quad P_2 = \frac{4\pi N}{3}\, \alpha_2 \tag{10.3}$$

The density of the mixture is

$$d = \frac{n_1 M_1 + n_2 M_2}{N} \tag{10.4}$$

in which M_1 and M_2 are the molecular weights.   Substituting

$$n_1 = c_1(n_1 + n_2) \quad \text{and} \quad n_2 = c_2(n_1 + n_2)$$

in Eqs. (10.1) and (10.4), dividing one by the other, and rearranging, we obtain

$$\frac{\epsilon - 1}{\epsilon + 2} \frac{c_1 M_1 + c_2 M_2}{d} = \frac{4\pi N}{3}\, c_1 \alpha_1 + \frac{4\pi N}{3}\, c_2 \alpha_2 \tag{10.5}$$

or

$$\frac{\epsilon - 1}{\epsilon + 2} \frac{c_1 M_1 + c_2 M_2}{d} = c_1 P_1 + c_2 P_2 = P_{12} \tag{10.6}$$

and since $c_1 = 1 - c_2$,

$$P_{12} = P_1 + (P_2 - P_1)c_2 \tag{10.7}$$

where P_{12} is the polarization of the mixture.   As P_{12} is calculated directly from the experimental values of the dielectric constant and density of the mixture, either P_1 or P_2 may be calculated if the other is known.

If substances 1 and 2 are both polar, the molecules of each substance may be expected to affect those of the other, so that, normally, the polarization of neither is what it would be if the molecules were separated from one another. If substance 1 is nonpolar, it will be assumed that its polarization P_1 is constant and independent of concentration, although it will subsequently be shown that this is an approximation (Sec. 18). Any deviation from the linear relation between P_{12} and c_2 expressed in Eq. (10.7) is attributed to variation in P_2, resulting from change in dipole-dipole interaction with concentration. P_2 is calculated from P_{12} and the value of P_1 for pure substance 1. P_2 may be plotted against c_2, and the resultant curve may be extrapolated to infinite dilution at $c_2 = 0$ to obtain the so-called polarization at infinite dilution, P_∞, from which the effect of interaction between permanent dipoles is approximately eliminated.   The value of the dipole moment of the polar molecule may then be calculated from this quantity.   The value thus obtained is close enough to the value measured in the vapor to justify the method as a fair approximation.   The reasons for the differences between the vapor moments and the solution moments will be discussed later (Sec. 18).   A less-approximate treatment of liquids will be given in subsequent sections of this chapter, and the actual calculation of moments for use in structure determinations will be treated in Chap. VII.

Most of the early measurements of dipole moments by different investigators in different solvents or occasionally in the vapor state showed differences among themselves no greater than the possible experimental errors.   Consequently, it was customary to disregard the effect of the solvent on the moment value and even to use the variation of polarization with temperature in solution to obtain the moment, as in the case of vapors.   Measurements by Müller[1] on a number of substances in solution in several different solvents showed that the apparent dipole moment values of many substances decreased with increase in the dielectric constant of the solvent.   It was even found possible to represent the relation of the apparent dipole moment in solution, μ_s, to that of the gas, μ_0, by an empirical equation

$$\mu_s = \mu_0[1 - C(\epsilon - 1)^2] \tag{10.8}$$

in which ϵ is the dielectric constant of the solvent and C is an empirical constant, for which Müller gave a value 0.038.   This constant held approximately for several substances, but many deviations occurred, and the relation failed entirely for some substances, in particular, the ketones. However, it became obvious that the variation of the effect of solvent (cf. Sec. 18) with temperature would render inaccurate the determination of moment from the variation with temperature of the polarization in solution.

11. Limitations of the Debye Equation.   Formally, the linear dependence of the polarization upon the reciprocal of the absolute temperature required by the Debye equation is shown by gases, by solutions of polar substances, by at least some polar liquids, and even by a few polar solids, where some molecular freedom occurs.   However, the small but often appreciable differences between moment values calculated from gas dielectric constants and from solution dielectric constants show that the application of the Debye equation to dilute solutions is an approximation, sometimes but not always good.   Of course, for pure polar liquids, the Debye equation cannot be expected to hold.

The impossibility of applying the Debye equation to liquids of considerable polarity becomes evident when an attempt is made to use it to calculate the dipole moment from the dielectric constant of the pure liquid.   If we take the measured dielectric constant of water as 80, the density as 1, and neglect the small induced moment, the inclusion of which would lower the calculated moment value a little, the Debye equa-

---

[1] F. H. Müller, *Physik. Z.*, **34,** 689 (1933); *Trans. Faraday Soc.*, **30,** 731 (1934).

tion gives a moment value 0.95×10^{-18} for the molecule as compared to the value 1.84×10^{-18} measured in the vapor state. Since $(\epsilon - 1)/(\epsilon + 2)$ approaches 1 as ϵ approaches ∞, an infinite value for the dielectric constant of water would raise the calculated moment value only to 0.96×10^{-18}.

A general difficulty in the application of the Debye equation to polar liquids becomes evident if, neglecting the induced polarization for the sake of simplicity, we write

$$\frac{\epsilon - 1}{\epsilon + 2} = \frac{4\pi N_1 \mu^2}{9kT} \tag{11.1}$$

and

$$\frac{4\pi N_1 \mu^2}{9k} = T_c \tag{11.2}$$

so that

$$\frac{\epsilon - 1}{\epsilon + 2} = \frac{T_c}{T} \tag{11.3}$$

According to this equation, when T is equal to or less than T_c, ϵ should be infinitely large, that is, T_c should be a Curie point. Van Vleck* has pointed out that this does not actually mean that the dielectric constant must really increase without limit, but, rather, that at temperatures below T_c the polarization cannot be treated as linearly dependent upon field strength, as assumed in the derivation of the Debye equation, since saturation effects should occur, producing an electric analog of ferromagnetism, that is, a stable state of permanent electric polarization. No such ferroelectric behavior has been found in liquids, and among pure solid substances it has thus far been observed only in Rochelle salt, in certain acid phosphates and arsenates, and in barium titanate (see Sec. V.9). The difficulty may be illustrated by the case of water. Putting the values of the constants into Eq. (11.2) gives $T_c = 1{,}140$, which means that, if the Debye equation were applicable, water should show ferroelectric behavior throughout its liquid range. For most substances, N_1 is smaller than for water, which would lower the value of T_c but still require ferroelectric behavior of most polar liquids.

12. Equation of van Arkel and Snoek. The false prediction of ferroelectric behavior in liquids is at least partially avoided in the semi-empirical equation of van Arkel and Snoek,[1] who have modified the Debye equation by the introduction into the denominator of an additional energy term $cn\mu^2$, corresponding roughly to dipole-dipole interaction energy. The resultant equation is

$$\frac{\epsilon - 1}{\epsilon + 2}\frac{M}{d} = \frac{4\pi N}{3}\alpha_0 + \frac{4\pi N}{3}\frac{\mu^2}{3kT + cn\mu^2} \tag{12.1}$$

---

* J. H. Van Vleck, *Ann. N.Y. Acad. Sci.*, **40**, 293 (1940).

[1] A. E. van Arkel and J. L. Snoek, *Physik. Z.*, **33**, 662 (1932); *ibid.*, **35**, 187 (1934); *Trans. Faraday Soc.*, **30**, 707 (1934).

in which n is the number of polar molecules per cc. and c is a constant. c was regarded as independent of n and of the nature of the solvent if the liquid was a solution and largely independent of the nature of the polar molecule, although it might vary greatly for an associated substance. For twenty-three substances, they reported values of c which were actually $3c/4\pi$. The values lay between 1.0 and 1.7 but tended to be not far from 1.35 except for the alcohols, which gave negative values, and the nitriles, which gave values varying with concentration and with solvent. It was subsequently shown* that for solutions of ethyl bromide in hexane the quantity varied from 1.3 to 5.1 according to concentration and temperature. Although the equation has the merit that it does not predict ferroelectric behavior as long as $4\pi n\alpha_0 + 4\pi/c < 3$, it is extremely approximate in spite of its empirical character.

A somewhat similar equation, III(1.2), was developed earlier by Danforth† to account for the decrease in polarization which he observed for several liquids under very high pressures. It will be discussed briefly in Sec. III.1, together with the measurements upon which it is based.

13. Equations Based on Restriction of Molecular Rotation. Debye[1,2] and Fowler[3] independently modified the original Debye equation with a factor to take account of the hindrance of molecular orientation by the presence of potential energy barriers in the liquid and solid states. The magnitude of the potential energy arising from dipole-dipole interaction may be estimated approximately. The local field due to a dipole moment μ is μ/r^3, where r is the distance from the dipole. If μ is taken as 10^{-18} and r is taken as the average distance between immediately neighboring molecules, about 2×10^{-8} cm., the local field is about $10^{-18}/8 \times 10^{-24} \approx 10^5$ c.g.s., or 3×10^7 volts per cm. The product of this field by the moment of a neighboring molecule is $10^5 \times 10^{-18} = 10^{-13} \approx 10\ kT$ at room temperatures.

Kincaid and Eyring[4] introduced a modifying factor based on a "free-angle ratio," which expressed the effect of restriction of molecular rotation upon various physical properties. Van Vleck[5] has pointed out the necessity that the internal field restricting molecular rotation be unilateral rather than bilateral, that is, that it should have a potential function whose period is 360° rather than 180° when the molecule is rotated. This is shown by the simple derivation of polarization based on two potential minima given in Sec. 4.

* C. P. Smyth, *J. Phys. Chem.*, **43**, 131 (1939).
† W. E. Danforth, *Phys. Rev.*, **38**, 1224 (1931).
[1] P. Debye, *Physik. Z.*, **36**, 100, 193 (1935); *Chem. Revs.*, **19**, 171 (1936).
[2] P. Debye and W. Ramm, *Ann. Physik*, **28**, 28 (1937).
[3] R. H. Fowler, *Proc. Roy. Soc. (London)*, **149A**, 1 (1935).
[4] J. F. Kincaid and H. Eyring, *J. Chem. Phys.*, **6**, 620 (1938).
[5] J. H. Van Vleck, *Ann. N.Y. Acad. Sci.*, **40**, 293 (1940).

The Debye theory of hindered rotation gives for the orientation polarization

$$P_M = \frac{4\pi N\mu^2}{9kT}\left(1 - \frac{E^2}{9k^2T^2}\right) \tag{13.1}$$

when E, the potential barrier or the variation in the potential energy of the molecules when they rotate through an angle of 360°, is small, that is, for dilute solutions of polar molecules in a nonpolar liquid. When E is large, that is, for concentrated solutions, the Debye theory gives

$$P_M = \frac{4\pi N\mu^2}{9kT}\frac{2kT}{E} \tag{13.2}$$

F. H. Müller[6] combined the above relationship with the van Arkel and Snoek equation for the case of very strong dipole interaction (when $3kT$ could be neglected in comparison with $cn\mu^2$) to obtain

$$E = \frac{2cn\mu^2}{3} \tag{13.3}$$

This relation results directly from dropping $3kT$ in the denominator of the second term of Eq. (12.1) and equating this term, which is P_M, to the expression for P_M given by Eq. (13.2). For dilute solutions, one may write

$$E^2 = E_0^2 + \frac{\beta n\mu^2}{kT} \tag{13.4}$$

in which E_0 is the value of E for infinite dilution and

$$\beta = \frac{81}{4\pi N}\left(\frac{kT}{\mu}\right)^4 \frac{\delta P_2}{\delta n} \tag{13.5}$$

β is obtained experimentally, $\delta P_2/\delta n$ being treated as independent of concentration, as is normally the case in dilute solution.[7]

White[8] approximated a liquid by considering it to consist of polar molecules unable to move except to rotate from one to the other of two equilibrium orientations separated by an angle β and differing in potential energy by an amount E. The orientational polarizability was then given by

$$\alpha = \frac{1 - \cos\beta}{\cosh^2(E/2kT)}\frac{\mu^2}{6kT} \tag{13.6}$$

The model accounted for the reduction of α in liquids and solids from the

[6] F. H. Müller, *Physik. Z.*, **38**, 498 (1937).
[7] G. Hedestrand, *Z. physik. Chem.*, **2B**, 428 (1929).
[8] A. H. White, *J. Chem. Phys.*, **7**, 58 (1939).

value $\mu^2/3kT$ observed in gases and provided for anomalous dispersion in terms of discontinuous molecular processes.

The treatment of dielectric behavior in terms of hindered molecular rotation has much to recommend it, since it avoids the incorrect prediction of ferroelectric behavior. Debye used it successfully in discussing the deviation of dielectric constant from linear dependence on field strength in a very strong applied field. Although the values obtained for E, the height of the potential energy barrier, are of reasonable magnitude (of the order of 10 kT), E has to be treated as an adjustable parameter and even then is often not successful in the quantitative prediction of dielectric behavior. It is reasonable, however, to picture the molecules in the liquid and solid states as executing rotatory oscillation in potential energy troughs with a probability, which may be large, small, or almost zero, of passing over the restricting potential barriers. The complexity of molecular shape and the inadequacy of the Lorentz treatment of the local field acting on the molecules are sufficient to account for the very approximate character of these equations for dielectric behavior.

14. Onsager Equation. The re-examination by Onsager of the problem of the internal field led to a considerable advance in dielectric theory.[1] Onsager limits his treatment of polar molecules to those which are spherical in form. With molecular radius a, the polarizability [cf. Eqs. (5.9), (5.11), and (5.12)] is

$$\alpha_0 = \frac{n^2 - 1}{n^2 + 2} a^3 \tag{14.1}$$

where n is an "internal refractive index." For a nonpolar liquid, $n^2 = \epsilon$, and, for a polar liquid, n^2 is equal to the dielectric constant ϵ_∞ measured at frequencies so high that the permanent dipoles are unable to contribute. ϵ_∞ may also be termed the optical dielectric constant and defined by the equation

$$\frac{n^2 - 1}{n^2 + 2} \frac{M}{d} = P_E + P_A = \frac{\epsilon_\infty - 1}{\epsilon_\infty + 2} \frac{M}{d} = \frac{4\pi N}{3} \alpha_0 \tag{14.2}$$

ϵ_∞ will be used in this book in the place of n^2, the square of the "internal refractive index." In an electric field F, the total electric moment per molecule in the direction of the field is

$$\mathsf{m} = \mu_0 \mathsf{u} + \alpha_0 \mathsf{F} \tag{14.3}$$

where μ_0 is the permanent electric moment of the molecule in vacuo and u denotes a unit vector in the direction of the dipole axis. Let us introduce a rigid dipole of moment m into a cavity of radius a in an unpolarized medium of dielectric constant ϵ. With the dipole treated as a point singularity of the electric field, situated at the center of the cavity,

[1] L. Onsager, *J. Am. Chem. Soc.*, **58**, 1486 (1936).

Onsager obtains the expressions

$$m^* = \frac{3\epsilon}{2\epsilon + 1} m \tag{14.4}$$

$$R = \frac{2(\epsilon - 1)m}{2(\epsilon + 1)a^3} \tag{14.5}$$

m^*, which may be called the external moment of the immersed dipole, determines the force which the dipole will exert upon a distant charge in the dielectric. R, which is called the reaction field, measures the electric field which acts upon the dipole as a result of the electric displacements induced by its own presence. The same relations are taken to hold for the case of a spherical molecule of actual dipole moment m.

If now we consider the modification of a homogeneous field E by the introduction into the dielectric of an empty spherical cavity of radius a, we obtain

$$M = \frac{\epsilon - 1}{2\epsilon + 1} Ea^3 \tag{14.6}$$

$$G = \frac{3\epsilon}{2\epsilon + 1} E \tag{14.7}$$

where M is the electric moment of the spherical region and G is the cavity field. Combination of the results for the dipolar molecule in the unpolarized dielectric and the spherical cavity in the polarized dielectric gives for the total field acting upon a spherical polar molecule in a polarized dielectric

$$\mathbf{F} = \mathbf{G} + \mathbf{R} = \frac{3\epsilon}{2\epsilon + 1} \mathbf{E} + \frac{2(\epsilon - 1)}{(2\epsilon + 1)a^3} \mathbf{m} \tag{14.8}$$

This equation formulates the conditions for equilibrium in the environment of the molecule, while Eq. (14.3) gives the condition for internal equilibrium of the molecule. For a given instantaneous direction $\mathbf{u}$ of the permanent dipole axis, substituting in Eq. (14.3) the value of $\mathbf{F}$ given by (14.8) and the value of α_0 given by (14.1) and writing $n^2 = \epsilon_\infty$, we have

$$\mathbf{m} = \frac{(\epsilon_\infty + 2)(2\epsilon + 1)}{3(2\epsilon + \epsilon_\infty)} \mu_0 \mathbf{u} + \frac{\epsilon(\epsilon_\infty - 1)}{2\epsilon + \epsilon_\infty} a^3 \mathbf{E} \tag{14.9}$$

It is evident that the first term in (14.9) is the contribution of the actual dipole moment μ of the molecule due to the permanent dipole moment μ_0. We may therefore write

$$\mu = \frac{(\epsilon_\infty + 2)(2\epsilon + 1)}{3(2\epsilon + \epsilon_\infty)} \mu_0 \tag{14.10}$$

Substituting for a in (14.9) its value given by (14.1),

$$\mathbf{m} = \mu \mathbf{u} + \frac{\epsilon(\epsilon_\infty + 2)}{2\epsilon + \epsilon_\infty} \alpha \mathbf{E} \tag{14.11}$$

The problem now is to calculate the effective energy of interaction between the molecule and the field and the resulting average orientation of the molecule. Onsager points out that for this purpose it is not admissible to assume, as Debye did, that the orienting force is proportional to the time average of **F**. Since **F** depends on the orientation, the orienting force-couple must be calculated for each individual direction of **u**. Since the reaction field **R**, being parallel to the dipole **m**, does not contribute to the orienting force-couple, the latter is

$$M = G \times m = \frac{3\epsilon}{2\epsilon + 1} E \times m$$

$$= \mu G \times u = \mu^* E \times u \tag{14.12}$$

From (14.4) it follows that μ^*, the external characteristic moment of the molecule, is

$$\mu^* = \frac{3\epsilon}{2\epsilon + 1} \mu \tag{14.13}$$

Dropping the vector notation, Onsager writes Eq. (14.12)

$$M = \mu^* E \sin \theta \tag{14.14}$$

where θ is the angle between the direction of μ^* and that of E. If w is the work of orientation,

$$M = \delta w / \delta \theta \tag{14.15}$$

and, therefore, $\qquad\qquad w = -\mu^* E \cos \theta \tag{14.16}$

The mean orientation of the molecules in the field is given by Boltzmann's formula

$$\overline{\cos \theta} = \frac{\int \cos \theta e^{-w/kT} \sin \theta \, d\theta \, d\varphi}{\int e^{-w/kT} \sin \theta \, d\theta \, d\varphi} = L(\mu^* E / kT) \tag{14.17}$$

The result is the Langevin function, which occurred [Eqs. (6.7) and (6.8)] in the development of the Debye equation. Consequently, for the low field intensities used in ordinary measurements,

$$\overline{\cos \theta} = \frac{\mu^* E}{3kT} \tag{14.18}$$

Referring back to Eq. (14.11) and replacing **u** by $\overline{\cos \theta}$, we can write for the polarization per unit volume

$$P = N_1 m = N_1 \left[\frac{\mu \mu^*}{3kT} + \frac{\epsilon(\epsilon_\infty + 2)}{2\epsilon + \epsilon_\infty} \alpha_0 \right] E \tag{14.19}$$

Equations (14.10) and (14.19) give

$$\epsilon - 1 = \frac{4\pi P}{E} = 4\pi N_1 \left[\frac{\mu \mu^*}{3kT} + \frac{\epsilon(\epsilon_\infty + 2)}{2\epsilon + \epsilon_\infty} \alpha_0 \right] \tag{14.20}$$

Replacement of α_0 by the expression given by Eq. (14.1), of n^2 by ϵ_∞, and of a^3 by the expression for it obtained from

$$N_1 \times \frac{4\pi a^3}{3} = 1 \tag{14.21}$$

gives

$$\epsilon - 1 = 4\pi N_1 \frac{\mu\mu^*}{3kT} + \frac{3\epsilon(\epsilon_\infty - 1)}{2\epsilon + \epsilon_\infty} \tag{14.22}$$

Substitution for μ^* of the expression given by Eq. (14.13) and for μ of the expression given by Eq. (14.10) yields

$$\frac{(\epsilon - \epsilon_\infty)(2\epsilon + \epsilon_\infty)}{\epsilon(\epsilon_\infty + 2)^2} = \frac{4\pi N_1}{3} \frac{\mu_0^2}{3kT} \tag{14.23}$$

Rearrangement gives

$$\frac{\epsilon - 1}{\epsilon + 2} - \frac{\epsilon_\infty - 1}{\epsilon_\infty + 2} = \frac{3\epsilon(\epsilon_\infty + 2)}{(2\epsilon + \epsilon_\infty)(\epsilon + 2)} \frac{4\pi N_1 \mu_0^2}{9kT} \tag{14.24}$$

Multiplying through by the molar volume M/d gives

$$\frac{\epsilon - 1}{\epsilon + 2} \frac{M}{d} - \frac{\epsilon_\infty - 1}{\epsilon_\infty + 2} \frac{M}{d} = \frac{3\epsilon(\epsilon_\infty + 2)}{(2\epsilon + \epsilon_\infty)(\epsilon + 2)} \frac{4\pi N\mu_0^2}{9kT} \tag{14.25}$$

In other words, the Onsager equation differs from that of Debye by the factor $3\epsilon(\epsilon_\infty + 2)/[(2\epsilon + \epsilon_\infty)(\epsilon + 2)]$ on the right-hand side of (14.25), since μ of the Debye equation is not distinguished from μ_0 of the Onsager equation. As ϵ approaches ϵ_∞, this factor approaches 1, that is, the difference between the two equations approaches zero. For gases at atmospheric pressure or below, ϵ and ϵ_∞ are so close to 1 that the factor becomes indistinguishable from 1 and the two equations become identical. The static dielectric constant $\epsilon = \epsilon_\infty$ only when $\mu_0 = 0$, and then the Onsager equation reduces to the Clausius-Mosotti equation.

When ϵ is large in comparison with ϵ_∞, which is always small, Eq. (14.23) can be written, as a rough approximation,

$$\frac{\epsilon}{(\epsilon_\infty + 2)^2} \approx \frac{2\pi N_1 \mu_0^2}{9kT} \tag{14.26}$$

Onsager pointed out that this equation was practically the same as an empirical equation developed by Wyman:[2]

$$p = \frac{\epsilon + 1}{A} \tag{14.27}$$

in which A is an empirical constant having a value of 8.5 for a large number of liquids, with a spread for nonassociated liquids given by the limits $A = 6.2$ and 11, and p is calculated from the measured dipole

[2] J. Wyman, Jr., *J. Am. Chem. Soc.*, **58**, 1482 (1936).

moment value by the relation

$$p = \frac{4\pi N_1 \alpha_0}{3} + \frac{4\pi N_1 \mu^2}{9kT} \qquad (14.28)$$

The virtual identity of the two approximations is more obvious when we write

$$\frac{\epsilon}{A} = \frac{2\epsilon}{(\epsilon_\infty + 2)^2} \approx \frac{4\pi N_1 \mu_0^2}{9kT} \qquad (14.29)$$

The Wyman equation fails to apply to associated liquids such as water, alcohol, and liquid ammonia, but its approximate representation of the dielectric constants of a large number of normal liquids is evidence of the approximate validity of Eq. (14.26). Evidence of the approximate validity of the Onsager relationship is given by the extent of the agreement of dipole moment values calculated from the dielectric constants of pure liquids by means of Eq. (14.23) or (14.25) with the values obtained by the Debye equation from measurements on gases or dilute solutions.[3] Such calculations will be examined in Sec. 16.

Equation (14.26) is useful in making evident approximate relationships: the direct proportionality of the dielectric constant to the number of polar molecules per unit volume, to the square of the permanent dipole moment, and to the reciprocal of the absolute temperature. The linear

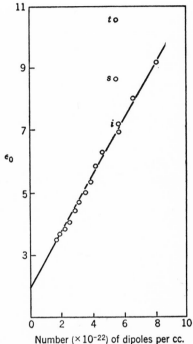

FIG. 14.1. The linear dependence of the dielectric constants of alkyl bromides upon the number of dipoles per cc. at 25°. (i, isobutyl; s, sec-butyl; t, tert-butyl.) [W. M. Heston, Jr., E. J. Hennelly, and C. P. Smyth, J. Am. Chem. Soc., **72**, 2071 (1950).]

dependence of the dielectric constants of the liquid n-alkyl bromides upon the number of molecules per cc. is shown[4] in Fig. 14.1. However, the effect of molecular shape is shown by these measurements, as the values for the branched-chain alkyl bromides lie above the line for the straight-chain molecules. Onsager pointed out that his assumption of spherical molecules could cause errors. These errors will be examined subse-

[3] C. J. F. Böttcher, *Physica*, **6**, 59 (1939).
[4] W. M. Heston, Jr., E. J. Hennelly, and C. P. Smyth, *J. Am. Chem. Soc.*, **72**, 2071 (1950).

quently in a discussion of "solvent effect." Other approximations are the treatment of the environment of the molecule as a homogeneous continuum and the neglect of local saturation effects.

Onsager extended his treatment to obtain an expression for the dielectric constant of a solution. For a dilute solution of a polar substance 2 in a nonpolar solvent 1, he obtained an expression which may be written

$$\epsilon = \epsilon_\infty + \frac{4\pi n_2 {\mu_2}^2}{3kT}\left[\frac{\epsilon_1(\epsilon_{\infty 2} + 2)}{2\epsilon_1 + \epsilon_{\infty 2}}\right]^2 \tag{14.30}$$

in which n_2 is the number of polar molecules per cc. of solution. It is evident that the dielectric constants of the dilute solutions should be linear functions of concentration, a fact which is employed in one method of calculating dipole moment from solution measurements. No general use has been made of Eq. (14.30) as such, but the principle of the linear dependence of dielectric constant upon the concentration of the polar solute is employed in the method of moment calculation of Hedestrand[5] and Halverstadt and Kumler,[6] described in Sec. VII.2.

Frenkel[7] criticized Debye's theory based on hindered rotation as self-contradictory, combined it with that of Onsager to obtain an equation of somewhat doubtful significance, and found that the disagreement between the dielectric constants calculated by this equation and the observed was greater than in the case of the unmodified Onsager equation.

15. Kirkwood Equation.

Kirkwood[1] has pointed out that hindered rotation must play a part in the dielectric polarization of polar liquids, that it must be responsible for large departures from the Lorentz field, and that it should be introduced not to supplement, but to correct the Lorentz field. Van Vleck's[2] treatment, which implied hindered rotation and deviations from the Lorentz field, gave a correction to the Lorentz field and eliminated the false prediction of a Curie point, but could be actually applied to liquids only empirically. Kirkwood has generalized the Onsager theory by eliminating the approximation of a uniform local dielectric constant identical with the macroscopic dielectric constant of the medium, obtaining

$$\frac{(\epsilon - 1)(2\epsilon + 1)}{9\epsilon}\frac{M}{d} = \frac{4\pi N}{3}\left(\alpha_0 + \frac{\mu\bar{\mu}}{3kT}\right) \tag{15.1}$$

where μ is the molecular dipole moment in the liquid and $\bar{\mu}$ is the sum of the molecular dipole moment and the moment induced as the result of

[5] G. Hedestrand, Z. physik. Chem., **2B**, 428 (1929).

[6] I. F. Halverstadt and W. D. Kumler, J. Am. Chem. Soc., **64**, 2988 (1942).

[7] J. Frenkel, "Kinetic Theory of Liquids," Oxford, London, 1946, p. 255.

[1] J. G. Kirkwood, J. Chem. Phys., **7**, 911 (1939); Ann. N.Y. Acad. Sci., **40**, 315 (1940); Trans. Faraday Soc., **42A**, 7 (1946).

[2] J. H. Van Vleck, J. Chem. Phys., **5**, 556 (1937).

hindered rotation in the spherical region surrounding the molecule. $\mu\bar{\mu}$ may be replaced by

$$\mu\bar{\mu} = g\mu^2 \tag{15.2}$$

The precise calculation of the correlation parameter g is, in principle, provided for by statistical mechanics, but is usually prevented by insufficient knowledge of liquid structure. Positive deviations of g from unity result when short-range hindering torques favor parallel orientation of the dipoles of neighboring molecules, and negative deviations result when the hindering torques favor antiparallel orientation. The theory may be based upon a rough quasi-crystalline model of local liquid structure, in which each molecule is surrounded by a shell of z nearest neighbors beyond which orientational effects do not extend. This model gives

$$g = 1 + z\,\overline{\cos\gamma} \tag{15.3}$$

and

$$\overline{\cos\gamma} = \int\cos\gamma\, e^{-W/kT}\, d\omega \tag{15.4}$$

where γ is the angle between the dipole moments of a neighboring pair of molecules, the integral defining $\overline{\cos\gamma}$ extends over all relative orientations of the pair, and W is the potential of average torque hindering their relative rotation, with a constant term adjusted to normalize the integral of $e^{-W/kT}$ to unity. Substitution of Eq. (15.2) in (15.1) gives

$$\frac{(\epsilon - 1)(\epsilon + 2)}{9\epsilon}\frac{M}{d} = \frac{4\pi N}{3}\left(\alpha_0 + \frac{g\mu^2}{3kT}\right) \tag{15.5}$$

In the case of water, Kirkwood obtains

$$g = 1 + z\cos^2\frac{\theta}{2} \tag{15.6}$$

where θ is the H—O—H bond angle, taken as 105°, and z differs slightly from 4 due to superposition on the tetrahedral structure of contributions from more closely packed structures. The dielectric constant of liquid water calculated from the molecular dipole moment by means of Eqs. (15.1), (15.2), and (15.5) differs by only 0.4 per cent from the observed value at 25°C. but is 12 per cent higher at 83°. Similar calculations for five alcohols show differences between calculated and observed values of 10 to 20 per cent. Kirkwood points out that the unmodified Onsager theory leads to a value of 31 for the dielectric constant of water at 25° as compared to an observed value of 78.2.

By statistical reasoning Fröhlich[3] has obtained a more general expression

$$\frac{(\epsilon - 1)(2\epsilon + 1)}{3\epsilon} = \frac{4\pi N_1}{3}\frac{\overline{mm^*}}{kT} \tag{15.7}$$

---

[3] H. Fröhlich, *Trans. Faraday Soc.*, **44**, 238 (1948); "Theory of Dielectrics," Oxford, London, 1949, pp. 36–53.

where N_1 is the number of units per unit volume and $\mathbf{m}^*$ is the average dipole moment of a spherical region embedded in its own medium, if one of its units is kept in a given configuration leading to a dipole moment $\mathbf{m}$. $\overline{\mathbf{m}\mathbf{m}^*}$ is the average value of the product $\mathbf{m}\mathbf{m}^*$ taking into account all possible configurations and weighting them according to the probability of finding the unit in such a configuration. $\mathbf{m}^*$ differs from $\mathbf{m}$ because of short-range forces or because of nonspherical molecular shape.   Introduction of the effect of the elastic displacement of charge leads to

$$\frac{(\epsilon - \epsilon_\infty)(2\epsilon + \epsilon_\infty)}{3\epsilon} = \frac{4\pi N_1}{3} \frac{\overline{\mathbf{m}\mathbf{m}^*}}{kT} \tag{15.8}$$

and establishment of the relation

$$\overline{\mathbf{m}\mathbf{m}^*} = \overline{\mathbf{\mu}\mathbf{\mu}^*} = \mathbf{\mu}\mathbf{\mu}^* \tag{15.9}$$

gives

$$\frac{(\epsilon - \epsilon_\infty)(2\epsilon + \epsilon_\infty)}{3\epsilon} = \frac{4\pi N_1 \mathbf{\mu}\mathbf{\mu}^*}{3kT} \tag{15.10}$$

Fröhlich then writes

$$\mathbf{\mu}\mathbf{\mu}^* = \mu^2(1 + z \overline{\cos \gamma}) \tag{15.11}$$

and, for spherical molecules, replaces μ by its value obtained from

$$\mu_0 = \frac{3}{\epsilon_\infty + 2} \mu \tag{15.12}$$

which is the moment in vacuum μ_0 of a spherical molecule consisting of material of dielectric constant ϵ_∞ having a dipole moment μ at its center. Using Eq. (15.5) and the Avogadro number N, we may write

$$\frac{\epsilon - 1}{\epsilon + 2} \frac{M}{d} - \frac{\epsilon_\infty - 1}{\epsilon_\infty + 2} \frac{M}{d} = \frac{3\epsilon(\epsilon_\infty + 2)}{(2\epsilon + \epsilon_\infty)(\epsilon + 2)} \frac{4\pi N g \mu_0^2}{9kT} \tag{15.13}$$

which becomes identical with the Onsager equation (14.25) if $g = 1$.

It is evident that the Kirkwood equation represents a theoretical advance beyond the Onsager equation in that it takes into account the hindrance of molecular orientation by neighboring molecules. Since, however, the correlation parameter g which expresses this effect can be calculated only roughly from knowledge of the liquid structure, which is usually lacking, the principal value of the equation consists in the introduction of a correction factor which is normally empirical. Kirkwood points out that the departure of g from unity is a measure of the degree of hindered relative molecular rotation arising from short-range intermolecular forces. "Normal" liquids show values of g which do not depart much from unity, while "abnormal" or "associated" liquids show values which depart significantly from unity.[4] Like the Onsager equa-

[4] G. Oster and J. G. Kirkwood, *J. Chem. Phys.*, **11**, 175 (1943); G. Oster, *J. Am. Chem. Soc.*, **68**, 2036 (1946).

tion, the Kirkwood equation contains the approximation involved in treating the polar molecules as spherical.

16. Experimental Comparison of the Debye, Onsager, and Kirkwood Equations.   Instead of testing the equations by using them to calculate the dielectric constants of pure liquids from dipole moment values measured in the vapor state or in dilute solution in nonpolar solvents, the accuracy of the dipole moment values calculated from the dielectric constants of the pure liquids may be used as a criterion for judging the equations.   In Table 16.1 are given the previously mentioned dipole moment

TABLE 16.1. MOMENTS ($\times 10^{18}$) CALCULATED BY THE ONSAGER EQUATION FOR PURE LIQUIDS AND VALUES OBTAINED FROM VAPOR AND SOLUTION MEASUREMENTS

Substance	Onsager	Solution	Vapor
Nitromethane	3.7	3.2	3.5
Nitrobenzene	4.2	3.9–4.1	4.2
Acetone	3.0–3.1	2.7–2.8	2.84
Methylethylketone	3.2	2.7–2.8	2.78
Acetophenone	3.2	2.9–3.0	3.00
Aniline	1.5	1.5–1.6	1.48
Acetonitrile	3.6	3.4–3.5	3.94
Benzonitrile	3.6–3.7	4.0	4.39
Acetaldehyde	2.7	2.72	2.5
Ethyl acetate	1.8	1.9	1.76
Ethyl ether	1.4–1.5	1.2	1.15
Anisol	1.5	1.25	1.35
Chloroform	1.2–1.3	1.1–1.3	1.02
Methylene chloride	1.7	1.5–1.6	1.58
Methylene bromide	1.4	1.4	1.43
Methyl bromide	1.6	1.5	1.80
Ethyl bromide	1.8–1.9	1.8–1.9	2.02
Ethyl iodide	1.5–1.7	1.8	1.87
Chlorobenzene	1.5–1.6	1.5–1.6	1.72
Bromobenzene	1.4	1.5–1.6	1.75
o-Dichlorobenzene	2.2	2.25	2.51
Water	3.0–3.1	1.7–1.9	1.84
Ethyl alcohol	2.8–3.1	1.7	1.70

values calculated by Böttcher[1] with the Onsager equation, and here compared with values obtained by means of the Debye equation from gas or dilute-solution measurements.   Several of the substances treated by Böttcher are omitted, and many of the solution and vapor values have been revised in the light of subsequent measurements.   Because of evident inaccuracies, discrepancies between the measurements of different observers, or differences between values obtained in different solvents

[1] C. J. F. Böttcher, *Physica*, **6**, 59 (1939).

because of solvent effect, many of the moments are given to only one decimal place or are represented by a range of values. The absence of a range of values in the solution column is not to be taken as evidence of the absence of variation from one solvent to another. Instead of ϵ_∞, which contains a contribution from the atomic polarization, Böttcher used n_∞^2, obtained by extrapolation of the refractive index for visible light to infinite wavelength. The values listed under "Onsager" are, therefore, slightly higher than they would be with due allowance for atomic polarization.

Forty per cent of the values calculated by the Onsager equation for normal liquids in Table 16.1 are nearer or as near to the vapor values as are the solution values. Between the freezing point and the boiling point of the liquid these Onsager values may increase by as much as 4 to 8 per cent with increasing temperature. A smaller but detectable rise in apparent moment may, however, be observed in solution with rising temperature, presumably because of decrease in solvent effect with decreasing dielectric constant.

The unmodified Onsager equation cannot be expected to hold for associated liquids like water and ethyl alcohol. For such liquids, the Kirkwood parameter g is very different from 1. Onsager suggested that the formation of a hydrogen bond increased the moment of the group carrying the hydrogen, an increase now known to be usually small and often undetectable, but it was pointed out[2] that complex formation would account qualitatively for the apparent increase of moment in the pure liquid as compared to the vapor or dilute solution. For example, if N molecules possessing dipole moment μ polymerized to form $N/2$ double molecules in which the two dipoles pointed in the same direction to give moment 2μ to each of the double molecules, the apparent value of the orientation polarization would double and the value calculated for the moment without consideration of these changes would be $\sqrt{2}\,\mu$, even though no change in bond moment had occurred.

A group of measurements[3] upon a considerable number of pure liquids has been used to compare the Debye, Onsager, and Kirkwood equations written in the forms

$$\mu_0{}^2 = \frac{9kT}{4\pi N}\frac{M}{d}\left(\frac{\epsilon - 1}{\epsilon + 2} - \frac{\epsilon_\infty - 1}{\epsilon_\infty + 2}\right) \qquad \text{(Debye)} \qquad (16.1)$$

$$\mu_0{}^2 = \frac{9kT}{4\pi N}\frac{M}{d}\frac{(2\epsilon + \epsilon_\infty)(\epsilon + 2)}{3\epsilon(\epsilon_\infty + 2)}\left(\frac{\epsilon - 1}{\epsilon + 2} - \frac{\epsilon_\infty - 1}{\epsilon_\infty + 2}\right) \qquad \text{(Onsager)} \qquad (16.2)$$

$$g\mu^2 = \frac{9kT}{4\pi N}\frac{M}{d}\left[\frac{(\epsilon - 1)(2\epsilon + 1)}{9\epsilon} - \frac{\epsilon_\infty - 1}{\epsilon_\infty + 2}\right] \qquad \text{(Kirkwood)} \qquad (16.3)$$

[2] C. P. Smyth, J. Chem. Phys., 43, 131 (1939).

[3] W. M. Heston, Jr., E. J. Hennelly, and C. P. Smyth, J. Am. Chem. Soc., 72, 2071 (1950).

Since there is no way of calculating g with accuracy for these liquids, it is lumped with the moment. By means of Eq. (14.10) μ_0 is calculated from μ. Table 16.2 gives the values of the vacuum or vapor dipole moment μ_0 under the headings Debye and Onsager, calculated from the values at 25°C. of the density d, the static dielectric constant ϵ, and the optical dielectric constant ϵ_∞, which arises primarily from electronic polarization

TABLE 16.2. COMPARISON OF DIPOLE MOMENTS ($\times 10^{18}$) CALCULATED BY DEBYE, ONSAGER, AND KIRKWOOD EQUATIONS WITH OBSERVED VALUES

Substance	Debye		Onsager		Kirk-wood	Obs.
	25°C.	55° − 1°C.	25°C.	55° − 1°C.		
Ethyl bromide	1.28	(0.11)	1.80	(0.02)	1.90	2.02 g
n-Propyl bromide	1.36	0.10	1.83	0.02	2.02	2.15 g
i-Propyl bromide	1.45	0.12	2.06	0.02	2.10	2.19 g
n-Butyl bromide	1.41	0.12	1.80	0.06	1.92	2.15 g
i-Butyl bromide	1.44	0.11	1.86	0.03	1.92	1.97 s
s-Butyl bromide	1.52	0.13	2.10	0.05	2.14	2.20 g
t-Butyl bromide	1.62	0.14	2.39	−0.02	2.40	2.21 s
n-Amyl bromide	1.46	0.10	1.82	0.03	1.99	2.19 g
n-Hexyl bromide	1.51	0.10	1.83	0.04	1.99	1.97 s
n-Heptyl bromide	1.53	0.09	1.81	0.04	1.90	2.15 g
n-Octyl bromide	1.56	0.10	1.81	0.05	1.88	1.96 s
n-Nonyl bromide	1.58	0.10	1.81	0.06	1.89	1.89 s
n-Decyl bromide	1.59	0.08	1.79	0.03	1.90	1.90 s
n-Dodecyl bromide	1.61	0.07	1.79	0.03	1.89	
n-Tetradecyl bromide	1.63	0.08	1.78	0.05	1.83	
n-Hexadecyl bromide	1.66	(0.07)	1.80	(0.03)	1.87	
n-Octyl chloride	1.58	0.07	1.84	0.01	2.14	
n-Octyl iodide	1.46	0.07	1.65	0.04	1.80	
n-Dodecyl chloride	1.65	0.07	1.84	0.03	2.11	
Cyclohexyl bromide	1.52	0.11	2.00	0.04	2.08	2.11 s
Chlorobenzene	1.22	0.06	1.45	0.01	1.54	1.72 g
Bromobenzene	1.17	0.07	1.37	0.05	1.52	1.77 g
α-Chloronaphthalene	1.20	0.07	1.35	0.05	1.33	1.50 s
α-Bromonaphthalene	1.13	(0.06)	1.25	0.05	1.29	1.48 s

but contains also a small contribution from atomic polarization. After each value for 25° is given the difference between the values calculated for 55° and for 1°, a difference which should be zero if the equations were exact. The values calculated with the Kirkwood equation are not exactly comparable with these since they were obtained by plotting $\dfrac{(\epsilon - 1)(2\epsilon + 1)}{9\epsilon} \dfrac{M}{d}$ against $1/T$ and calculating $g\mu^2$ from the slope of the straight line thus obtained and $g^{1/2}\mu_0$ from $g\mu^2$ by means of Eq. (14.10). These values of $g^{1/2}\mu_0$ are listed as the moment values calculated by the Kirkwood equation. In the last column, the values followed by "g" are gas measurements, which should be accurate values of μ_0, and those followed by "s" are solution measurements, which tend to be somewhat better approximations to μ_0 than the values calculated from data on the pure liquids.

Since the Debye equation is not expected to be applicable to pure polar liquids, the moment values calculated by it in Table 16.2 are of interest merely for their trends and for contrast with the results of the other equations. The Debye values increase with increase in molecular size, which increases the dipole separation, and with increase in temperature. The effect of temperature is slightly less for the larger molecules for which the values are not as far below the correct ones as they are for the smaller molecules. For the straight-chain bromides, the Onsager values are about 10 per cent below the gas values and show no significant increase with increase in chain length. They increase slightly with temperature, but little more than do some solution values. Wilson[4] has shown that the Onsager moments for ethyl ether and nitrobenzene decrease with rising temperature, while six other substances examined increase. The Kirkwood values calculated from temperature dependence are higher than the Onsager values and so nearer to the observed values, indeed, differing, apparently, from the gas values by no more than would the solution values. t-Butyl bromide has, presumably, the most nearly spherical molecule of any substance in the list, but both the Onsager and Kirkwood equations, which are based on the assumption of spherical molecular shape, give values 8 per cent high for this substance and also for the similarly spherical t-butyl chloride, which is not included in Table 16.2. The difference between the molecular moment in the pure polar liquid and in the vapor may be illustrated by the values of $g^{1/2}\mu$ and $g^{1/2}\mu_0$ for some of the substances in Table 16.2. For ethyl bromide, $g^{1/2}\mu$ is 2.52 and $g^{1/2}\mu_0$ is 1.90; for hexadecyl bromide, the values are 2.25 and 1.87, respectively; and, for bromobenzene, 2.02 and 1.52. The nearness of the Kirkwood values, $g^{1/2}\mu_0$, to the observed values shows that the parameter g is close to 1 for these normal liquids. In general, the calculation of g is so difficult or impossible that the procedure for normal liquids would be to assume g to be 1 and use the Onsager equation, which is an approximation, often no worse than the solution measurement but occasionally leading to a considerable error.

17. Other Equations Relating Dielectric Constant and Dipole Moment. The Debye equation and the refinement of it by Onsager and Kirkwood have been discussed in some detail, and certain other closely related equations have been treated briefly. Others more or less generally employed will be treated briefly in the present section.

A rather complicated equation, (18.3), developed by Raman and Krish-

[4] J. N. Wilson, *Chem. Revs.*, **25**, 377 (1939).

nan[1] treated the molecule as both optically and electrically anisotropic. The equation was criticized by Hans Mueller[2] and by Jenkins and Bauer.[3] It was of interest in its departure from the treatment of a molecule as a sphere with a dipole at the center.

The effect of optical anisotropy was introduced by Wilson[4] into the Onsager equation. He assumed that the optical polarizability α_1 along the dipole axis of the molecule was different from the polarizability α_0 averaged over all directions, the quantity used in the Debye and Onsager equations, and obtained the equation

$$\frac{\epsilon - 1}{\epsilon} - \frac{3(\epsilon_\infty - 1)}{2\epsilon + \epsilon_\infty} = \frac{4\pi N_1 \mu^2}{9kT} \frac{(2\epsilon + 1)(\epsilon_1 + 2)^2}{(2\epsilon + \epsilon_1)^2} \qquad (17.1)$$

where ϵ_1 is the value of the optical dielectric constant ϵ_∞ corresponding to the polarizability along the molecular axis in which the dipole moment lies. Inclusion in the treatment of three different polarizabilities α_1, α_2, and α_3, along mutually perpendicular axes 1, 2, and 3, with the permanent moment in axis 1, changed Eq. (17.1) only in replacing

$$\frac{3(\epsilon_\infty - 1)}{2\epsilon + \epsilon_\infty} \qquad \text{by} \qquad \left(\frac{\epsilon_1 - 1}{2\epsilon + \epsilon_1} + \frac{\epsilon_2 - 1}{2\epsilon + \epsilon_2} + \frac{\epsilon_3 - 1}{2\epsilon + \epsilon_3} \right)$$

where ϵ_1, ϵ_2, and ϵ_3 are the optical dielectric constants along the three axes. This correction appeared to be unimportant for polar liquids at usual temperatures when ϵ was large. Wilson has taken polarizabilities from the data compiled by Stuart and Volkmann[5,6] and used Eq. (17.1) to calculate modified Onsager moment values, which still are markedly different from the gas values. These modified values trend toward the gas values with increasing temperature, the too high ether and chloroform moment values decreasing and the too low acetone, methyl chloride, methyl bromide, ethyl bromide, and chlorobenzene increasing, while the too low nitrobenzene remains almost constant. For these substances, the ratio of the square of the modified Onsager moment to that of the gas moment lies between 0.5 and 1.5. The discrepancies between calculated and observed values are about as large as in the case of the unmodified Onsager equation.

Scholte[7] and Abbott and Bolton[8] also have extended the Onsager treatment to ellipsoidal molecules, obtaining somewhat better agreement with

[1] C. V. Raman and K. S. Krishnan, *Proc. Roy. Soc. (London)*, **117A**, 589 (1928).

[2] Hans Mueller, *Phys. Rev.*, **50**, 547 (1936).

[3] H. O. Jenkins and S. H. Bauer, *J. Am. Chem. Soc.*, **58**, 2435 (1936).

[4] J. N. Wilson, *Chem. Revs.*, **25**, 377 (1939).

[5] H. A. Stuart and H. Volkmann, *Ann. Physik*, [5]**18**, 121 (1933).

[6] H. A. Stuart, "Molekülstruktur," Springer, Berlin, 1934, pp. 221–222.

[7] T. G. Scholte, *Physica*, **15**, 437 (1949).

[8] J. A. Abbott and H. C. Bolton, *Trans. Faraday Soc.*, **48**, 422 (1952).

the gas moment values for a few substances than that obtained by means of the Onsager equation for a spherical model. Abbott and Bolton conclude that the 5 to 15 per cent discrepancy which they observe is the apparent limit of accuracy of a purely electrostatic theory of polar liquids. Frood and Dekker[8a] have concluded that the Onsager equation holds not only for a mathematical dipole at the center of a spherical molecule, but also for extended dipoles of arbitrary position and direction in a spherical molecule.

Van Vleck and Cole[9] interpolated between the results of Lorentz and those of Onsager by the introduction of an empirical correction factor q having values between 0 and 1. The unmodified Onsager equation written in the form

$$\frac{\epsilon - 1}{\epsilon + 2} \frac{M}{d} - \frac{\epsilon_\infty - 1}{\epsilon_\infty + 2} \frac{M}{d} - \frac{4\pi N \mu_0^2}{9kT} = (f - 1) \frac{4\pi N \mu_0^2}{9kT} \qquad (17.2)$$

where
$$f = \frac{3\epsilon(\epsilon_\infty + 2)}{(2\epsilon + \epsilon_\infty)(\epsilon + 2)} \qquad (17.3)$$

was changed to

$$\frac{\epsilon - 1}{\epsilon + 2} \frac{M}{d} - \frac{\epsilon_\infty - 1}{\epsilon_\infty + 2} \frac{M}{d} - \frac{4\pi N \mu_0^2}{9kT} = q(f - 1) \frac{4\pi N \mu_0^2}{9kT} \qquad (17.4)$$

When $q = 1$, this equation is identical with the Onsager equation. When $q = 0$, it reduces to the Debye equation. Cole showed that, with certain justifiable approximations, it reduced to the empirical equation of van Arkel and Snoek (Sec. 12).

Jaffé[10] has extended Onsager's treatment and has obtained an equation somewhat resembling Kirkwoods's:

$$\frac{\epsilon - 1}{9\epsilon} = \frac{4\pi N_1}{3} \left[\frac{\mu^2}{3kT} + \varphi(z_1, q)\alpha \right] \qquad (17.5)$$

in which
$$\mu = \mu_0 \varphi(z_1, q) \qquad (17.6)$$

$$z_1 = \frac{4\pi N_1 s_1^3}{3} \qquad (17.7)$$

where s_1 is the distance of nearest approach to two molecules,

$$q = \frac{2(\epsilon - 1)}{2\epsilon + 1} \frac{4\pi N_1 \alpha}{3} \qquad (17.8)$$

$$\varphi(z_1, q) = 1 - q e^{z_1 - q} Ei(q - z) \qquad (17.9)$$

where
$$-Ei(-x) = \int_x^\infty \frac{e^{-t}}{t} \, dt \qquad (17.10)$$

[8a] D. G. Frood and A. J. Dekker, *J. Chem. Phys.*, **20**, 1030 (1952).

[9] J. H. Van Vleck, *J. Chem. Phys.*, **5**, 556 (1937); *Ann. N.Y. Acad. Sci.*, **40**, 293 (1940); R. H. Cole, *J. Chem. Phys.*, **6**, 385 (1938).

[10] G. Jaffé, *J. Chem. Phys.*, **8**, 879 (1940).

is a logarithmic integral which can be found in tables.[11] Jaffé has used this equation to calculate values of the vapor moment μ_0 from the dielectric constants of pure liquid benzonitrile, methyl bromide, methyl iodide, ethyl bromide, ethyl iodide, and chlorobenzene and, by using s_1 as an adjustable constant, has obtained results in exact agreement with the values observed for the vapors. As no unreasonable values had to be assigned to s_1 to obtain this agreement, the equation would appear to be accurate, though somewhat complicated to use.

In an apparently empirical approach, Syrkin[12] has proposed an equation which may be written

$$\frac{\left(\dfrac{\epsilon - 1}{\epsilon + 2} - \dfrac{\epsilon_\infty - 1}{\epsilon_\infty + 2}\right)\dfrac{M}{d}}{1 - \left(\dfrac{\epsilon - 1}{\epsilon + 2}\right)^2} = \frac{4\pi N \mu^2}{9kT} \tag{17.11}$$

or

$$\frac{\epsilon - \epsilon_\infty}{\epsilon_\infty + 2}\frac{\epsilon + 2}{2\epsilon + 1} = \frac{4\pi N_1 \mu^2}{9kT} \tag{17.12}$$

Using $n_D{}^2$, the square of the refractive index for the sodium D line, instead of ϵ_∞, he has calculated a large number of dipole moments from the dielectric constants of the pure polar liquids, obtaining values which usually differ by less than 0.1×10^{-18} from those measured in dilute solution, an agreement which compares favorably with that given by the Onsager equation. Syrkin also proposes, without demonstration of its accuracy, an equation for mixtures of polar components 1 and 2,

$$\frac{\dfrac{\epsilon - 1}{\epsilon + 2}\dfrac{c_1 M_1 + c_2 M_2}{d} - c_1 R_1 - c_2 R_2}{1 - \left(\dfrac{\epsilon - 1}{\epsilon + 2}\right)^2} = \frac{4\pi N}{9kT}(c_1\mu_1{}^2 + c_2\mu_2{}^2) \tag{17.13}$$

where R is the molar refraction.

G. B. Brown[13] made the approximation that the internal field in a polar liquid is $F = E$, instead of $F = (\epsilon + 2)E/3$ as in the case of the Lorentz field used by Debye [see Eq. (5.1)], and thus obtained the equation

$$(\epsilon - 1)\frac{M}{d} = 4\pi N\left(\alpha_0 + \frac{\mu^2}{3kT}\right) \tag{17.14}$$

which is the expression to which the Debye equation may be reduced in the case of a gas.

[11] E. Jahnke and F. Emde, "Funktionentafeln mit Formeln und Kurven," 2d ed. (with English text), Teubner Verlagsgesellschaft, Leipzig, 1933.

[12] V. K. Syrkin, *Compt. rend. acad. sci. U.R.S.S.*, **35**, 43 (1942).

[13] G. B. Brown, *Nature*, **150**, 661 (1942).

Jatkar, Iyengar, and Sathe[14,15] derived an equation using an internal field based on a thin, long cylindrical cavity and followed Debye's treatment[16] of ice in assuming that the molecule can point in only two directions, along the field and opposite to it, an entirely arbitrary assumption for liquids and gases. The equation obtained,

$$(\epsilon - 1)\frac{M}{d} = 4\pi N\left(\alpha_0 + \frac{\mu^2}{kT}\right) \tag{17.15}$$

is identical with that of G. B. Brown [Eq. (17.14)] except for the absence of 3 in the denominator of the expression on the right, an absence which would result in dipole moment values different from those obtained by the generally accepted equations. In an arbitrary application of quantum theory, Jatkar and his co-workers have obtained an equation equivalent to the Debye equation [or Eq. (17.14)] for gases and one equivalent to (17.15) for liquids and solids. They have applied[15] the latter with considerable success to calculating moment values from the dielectric constants of the hydrogen halides in the liquid and solid states, which may indicate that the expression has some value as an empirical equation.

Fröhlich and Sack[17] extended the Onsager equation to solids and applied it to the model having only two equilibrium orientations for the molecule separated by an angle of 180°. Their equation may be written

$$\frac{(\epsilon - \epsilon_\infty)(2\epsilon + \epsilon_\infty)}{3\epsilon} = \left[1 + \frac{(\epsilon - \epsilon_\infty)^2}{3\epsilon\epsilon_\infty}\right]\frac{\mu^2}{a^3 kT} \tag{17.16}$$

where a is the molecular radius. The equation may be applied to liquids of high viscosity as well as to solids, but, for liquids of low viscosity, it reduces to the Onsager equation.

Bauer and Massignon[18] have examined solids and liquids in terms of a "crystalline field." Böttcher[19] has studied the internal field and has particularly investigated the polarization of nonpolar liquids.

W. F. Brown[20] has calculated the dielectric constants of nonpolar fluids

[14] S. K. K. Jatkar, B. R. Y. Iyengar, and N. V. Sathe, *J. Indian Inst. Sci.*, **28A**, II, 1 (1946).

[15] S. K. K. Jatkar and B. R. Y. Iyengar, *J. Indian Inst. Sci.*, **30A**, 27 (1948); S. K. K. Jatkar and S. B. Kulkarni, *J. Indian Chem. Soc.*, **27**, 563 (1950).

[16] P. Debye, "Polar Molecules," Chemical Catalog, New York, 1929, pp. 104–106.

[17] H. Fröhlich and R. Sack, *Proc. Roy. Soc. (London)*, **182A**, 388 (1944).

[18] E. Bauer and D. Massignon, *Trans. Faraday Soc.*, **42A**, 12 (1946).

[19] C. J. F. Böttcher, *Physica*, **9**, 937, 945 (1942); *Trans. Faraday Soc.*, **42A**, 16 (1946); *Chem. Weekblad*, **43**, 652 (1947).

[20] W. F. Brown, Jr., *J. Chem. Phys.*, **18**, 1193, 1200 (1950).

and has critically examined the formulas of Lorentz,[21] Yvon,[22] Kirkwood,[23] and Böttcher,[19] concluding that the success of the latter's approximation is partly the result of an approximate cancellation of errors. He further concludes that an accurate calculation of the deviation from the Clausius-Mosotti formula requires knowledge of molecular distribution functions of various orders, but that an approximate calculation is possible on the basis of the radial distribution function alone.

Henriquez[24] modified the expression for the force at the center of the spherical cavity by the introduction of an empirical constant a so that the molar polarization is written

$$P = \frac{\epsilon - 1}{a(\epsilon - 1) + 3} \frac{M}{d} \tag{17.17}$$

The best agreement with experimental data was obtained by setting

$$a = \frac{5}{\epsilon + 4} \tag{17.18}$$

This gave for a liquid

$$\left[\frac{(\epsilon - 1)(\epsilon + 4)}{8\epsilon + 7} - \frac{(n^2 - 1)(n^2 + 2)}{8n^2 + 7} \right] \frac{M}{d} = \frac{4\pi N \mu^2}{9kT} \tag{17.19}$$

When ϵ was greater than 20, $0.0017(\epsilon - 1)^3$ was added to the denominator of the dielectric-constant term. In spite of these empirical adjustments, the equation gave agreement between dipole moment values calculated from liquid data and those measured for the gas no better than that obtained with the Onsager equation.

For an equation derived by Guggenheim, see Eq. (18.2).

18. Solvent Effect. The term "solvent effect" came into use when, as previously described (Sec. 10), F. H. Müller[1,2,3] showed that the dipole moment values of many molecules measured in solution were consistently different from those measured in the vapor state and varied from one solvent to another. The solution moment values were calculated from polarization values P_∞, obtained by extrapolating to infinite dilution the solute polarizations calculated by the Debye equation from measurements of dielectric constant and density at different concentrations. Since the polarization of the nonpolar solvent molecules was assumed to be

[21] H. A. Lorentz, "Theory of Electrons," Teubner Verlagsgesellschaft, Leipzig, 1909, p. 137.

[22] J. Yvon, *Compt. rend.*, **202**, 35 (1936).

[23] J. G. Kirkwood, *J. Chem. Phys.*, **4**, 592 (1936).

[24] P. C. Henriquez, *Rec. trav. chim.*, **54**, 574 (1935).

[1] F. H. Müller, *Physik. Z.*, **34**, 689 (1933); *ibid.*, **35**, 346 (1934); *Trans. Faraday Soc.*, **30**, 731 (1934).

[2] F. H. Müller and P. Mortier, *Physik. Z.*, **36**, 371 (1935).

[3] F. H. Müller, *Physik. Z.*, **38**, 283 (1937).

constant and unaffected by the presence of the polar solute molecules, any moments induced in the solvent molecules by the solute dipoles were resolved with the permanent moment of the solute molecule into an apparent moment, which was taken as the solution moment value. The difference observed between this value and the moment of the molecule measured in the vapor constitutes the so-called solvent effect.

As previously stated, Müller's empirical equation for the apparent dipole moment in solution,

$$\mu_s = \mu_0[1 - C(\epsilon - 1)^2] \tag{18.1}$$

in which μ_0 is the gas or vacuum dipole moment, C an empirical constant, and ϵ the dielectric constant of the solvent, held approximately for a number of substances, but failed for others.[4] A value of 0.038 for C gave an approximate representation of the values for several substances in a variety of nonpolar solvents, and, for fluorobenzene, chlorobenzene, and nitrobenzene, made possible the calculation[5] of fairly satisfactory gas values from solution measurements, but other values were necessary for other substances. Müller[3] determined the value of P_∞ for chlorobenzene at 20° in twenty-five different pure solvents and nine mixed solvents and obtained values which, with the exception of two points, lay close to a smooth S-shaped curve drawn through the gas value at one end, for which $\epsilon = 1.00$, and a 28 per cent lower value for the solutions in ether, for which $\epsilon = 4.25$, at the other end. In the region where most of the experimental points lay, between $\epsilon = 1.8$ and $\epsilon = 2.9$, Müller's equation fitted fairly well to the observed-data curves of the polarization as a linear function of: (a) $(\epsilon - 1)/(\epsilon + 2)$ according to an empirical relation proposed by Sugden;[6] (b) $1/\epsilon$, as proposed by Jenkins;[7] (c) $3/(\epsilon + 2)$, a special case of the relation proposed by Le Fèvre and Le Fèvre;[8] and (d) $(\epsilon - 1)^2$, as proposed by himself. He found, however, that none of them reproduced the value for the gas closely.

An equation derived by Guggenheim,[9] which might well have been treated in Sec. 17, is

$$\frac{(\epsilon - \epsilon_1 - n^2 + n_1^2)C}{\epsilon_1} = \frac{4\pi\mu^2}{3kT} \tag{18.2}$$

in which ϵ and n are the dielectric constant and refractive index of the solution, ϵ_1 and n_1 are the corresponding quantities for the solvent, and C is the number of molecules of polar solute per cc. of solution. As an

[4] K. Higasi, *Bull. Inst. Phys. Chem. Research (Tokyo)*, **13**, 1167 (1934).
[5] K. B. McAlpine and C. P. Smyth, *J. Chem. Phys.*, **3**, 55 (1935).
[6] S. Sugden, *Nature*, **133**, 415 (1934); *Trans. Faraday Soc.*, **30**, 720 (1934).
[7] H. O. Jenkins, *Nature*, **133**, 106 (1934).
[8] C. G. Le Fèvre and R. J. W. Le Fèvre, *J. Chem. Soc.*, 1747 (1935).
[9] E. A. Guggenheim, *Nature*, **137**, 459 (1936).

approximation, the ratio of the moment calculated by Eq. (18.2) to that calculated by the Debye equation is

$$\frac{\mu \text{ (Guggenheim)}}{\mu \text{ (Debye)}} = \frac{(\epsilon_1 + 2)}{3\epsilon_1^{\frac{1}{2}}}$$

so that for the usual nonpolar solvents of dielectric constant 1.9 to 2.3, the solution moment would vary from about 0.942 to 0.947 of the gas moment.

The previously mentioned (Sec. 17) equation of Raman and Krishnan[10] may be examined at this point because of its relation to subsequently developed treatments of solvent effect. The equation may be written

$$\frac{\epsilon - 1}{\epsilon + 2}\frac{M}{d} = \frac{4\pi N}{3}\left(\frac{\alpha_1 + \alpha_2 + \alpha_3}{3} + \frac{\mu^2}{3kT}\right) + \frac{\epsilon - 1}{\epsilon + 2}N\left(\Psi + \frac{\Theta}{3kT}\right) \quad (18.3)$$

where α_1, α_2, and α_3 are the polarizabilities along three mutually perpendicular axes in the molecule,

$$\Psi = \tfrac{1}{3}(\alpha_1 S_1 + \alpha_2 S_2 + \alpha_3 S_3) \quad (18.4)$$

$$\Theta = \mu_1^2 S_1 + \mu_2^2 S_2 + \mu_3^2 S_3 + 2(\mu_1\mu_2 q_{12} + \mu_2\mu_3 q_{23} + \mu_3\mu_1 q_{31}) \quad (18.5)$$

S_1, S_2, S_3 = numerical factors which determine polarization fields acting along the three axes

and $\quad q_{11} = 4\pi/3 + S_1 \qquad q_{22} = 4\pi/3 + S_2 \qquad q_{33} = 4\pi/3 + S_3 \quad (18.6)$

If the second term on the right of Eq. (18.3) becomes zero and the approximation

$$\frac{\alpha_1 + \alpha_2 + \alpha_3}{3} = \alpha_0 \quad (18.7)$$

holds, the equation becomes identical with that of Debye. The equation obviously contains too many unknown constants for exact use without simplification by approximations, but it includes some of the subsequently developed equations for solvent effect as special cases.

Govinda Rau[11] based directly on this equation of Raman and Krishnan an equation for $P_{2\,\text{gas}}$ of a polar solute 2 in solution in a nonpolar solvent 1 as follows:

$$P_{2\,\text{gas}} = P_{2\infty} - N\Psi_1 \frac{3a\epsilon_1}{(\epsilon_1 + 2)^2} - \frac{\epsilon_1 - 1}{\epsilon_1 + 2}N\Psi_2 - \frac{\epsilon_1 - 1}{\epsilon_1 + 2}\frac{N\Theta}{3kT} \quad (18.8)$$

where a is defined by the equation

$$\epsilon = \epsilon_1(1 + ac_2) \quad (18.9)$$

He found this equation to give fairly satisfactory results when applied to solutions of nitrobenzene in several different solvents, the values of Ψ and Θ having been taken from published data or estimated.

[10] C. V. Raman and K. S. Krishnan, *Proc. Roy. Soc. (London)*, **117A**, 589 (1928).
[11] M. A. Govinda Rau, *Proc. Indian Acad. Sci.*, **1**, 498 (1934).

Hans Mueller[12] and Jenkins and Bauer[13] raised theoretical objections to the Raman and Krishnan theory, and the latter concluded from empirical tests that it gave only the order of magnitude of the solvent effect.

Weigle[14] took account of molecular anisotropy in calculating the inductive effects of the polar solute molecules upon the nonpolar solvent molecules and obtained effects of the same magnitude as the observed solvent effects.

Goss[15] pointed out that Sugden's equation[6] for the solute polarization could be written

$$P_2 = A + B\frac{\epsilon - 1}{\epsilon + 2} \tag{18.10}$$

where
$$A = P_E + P_A + P_M \tag{18.11}$$

and that neglect of Ψ, which is small, in the Raman and Krishnan equation (18.3) made it similar to the Sugden equation if, in the latter,

$$B = \frac{N\Theta}{3kT} \tag{18.12}$$

and not
$$B = \frac{-4\pi N\mu^2}{9kT}$$

as suggested by Sugden.[6]

Le Fèvre[16] concluded that the orientation polarizations P_{M_1} and P_{M_2} of a solute in two different solvents of dielectric constants ϵ_1 and ϵ_2 could be represented by

$$\frac{P_{M_1}}{P_{M_2}} = K\frac{\epsilon_2 + 2}{\epsilon_1 + 2} \tag{18.13}$$

where the constant K was close to unity. Le Fèvre and Le Fèvre,[8] writing

$$P_{M\,\text{gas}} = \frac{4\pi N\mu^2}{9kT} \tag{18.14}$$

obtained from the Raman and Krishnan equation

$$\frac{P_{M\,\text{liq}}}{P_{M\,\text{gas}}} = 1 + \frac{3\Theta}{4\pi\mu^2}\frac{\epsilon - 1}{\epsilon + 2} \tag{18.15}$$

and showed that when, as in many cases, Θ could be considered of the order of $-4\pi\mu^2/3$, this equation gave approximately

$$\frac{P_{M\,\text{liq}}}{P_{M\,\text{gas}}} = \frac{3}{\epsilon + 2} \tag{18.16}$$

[12] H. Mueller, *Phys. Rev.*, **50**, 547 (1936).
[13] H. O. Jenkins and S. H. Bauer, *J. Am. Chem. Soc.*, **58**, 2435 (1936).
[14] J. Weigle, *Helv. Phys. Acta*, **6**, 68 (1933).
[15] F. R. Goss, *J. Chem. Soc.*, 696 (1934); *Trans. Faraday Soc.*, **30**, 75 (1934).
[16] R. J. W. Le Fèvre, *J. Chem. Soc.*, 773 (1935).

Goss[17] has developed empirical equations

$$P_S = P_E + P_A + Z \left(\frac{\epsilon - 1}{\epsilon + 2}\right)^4 + \frac{Y}{\epsilon} \qquad (18.17)$$

$$\frac{(Y/P_M) - 1}{[(Z + P_E + P_A)/(P_E + P_A)]^{1/4} - 1} = C \qquad (18.18)$$

where P_S is the partial molar polarization of the liquid when mixed at molar concentration c_2 with a nonpolar, electrically isotropic liquid, the evaluation of P_S being made by the method of intercepts; Z and Y are characteristic of each polar liquid and are calculated by means of Eq. (18.17) from corresponding values of P_S and ϵ; and C is a ratio having a value not far from 3. Goss and Audsley[18] have used these equations to calculate P_M, the gas orientation polarization, from measurements on solutions and have thus obtained values of the gas dipole moment in fair agreement with the values actually measured for the gas.

Frank[19] and Higasi,[20] independently, have worked out treatments of solvent effect, which roughly resemble in approach that of Weigle.[14] Because Higasi applied his equations with success to the results of a large number of measurements, his treatment is summarized here. Higasi's expression for the apparent moment observed in solution may be written

$$\mu_s = \mu_0 + \mu_i \qquad (18.19)$$

where μ_0 is the moment measured in the vapor state and μ_i is the effective moment arising from the moments induced in the solvent by the solute moment. If a dipole of moment μ is located at the origin of a system of polar coordinates pointing in the direction of the z axis, the field E due to it at a point r, θ, ϕ, where θ is the angle between r and the z axis and ϕ is the angle between the projection of r in the xy plane and the x axis, has the components

$$E_x = \frac{3\mu}{r^3} \cos \theta \sin \theta \cos \phi \qquad (18.20)$$

$$E_y = \frac{3\mu}{r^3} \cos \theta \sin \theta \sin \phi \qquad (18.21)$$

$$E_z = \frac{\mu}{r^3} (3 \cos^2 \theta - 1) \qquad (18.22)$$

Higasi treats the solvent as a medium of polarizability α, containing n molecules per cc., locates the dipole at the center of the coordinate system, and integrates to obtain the total components of the induced moments.

---

[17] F. R. Goss, *J. Chem. Soc.*, 1915 (1937); *ibid.*, 752 (1940).

[18] F. R. Goss, *J. Chem. Soc.*, 752, 888 (1940); A. Audsley and F. R. Goss, *J. Chem Soc.*, 864 (1941); *ibid.*, 358, 497 (1942).

[19] F. C. Frank, *Proc. Roy. Soc. (London)*, **152A**, 171 (1935).

[20] K. Higasi, *Sci. Papers Inst. Phys. Chem. Research (Tokyo)*, **28**, 284 (1936).

He explores the various possibilities by treating special cases of the polar solute molecule surrounded by nonpolar solvent and obtains results as follows:

1. A spherical solute molecule with a dipole at its center.

$$\mu_i = 0 \tag{18.23}$$

2. A solute molecule having the shape of an ellipsoid of rotation with a dipole at its center along its axis of symmetry.

(a) The molecular radius a along the axis of symmetry is greater than the radius c perpendicular to it.

$$\mu_i = 4\pi n \alpha \mu A \tag{18.24}$$

where $\quad A = \dfrac{-1}{k^2 - 1}\left\{1 - \dfrac{k}{(k^2 - 1)^{1/2}} \log\,[k + (k^2 - 1)^{1/2}]\right\} - \dfrac{1}{3} \quad$ (18.25)

and

$$k = \frac{a}{c} > 1 \tag{18.26}$$

(b) $\quad a < c$

$$\mu_i = 4\pi n \alpha \mu B \tag{18.27}$$

where $\quad B = \dfrac{k'^2}{k'^2 - 1}\left[1 - \dfrac{1}{(k'^2 - 1)^{1/2}} \sin^{-1} \dfrac{(k'^2 - 1)^{1/2}}{k'}\right] - \dfrac{1}{3} \quad$ (18.28)

and

$$k' = \frac{c}{a} > 1 \tag{18.29}$$

3. A solute molecule having the shape of an ellipsoid of rotation with a dipole in its axis of symmetry at a distance a_1 from one end of the diameter and a_2 from the other end (diameter along axis of symmetry $2a = a_1 + a_2$).

(a) $\quad a > c,\ a_1 > c,\ a_2 > c$

$$\mu_i = 2\pi n \alpha \mu (A_1 + A_2) \tag{18.30}$$

where

$$A_1 = \frac{-c_2}{a_1{}^2 + c^2}\left[1 - \frac{a_1}{(a_1{}^2 - c^2)^{1/2}} \log \frac{a_1 + (a_1{}^2 - c^2)^{1/2}}{c}\right] - \frac{1}{3}, \text{ etc.} \tag{18.31}$$

$$A_1 < 0,\ A_2 < 0 \qquad \text{therefore } \mu_s < \mu_0 \tag{18.32}$$

(b) $\quad a > c,\ a_1 > c,\ a_2 < c$

$$\mu_i = 2\pi n \alpha \mu (A_1 + B_2) \tag{18.33}$$

where $\quad B_2 = \dfrac{c_2}{c^2 - a_2{}^2}\left(1 - \dfrac{a_2}{c^2 - a_2{}^2} \sin^{-1} \dfrac{c^2 - a_2{}^2}{c}\right) - \dfrac{1}{3} \quad$ (18.34)

$$A_1 < 0,\ B_2 > 0 \qquad \text{when } |A_1| \gtreqless |B_2| \qquad \mu_s \lesseqgtr \mu_0 \tag{18.35}$$

(c) $\quad a < c,\ a_1 < c,\ a_2 < c$

$$\mu_1 = 2\pi n \alpha \mu (B_1 + B_2) \tag{18.36}$$
$$B_1 + B_2 > 0 \qquad \mu_s > \mu_0 \tag{18.37}$$

(d) $a < c, a_1 < c, a_2 > c$

$$\mu_i = 2\pi n\alpha\mu(B_1 + A_2) \tag{18.38}$$

When $B_1 \gtrless |A_2|$ $B_1 + A_2 \gtrless 0$

When $B_1 \gtrless |A_2|$ $\mu_s \gtrless \mu_0$ (18.39)

These specific conclusions may be summarized in the statement

$$a \lessgtr c \qquad \mu_s \gtrless \mu_0 \tag{18.40}$$

Substitution of

$$\alpha = \frac{3}{4\pi n}\frac{\epsilon - 1}{\epsilon + 2} \tag{18.41}$$

where ϵ is the dielectric constant of the solvent, and $A = A$ in Eq. (18.24) $= B$ in (18.27) $= (A_1 + A_2)/2$ in (18.30) $= (A_1 + B_2)/2$ in (18.33) $= (B_1 + B_2)/2$ in (18.36) $= (B_1 + A_2)/2$ in (18.38), gives

$$\frac{\mu_s}{\mu_0} = 1 + 3A\frac{\epsilon - 1}{\epsilon + 2} \tag{18.42}$$

This may recall some of the previously discussed equations, which contain $(\epsilon - 1)/(\epsilon + 2)$. However, in the empirical Sugden equation (18.10), the solution moment is a function of the square root of this quantity, as it is also in the equation of Le Fèvre and Le Fèvre (18.15) obtained from the Raman and Krishnan equation, while in the Goss equation (18.17) the solution moment is a function of the square of this quantity.

Higasi, for the most part, used optical polarizabilities to obtain the values of k and k', assuming

$$\frac{a}{c} = \frac{b_1}{b_2} \tag{18.43}$$

where b_1 is the optical polarizability of the molecule along its axis of symmetry and b_2 is the polarizability perpendicular to this axis. The Kerr constant is

$$K = 3\pi N_1(\Theta_1 + \Theta_2) \tag{18.44}$$

For these ellipsoidal molecules under consideration, it may easily be shown that

$$\Theta_1 = \frac{2}{45kT}\frac{n_\infty - 1}{n - 1}(b_1 - b_2)^2 \tag{18.45}$$

$$\Theta_2 = \frac{2\mu^2}{45k^2T^2}(b_1 - b_2) \tag{18.46}$$

The values of the polarizabilities obtained from Kerr constants[21] may be used to calculate solvent effect quantitatively, but, qualitatively, it would appear from Eqs. (18.40) and (18.43) to (18.46) that, when the

[21] H. A. Stuart, "Molekülstruktur," Springer, 1934, pp. 221–222.

Kerr constant is negative, the solution moment is larger and, when it is positive, the solution moment is smaller than the gas moment.   However, it will be seen shortly from Eq. (18.58) that this is not necessarily true. The agreement of Higasi's calculations with the experimental values will be shown (Table 18.1) in comparison with the results of Eq. (18.54).

Frank[19] derived the equation

$$\mu_i = A'\mu \frac{\epsilon - 1}{\epsilon} \tag{18.47}$$

in which A' is a numerical factor,

$$A' = A_1 + A_2 \tag{18.48}$$

where A_1 depends only on the geometry of the polar solute molecule without reference to its size and A_2 depends similarly on the external boundary conditions. A_2 is small and is generally neglected by Frank in his calculations.   Substitution in Eq. (18.19) gives the equation in the same general form as that of Higasi (18.42)

$$\frac{\mu_s}{\mu_0} = 1 + A' \frac{\epsilon - 1}{\epsilon} \tag{18.49}$$

The equation differs from that of Higasi in having ϵ instead of $\epsilon + 2$ in the denominator.

A simple structural picture helps to qualitative conclusions as to the size and magnitude of the solvent effect.   Let us suppose that a spherical solute molecule with a dipole at the center has six spherical solvent molecules of polarizability α symmetrically located around it so that the solute molecule is at the center of a regular octahedron, with a solvent molecule at each of the six corners, at a distance r from the permanent moment μ, and with the solute dipole in an axis of symmetry connecting opposite corners of the octahedron.   The field in the direction of the dipole axis is given by Eq. (18.22).   The field perpendicular to this direction is shown by Eqs. (18.20) and (18.21) to be zero.   For the two solvent molecules at the ends of the symmetry axis containing the dipole, θ is 0° and 180° and the dipole moment induced in each is, therefore,

$$m = \frac{\mu}{r^3} (3 \cos^2 \theta - 1)\alpha = \frac{2\mu}{r^3} \alpha \tag{18.50}$$

For each of the four solvent molecules in the plane perpendicular to the dipole axis, θ is 90° and the moment induced in each is, therefore,

$$m = \frac{-\mu}{r^3} \alpha \tag{18.51}$$

that is, acting in the direction opposite to the permanent solute moment. The sum of the six induced moments is obviously zero, that is, the solvent effect should be zero for a spherical solute molecule with a dipole at the center. This is observed for the symmetrical t-butyl chloride molecule.[22] If the solute molecule is elongated so that the two solvent molecules in the line of the dipole axis are farther from the dipole, r in Eq. (18.50) is increased and the moments induced in these two molecules are decreased below the sum of the opposing moments in the other four molecules, so that the total resultant induced moment opposes the permanent solute moment, giving a negative solvent effect. In the majority of molecules, the dipole tends to lie more nearly in the direction of the longest molecular axis than perpendicular to it, so that the solution moment is usually lower than the gas moment, as in the case of chlorobenzene. If the molecular axis in which the dipole lies is shortened, r is decreased and the solvent moments induced in the direction of the permanent solute dipole increase to give a positive solvent effect, as in the case of chloroform.

Hobbs[23] has used the Onsager reaction field R [cf. Eq. (14.5)] and an empirical constant C' to calculate the orientation polarization P_M in solution in different solvents, making use of an equation of Böttcher[24] and arbitrarily introducing C' to give

$$P_{M_\infty} = \frac{4\pi N}{3} \frac{\mu^2}{3kT + C'\mu R} \tag{18.52}$$

in which the energy μR is calculated from the equation [cf. Eq. (14.5)]

$$\mu R = \frac{25.2\mu^2}{10^{-23}V} \frac{2\epsilon - 2}{2\epsilon + 1} \tag{18.53}$$

where V is the molar volume and ϵ is the dielectric constant of the nonpolar solvent. The equation can be used to calculate $P_{M\,gas}$ and the gaseous dipole moment by measuring $P_{M\,soln}$ in two or more different solvents. The constant C' is wholly empirical, which, in principle, is a drawback to the method.

Conner and Smyth,[25] using a treatment analogous to that of Kirkwood[26] (cf. Sec. 15) and considering molecular anisotropy, developed an equation for ellipsoidal solute molecules containing the reciprocal of the eccentricity of the ellipsoid in a factor identical with A in Eq. (18.42). It may, as a fair approximation, be written

$$\frac{\mu_s}{\mu_0} = 1 + \frac{\epsilon - 1}{2} A(0.85) = 1 + 0.43A(\epsilon - 1) \tag{18.54}$$

which has a factor 0.43 where the Higasi equation (18.42) has $3/(\epsilon + 2)$ and the Frank equation (18.49) $1/\epsilon$. As the dielectric constant of the

[22] R. H. Wiswall and C. P. Smyth, *J. Chem. Phys.*, **9**, 356 (1941).
[23] M. E. Hobbs, *J. Chem. Phys.*, **7**, 849 (1939).
[24] C. J. F. Böttcher, *Physica*, **5**, 635 (1938).
[25] W. P. Conner, R. P. Clarke, and C. P. Smyth, *J. Am. Chem. Soc.*, **64**, 1379 (1942).
[26] J. G. Kirkwood, *J. Chem. Phys.*, **7**, 911 (1939).

solvent usually has a value between 1.9 and 2.5, this equation gives a solvent effect correction from 0.55 to 0.64 of that given by the Higasi equation and nearly the same as that given by the Frank equation if A' in the latter does not differ from A. The only quantitative values of μ_s/μ_0 that Frank has calculated for molecules listed in Table 18.1 are 0.96 for methyl chloride as compared to 0.95 calculated by the Higasi equation, 0.97 by the Conner and Smyth equation, and 0.88 observed; and 0.90 for chlorobenzene as compared to 0.91 (Higasi), 0.94 (Conner and Smyth), and 0.92 observed.

TABLE 18.1. SOLVENT EFFECTS

Substance	Moment ($\times 10^{18}$)		μ_s/μ_0		
	Gas	Benzene	Obs.	Higasi	Conner and Smyth
CH_3Cl	1.86	1.64(C_6H_{14})	0.88	0.95	0.97
CH_3Br	1.78	1.78(C_6H_{14})	1.00	0.94	0.97
CH_3I	1.59	1.58(C_6H_{14})	1.00	0.99	1.00
$CHCl_3$	1.08	1.21	1.12	1.08	1.05
C_2H_5Br	2.02	1.89	0.94	0.94	0.96
C_2H_5I	1.90	1.78	0.94	0.89	0.93
C_6H_5F	1.57	1.45	0.92	0.96	0.97
C_6H_5Cl	1.70	1.56	0.92	0.91	0.94
C_6H_5Br	1.71	1.51	0.88	0.92	0.95
$C_6H_5NO_2$	4.23	3.98	0.94	0.89 (0.94)	0.96
C_6H_5CN	4.39	3.94	0.90	0.92	0.95
HCN	2.93	2.59	0.88	0.85	0.91
n-C_4H_9CN	4.09	3.57	0.87	0.87	0.92
CH_3NO_2	3.54	3.13	0.88	0.95	0.97
CH_3COCH_3	2.85	2.76	0.96	0.96	0.98
$C_6H_5COCH_3$	3.00	2.95	0.98	0.98	0.99
$(C_2H_5)_2O$	1.16	1.22	1.06	1.05	1.04
CH_3OH	1.69	1.62	0.96	1.01	1.01
C_2H_5OH	1.69	1.66	0.98	1.02	1.01
n-C_3H_7OH	1.66	1.66	1.00	1.04	1.02
i-C_4H_9OH	1.63	1.70	1.04	1.04	1.02

Table 18.1 gives for a variety of molecules the moments calculated by the Debye equation from measurements on gases and on benzene solutions and the ratios of the solution moments to the gas moments as observed and as calculated by the Higasi equation (18.42) and by the Conner and Smyth equation (18.54). Most of the Higasi values are taken from Higasi's calculations[20] based, with the exception of those for hydrogen cyanide, on the polarization ellipsoids of the molecules, while the other Higasi values and all the Smyth and Conner values are taken from calculations by Eckstein[27] based on the dimensions of reasonable molecular

[27] B. Eckstein, Senior Thesis, Princeton University, 1948.

models, when the values of A were not available in Higasi's calculations. Errors or approximations in the molecular models may cause errors in the results larger than the differences between the results of the two equations. This is shown by the values for nitrobenzene in Table 18.1, where the value 0.89 was calculated by Higasi, and the value 0.94 in parentheses was calculated by Eckstein. Solutions in benzene are chosen for comparison with the gas because of the general use of benzene as a solvent. For the first three substances listed, it has been necessary to use data measured in hexane.

It is evident from Table 18.1 that both the equations of Higasi and of Conner and Smyth give the magnitude and direction of the solvent effect. Although, in many cases, the solvent effect calculated by the Conner and Smyth equation is in better agreement with the observed effect than is the result of the Higasi equation, the larger solvent effect calculated by the Higasi equation seems, on an average, to be a little nearer the observed effect. Theoretically, it should be possible to distinguish between the equations of Frank, Higasi, and Conner and Smyth by plotting the experimental values of μ_s/μ_0 against $(\epsilon - 1)/\epsilon$, $(\epsilon - 1)/(\epsilon + 2)$, and ϵ, where ϵ is the dielectric constant of the solvent, and choosing that function which gives the best approximation to a straight line. However, the solvent effect is so small that the experimental errors in the data now available obscure the exact shape of the curve, and the fact that a straight line usually represents the relationship between μ_s and ϵ as well as any other form of curve cannot be taken as establishing the correctness of the Conner and Smyth equation. In view of the simplicity of the latter equation, it seems to provide slightly the most convenient empirical equation for calculating the gas moment from measurements in two or more solvents, when written in the form

$$\mu_0 = \frac{\mu_s}{1 + C(\epsilon - 1)} \tag{18.55}$$

However, if the molecular dimensions or axial polarizabilities are known or, as is commonly the case, capable of approximate estimation, A can evidently be calculated and used to obtain a fair value of μ_0 from a single value of μ_s.

A summary review of many of the equations dealing with or related to solvent effect has been given by J. W. Smith,[28] and a brief critical review of several equations is included in a paper by Ross and Sack.[29] The latter writers call attention to similarity between the equation of Raman and Krishnan and that of Higasi but point out that the Higasi equation gives calculated solvent effects exactly twice those given by the Raman

[28] J. W. Smith, *Science Prog.*, **36**, 483 (1948).
[29] I. G. Ross and R. A. Sack, *Proc. Phys. Soc.* (*London*), **36B**, 893 (1950).

and Krishnan equation. They conclude that two errors in the derivation of the Higasi equation (18.42) are corrected when his expression for μ_i is multiplied by $(\epsilon + 2)/3\epsilon$, which makes it identical in form with the Frank equation (18.49).

Ross and Sack[29] express the effect of the anisotropy of the solute molecule by means of an "internal-field function" in the equation for the internal field within an ellipsoidal cavity,

$$F = E + 4\pi \xi P \tag{18.56}$$

where $\xi = \xi_a$, ξ_b, or ξ_c according as the field E is applied parallel to the ellipsoidal axis a, b, or c. When ξ is $\frac{1}{3}$, Eq. (18.56) is identical with the Lorentz expression for the internal field in a spherical cavity [Eq. (5.17)]. Ross and Sack have derived expressions for ξ_a, ξ_b, and ξ_c and evaluated them as functions of the axial ratios. Confining themselves to the case where the dipole is parallel to one of the principal axes of the ellipsoid and using a treatment analogous to that of Onsager, they have obtained an expression which may be written

$$\frac{\mu_s}{\mu_0} = \frac{3\epsilon[1 - (\epsilon_\infty - 1)\xi]}{(\epsilon + 2)[\epsilon + (\epsilon_\infty - \epsilon)\xi]} \tag{18.57}$$

or

$$\frac{\mu_i}{\mu_0} = \frac{(\epsilon - 1)[(\epsilon + 2\epsilon_\infty)\xi - \epsilon]}{(\epsilon + 2)[\epsilon + (\epsilon_\infty - \epsilon)\xi]} \tag{18.58}$$

in which ϵ_∞ is the optical dielectric constant of the solute. As ϵ approaches ϵ_∞, Eq. (18.57) approaches the Higasi equation (18.42), $\xi - \frac{1}{3}$ being taken as equivalent to A. Since $\xi < 1$, it is evident from Eq. (18.58) that the sign of the solvent effect μ_i is determined by that of the factor $(\epsilon + 2\epsilon_\infty)\xi - \epsilon$ and not by that of ξ alone or of the Kerr constant, although a parallelism is rather commonly observed.

Ross and Sack compared the effectiveness of their equation with that of Higasi's by calculating μ_s/μ_0 for ten substances by means of each equation. In calculating the axial ratios of the molecules and, from these, the values of ξ, they used the axial polarizabilities, the bond and packing radii, and the bond angles. When the values of ξ obtained from polarizabilities were used, the Ross and Sack equation gave appreciably better agreement with the observed values of μ_s/μ_0 than did the Higasi equation. When the values obtained from estimated molecular dimensions were used, the superiority of the Ross and Sack equation was negligible.

Smith and Witten[30] have measured the apparent moments of t-butyl chloride and acetonitrile in various solvents and solvent mixtures and concluded that the shape of the solvent molecule, as well as that of the solute molecule, is a factor in determining the solvent effect. This

[30] J. W. Smith and L. B. Witten, *Trans. Faraday Soc.*, **47**, 1304 (1951).

emphasizes the necessarily approximate character of the equations for solvent effect which have been considered, but does not invalidate their use for the approximate calculation of the relatively small effects.

A fairly accurate estimate of solvent effect can probably be made by assuming the unknown solvent effect of a molecule to be the same as that known for a molecule of similar structure. This method of estimation may be illustrated by the case of the o-dichlorobenzene molecule. The moment of the molecule in benzene solution was well established as close to 2.25×10^{-18}, but the only gas value in the literature was 2.16. The similarity of the molecular shape and dipole location of o-dichlorobenzene to those of chlorobenzene led the writer to use the solvent effect of the latter to estimate a gas dipole moment for o-dichlorobenzene of about 2.45. Subsequent measurements of the vapor gave 2.51[31] and 2.48.[32]

19. Conclusions. It may be concluded that the static dielectric constant of a gas may be accurately calculated by means of the Debye equation (6.13) from the molecular polarizability and permanent dipole moment. The Debye equation may be used to calculate approximate values of the molecular dipole moment from the dielectric constants and densities of dilute solutions of the polar molecules in nonpolar solvents. The small differences between these approximate solution values and the gas values may be calculated correctly as to magnitude and sign by the equations of Higasi (18.42), of Conner and Smyth (18.54), and of Ross and Sack (18.58), but none of these equations takes strict account of all the factors involved. The Debye equation is not applicable to pure polar liquids, but the Onsager equation (14.23) gives the approximate relation between the dielectric constant of a normal polar liquid and the molecular dipole moment. The dipole moment value calculated by it from the dielectric constant of the pure liquid is commonly only a little more approximate than the uncorrected Debye solution values. The Kirkwood equation (15.5) is more exact than the Onsager equation in that it contains a factor to take into account the restriction of molecular orientation by neighboring molecules. In the usual absence of knowledge of liquid structure this factor is unknown and useful only as an empirical constant.

[31] E. C. Hurdis and C. P. Smyth, *J. Am. Chem. Soc.*, **64**, 2212 (1942).
[32] E. M. Moore and M. E. Hobbs, *J. Am. Chem. Soc.*, **71**, 411 (1949).

CHAPTER II

DIELECTRIC CONSTANT AND LOSS

1. Relaxation of Polarization. The first chapter has considered the static or low-frequency dielectric constant which is observed when the dielectric is in equilibrium with the externally applied field. The present chapter will discuss dielectric behavior when the frequency of the externally applied alternating field is such that there is an observable lag in the attainment of equilibrium. This lag is commonly referred to as relaxation, which, in general, may be defined as the lag in the response of a system to change in the forces to which it is subjected.[1] The existence of relaxation becomes apparent when its rate is not far from being of the same order of magnitude as that of the change of the applied forces. Since we are concerned with the polarization of matter as in the case of the static dielectric constant, it is desirable to classify the various types of polarization with reference to the time required for the polarization process.

The polarization process always involves rapidly forming polarization and may also involve slowly forming polarization.[2] Rapidly forming polarization consists in part, and often in large part, of electronic polarization due to the displacement of the electrons in the atoms relative to the positive nuclei, a process requiring about 10^{-15} sec. and corresponding approximately to the frequency of ultraviolet light. A relatively small atomic polarization arises from the displacement of atoms relative to one another in the molecule, a process requiring about 10^{-12} to 10^{-14} sec. and corresponding to the frequency of infrared light. In ionic crystals, a similar but usually larger polarization arises from the displacement in the lattice of the ions of one sign relative to those of the opposite sign, a process requiring about 10^{-12} sec. and corresponding to the frequency of the far infrared region. The time required for the dipole or orientation-polarization process depends upon the frictional resistance of the medium to the change of molecular orientation. For a gas, the time required is of the order of 10^{-12} sec., corresponding to the frequency of the

[1] W. Kauzmann, *Revs. Mod. Phys.*, **14**, 12 (1942).

[2] E. J. Murphy and S. O. Morgan, *Bell System Tech. J.*, **16**, 493 (1937).

far infrared region. Resonance absorption corresponding to changes in rotational energy levels may occur in the microwave region to give rise to microwave spectra, but the energy loss is normally small. For small molecules in liquids of low viscosity, the time required is about 10^{-11} to 10^{-10} sec., corresponding to the frequency of the microwave region. For large molecules or viscous liquids, the time required is of the order of 10^{-6} sec., corresponding to radio frequencies. The high internal frictional resistance of very viscous liquids, glasses, and solids may lengthen the time required for the polarization process to seconds, minutes, or longer, so that it may not make itself evident under the conditions of observation. In a heterogeneous material, an additional type of polarization, interfacial polarization, arises from the accumulation of charge at the interfaces between phases. It arises only when two phases differ from each other in dielectric constant and conductivity, and, for a two-layer dielectric in particular, when the product of the dielectric constant ϵ_1 of one phase and the conductivity k_2 of the second phase is unequal to the product of the dielectric constant ϵ_2 of the second phase and the conductivity k_1 of the first phase, that is, $\epsilon_1 k_2 \neq \epsilon_2 k_1$. This accumulation of charge requires flow of current through the dielectric phases, a process which may require seconds or minutes so that it may be observed only at very low frequencies. However, if one phase has a high conductivity, the polarization may occur so rapidly as to be observed in the radio-frequency range.[2] Because interfacial polarization is attributable to the heterogeneous and often indeterminate character of the dielectric material, it seems preferable to restrict this discussion to the well-defined dipole or orientation polarization observable at frequencies from the microwave region to those of very-low-frequency alternating currents, except for the occasional interfacial polarization caused by the appearance of a new phase with change of temperature.

Dielectric relaxation is the exponential decay with time of the polarization in a dielectric when an externally applied field is removed. The relaxation time may be defined as the time in which this polarization is reduced to $1/e$ times its original value, e being the natural logarithmic base [see Eqs. (2.12) and (3.1)]. Dielectric relaxation is the cause of anomalous dispersion in which the dielectric constant decreases with increasing frequency. From a structural point of view, the most interesting dielectric relaxation is that involving orientation polarization, which depends on the internal structures of the molecules and on the molecular arrangement or structure of the dielectric. In terms of the theory of this phenomenon as developed by Debye,[3] dielectric relaxation is the lag in dipole orientation behind an alternating electric field. Under the influence of such a field, the polar molecules of a system rotate toward an

[3] P. Debye, "Polar Molecules," Chemical Catalog, New York, 1929, chap. V.

equilibrium distribution in molecular orientation with a corresponding dielectric polarization.[4]   When the polar molecules are very large, or the frequency of the alternating field is very high, or the viscosity of the medium is very great, the rotatory motion of the molecules is not sufficiently rapid for the attainment of equilibrium with the field.   The polarization then acquires a component out of phase with the field, and the displacement current acquires a conductance component in phase with the field, resulting in thermal dissipation of energy.

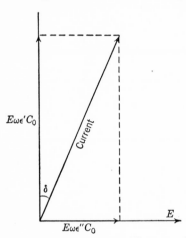

FIG. 2.1. Current-voltage diagram of a dielectric with loss.

2. Dielectric Constant and Loss.   In an ideal condenser of geometrical capacitance C_0, in which the polarization is instantaneous, the charging or capacitive current $E\omega\epsilon'C_0$ [see Eq. (2.3)] is 90° out of phase with the alternating potential (Fig. 2.1).   In a condenser in which absorptive polarization occurs, the current also has a component $E\omega\epsilon''C_0$ in phase with the potential and determined by Ohm's law.   This ohmic or loss current, which measures the absorption, is due to the dissipation of part of the energy of the field as heat.   In vector notation, the total current is the sum of the charging current and the loss current.   The angle δ between the vector for the amplitude of the total current and that for the amplitude of the charging current is the loss angle, and the tangent of this angle is the loss tangent

$$\tan \delta = \frac{\text{loss current}}{\text{charging current}} = \frac{\epsilon''}{\epsilon'} \tag{2.1}$$

where ϵ' is the measured dielectric constant of the dielectric material in the condenser and ϵ'' is its loss factor.   A complex dielectric constant is defined as

$$\epsilon^* = \epsilon' - i\epsilon'' \tag{2.2}$$

The classical development of the relations between dielectric constant, loss, frequency, dipole moment, molecular size, and viscosity of the dielectric is due to Debye.[1]   A convenient development of the Debye equations given by Fröhlich[2] is shown below with slightly altered defini-

---

[4] J. G. Kirkwood and R. M. Fuoss, *J. Chem. Phys.*, **9**, 329 (1941).

[1] See footnote 3, Sec. 1.

[2] H. Fröhlich, "Theory of Dielectrics," Oxford, London, 1949, sec. 10.

tions.   A periodic field,

$$E = E_0 \cos \omega t \tag{2.3}$$

where E_0 is independent of time t, and ω, the angular frequency, is 2π times the frequency in cycles per second.   Instead of Eq. (2.3), we may write

$$E = E_0 e^{i\omega t} \tag{2.4}$$

The displacement D is also periodic in time and will normally be out of phase with E, the phase shift being ϕ, so that

$$D = D_0 \cos (\omega t - \phi) = D_1 \cos \omega t + D_2 \sin \omega t \tag{2.5}$$

where $\qquad D_1 = D_0 \cos \phi \qquad D_2 = D_0 \sin \phi \tag{2.6}$

Two different dielectric constants may be written

$$\epsilon' = D_1/E_0 \qquad \text{and} \qquad \epsilon'' = D_2/E_0 \tag{2.7}$$

It follows then from (2.6) that

$$\frac{\epsilon''}{\epsilon'} = \tan \phi \tag{2.8}$$

which is the expression for the loss tangent [Eq. (2.1)].   As the frequency approaches zero, ϵ'' approaches zero and ϵ' approaches the static dielectric constant ϵ_0, represented in Chap. I by ϵ; and, as the frequency approaches infinity, ϵ' approaches ϵ_∞, the optical dielectric constant. ϵ_0 and ϵ_∞ may be defined in terms of the quantities and equations of Chap. I by

$$\frac{\epsilon_\infty - 1}{\epsilon_\infty + 2} \frac{M}{d} = \frac{4\pi N}{3} \alpha_0 \tag{2.9}$$

$$\frac{\epsilon_0 - 1}{\epsilon_0 + 2} \frac{M}{d} = \frac{4\pi N}{3} \alpha_0 + \frac{4\pi N}{9kT} \mu^2 \tag{2.10}$$

With an electric field $E(t)$ which is dependent on time, a field $E(u)$ which is applied during a time interval between u and $u + du$, and a corresponding electric displacement $D(t)$, we may write

$$D(t) = \epsilon_\infty E(t) + \int_{-\infty}^{t} E(u)f(t - u)\, du \tag{2.11}$$

The first term on the right of (2.11) is the instantaneous displacement, while the second is the absorptive term.   It is convenient to assume that the attainment of equilibrium is exponential with time and has the decay function

$$f(t) \propto e^{-t/\tau} \tag{2.12}$$

where τ is independent of time, but dependent upon temperature.   Differentiating (2.11) and (2.12) with respect to time, combining the results, and multiplying by τ, we obtain

$$\tau \frac{dD(t)}{dt} = \epsilon_\infty \tau \frac{dE(t)}{dt} + \tau f(0)Et - \int_{-\infty}^{t} E(u)f(t - u)\, du \tag{2.13}$$

Addition of (2.11) and (2.13) gives

$$\tau \frac{d}{dt}(D - \epsilon_\infty E) + (D - \epsilon_\infty E) = \tau f(0)E \tag{2.14}$$

The constant $f(0)$ is the value of the decay function when the field is constant. Under these circumstances,

$$\frac{d}{dt}(D - \epsilon_\infty E) = 0 \quad \text{and} \quad D = \epsilon_0 E \tag{2.15}$$

Substitution of (2.15) in (2.14) gives

$$\tau f(0) = \epsilon_0 - \epsilon_\infty \tag{2.16}$$

Insertion of (2.16) into (2.14) gives

$$\tau \frac{d}{dt}(D - \epsilon_\infty E) + (D - \epsilon_\infty E) = (\epsilon_0 - \epsilon_\infty)E \tag{2.17}$$

Differentiating E in (2.4) with respect to time and substituting the result

$$\frac{dE}{dt} = i\omega E \tag{2.18}$$

in the expression for dD/dt obtained by differentiating D in the expression

$$D = \epsilon^* E \tag{2.19}$$

we obtain

$$\frac{dD}{dt} = i\omega \epsilon^* E \tag{2.20}$$

Substitution of these relations in (2.17) and rearrangement gives

$$\epsilon^* = \epsilon_\infty + \frac{\epsilon_0 - \epsilon_\infty}{1 + i\omega\tau} \tag{2.21}$$

Substitution of (2.2) in (2.21) and separation of real and imaginary parts gives

$$\epsilon' = \epsilon_\infty + \frac{\epsilon_0 - \epsilon_\infty}{1 + \omega^2\tau^2} \tag{2.22}$$

$$\epsilon'' = \frac{(\epsilon_0 - \epsilon_\infty)\omega\tau}{1 + \omega^2\tau^2} \tag{2.23}$$

Examination of Eq. (2.23) shows that ϵ'' approaches zero both for small and for large values of $\omega\tau$, while it is a maximum for

$$\omega\tau = 1 \tag{2.24}$$

For this value of $\omega\tau$, (2.23) gives

$$\epsilon''_m = \frac{\epsilon_0 - \epsilon_\infty}{2} \tag{2.25}$$

and (2.22) gives

$$\epsilon'_m = \frac{\epsilon_0 + \epsilon_\infty}{2} \tag{2.26}$$

Equation (2.22) requires that ϵ' decrease from ϵ_0 to ϵ_∞ with increasing frequency, most of the decrease occurring within a 100-fold frequency range, or within two logarithmic units of frequency or wavelength as shown by the solid line A in Fig. 2.2.[3] In this same range, Eq. (2.23) requires that ϵ'' change from a small value through a maximum to a small value again (Fig. 2.2B).   Although liquids may conform to the behavior demanded by these equations, as does i-butyl bromide approximately in

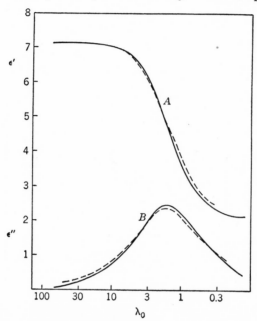

FIG. 2.2. Dependence of dielectric constant (A) and loss factor (B) of i-butyl bromide upon the logarithm of the wavelength (cm.). [$E. J. Hennelly, W. M. Heston, Jr., and C. P. Smyth, J. Am. Chem. Soc.,$ **70**, 4102 (1948).]

Fig. 2.2, the dispersion commonly occurs over a wider frequency range, with a maximum value of ϵ'' lower than that predicted by Eq. (2.23), as shown in Fig. 2.3.[3] This effect has been attributed to a distribution of relaxation times, a phenomenon which will be discussed shortly.

Equation (2.12) shows that, when $t = \tau$,

$$f(t) \propto \frac{1}{e} \tag{2.27}$$

that is, during the time τ, the polarization has changed to $1/e$ of its original value.   It is evident, therefore, that τ is the relaxation time which has been defined in the preceding section.   It is an experimentally observable

[3] E. J. Hennelly, W. M. Heston, Jr., and C. P. Smyth, *J. Am. Chem. Soc.,* **70**, 4102 (1948).

quantity for the macroscopic relaxation process.   A directly measurable value of τ is given by (2.24), which requires that the value ω_m of the angular frequency for which the loss factor is a maximum, called the critical frequency, should be

$$\omega_m = \frac{1}{\tau} \qquad (2.28)$$

Division of Eq. (2.23) by (2.22) in rearranged form gives

$$\frac{\epsilon''}{\epsilon' - \epsilon_\infty} = \omega\tau \qquad (2.29)$$

According to this equation, $\epsilon''/(\epsilon' - \epsilon_\infty)$, when plotted against the angular frequency, should give a straight line of slope τ passing through the origin.

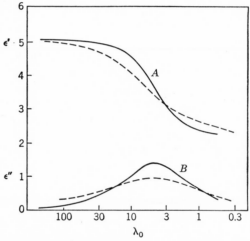

FIG. 2.3. Dependence of dielectric constant (A) and loss factor (B) of n-octyl bromide at 25° upon the logarithm of the wavelength (cm.).   [*E. J. Hennelly, W. M. Heston, Jr., and C. P. Smyth, J. Am. Chem. Soc.*, **70**, 4102 (1948).]

In examining experimental data it may be convenient to use, instead of ω_m, the critical frequency

$$f_m = \frac{\omega_m}{2\pi} = \frac{1}{2\pi\tau} \qquad (2.30)$$

or the critical wavelength

$$\lambda_m = \frac{3 \times 10^{10}}{f_m} = 2\pi \times 3 \times 10^{10}\tau \qquad (2.31)$$

for which the loss factor is a maximum.   In the latter case, since

$$\omega_m = \frac{2\pi c}{\lambda_m} \qquad (2.32)$$

and

$$\omega = \frac{2\pi c}{\lambda_0} \qquad (2.33)$$

where c is the velocity of light, 3×10^{10} cm. per sec., and λ_0 is the free-space wavelength, we may write

$$\epsilon' = \epsilon_\infty + \frac{\epsilon_0 - \epsilon_\infty}{1 + (\lambda_m/\lambda_0)^2} \tag{2.34}$$

$$\epsilon'' = \frac{(\epsilon_0 - \epsilon_\infty)\lambda_m/\lambda_0}{1 + (\lambda_m/\lambda_0)^2} \tag{2.35}$$

Although Eqs. (2.22) and (2.23) are sometimes called the Debye equations, they are somewhat simpler than those originally derived by Debye[1] for a molecular orientation process. By assuming the dipolar molecule to be a sphere of radius a moving in a continuous viscous fluid possessing a coefficient of internal friction η, he obtained for the process of molecular relaxation the relationship

$$\tau = \frac{4\pi\eta a^3}{kT} \tag{2.36}$$

It has been customary to use for η the experimentally measured macroscopic viscosity instead of the unknown microscopic internal friction coefficient or viscosity, with very unsatisfactory results in most cases, as will be shown later. Quite irrespective of the validity of Eq. (2.36), Debye obtained a complex polarization

$$\frac{\epsilon^* - 1}{\epsilon^* + 2}\frac{M}{d} = P(\omega) = \frac{4\pi N}{3}\alpha_0 + \frac{4\pi N\mu^2}{9kT}\frac{1}{1 + i\omega\tau} \tag{2.37}$$

which differs from Eq. (2.10) only by the factor $1/(1 + i\omega\tau)$ in the second term on the right, which makes ϵ complex. Substitution of Eqs. (2.2), (2.9), and (2.10) into (2.37) and separation of real and imaginary parts gives

$$\epsilon' = \epsilon_\infty + \frac{\epsilon_0 - \epsilon_\infty}{1 + X^2} \tag{2.38}$$

$$\epsilon'' = \frac{(\epsilon_0 - \epsilon_\infty)X}{1 + X^2} \tag{2.39}$$

where

$$X = \frac{\epsilon_0 + 2}{\epsilon_\infty + 2}\omega\tau \tag{2.40}$$

Equations (2.38) and (2.39) differ from (2.22) and (2.23) only in containing the quantity $\tau(\epsilon_0 + 2)/(\epsilon_\infty + 2)$ instead of τ. This difference arises because the relaxation time which Fröhlich uses is for the macroscopic relaxation process, while the relaxation time used by Debye is that of the microscopic or molecular process, which makes the result dependent upon the internal field. Since both quantities are independent of frequency, the two pairs of equations give the same dependence of ϵ' and ϵ'' upon frequency and cannot be directly distinguished from each other experimentally. However, Eqs. (2.38) and (2.39) require that ϵ''_m be reached when $X = 1$, that is,

$$\tau = \frac{\epsilon_\infty + 2}{\epsilon_0 + 2} \frac{1}{\omega_m} \tag{2.41}$$

which will give a smaller value of τ than is given by (2.28), since ϵ_0 is larger than ϵ_∞. Since it will be seen later that the values of molecular radii calculated from τ by means of (2.36) tend to be too small even when (2.28) is used to obtain τ, the experimental results would seem to favor the use of the simpler equations (2.22) and (2.23).

Powles[4] has proposed a new expression for the internal field in a dielectric subjected to an alternating electric field which leads to

$$\frac{1}{\omega_m} = \frac{3\epsilon_0}{2\epsilon_0 + \epsilon_\infty} \tau \tag{2.42}$$

instead of
$$\frac{1}{\omega_m} = \frac{\epsilon_0 + 2}{\epsilon_\infty + 2} \tau$$

given by the Debye relationship [Eq. (2.41)]. Equation (2.42) indicates that the difference between the macroscopic relaxation time given by Eq. (2.28) and the molecular relaxation time is small, the ratio never being greater than a limiting value of $\frac{3}{2}$, while Eq. (2.41) would require the macroscopic relaxation time for water to be twenty times the molecular. It is reassuring to obtain this additional justification for the common neglect of the difference between the two relaxation times, which, in terms of Powles's internal field, is small for most polar liquids and negligible for solutions in nonpolar solvents. It seems likely that a more rigorous theory of dielectric relaxation will show that the difference between the two relaxation times is not large.

For some purposes it is convenient to discuss[1] dielectric absorption in the terminology of optics, using the absorption coefficient κ and the refractive index n. In terms of these quantities, the complex dielectric constant is

$$\epsilon^* = n^2(1 - i\kappa)^2 \tag{2.43}$$

This ordinary refractive index is given by

$$n = \frac{\lambda_0}{\lambda} \tag{2.44}$$

where λ_0 is the free-space wavelength and λ is the wavelength in the material in question. The significance of κ is given by the fact that after the wave has traveled over a distance λ through the material, its amplitude is multiplied by $e^{-2\pi\kappa}$. Debye[1] has shown that the absorptive coefficient should, when the factor $(\epsilon_0 + 2)/(\epsilon_\infty + 2)$ is retained, have a maxi-

[4] J. G. Powles, J. Chem. Phys., 21, 633 (1953).

mum at a frequency

$$\omega = \frac{(\epsilon_\infty + 2)\epsilon_0^{1/2}}{\tau(\epsilon_0 + 2)\epsilon_\infty^{1/2}} \quad (2.45)$$

while the maximum value of κ should be

$$\kappa_m = \frac{\epsilon_0^{1/2} - \epsilon_\infty^{1/2}}{\epsilon_0^{1/2} + \epsilon_\infty^{1/2}} \quad (2.46)$$

Cole[5] has shown that the Onsager equation may be obtained in a form with a complex factor analogous to that of (2.37) and may be reduced approximately to (2.21) when ϵ_0 is so large that $3\epsilon_0/(2\epsilon_0 + \epsilon_\infty)$ may be replaced by $3/2$, usually a very rough approximation. He has generalized the treatment [cf. Eq. I(14.27)] by replacing X in Eqs. (2.38) and (2.39) by the quantity z, where

$$z = \frac{\omega\tau}{(1 - \delta)} \quad (2.47)$$

$$\delta = \frac{1}{3}\beta(\epsilon_\infty + 2)(1 - q) \quad (2.48)$$

in which q is an empirical factor having a value between 0 and 1.1, and β is the orientation polarization, equal to the second term on the right of Eq. (2.10). When $q = 0$, z becomes equivalent to X, giving Eqs. (2.38) and (2.39). When $q = 1$, $z = \omega\tau$, a relation corresponding to the Onsager treatment of the internal field, and, for intermediate values of q, the relation corresponds to a modified Onsager treatment according to the rough approximation which has just been mentioned.

For certain considerations it is useful to rearrange Eq. (2.36) and write it in the form

$$V_D = \frac{4\pi a^3 N}{3} = \frac{\tau RT}{3\eta} \quad (2.49)$$

where V_D is the hypothetical volume of the N molecules in a mole as calculated from relaxation time and viscosity measurements.[6] Departure of V_D from the molar volume given by the density of the liquid should be an indication either of departure from the assumed mechanism of orientation or of the inadequacy of the macroscopic viscosity as a substitute for the microscopic.

3. Rate Theory of Dielectric Relaxation. Kauzmann[1] has given an extensive analysis of dipole orientation as a rate phenomenon,[2-4] con-

[5] R. H. Cole, *J. Chem. Phys.*, **6**, 385 (1938).

[6] W. P. Conner and C. P. Smyth, *J. Am. Chem. Soc.*, **65**, 382 (1943).

[1] W. Kauzmann, *Revs. Mod. Phys.*, **14**, 12 (1942).

[2] H. Eyring, *J. Chem. Phys.*, **4**, 283 (1936).

[3] F. C. Frank, *Trans. Faraday Soc.*, **32**, 1634 (1936).

[4] S. Glasstone, K. J. Laidler, and H. Eyring, "The Theory of Rate Processes," McGraw-Hill, New York, 1941, chap. IX.

sidering (cf. Sec. I.4) that molecular dipole orientation involves passage over a potential energy barrier with a certain probability of jumping from one orientation to another. With the aid of simplifying assumptions, he obtains the polarization $P(t)$, the electric moment per cubic centimeter due to dipole orientation, as a function of time as

$$P(t) = P_0 e^{-k_0 t} \tag{3.1}$$

where P_0 is the orientation polarization at the time $t = 0$, and k_0 is the rate constant for the activation of dipoles, that is, the jump rate, or the mean number of jumps made by a dipole in unit time. When t has such a value that $k_0 t = 1$, $P(t)$ must have decayed to P_0/e. This value of t is a relaxation time, which may be defined as $\tau = 1/k_0$. Kauzmann,[1] using the Lorentz expression for the internal field, shows that the rate of change of the orientation polarization per cubic centimeter, P_m, with time, after the removal at $t = 0$ of a constant external field E which has been acting on the dielectric material, may be written

$$\frac{dP_m}{dt} = -k_0 \frac{\epsilon_\infty + 2}{\epsilon_0 + 2} P_m = -k_0' P_m \tag{3.2}$$

and, when the external field E is not zero,

$$\frac{dP_m}{dt} = -k_0' \left(P_m - N_1 \frac{\mu^2}{3kT} \frac{\epsilon_0 + 2}{3} E \right) \tag{3.3}$$

When E is periodic, so that

$$E = \mathrm{Re}\ (E_0 e^{i\omega \tau}) \tag{3.4}$$

where Re ( ) represents the real part of the expression in parentheses, he obtains for the total polarization per cubic centimeter

$$P_1 = N_1 \alpha_0 \left(E_0 + \frac{4\pi P_1}{3} \right) + \frac{N_1 \mu^2/3kT}{1 + i\omega/k_0'} \frac{\epsilon_0 + 2}{3} E_0 \tag{3.5}$$

Substitution from Eqs. I(5.3), II(2.9), and II(2.10), replacement of ϵ by ϵ^*, which is now complex, and rearrangement give

$$\epsilon^* = \epsilon_\infty + \frac{\epsilon_0 - \epsilon_\infty}{1 + i\omega/k_0'} \tag{3.6}$$

which is identical with (2.21) except that we have $1/k_0'$ instead of τ. Separation of real and imaginary parts gives equations which are seen to be identical with those of Debye [(2.38) and (2.39)] when it is remembered that, from Eq. (3.2),

$$k_0' = \frac{\epsilon_\infty + 2}{\epsilon_0 + 2} k_0 \tag{3.7}$$

and that $1/k_0 = \tau$.

Since it is assumed that the process of molecular rotation requires an activation energy sufficient to overcome the energy barrier separating the two mean equilibrium positions, the number of times such a rotation will occur per second is given by the rate expression[1,4]

$$k = \frac{1}{\tau} = \frac{kT}{h} e^{-\Delta F_\epsilon \ddagger/RT} \tag{3.8}$$

where h is the Planck constant and $\Delta F_\epsilon^\ddagger$ is the molar free energy of activation for dipole relaxation. Since $\Delta F = \Delta H - T \Delta S$, the equation may be rewritten

$$\tau = \frac{h}{kT} e^{\Delta H_\epsilon \ddagger/RT} e^{-\Delta S_\epsilon \ddagger/R} \tag{3.9}$$

where $\Delta H_\epsilon^\ddagger$ is the heat of activation for dipole relaxation and $\Delta S_\epsilon^\ddagger$ is the entropy of activation for dipole relaxation. $\Delta S_\epsilon^\ddagger$ may be calculated since $\Delta F_\epsilon^\ddagger$ is now known, and $\Delta H_\epsilon^\ddagger$ is obtained from the slope of the curve for $\ln \tau$ plotted against $1/T$, since differentiation of Eq. (3.9) gives

$$\Delta H_\epsilon^\ddagger = \frac{R d \ln \tau}{d(1/T)} - RT \tag{3.10}$$

The approximate linearity of this plot of $\ln \tau$ against $1/T$ has been repeatedly established by measurements, which will be discussed in a subsequent chapter. Actually, the slope of the plot of $\ln \tau$ against $1/T$ should increase slightly as the temperature is raised, since

$$\ln \tau = \frac{1}{T} \frac{\Delta H_\epsilon^\ddagger}{R} - \ln T + \left(\ln \frac{h}{k} - \frac{\Delta S_\epsilon^\ddagger}{R} \right) \tag{3.11}$$

An exact linear relationship should be obtained by plotting $\ln T\tau$ against $1/T$, but the accuracy of the results thus far obtained has been insufficient to establish clearly any departure from linearity in the $\ln \tau$ against $1/T$ relationship.

4. Dielectric Constants and Losses of Solutions in Nonpolar Solvents. Since the equations of the preceding section are subject to the same errors when applied to pure polar liquids as the Debye equation for static dielectric constant (Chap. I) it is desirable to obtain expressions for ϵ' and ϵ'' which should be applicable to dilute solutions of polar molecules in a nonpolar solvent. Replacement of N_1 in the second term of Eq. (3.5) by cN_1, where c is the concentration of polar solute in moles per cc., and of $1/k_0'$ by τ, neglecting the small difference between ϵ_0 and ϵ_∞ for the dilute solution, gives

$$P_m = \frac{cN_1\mu^2/3kT}{1 + i\omega\tau} \frac{\epsilon_0 + 2}{3} E_0 \tag{4.1}$$

Introducing this expression for P_m into (3.5) and treating as before in the derivation of (3.6), we obtain

$$\epsilon^* = \epsilon_\infty + \frac{4\pi c N_1 \mu^2}{27kT} \frac{(\epsilon_0 + 2)(\epsilon_\infty + 2)}{1 + i\omega\tau} \tag{4.2}$$

Substitution of (2.2) and separation of real and imaginary parts gives

$$\epsilon' = \epsilon_\infty + \frac{4\pi c N_1 \mu^2}{27kT} \frac{(\epsilon_0 + 2)(\epsilon_\infty + 2)}{1 + \omega^2\tau^2} \tag{4.3}$$

$$\epsilon'' = \frac{4\pi c N_1 \mu^2}{27kT} \frac{(\epsilon_0 + 2)(\epsilon_\infty + 2)\omega\tau}{1 + \omega^2\tau^2} \tag{4.4}$$

Since the loss tangent ϵ''/ϵ' is often used instead of the loss factor, we may divide (4.4) by ϵ' and write

$$\tan\delta = \frac{(\epsilon_0 + 2)(\epsilon_\infty + 2)}{\epsilon'} \frac{4\pi c N_1 \mu^2}{27kT} \frac{\omega\tau}{1 + \omega^2\tau^2} \tag{4.5}$$

Since for dilute solutions of a polar solute in a nonpolar solvent the difference between ϵ_0 and ϵ_∞ is small and ϵ' lies between ϵ_0 and ϵ_∞, the error resulting from the replacement of ϵ_0 and ϵ_∞ by ϵ' should not be large in comparison to the experimental error in $\tan\delta$. We may therefore write as a fair approximation

$$\tan\delta = \frac{(\epsilon' + 2)^2}{\epsilon'} \frac{4\pi c N_1 \mu^2}{27kT} \frac{\omega\tau}{1 + \omega^2\tau^2} \tag{4.6}$$

which has been used[1,2] in the interpretation of loss measurements.

Bolton[3] has used Cole's generalization[4] of the Onsager equation without the approximation $3\epsilon_0/(2\epsilon_0 + \epsilon_\infty) = \frac{3}{2}$. Plotting $\epsilon''/\epsilon_\infty$ against $\epsilon'/\epsilon_\infty$ for water, ethyl alcohol, and t-butyl alcohol, he obtained curves which lay slightly above the ideal semicircle given by the Debye equations and concluded that, since the experimental points lay below or on the semicircles, the Debye theory gave better agreement with experiment in these cases. On the other hand, his use of the Onsager equation gave values of $\omega\tau$ close to 1 as required by Cole's approximation, τ being the molecular relaxation time. The molecular volumes calculated from the relaxation times given by the two methods were: for water, 12×10^{-24} by the Onsager method and 0.6×10^{-24} by the Debye method, as compared to 14×10^{-24} cc. calculated from the van der Waals b coefficient; and, for ethyl alcohol, 160×10^{-24} by the Onsager method and 23×10^{-24} by the Debye method, as compared to 35×10^{-24} cc. from the van der Waals b. As far as this very limited examination of the use of the Onsager equation goes,

[1] W. Jackson and J. G. Powles, *Trans. Faraday Soc.*, **42A**, 101 (1946).

[2] D. H. Whiffen and H. W. Thompson, *Trans. Faraday Soc.*, **42A**, 114 (1946).

[3] H. C. Bolton, *J. Chem. Phys.*, **16**, 486 (1948).

[4] R. H. Cole, *J. Chem. Phys.*, **6**, 385 (1938).

it appears to offer no advantage in its exact form over the approximate use of it made by Cole and Cole.

Fuoss and Kirkwood[5] have applied the Kirkwood equation to binary systems with special reference to polymeric systems. From Eq. I(15.1), one may write

$$\frac{(\epsilon - 1)(2\epsilon + 1)}{9\epsilon} - \frac{(\epsilon_\infty - 1)(2\epsilon_\infty + 1)}{9\epsilon_\infty} = \frac{P'_2 c_2}{V} \tag{4.7}$$

where

$$P'_2 = \frac{4\pi N \mu \bar\mu}{9kT} \tag{4.8}$$

and [cf. Eq. I(10.5)] the molar volume is

$$V = \frac{c_1 M_1 + c_2 M_2}{d} \tag{4.9}$$

Setting

$$\varphi(\epsilon) = \frac{(\epsilon - 1)(2\epsilon + 1)}{\epsilon} \tag{4.10}$$

and

$$\varphi(\epsilon_\infty) = \frac{(\epsilon_\infty - 1)(2\epsilon_\infty + 1)}{\epsilon_\infty} \tag{4.11}$$

Eq. (4.7) becomes

$$[\varphi(\epsilon) - \varphi(\epsilon_\infty)]V = 9P'_2 c_2 \tag{4.12}$$

Fuoss and Kirkwood extend the above equations to the general a.c. case, denoting by $P'_2(\omega)$ the polarization at frequency $f = \omega/2\pi$ and defining a reduced polarization as

$$Q(\omega) = \frac{P'_2(\omega)}{P'_2(0)} = \frac{\varphi(\epsilon) - \varphi(\epsilon_\infty)}{\varphi(\epsilon_0) - \varphi(\epsilon_\infty)} \tag{4.13}$$

where $P'_2(0)$ is the value of P'_2 at zero frequency, corresponding to the static dielectric constant ϵ_0. It is convenient to write for a given system the normalizing constant

$$Z = \frac{\varphi(\epsilon_0) - \varphi(\epsilon_\infty)}{9} \tag{4.14}$$

which is independent of frequency. Q may be separated into its components as

$$Q(\omega) = J(X) - iH(X) \tag{4.15}$$

where

$$X = \ln \frac{\omega_m}{\omega} \tag{4.16}$$

and ω_m is 2π times the frequency at maximum H, which corresponds to ϵ_m. Using the expression for the complex dielectric constant [Eq. (2.2)] we may separate $\varphi(\epsilon)$ to obtain

$$\varphi(\epsilon) = 2\epsilon' - 1 - \frac{\epsilon'}{\epsilon'^2 + \epsilon''^2} - i\epsilon'' \left(2 + \frac{1}{\epsilon'^2 + \epsilon''^2}\right) \tag{4.17}$$

When

$$\epsilon'^2 \gg \epsilon''^2 \tag{4.18}$$

[5] R. M. Fuoss and J. G. Kirkwood, *J. Am. Chem. Soc.*, **63**, 385 (1941).

we may write, to a rather close approximation,

$$\varphi(\epsilon) = 2\epsilon' - 1 - \frac{1}{\epsilon'} - i(2\epsilon'') \qquad (4.19)$$

Comparing real and imaginary parts of Eqs. (4.15) and (4.17) and using the approximation (4.18), we obtain

$$J(X) = \frac{2\epsilon' - 1 - 1/\epsilon' - \varphi(\epsilon_\infty)}{9Z} \qquad (4.20)$$

and

$$H(X) = \frac{2\epsilon''}{9Z} \qquad (4.21)$$

$Q(\omega)$ is simply related to P_2' by (4.13), and P_2' to the moment by (4.8). Q, J, and H are convenient functions to use when a distribution of relaxation times is involved.

5. Distribution of Relaxation Times. If a molecule is not spherical, the processes of orientation by rotation about different axes should require different relaxation times. Perrin[1] has treated the dipolar molecule as an ellipsoid with half axes a, b, and c and has thus replaced $\mu^2/(1 + i\omega\tau)$ in Eq. (2.37) by

$$\frac{\mu_1{}^2}{1 + i\omega\tau_1} + \frac{\mu_2{}^2}{1 + i\omega\tau_2} + \frac{\mu_3{}^2}{1 + i\omega\tau_3} \qquad (5.1)$$

where μ_1, μ_2, and μ_3 are the components of μ along these axes and τ_1, τ_2, and τ_3 are the corresponding relaxation times. The use of this relationship in determining molecular shape will be considered later.

Variations in the local environment of the molecules should give rise to variations in the relaxation times. Wagner[2] and Yager[3] have shown that a Gaussian error distribution reproduces some experimental data satisfactorily when written

$$f(S) = \pi^{1/2}be^{-b^2S^2} \qquad (5.2)$$

where b is a constant which determines the breadth of the distribution and

$$S = \ln \frac{\tau_0}{\tau} \qquad (5.3)$$

in which τ_0 is the most probable relaxation time. $f(S) \, dS$ is the probability of finding a relaxation time τ such that $\ln (\tau_0/\tau)$ lies between S and $S + dS$.

A useful empirical relation developed by Cole and Cole,[4] which will be discussed later in this section, corresponds to the distribution

$$f(S) \, dS = \frac{1}{2\pi} \frac{\sin \alpha\pi}{\cosh (1 - \alpha)S - \cos \alpha\pi} \qquad (5.4)$$

[1] F. Perrin, *J. phys. radium*, **5**, 497 (1934).
[2] K. W. Wagner, *Ann. Physik*, **40**, 817 (1913); *Arch. Elektrotech.*, **3**, 83 (1914).
[3] W. A. Yager, *Physics*, **7**, 434 (1936).
[4] K. S. Cole and R. H. Cole, *J. Chem. Phys.*, **9**, 341 (1941).

Fuoss and Kirkwood[5] found a satisfactory interpolation formula to be

$$H(X) = H(0) \text{ sech } \alpha X \qquad (5.5)$$

where $H(0)$ is the maximum value of $H(X)$, corresponding to $f = f_m$, and α is a parameter determining the width of the H curve at half height [cf. Eq. (4.15)]. Making use of this relation, they derived the expression

$$\frac{F(S)}{H(0)} = \frac{2}{\pi} \frac{\cos{(\alpha\pi/2)} \cosh{\alpha S}}{\cos^2{(\alpha\pi/2)} + \sinh^2{\alpha S}} \qquad (5.6)$$

and showed that

$$H(0) = \frac{\alpha}{2} \qquad (5.7)$$

Substitution of this value for $H(0)$ in Eq. (4.21) gives

$$\frac{4\epsilon_m''}{9Z} = \alpha \qquad (5.8)$$

and similar substitution in (5.6) gives

$$F(S) = \frac{\alpha}{\pi} \frac{\cos{(\alpha\pi/2)} \cosh{\alpha S}}{\cos^2{(\alpha\pi/2)} + \sinh^2{\alpha S}} \qquad (5.9)$$

Kauzmann[6] has analyzed these treatments and has shown that, when the parameters in these three distribution functions are adjusted so as to give the best possible fit, the resulting distributions are rather closely similar. Fuoss and Kirkwood determined α as the slope of the straight line obtained by plotting

$$\cosh^{-1}\frac{H(0)}{H(X)} = \cosh^{-1}\frac{\epsilon_m''(2 + 1/\epsilon_m'^2)}{\epsilon''(2 + 1/\epsilon'^2)} \qquad (5.10)$$

against the logarithm of the frequency. The intersection of the line with the $\log f$ axis determines f_m. With the experimental values of ϵ_m'' and of α, Z can be calculated by means of (5.8). By means of (4.14) and (4.12), this gives a value of the polarization for a static field, from which the mean moment per molecule may be calculated by means of Eqs. II(4.8) and I(15.2).

Fröhlich[7] has given an analysis of the distribution of relaxation times which is helpful in the visualization of the behavior of a concrete model.[8] If $y(\tau)\,d\tau$ is the contribution to the static dielectric constant of the group of dipoles having individual relaxation times in a range $d\tau$ near τ, the total contribution of all the dipoles is

$$\epsilon_0 - \epsilon_\infty = \int_0^\infty y(\tau)\,d\tau \qquad (5.11)$$

[5] See footnote 5, Sec. 4.

[6] W. Kauzmann, *Revs. Mod. Phys.*, **14**, 12 (1942).

[7] H. Fröhlich, "Theory of Dielectrics," Oxford, 1949, sec. 12.

[8] Cf. H. Kramers, *Atti congr. fisici, Como,* 545 (1927); F. H. Branin, Jr., and C. P. Smyth, *J. Chem. Phys.*, **20**, 1121 (1952).

It follows that Eqs. (2.22) and (2.23) become

$$\epsilon' = \epsilon_\infty + \int_0^\infty \frac{y(\tau)\,d\tau}{1 + \omega^2\tau^2} \tag{5.12}$$

$$\epsilon'' = \int_0^\infty \frac{y(\tau)\omega\tau\,d\tau}{1 + \omega^2\tau^2} \tag{5.13}$$

The values for ϵ'' evidently consist of a superposition of Debye curves $\omega\tau/(1 + \omega^2\tau^2)$, with different positions and heights of their respective maxima, and thus give the lower, broader total maximum commonly observed. A model may now be examined in which each molecule has two equilibrium positions with equal energies and opposite dipole directions.[7] It is assumed that the potential barrier between the two positions has a different height for each molecule and that the heights h of the barriers are equally distributed over a range between h_0 and $h_0 + v_0$, that is

$$h = h_0 + v \qquad 0 \leq v \leq v_0 \tag{5.14}$$

The individual relaxation times τ are given by

$$\tau = \tau_0 e^{v/kT} \tag{5.15}$$

and cover a range

$$\tau_0 \leq \tau \leq \tau_1 \qquad \text{where } \tau_1 = \tau_0 e^{v_0/kT} \tag{5.16}$$

For these conditions, it is readily shown[7] that

$$y(\tau) = (\epsilon_0 - \epsilon_\infty)\frac{kT}{v_0}\frac{1}{\tau} \tag{5.17}$$

This corresponds to an equal distribution of potential barriers over a range v_0 with a relative width

$$\frac{\tau_1 - \tau_0}{\tau_0} = e^{v_0/kT} - 1 \tag{5.18}$$

It is evident that the relative width of the distribution should decrease with rising temperature as has been observed in certain liquids.[9] Decrease in v_0 as well as increase in T may contribute to this effect.

The previously mentioned empirical relationship developed by Cole and Cole[4] results in a modification of Eq. (2.21) to give

$$\epsilon^* = \epsilon_\infty + \frac{\epsilon_0 - \epsilon_\infty}{1 + (i\omega\tau_0)^{1-\alpha}} \tag{5.19}$$

where τ_0 is the most probable relaxation time, corresponding to the frequency at which $\epsilon'' = \epsilon_m''$ and α is an empirical constant with values between 0 and 1, a measure of the distribution of the relaxation times.

[9] E. J. Hennelly, W. M. Heston, Jr., and C. P. Smyth, *J. Am. Chem. Soc.*, **70**, 4102 (1948).

This leads to the following equations instead of (2.22) and (2.23):

$$\epsilon' - \epsilon_\infty = \frac{(\epsilon_0 - \epsilon_\infty)[1 + (\omega\tau_0)^{1-\alpha} \sin (\alpha\pi/2)]}{1 + 2(\omega\tau_0)^{1-\alpha} \sin (\alpha\pi/2) + (\omega\tau_0)^{2(1-\alpha)}}$$

$$= \frac{\epsilon_0 - \epsilon_\infty}{2} \left\{ 1 - \frac{\sinh [(1 - \alpha)X]}{\cosh [(1 - \alpha)X] + \sin (\alpha\pi/2)} \right\} \quad (5.20)$$

$$\epsilon'' = \frac{(\epsilon_0 - \epsilon_\infty)(\omega\tau_0)^{1-\alpha} \cos (\alpha\pi/2)}{1 + 2(\omega\tau_0)^{1-\alpha} \sin (\alpha\pi/2) + (\omega\tau_0)^{2(1-\alpha)}}$$

$$= \frac{(\epsilon_0 - \epsilon_\infty) \cos (\alpha\pi/2)}{2\{\cosh [(1 - \alpha)X] + \sin (\alpha\pi/2)\}} \quad (5.21)$$

when $X = \ln \omega\tau_0$. When $\alpha = 0$, these equations reduce to (2.22) and (2.23). Equation (5.20) differs from the original Cole and Cole expression in having $\sin (\alpha\pi/2)$ in the denominator instead of $\cos (\alpha\pi/2)$, which appears to be incorrect.[10]

Equations (2.22) and (2.23) can be combined and written in the form of the equation for a circle

$$\left(\epsilon' - \frac{\epsilon_0 + \epsilon_\infty}{2} \right)^2 + \epsilon''^2 = \left(\frac{\epsilon_0 - \epsilon_\infty}{2} \right)^2 \quad (5.22)$$

Since all values must be positive, this gives a semicircular plot of ϵ'' against ϵ'. An example of this is shown in Fig. 5.1 (cf. Fig. 2.2) for isobutyl bromide.[9] If the values of ϵ'' give a semicircle when plotted against those of ϵ', it means that the data conform to the Debye theory. Cole and Cole[4] found for a considerable number of liquids and solids that the values of ϵ'' commonly fell below the semicircle but could be represented by a semicircular arc intersecting the abscissa axis at the values of ϵ_∞ and ϵ_0. The center of the circle of which this arc was a part lay below the abscissa axis, and the diameter drawn through the center from the ϵ_∞ point made an angle $\alpha\pi/2$ with the abscissa axis. The arc plot is illustrated by Fig. 5.2 for n-octyl bromide (cf. Fig. 2.3).

To determine α, it may be assumed that lines drawn between adjacent plotted points are chords of a circle with its center below the real axis. The center of the circle is given by the intersection of the perpendicular bisectors of these chords and the perpendicular bisector of the abscissa axis between ϵ_∞ and ϵ_0. $\tan \alpha\pi/2$ is measured on the plot, and α is calculated from it. The relaxation time may be calculated from the relation

$$\frac{v}{u} = (\omega\tau_0)^{1-\alpha} \quad (5.23)$$

where v is the distance on the Cole and Cole plot between ϵ_0 and the experimental point, and u is the distance between the point and ϵ_∞. If α were zero, v/u would equal $\omega\tau_0$, which is true for the Debye equations.

[10] H. L. Laquer and C. P. Smyth, *J. Am. Chem. Soc.*, **70**, 4097 (1948).

It follows from simple geometry that

$$\frac{v}{u} = \left[\frac{(\epsilon_0 - \epsilon')^2 + \epsilon''^2}{(\epsilon' - \epsilon_\infty)^2 + \epsilon''^2} \right]^{\frac{1}{2}} \tag{5.24}$$

and from Eq. (5.23) that

$$\log \frac{v}{u} = (1 - \alpha) \log (\omega\tau_0) \tag{5.25}$$

or

$$\log \frac{v}{u} = (1 - \alpha) \log \omega + (1 - \alpha) \log \tau_0$$

$$= (1 - \alpha) \log \lambda_m - (1 - \alpha) \log \lambda \tag{5.26}$$

since $\omega = 2\pi c/\lambda$ and $\tau_0 = \lambda_m/2\pi c$, where c is the velocity of light. It is evident that the values of $\log (v/u)$ calculated from Eq. (5.24), when

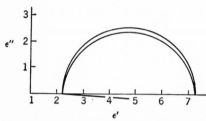

Fig. 5.1. Arc plot of i-butyl bromide. [E. J. Hennelly, W. M. Heston, Jr., and C. P. Smyth, J. Am. Chem. Soc., 70, 4102 (1948).]

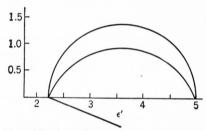

Fig. 5.2. Arc plot of n-octyl bromide. [E. J. Hennelly, W. M. Heston, Jr., and C. P. Smyth, J. Am. Chem. Soc., 70, 4102 (1948).]

plotted against $\log \omega$, should give a straight line of slope $1 - \alpha$ and an intercept at $\log \omega = 0$ equal to $(1 - \alpha) \log \tau_0$; and, when plotted against $\log \lambda$, the values should give a straight line of slope $\alpha - 1$ and an intercept at $\log \lambda = 0$ equal to $(1 - \alpha) \log \lambda_m$. This linearity has been demonstrated for ice and glycerine[4] and for several solutions.[11]

Gevers and Du Pré[12,13] have treated the distribution of relaxation times in solid amorphous dielectrics on the assumption of a statistical scattering of the activation energies determining the diffusion of ions or the rotation of dipoles, with results somewhat like those of Fröhlich[7] (see also Sec. V.7).

The significance of dipole relaxation with regard to the nature of liquids and solids will be considered in Chaps. IV and V.

6. Conductivity and Dielectric Loss. Since the dielectric loss is made evident in the loss current which results from the dissipation of part of

[11] A. D. Franklin, W. M. Heston, Jr., E. J. Hennelly, and C. P. Smyth, J. Am. Chem. Soc., 72, 3447 (1950).

[12] M. Gevers and F. K. Du Pré, Trans. Faraday Soc., 42A, 47 (1946).

[13] M. Gevers, Philips Research Repts., 1, 197, 279, 361, and 447 (1945–46).

the energy of the field as heat, it is desirable in this connection to examine the relation of the apparent conductivity to dielectric constant and loss in the light of the analysis given by Murphy and Morgan.[1] For conductors, the conductivity k is

$$k = \frac{I}{E} = \frac{W}{E^2} \qquad (6.1)$$

where I is the current density, E the voltage gradient, and W the heat developed per second in a unit cube of the material. This proportionality between current and heat developed in the conductor does not hold in a dielectric material, for, in a dielectric, the ratio of heat developed to current flowing varies with the material. In an ideal dielectric there would be no free-ion conduction, but, in actual insulating materials, Joule heat may be produced by the drift of electrons or free ions in the applied field. The total heat developed is the sum of the dielectric loss and the Joule heat. The dielectric loss is thus proportional to the total measured a.c. conductivity minus the d.c. conductivity.

Let a dielectric material of dielectric constant ϵ fill the space between the parallel plates of a two-plate condenser, which has a distance d cm. between the plates, each plate having an area A cm.[2] on each side. If a potential difference V is established between the plates, a charge q per unit area will appear on each plate and a polarization P will be created in the dielectric. The current flowing in the leads to the condenser is $A \, dq/dt$, if we assume that conductivity due to free ions may be neglected, and the conductivity is

$$k = \frac{1}{E} \frac{dq}{dt} \qquad (6.2)$$

Since the following familiar relations hold:

$$E = \frac{V}{d} = \frac{D}{\epsilon} \qquad D = 4\pi q = E + 4\pi P \qquad (6.3)$$

Eq. (6.2) becomes

$$kE = \frac{dq}{dt} = \frac{1}{4\pi} \frac{dD}{dt} = \frac{\epsilon}{4\pi d} \frac{dV}{dt} \qquad (6.4)$$

where all the electrical quantities are expressed in electrostatic units. When the applied potential is alternating, V may be expressed as the real part of

$$V = V_0 e^{i\omega t} \qquad (6.5)$$

and the dielectric constant is complex. The current density in the

[1] E. J. Murphy and S. O. Morgan, *Bell System Tech. J.*, **18**, 502 (1939).

dielectric is then

$$\frac{dq}{dt} = i\omega(\epsilon' - i\epsilon'') \frac{V_0 e^{i\omega t}}{4\pi d}$$

$$= \left(\frac{\epsilon''\omega}{4\pi} + \frac{i\epsilon'\omega}{4\pi}\right) E_0 e^{i\omega t}$$

$$= (k' + ik'') E_0 e^{i\omega t} \tag{6.6}$$

where

$$k' = \frac{\epsilon''\omega}{4\pi} \tag{6.7}$$

and

$$k'' = \frac{\epsilon'\omega}{4\pi} \tag{6.8}$$

We thus have a complex conductivity

$$k^* = k' + ik'' \tag{6.9}$$

For convenience in connection with a subsequent account of methods of measurement, the admittance of the condenser may be expressed in terms of an equivalent parallel capacitance C_p and conductance G_p, so that

$$\frac{dq}{dt} = \frac{0.9 \times 10^{12}}{A} (G_p + iC_p\omega) V_0 e^{i\omega t} \tag{6.10}$$

where G_p is in mhos, C_p is in farads, and 0.9×10^{12} is the ratio of the farad to the electrostatic unit of capacitance and of the mho to the electrostatic unit of conductance. By using the expression for the capacitance C_0 in farads of the empty condenser

$$C_0 = \frac{A}{4\pi d \times 0.9 \times 10^{12}} \tag{6.11}$$

and comparing (6.10) with (6.6), we obtain

$$\epsilon' = \frac{C_p}{C_0} \tag{6.12}$$

$$\epsilon'' = \frac{G_p}{C_0\omega} \tag{6.13}$$

$$k' = \frac{G_p}{4\pi C_0} \tag{6.14}$$

To obtain k' in ohms^{-1} cm.$^{-1}$ we write

$$k' = \frac{\epsilon''\omega}{4\pi \times 0.9 \times 10^{12}} = \frac{\epsilon'' f}{1.8 \times 10^{12}} = \frac{8.85 \times 10^{-2} G_p}{C_0 \,\mu\mu f} \tag{6.15}$$

where $C_0 \,\mu\mu f$ is the capacitance in micromicrofarads.

If we multiply the current given by (6.6) by the voltage $E_0 \cos \omega t$, we obtain the instantaneous power, or heat developed per second, and, from this, by integration over a whole number of half periods, the mean power, or heat developed per cycle:

$$\bar{W} \text{ per second } = k' \frac{E_0{}^2}{2} = \frac{\epsilon'' \omega}{4\pi} \frac{E_0{}^2}{2} \qquad \text{ergs per sec.} \qquad (6.16)$$

The heat developed per cycle in the dielectric is evidently

$$\bar{W} \text{ per cycle } = \frac{\epsilon'' E_0{}^2}{4} \qquad \text{ergs per cycle} \qquad (6.17)$$

These equations (6.16) and (6.17) show that k' is proportional to the heat developed per second and ϵ'' to that developed per cycle.

If we substitute Eq. (2.23) in (6.7), we obtain

$$k' = \frac{1}{4\pi} \frac{(\epsilon_0 - \epsilon_\infty)\omega^2 \tau}{1 + \omega^2 \tau^2} \qquad (6.18)$$

This shows that k' does not pass through a maximum as does ϵ'', but increases with ω, approaching a limiting value k_∞, the infinite-frequency conductivity, which is reached when 1 can be neglected in comparison with $\omega^2 \tau^2$, so that

$$k_\infty = \frac{\epsilon_0 - \epsilon_\infty}{4\pi\tau} \qquad (6.19)$$

As indicated in Sec. 1, the presence in a condenser of two phases may give rise to an apparent dielectric constant e' and loss factor e''. If the phases are present as parallel slabs filling a parallel-plate condenser, the effects may easily be analyzed in terms of an equivalent circuit.[2] Wagner[3,4] has analyzed the case where spherical particles of phase 2 having a real dielectric constant ϵ_2' and a conductivity k_2 are sparsely distributed throughout phase 1, which has a real dielectric constant ϵ_1' and a negligibly small conductivity. The apparent dielectric constant observed for the material as a whole is then found to be

$$e' = e_\infty \left(1 + \frac{K}{1 + \omega^2 T^2} \right) \qquad (6.20)$$

where
$$e_\infty = \epsilon_1' \left[1 + \frac{3q(\epsilon_2' - \epsilon_1')}{2\epsilon_1' + \epsilon_2'} \right] \qquad (6.21)$$

$$K = \frac{9q\epsilon_1'}{2\epsilon_1' + \epsilon_2'} \qquad (6.22)$$

$$T = \frac{2\epsilon_1' + \epsilon_2'}{4\pi \times 0.9 \times 10^{12} k_2} = \frac{2\epsilon_1' + \epsilon_2'}{1.13 \times 10^{13} k_2} \qquad (6.23)$$

[2] J. B. Whitehead, "Lectures on Dielectric Theory and Insulation," McGraw-Hill, 1927, lecture VII.
[3] K. W. Wagner, *Arch. Elektrotech.*, **2**, 371 (1914).
[4] R. W. Sillars, *J. Inst. Elec. Engrs. (London)*, **80**, 378 (1937).

k_2 is expressed in ohms^{-1} cm.$^{-1}$, and q is the volume fraction of phase 2. The loss factor observed for this mixture is

$$e'' = \frac{e_\infty K \omega T}{1 + \omega^2 T^2} \qquad (6.24)$$

and the loss tangent is

$$\tan \delta = \frac{e''}{e'} = \frac{K \omega T}{1 + K + \omega^2 T^2} \qquad (6.25)$$

In Eq. (6.20), it is clear that $e' = e_\infty(1 + K)$ when $\omega^2 T^2$ is small in comparison with 1 and that $e' = e_\infty$ when $\omega^2 T^2$ is large in comparison to 1. The apparent anomalous dispersion occurs at intermediate values of the frequency, which are usually so low that ϵ_1' and ϵ_2' are constant. Under these circumstances, e_∞, K, and T are constant. It is evident that these equations give a frequency dependence for the apparent dielectric constant and loss factors identical in form with that given by the Debye equations. For a simplified Wagner-model dielectric, Sillars[4] calculates that values of $\epsilon_1' = \epsilon_2' = 4$, $k_2 = 9.54 \times 10^5$ e.s.u. $= 1.06 \times 10^{-6}$ ohm^{-1} cm.$^{-1}$, and $q = 0.033$ correspond to $K = 0.1$ and $T = 10^{-6}$ sec. When $\epsilon_1' = \epsilon_2'$, $e_\infty = \epsilon_1' = 4$; consequently, a maximum value 0.2 occurs for e'' at a frequency of $2\pi \times 10^6$ cycles, and e' has a constant value 4.4 at low frequencies and $4.0 = \epsilon_\infty$ at high frequencies. Sillars[4] has calculated loss characteristics for different form factors and has tested them experimentally with suspensions of water droplets in wax. He concludes that the presence of a minute amount of conducting impurity in the form of fine needles could produce a serious loss at low frequencies, although the effect of the same quantity of impurity in spherical form would be negligible. It is evident that small quantities of impurities may seriously affect the dielectric properties of a material if they lead to the formation of an additional phase. The coexistence of two phases of different conductivities in the vicinity of the freezing point not infrequently leads to an apparent peak in the dielectric-constant values.

CHAPTER III

DIELECTRIC CONSTANTS OF GASES AND LIQUIDS

1. The Static Dielectric Constants and Polarizations of Pure Gases and Liquids. This chapter aims to examine the experimentally observed relations between the nature of gases and liquids and their dielectric constants and losses. The dielectric losses of liquids will be discussed in Chap. IV but must occasionally be introduced in this chapter. It has been shown in Chap. I that the Debye equation applies accurately to gases in the normal pressure range. Equation I(9.5) may be written

$$\epsilon = 1 + 4\pi N_1 \left(\alpha_0 + \frac{\mu^2}{3kT} \right) \tag{1.1}$$

This states that the dielectric constant of a gas is a linear function of the number of molecules per cc., N_1. When $N_1 = 0$, that is, for a vacuum, the dielectric constant is unity. For constant N_1, the dielectric constant of a nonpolar gas is independent of temperature, while, for a polar gas, it is a linear function of the reciprocal of the absolute temperature and increases as the square of the dipole moment.

At high pressures, the polarization of a gas may show a small variation with pressure. For air, nitrogen, and hydrogen, Tangl[1] found no measurable deviation from constancy for the Clausius-Mosotti expression $(\epsilon - 1)/(\epsilon + 2)d$ up to 100 atm., and similar constancy was found[2] for nitrogen, hydrogen, and methane up to 150, 200, or 250 atm. However, for the nonpolar carbon dioxide at 100°C., Keyes and Kirkwood[3] found a polarization of 7.485 cc. at 10 atm. pressure, while, at 151 atm., the polarization had increased to 7.729. At 35°, the effect of pressure was smaller, the polarization increasing from 7.488 at 10 atm. to 7.691 at 100 atm. In liquid carbon dioxide at 0°, an increase of pressure from 50 to 200 atm. lowered the polarization from 7.809 to 7.798, instead of raising it as in the case of the gas. Slightly larger increases of polarization with

[1] K. Tangl, *Ann. Physik*, **29**, 59 (1908).

[2] H. H. Uhlig, J. G. Kirkwood, and F. G. Keyes, *J. Chem. Phys.*, **1**, 155 (1933); A. Michels, P. Sanders, and A. Schipper, *Physica*, **2**, 753 (1935).

[3] F. G. Keyes and J. G. Kirkwood, *Phys. Rev.*, **36**, 754 (1930).

increasing pressure were observed in the polar gas ammonia.[1,4] On the basis of a statistical calculation of the average internal field, Keyes and Kirkwood[5] developed an equation which accounted qualitatively but not quantitatively for the small increase in polarization with pressure. An equation of Kirkwood's[5a] involving the effect of the translational fluctuations on the average local electric field was examined[5b] in the light of measurements on ethylene at temperatures of 25 and 50° and pressures up to 500 atm. These measurements showed the Clausius-Mosotti expression for ethylene to vary by about 2 per cent and pass through a maximum.

Kyropoulos[6] found very slight decreases in polarization for the nonpolar carbon disulfide and benzene with increasing pressure up to 3,000 kg. per cm.[2], a slight decrease for the somewhat polar ethyl ether, and considerable decreases for the polar water, methyl alcohol, ethyl alcohol, and acetone. This latter decrease is presumably due to the same cause as that observed in the polarization of a polar solute in a nonpolar solvent as the concentration increases. Danforth[7] carried out measurements at 3.71 and 247 kc. at pressures from 1 to 12,000 atm. and found similar decreases in the polarization with increase in pressure. When the reciprocal of the specific polarization was plotted against density, straight lines were obtained for the more polar liquids chlorobenzene, bromobenzene, ethyl alcohol, isobutyl alcohol, hexyl alcohol, eugenol, and glycerol, but not for the less polar and the nonpolar carbon disulfide and pentane. The effect of pressure is illustrated by the values of the dielectric constant and specific polarization in Table 1.1, selected from Danforth's data.[7]

A very interesting feature of the work is that measurements at a higher frequency, 247 kc., on isobutyl alcohol, glycerol, and eugenol show a decrease of dielectric constant at very high pressures at 0°, but not at 30°, for the first two substances, and at 0, 30, and 50° for eugenol. This anomalous dispersion is, presumably, due to the increase in viscosity of the liquids with increase in pressure.

Danforth derived an equation to account qualitatively for the variation in the specific polarization

$$\frac{\epsilon - 1}{\epsilon + 2} \frac{1}{d} = \frac{4\pi N_1 \alpha}{3 + (4\pi - 3c)N_1 \alpha d} \tag{1.2}$$

in which α is the total polarizability per molecule and c is the constant of

[4] F. G. Keyes and J. G. Kirkwood, *Phys. Rev.*, **36**, 1570 (1930).

[5] F. G. Keyes and J. G. Kirkwood, *Phys. Rev.*, **37**, 202 (1931).

[5a] J. G. Kirkwood, *J. Chem. Phys.*, **4**, 592 (1936).

[5b] H. G. David, S. D. Hamann, and J. F. Pearse, *J. Chem. Phys.*, **19**, 1491 (1951).

[6] S. Kyropoulos, *Z. Physik*, **40**, 507 (1926).

[7] W. E. Danforth, *Phys. Rev.*, **38**, 1224 (1931).

the inner field.   When $c = 4\pi/3$, this becomes identical with the Debye equation.   Danforth's equation, which is somewhat similar to the later equation of van Arkel and Snoek (Sec. I.12), shows that with constant polarizability the polarization will increase with pressure if c is greater than $4\pi/3$ and decrease if it is less.   As α, and possibly c, may change with these large pressure changes, the equation is useful mainly in a qualitative analysis of the possibilities.

TABLE 1.1. VARIATION[7] OF STATIC DIELECTRIC CONSTANT AND SPECIFIC POLARIZATION WITH PRESSURE AT 30°C.

Substance	Static dielectric constant			$(\epsilon - 1)/(\epsilon + 2)d$		
	1 atm.	4,000 atm.	12,000 atm.	1 atm.	4,000 atm.	12,000 atm.
CS_2	2.61	3.11	3.52	0.282	0.277	0.271
C_5H_{12}	1.82	2.12	2.33	0.356	0.345	0.339
$(C_2H_5)_2O$	4.15	6.05	7.68	0.710	0.700	0.655
C_6H_5Cl	5.41	6.33		0.592	0.554	
C_6H_5Br	5.22	5.88		0.399	0.365	
C_2H_5OH	23.2	28.7	33.7	1.127	0.959	0.857
$C_3H_5(OH)_3$	42.8	49.1	57.6	0.744	0.698	0.645

Earlier investigations[8-14] of the pressure dependence of the dielectric constants of liquids agree in indicating decrease of polarization with increase in pressure.

The polarization of a nonpolar liquid at ordinary pressures is approximately independent of temperature as required by the Clausius-Mosotti expression, which means that the dielectric constant changes with temperature only to the extent that the number of molecules per cc. changes. Danforth's values for the specific polarization of carbon disulfide were identical at 30 and 75°.   The polarizations of several nonpolar liquid hydrocarbons showed[15] a very small linear increase with temperature, the polarization-temperature curves being approximately parallel to one another.   For example, the molar polarization of n-heptane was found to be 34.09 at $-90°$ and 34.56 at 50°, while the dielectric-constant values were 2.073 at $-90°$ and 1.881 at 50°, and the densities were 0.7738 and 0.6577.   The dielectric constants of nonpolar liquids lie, for the most

[8] W. C. Roentgen, *Ann. Physik*, **52**, 593 (1894).

[9] F. Ratz, *Z. physik. Chem.*, **19**, 94 (1896).

[10] R. Ortvay, *Ann. Physik*, **36**, 1 (1911).

[11] G. Falckenberg, *Ann. Physik*, **61**, 145 (1920).

[12] F. Waibel, *Ann. Physik*, **72**, 161 (1923).

[13] M. Grenacher, *Ann. Physik*, **77**, 138 (1925).

[14] C. Francke, *Ann. Physik*, **77**, 159 (1925).

[15] R. W. Dornte and C. P. Smyth, *J. Am. Chem. Soc.*, **52**, 3546 (1930).

part, between 1.8 and 2.4.   However, the unusually high polarizability of the small carbon disulfide molecule leads to a value[16] 2.65 for the dielectric constant of the liquid at 10°.   The dielectric constants of liquids consisting of small nonpolar molecules may, however, be considerably smaller than the usual lower limit.   The dielectric constant of liquid oxygen,[17] for example, is only 1.505 at 80.7°K.   Liquid helium II at 1.97°K. has a dielectric constant of 1.0555, which increases as the density increases up to the temperature, 2.19°K., of the transition to liquid helium I.   Above this transition, the dielectric constant decreases as the density decreases with rising temperature.[18]   The molar polarization decreases by 1 per cent from 0.505 to 0.500 as the temperature rises from 1.97 to 4.21°K.   The polarization of the gas at 273°K. calculated from the measurements of Jelatis[19] is 0.516, a value which is identical with that of the molar refraction of the gas extrapolated to infinite wavelength.

The inaccuracy of the Debye equation for a polar liquid has been shown in Sec. I.16, but, in spite of this, the polarizations of some pure polar liquids[20] and even of certain polar solids[21] have been shown to vary linearly as the reciprocal of the absolute temperature.   The slopes of these lines would, however, give much too low values for the dipole moments.   The linearity of the Kirkwood expression $\dfrac{(\epsilon - 1)(2\epsilon + 1)}{9\epsilon} \dfrac{M}{d}$ (Sec. I.15) as a function of the reciprocal of the absolute temperature has been used to calculate dipole moments[22] (Sec. I.16).   The more or less linear dependence of the dielectric constant of a polar liquid upon the number of molecules per cc., the square of the dipole moment, and the reciprocal of the absolute temperature is shown by the moderate success of Wyman's empirical equation I(14.29), which is equivalent to the approximate form of the Onsager equation I(14.26) for liquids of high dielectric constant.   The linear dependence of the dielectric constant upon the number of molecules per cc. is well illustrated (Fig. 14.1, Chap. I) by the values for the normal alkyl bromides,[22] which have virtually the same dipole moment in molecules increasing regularly in size.   Increase in molecular size reduces the number of dipoles per cc. and, consequently, the dielectric constant.   The dielectric constants of thirteen of these liquids from ethyl to n-hexadecyl bromide give a satisfactory straight line

[16] A. E. Stearn and C. P. Smyth, *J. Am. Chem. Soc.*, **56**, 1667 (1934).

[17] G. L. Lewis and C. P. Smyth, *J. Am. Chem. Soc.*, **61**, 3063 (1939).

[18] W. H. Keesom, "Helium," Elsevier, New York, 1942, pp. 319–323.

[19] J. G. Jelatis, Measurements of Dielectric Constant and Dipole Moment of Gases by the Beat-frequency Method, *MIT Lab. Insulation Research Tech. Rept.* 7 (1947).

[20] C. P. Smyth and S. O. Morgan, *J. Am. Chem. Soc.*, **50**, 1547 (1928).

[21] C. P. Smyth and C. S. Hitchcock, *J. Am. Chem. Soc.*, **55**, 1830 (1933).

[22] W. M. Heston, Jr., E. J. Hennelly, and C. P. Smyth, *J. Am. Chem. Soc.*, **72**, 2071 (1950).

when plotted against the number of molecules per cubic centimeter, calculated from the densities of the liquids.

Although, as indicated in the preceding paragraph, the dielectric constant of a liquid is normally an approximately linear function of the reciprocal of the absolute temperature, Dodd and Roberts[23,24] have obtained linear plots of dielectric constant against temperature for several liquids over a temperature range of 20 to 30° above the freezing point. On supercooling, the polar liquids investigated showed a small but abrupt increase in the slope of the curve in the vicinity of the freezing point, but the nonpolar liquids did not. The increase in slope was[24] approximately proportional to $\epsilon_0 - n^2$. An analogous discontinuity in slope was observed for the viscosities[25] and the conductivities[26] of supercooled liquids. Any structural change in the supercooled liquid should affect the dielectric constant of a polar liquid much more than that of a nonpolar one, which is virtually independent of molecular orientation, but there appears to be no reason for an abrupt change, however small, in the absence of crystallization.

2. The Static Dielectric Constants and Polarizations of Nonaqueous Solutions. Early work on dielectric constants included attempts to represent the dielectric constant of a mixture as a function of the dielectric constants and concentrations of the individual components of the mixture. Summaries of such work may be found in papers by Lichtenecker[1] and Lowry.[2] If the components of the mixture are nonpolar, the polarizations should be very nearly additive, as are the refractions. The dielectric constant of the mixture is then calculable from its density, and the polarizations of the individual components can be found by means of Eq. I(10.6). If, however, one of the components is polar, the variation of its polarization with concentration makes impossible the calculation of the polarization of the mixture from those of its pure components. Onsager's equation I(14.30) shows that for a dilute solution the dielectric constant is a linear function of the number of polar molecules per cubic centimeter of solution. This has been demonstrated by Hedestrand[3] and Halverstadt and Kumler,[4] who have examined data for solutions in nonpolar solvents of over fifty polar compounds of widely different nature and have found, in every case, that the dielectric constant of the solution is a linear function of the weight fraction of solute as long as the

[23] C. Dodd and G. N. Roberts, *Proc. Phys. Soc. (London)*, **63B**, 814 (1950).

[24] G. N. Roberts, *J. Am. Chem. Soc.*, **75**, 2264 (1953).

[25] C. Dodd and Hu Pak Mi, *Proc. Phys. Soc. (London)*, **62B**, 454 (1949).

[26] N. N. Greenwood and R. L. Martin, *J. Chem. Soc.*, 1795 (1951).

[1] K. Lichtenecker, *Physik. Z.*, **27**, 115 (1926).

[2] H. H. Lowry, *J. Franklin Inst.*, **203**, 413 (1927).

[3] G. Hedestrand, *Z. physik. Chem.*, **2B**, 428 (1929).

[4] I. F. Halverstadt and W. D. Kumler, *J. Am. Chem. Soc.*, **64**, 2988 (1942).

weight fraction is less than 0.01. The linearity very often extends to weight fraction 0.08 or higher and may even cover the entire concentration range, as in the case of solutions of chlorobenzene in benzene,[5] which deviate from linearity by no more than 1 per cent. On the other hand solutions of chlorobenzene in hexane deviate by as much as 8 per cent from linear dependence upon mole fraction. The dielectric constants of solutions of the more polar molecules of o-dichlorobenzene in benzene deviate by a maximum of 2 per cent from linear dependence upon the mole fraction of the polar component, while for solutions in hexane the maximum deviation is about 11 per cent.[5] The polarizations P_{12} of the mixture and P_2 of the polar component show more deviation from linearity than does the dielectric constant in the cases of chlorobenzene, o-dichlorobenzene, and m-dichlorobenzene, but are linear in the case of the nonpolar p-dichlorobenzene. The smaller polar molecule of ethyl bromide gives a large deviation from linearity in the dielectric constant and polarizations of its solutions in heptane,[6] the P_{12} curve actually passing through a maximum. As the polarization of pure ethyl bromide increases slightly with rising temperature from -90 to $+20°$, while the polarizations of the solutions containing less than 0.95 ethyl bromide decrease, the polarization of a mixture containing about 0.95 mole fraction of ethyl bromide is virtually independent of temperature. The behavior of ethyl iodide in heptane[7] is very similar to that of ethyl bromide in hexane. The slightly smaller dipole moment of the molecule and slightly greater screening of the dipole by the larger-sized halogen atom reduces the molecular field somewhat, so that the curvature of the P_{12} curves is a little less pronounced and the polarization of pure ethyl iodide decreases very slowly with rising temperature instead of increasing as in the case of ethyl bromide. In the butyl halides[8] the polarization of the pure liquid decreases more rapidly with rising temperature and in the case of heptyl bromide still more rapidly, for as the molecular size increases the effect of the molecular field decreases and the liquid approaches more nearly the conditions represented by the Debye equation. It has been shown in Chap. I that the Onsager and Kirkwood equations are approximately applicable even to the pure polar liquids. The departure of the polarization from Debye behavior is greater, the larger and more exposed the molecular dipole and the smaller the molecule.

3. **Associated Liquids.** At one time it was customary for many investigators to attribute to molecular association any departure from what was considered to be normal behavior, such, for instance, as additivity

[5] C. P. Smyth, S. O. Morgan, and J. C. Boyce, *J. Am. Chem. Soc.*, **50**, 1536 (1928).
[6] C. P. Smyth and S. O. Morgan, *J. Am. Chem. Soc.*, **50**, 1547 (1928).
[7] C. P. Smyth and W. N. Stoops, *J. Am. Chem. Soc.*, **51**, 3312 (1930).
[8] C. P. Smyth and H. E. Rogers, *J. Am. Chem. Soc.*, **52**, 2227 (1930).

of properties in a binary mixture. The variation of polarization with concentration was attributed[1-3] to the pairing of molecules to give zero moment, but the only evidence for the formation of these paired molecules was, in most cases, the fact that the assumption of their existence made it possible to reproduce the experimental results by the use of empirically determined constants. The discussion in the preceding section has made it evident that departure of dielectric constant or polarization from linear dependence upon concentration is normally not to be attributed to molecular association or polymerization, but there are occasional

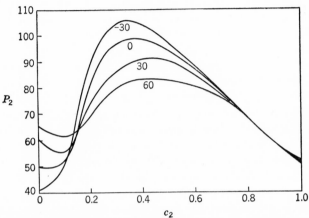

FIG. 3.1. Apparent polarization P_2 of ethyl alcohol in solution in hexane and heptane. [C. P. Smyth and W. N. Stoops, J. Am. Chem. Soc., **51**, 3312 (1929).]

instances of strong influence of molecular association upon the behavior of the polarization. An outstanding example of this is found in the case of the alcohols,[4] in which hydrogen bonding between hydroxyl groups produces polymers. The values of P_{12} and P_2 (Fig. 3.1) for fairly dilute ethyl alcohol solutions increase with rising temperature instead of decreasing in the normal fashion. In very dilute solutions and in the pure alcohol, the polarization increases with the temperature. At intermediate concentrations the polarization decreases with rising temperature, with the result that the P_2-c_2 curves intersect both in the dilute and concentrated regions. The values of P obtained by extrapolating these P_2 curves to zero concentration of alcohol obviously do not correspond to the unassociated state, since they increase with rising temperature instead of decreasing. The P_{12}-c_2 and the P_2-c_2 curves for butyl alcohol in heptane show a less sharply defined maximum and a greater dependence

[1] J. Rolinski, *Physik. Z.*, **29**, 658 (1928).

[2] K. Höjendahl, Thesis, Copenhagen, 1928.

[3] J. Errera, Leipziger Vorträge, Hirzel, Leipzig, 1929, p. 105.

[4] C. P. Smyth and W. N. Stoops, *J. Am. Chem. Soc.*, **51**, 3312, 3330 (1929).

of polarization upon temperature in the concentrated solutions, while for octyl alcohol in heptane the maximum disappears in the P_{12}-c_2 curves and is less pronounced in the P_2-c_2 curves. This decrease in the effect of orientation is also evident in the variation with temperature of the polarization in the pure alcohols. Whereas the polarization of ethyl alcohol increases with temperature over the entire range, that of butyl alcohol at first increases, then becomes practically constant, and finally decreases with rising temperature. The polarization of the n-octyl alcohol, however, decreases with rising temperature over the entire temperature range within which it is measured. Another indication of this effect is given by the variation in orientation polarization for these alcohols, the values of which for pure ethyl, butyl, and n-octyl alcohols at 20°C. are, respectively, 38.8, 55.1, and 78.6, although the dipole moments of the monomers are practically identical. In dilute solution this progressive variation of the effect of orientation does not occur, the curves for the three alcohols all being quite similar.

These complicated polarization curves can be represented quantitatively by the arbitrary assumption of a sufficient number of molecular complexes whose polarizations and relative concentrations provide the necessary adjustable parameters.[5,6] Rodebush, Eddy, and Eubank[7] made additional measurements on solutions containing less than 0.15 mole fraction of alcohol and concluded that the maximum could not be explained upon any reasonable assumption and must, therefore, be due to the failure of the Clausius-Mosotti expression and, hence, be illusory. They plotted a "molal polarizability"

$$\frac{\epsilon - 1}{4\pi} \frac{c_1 M_1 + c_2 M_2}{d} = \frac{(\epsilon - 1)V}{4\pi} \tag{3.1}$$

which showed no maximum or minimum, in contrast to the molar polarization. However, the curves for different temperatures intersected, and their behavior was attributed to the existence of a dimer in these moderately dilute solutions. Similarly, Schupp[8] found that the polarization of phenol, like that of methyl alcohol and of n-butyl alcohol, in solution in carbon tetrachloride showed a maximum at an intermediate concentration, while no maximum occurred when the dielectric constant of the polar solute calculated from the volume fraction was plotted against mole fraction. These dielectric-constant curves flattened out at very low concentrations in contrast to the minimum given at low temperatures by the

[5] K. L. Wolf and W. Herold, *Z. physik. Chem.*, **27B**, 58 (1934).

[6] O. Fuchs and K. L. Wolf, Dielektrische Polarisation, "Hand- und Jahrbuch der chemischen Physik," A. Eucken and K. L. Wolf, Akademische Verlagsgesellschaft m.b.H., Leipzig, 1935, vol. 6, pp. 422–428.

[7] W. H. Rodebush, C. R. Eddy, and L. D. Eubank, *J. Chem. Phys.*, **8**, 889 (1940).

[8] R. L. Schupp, *Z. Elektrochem.*, **53**, 12 (1949).

polarization curves. The maxima were attributed to the inapplicability of the Debye theory to the concentrated solutions.

Measurements by Müller,[9] Mortier,[10] and Hoecker[11] carried out at higher dilutions showed an apparent minimum in the polarization-concentration curve for methyl alcohol in benzene at mole fraction 0.006 of methyl alcohol and at about 0.005 of ethyl alcohol in benzene. However, the precise measurements of Maryott[12] extending down to 0.00013 mole fraction of alcohol gave constant polarization values in this region, indicating the existence of the alcohols in these very dilute solutions only as single molecules, so widely separated from one another as to behave practically like gaseous molecules.

Seemingly, the best attempt at a quantitative representation of the behavior of the straight-chain alcohols is Kirkwood's application[13] of his equation (Sec. I.15) based upon a rough quasi-crystalline model of local liquid structure, in which each molecule possesses a coordination shell of nearest neighbors beyond which orientational correlation does not extend. On the assumption that orientational correlation is appreciable only between an alcohol molecule and the members of the chain of which it forms a part through hydrogen bonding, Kirkwood has calculated dielectric-constant values for methyl, ethyl, n-propyl, n-butyl, and n-amyl alcohol molecules, which are 10 to 20 per cent below the observed values.

If no molecular association occurred, the polarizations and dielectric constants of the octyl alcohols should be approximately the same, being calculable by means of the Debye equation from the little-differing molar refractions and densities and the approximate moment value 1.7×10^{-18}, because of the dilution of the dipoles by the octyl groups. The values thus obtained are 5.9 for the dielectric constant and 100 for the polarization at 25°C. In Table 3.1 are listed the dielectric constants, molar polarizations, and molar refractions of twenty-two isomeric octyl alcohols.[4,14]

It is evident that the type of orientation predominating in the alcohol depends upon the location of the hydroxyl group in the molecule. When the dipoles are at the end of a long carbon chain and remote from any branch in the chain, they orient in such a way as to reinforce one another. However, when they are attached to a tertiary carbon, they appear to be so screened that they cannot line up in this way, but, rather, tend to oppose one another, making the dielectric constant and polarization

[9] F. H. Müller and P. Mortier, *Physik. Z.*, **36**, 371 (1935).

[10] P. Mortier, *Bull. Acad. Belg.*, **21**, 594 (1935).

[11] F. E. Hoecker, *J. Chem. Phys.*, **4**, 431 (1936); *ibid.*, **5**, 372 (1937).

[12] A. A. Maryott, *J. Am. Chem. Soc.*, **63**, 3079 (1941).

[13] J. G. Kirkwood, *Trans. Faraday Soc.*, **42A**, 7 (1946).

[14] C. P. Smyth, *Chem. Revs.*, **6**, 549 (1929).

TABLE 3.1. DIELECTRIC CONSTANTS AND POLARIZATION OF ISOMERIC OCTYL ALCOHOLS AT 25°C.

Substance	ϵ	P	Substance	ϵ	P
C—C—C—C—C—C—C—C—OH	9.8	118.3	C OH C—C—C—C—C—C—C	7.16	106.9
OH C—C—C—C—C—C—C—C	7.7	110.1	OH C—C—C—C—C—C—C C	3.46	72.8
OH C—C—C—C—C—C—C—C	6.8	104.9	C OH C—C—C—C—C—C—C	5.4	100.1
OH C—C—C—C—C—C—C—C	5.0	91.0	C OH C—C—C—C—C—C—C	6.00	99.6
C C—C—C—C—C—C—C—OH	9.8	118.6	C OH C—C—C—C—C—C—C	5.15	95.1
C C—C—C—C—C—C—C—OH	7.1	106.9	OH C—C—C—C—C—C—C C	3.76	75.4
C C—C—C—C—C—C—C—OH	4.37	85.4	OH C C—C—C—C—C—C—C	3.44	71.0
C C—C—C—C—C—C—C—OH	2.85	63.1	OH C—C—C—C—C—C—C C	2.92	61.8
C C—C—C—C—C—C—C—OH	4.95	92.6	OH C C—C—C—C—C—C—C	7.18	104.8
C OH C—C—C—C—C—C	5.9	100.5	OH C C—C—C—C—C—C	3.36	70.6
C OH C—C—C—C—C—C	3.58	75.5			

abnormally low. Every intermediate condition may be represented. As the rigidity of the chain and hence the shape of the molecule depend upon the positions both of the hydroxyl group and of the branching of the chain, the relation of the orientation to the structural formula is very complex.

The fatty acid molecules are known[15,16] to associate to form dimers

[15] E. N. Lassetre, *Chem. Revs.*, **20**, 259 (1937).

[16] L. Pauling, "The Nature of the Chemical Bond," 2d ed., Cornell University Press, Ithaca, N.Y., 1940, p. 306.

until the low concentrations of very dilute solutions are reached. Not only the polarizations, but also the dielectric constants of pure liquid acetic[17,18] and butyric[17] acids, increase with increasing temperature.[17] On dilution with benzene, not only the dielectric constants but also the polarizations drop and continue to drop with increasing dilution until very low solute concentrations are reached.   Pohl, Hobbs, and Gross[19] have found, for formic, acetic, propionic, butyric, trimethylacetic, monochloroacetic, and benzoic acids in benzene solution, that the polarizations are increasing gradually with increasing dilution at mole fraction 0.01 and, below mole fraction 0.004, rise rapidly to values belonging to the monomer alone.   In heptane solution, the polarizations of formic and acetic acids are lower and do not rise rapidly until the concentrations approach a value as low as 0.001 mole fraction.   In ether solution, where the molecules are not dimerized,[15] the polarization of acetic acid shows[17] the normal increase with increasing dilution, reaching a polarization at infinite dilution close to that subsequently found in benzene solution.[19] Very high values reported[20] for the dielectric constant of trifluoroacetic acid were subsequently shown to arise from a large error caused by electrode polarization.[18]

There seems to be no doubt that, at extremely low concentrations in benzene solution, the carboxylic acid molecules exist in monomeric form. With increasing concentration, the monomers tend to dimerize into the almost, if not quite, nonpolar ring structure containing two hydrogen bonds indicated by electron diffraction:[21]

The polarizations of the dilute solutions are calculable[19] in terms of the equilibrium constant

$$K = \frac{c_1{}^2}{c_2}$$

where c_1 is the number of moles of monomer and c_2 is the number of moles of dimer per unit volume.   It would appear that as the acid concentration increases, the opportunity increases for the formation of higher polymers in which only one hydrogen bond exists between any two molecules.

[17] C. P. Smyth and H. E. Rogers, *J. Am. Chem. Soc.*, **52**, 1824 (1930).
[18] W. Dannhauser and R. H. Cole, *J. Am. Chem. Soc.*, **74**, 6015 (1952).
[19] H. A. Pohl, M. E. Hobbs, and P. M. Gross, *Ann. N.Y. Acad. Sci.*, **40**, 389 (1940).
[20] J. H. Simons and K. E. Lorentzen, *J. Am. Chem. Soc.*, **72**, 1426 (1950).
[21] L. Pauling and L. O. Brockway, *Proc. Nat. Acad. Sci. U.S.*, **20**, 336 (1934).

Polar polymeric chains would thus be formed, with corresponding increase in the molar polarization of the acid. Since these chains would have slightly higher energy than the rings because of the nonbonding hydrogen at one end, their formation would be favored by increasing temperature, with consequent tendency toward increase in the dielectric constant and polarization of the acid.

The most important associated liquid is, of course, water. Because of its considerable dipole moment, 1.85×10^{-18}, and small molecular size, the dielectric constant should be large and should decrease fairly rapidly with rising temperature. Wyman[22] has represented his accurate measurements of the dielectric constant of water at 1.4 to 81×10^8 cycles by the equation

$$\epsilon = 78.54[1 - 0.00460(t - 25) + 0.0000088(t - 25)^2]$$

These values are in good agreement with those of Drake, Pierce, and Dow[23] measured at 0.118 to 0.766×10^8 cycles. In spite of the high frequencies, these may be regarded as static dielectric-constant values. Akerlof and Oshry[24] have used the method of Wyman at frequencies from 430 to 840 megacycles to measure the dielectric constant of water in equilibrium with its vapor in the temperature range from the normal boiling point to the critical temperature, obtaining values which are represented as a function of the absolute temperature T by the equation

$$\epsilon = 5321/T + 233.76 - 0.9297T + 0.001417T^2 - 0.0000008292T^3$$

At 370°, the dielectric constant has decreased to 9.74. Values computed from Wyman's equation fall on the curve given by this equation.

It has been mentioned in Sec. I.15 that use of the Onsager equation to calculate the dielectric constant from the molecular dipole moment gives a value of 31 for the dielectric constant of water at 25° as compared to 78.5 observed, while the Kirkwood equation gives 78.2 at 25°, and a 12 per cent too high value at 83°.

It has been pointed out[25] that the linear attachment of two molecular dipoles, each of moment μ, to each other to give a dimer of moment 2μ would increase the orientation polarization from $4\pi N\mu^2/9kT$ to $4\pi(N/2)(2\mu)^2/9kT$, that is, would double it, and would thus change the apparent moment calculated on the basis of single molecules to $\sqrt{2}\mu$. The formation of higher polymers would effect correspondingly greater changes, 2 being replaced by n, the number of single molecules in the polymer. An angle other than zero between the directions of the associated dipole axes, of course, diminishes the resultant effect.

[22] J. Wyman, *Phys. Rev.*, **35**, 623 (1930).
[23] F. H. Drake, G. W. Pierce, and M. T. Dow, *Phys. Rev.*, **35**, 613 (1930).
[24] G. C. Akerlof and H. I. Oshry, *J. Am. Chem. Soc.*, **72**, 2844 (1950).
[25] C. P. Smyth, *J. Phys. Chem.*, **43**, 131 (1939).

Other liquids having still larger dielectric constants because of still larger molecular dipoles, small molecular size, and hydrogen bonding are hydrogen fluoride, hydrogen cyanide, and the N-methylamides. Hydrogen fluoride, with a dipole moment 1.94×10^{-18} for the single molecule in the vapor,[26,27] has dielectric-constant values[28] for the liquid as follows: 174.8 at $-73°$, 134.2 at $-42°$, 110.6 at $-27°$, and 83.6 at $0°$. The molecular dipole moment and the dielectric constant at $0°$ have values slightly higher than those of water. The solid and the vapor near the boiling point are known[29] to contain long polymeric, zigzag chains. The orientation of these chains or of their segments in the measuring electric field is the presumable cause of a dielectric constant higher than the rather high value which should arise merely from the large dipole moment and small molecular size. Hydrogen cyanide, with a large dipole moment (2.93×10^{-18}) for the single molecule in the vapor,[30] has the following dielectric-constant values for the liquid:[31] 213.2 at $-15°$ (supercooled), 158.1 at $0°$, 114.9 at $20°$, and 105.7 at $25.7°$, the boiling point. Since the HCN molecules should form linear polymers, a little association should raise the dielectric constant considerably. The existence in the liquid at any instant of transitory linear polymers containing two to four HCN molecules and having dipole moments of 6 to 12×10^{-18} is sufficient to account for the abnormally high dielectric constant and temperature coefficient of dielectric constant. Increased association with decreasing temperature accounts for the rapid increase in dielectric constant.

The dielectric constant[32] of N-methylformamide, $HCONH(CH_3)$, decreases from 200.1 at $15°$ to 167.1 at $35°$; that of N-methylpropionamide decreases from 188.1 at $15°$ to 156.7 at $35°$. At $25°$, the values for these and some related compounds[32,33] are: formamide, 110; acetamide, 74 (extrapolated); N-methylformamide, 182.4; N-methylpropionamide, 172.2; N,N-dimethylformamide, 36.71; N,N-dimethylacetamide, 37.78. The high values for the monosubstituted amides are attributed to association as chain polymers, while the two amino hydrogens in the unsubstituted amides permit a greater variety of associated forms, some of which have low moments.[32] The much smaller values of the disubstituted amides result from the elimination of the hydrogen bonds formed by the amino hydrogens.

[26] N. B. Hannay and C. P. Smyth, *J. Am. Chem. Soc.*, **68**, 171 (1946).

[27] R. A. Oriani and C. P. Smyth, *J. Chem. Phys.*, **16**, 1167 (1948).

[28] K. Fredenhagen and J. Dahmlos, *Z. anorg. allgem. Chem.*, **178**, 272 (1929).

[29] See R. A. Oriani and C. P. Smyth, *J. Am. Chem. Soc.*, **70**, 125 (1948).

[30] C. P. Smyth and K. B. McAlpine, *J. Am. Chem. Soc.*, **56**, 1697 (1934).

[31] G. E. Coates and J. E. Coates, *J. Chem. Soc.*, 77 (1944).

[32] G. R. Leader and J. F. Gormley, *J. Am. Chem. Soc.*, **73**, 5731 (1951).

[33] G. R. Leader, *J. Am. Chem. Soc.*, **73**, 856 (1951).

4. The Dielectric Constant in Strong Electric Fields. In Chap. I, it was pointed out that the dielectric constant was practically independent of the intensity of the measuring field for ordinary field strengths. For very strong fields, however, saturation effects are detectable. Böttcher[1] has examined the work of Debye[2] and of Van Vleck[3] on the saturation effect and derived a new expression for the change $\Delta\epsilon$ of the dielectric constant ϵ_0 produced by a field E:

$$\frac{\Delta\epsilon}{E^2} = -\frac{4\pi N_1 \mu^4}{45 k^3 T^3} A \tag{4.1}$$

where A has the values

$$A_1 = \frac{(\epsilon_0 + 2)^4}{81} \qquad \text{(Debye)} \tag{4.2}$$

$$A_2 = \frac{27\epsilon_0{}^4}{(2\epsilon_0{}^2 + 1)(2\epsilon_0 + 1)^2} \qquad \text{(Van Vleck)} \tag{4.3}$$

$$A_3 = \frac{(\epsilon_\infty + 2)^3 \epsilon_0{}^4}{(2\epsilon_0{}^2 + \epsilon_\infty{}^2)(2\epsilon_0 + \epsilon_\infty)(2\epsilon_0 + 1)} \qquad \text{(Böttcher)} \tag{4.4}$$

Debye[2] calculated for ethyl ether at 20° that, in order to lower the dielectric constant by 1 part in 10^5, the applied field would have to be

$$E = 115 \text{ e.s.u.} = 34{,}500 \text{ volts per cm.}$$

Measurements carried out by Herweg[4] indicated the existence of the lowering. Kautzsch[5] found the expected decreases in the dielectric constants of ethyl ether, chloroform, and chlorobenzene, whose molecules are polar, and the expected absence of change in the nonpolar hexane. The slight increase which he observed in the nonpolar carbon disulphide is attributable to the orientation responsible for Kerr effect. The optically anisotropic molecule tends to orient its SCS axis, along which it is much more polarizable than along the other axes, in the direction of the field. Using a field of intensity 100,000 volts per cm., Malsch[6] observed no change in the dielectric constants of ether, water, and glycerine, his accuracy of 5 parts in 1,000 being insufficient to detect the effect. In further investigation with an improved experimental method,

---

[1] C. J. F. Böttcher, "Theory of Electric Polarisation," Elsevier, Houston, 1952, sec. 38.

[2] P. Debye, "Polar Molecules," Chemical Catalog, New York, 1929, chap. VI; "Handbuch der Radiologie," 2d ed., Akademische Verlagsgesellschaft m.b.H., Leipzig, 1934, vol. VI/2, p. 189.

[3] J. H. Van Vleck, *J. Chem. Phys.*, **5**, 556 (1937).

[4] J. Herweg, *Z. Physik*, **3**, 36 (1920); J. Herweg and W. Pötzsch, *Z. Physik*, **8**, 1 (1922).

[5] F. Kautzsch, *Physik. Z.*, **29**, 105 (1928).

[6] J. Malsch, *Ann. Physik*, **84**, 841 (1927).

however, he found[7] that a field of 250,000 volts per cm. produced a decrease of 0.7 per cent in the dielectric constant of water, 1.0 per cent in that of nitrobenzene, and 1.5 per cent in that of ethyl alcohol. Gundermann[8] has made semiquantitative measurements upon ether, chlorobenzene, aniline, and several alcohols, some of which were measured also in solutions of different concentrations. For liquids of low dielectric constant, the depression of the dielectric constant by a strong field was found to be of the magnitude required by the Debye theory, but liquids of higher dielectric constant showed depressions considerably smaller than those required by the Debye theory. Although the attribution of the discrepancies to the effects of molecular association was at least partly correct in the case of the alcohols, one must bear in mind that the Debye theory lays no claim to accuracy for such liquids. Böttcher concludes that the available experimental data are not of sufficient accuracy to decide between the three equations (4.2), (4.3), and (4.4). For most purposes, it is sufficient to know that the effect of field intensity is undetectable in the range of field intensities used in ordinary measurements. It is evident that the tremendous local fields existing around ions and dipoles in solution may have large effects upon the dielectric constant.

As a starting point for the investigation of the effect of the ionic fields upon the dielectric constant of ionic solutions, Ritson and Hasted[9] have arranged the Onsager equation to give

$$\epsilon E = \frac{4\pi}{V} \frac{(\epsilon_\infty + 2)(2\epsilon + 1)}{3(2\epsilon + \epsilon_\infty)} L \left[\frac{\epsilon(\epsilon_\infty + 2)}{2\epsilon + \epsilon_\infty} \frac{\mu_0^2}{kT} E \right] + \frac{3\epsilon(\epsilon_\infty - 1)E}{2\epsilon + \epsilon_\infty} \quad (4.5)$$

where L is the Langevin function.

5. Dielectric Constants of Aqueous Solutions of Nonelectrolytes. The dielectric constants of many aqueous solutions of nonelectrolytes have been measured. Although the conductivities of these solutions are low in comparison to those of electrolytes, they may be sufficient to have caused errors in some of the measurements. Akerlof[1] used a resonance method at a wavelength of 150 m. to measure the dielectric constants over a range of temperature of series of mixtures of water with methyl, ethyl, n-propyl, isopropyl, and t-butyl alcohol, ethylene glycol, glycerol, acetone, and dioxane and of aqueous solutions of mannitol and cane sugar. The dielectric constant of the dioxane-water mixtures was found to decrease almost linearly with increase in the percentage of dioxane in the mixtures containing less than 50 per cent by weight of dioxane, but above 60 per

---

[7] J. Malsch, *Physik. Z.*, **29**, 770 (1928).

[8] H. Gundermann, *Ann. Physik*, **6**, 545 (1930).

[9] J. B. Hasted, D. M. Ritson, and C. H. Collie, *J. Chem. Phys.*, **16**, 11 (1948).

[1] G. Akerlof, *J. Am. Chem. Soc.*, **54**, 4125 (1932); G. Akerlof and O. A. Short, *J. Am. Chem. Soc.*, **58**, 1241 (1936).

cent a marked curvature appeared, the decrease becoming less than linear.   The dielectric-constant values found by Akerlof and Short for dioxane are about 5 per cent lower than those found by other investigators.[2]   Measurements on dioxane-water mixtures at microwave frequencies are mentioned in Sec. 6.   Although the Debye polarization is of very dubious significance for these highly polar liquids, it may be noted that the curve for the polarization P_{12} of the mixture as a function of concentration goes through a pronounced maximum in the case of the dioxane-water mixtures, although the polarization P_2 of the water increases linearly with increasing dilution over the whole range of concentration.   The polarization P_{12} of the glycerol-water mixtures was found to be a linear function of concentration.

Fürth,[3] using the second Drude method of measurement at a wavelength of 76 cm., found that the dielectric constants of aqueous solutions of dextrose, levulose, and sucrose decreased with increasing concentration, those of urea and glycine solutions increased with increasing concentration, and that of saccharin increased to a maximum and then decreased. Decrease in dielectric constant resulted from dilution of the water by a substance of lower dielectric constant.   The very large dipole moments of the urea and glycine molecules cause the increase in the dielectric constants of the solutions over that of pure water (see Chap. XIII).   The initial increase in the dielectric constant of the saccharin solutions with increasing concentration is presumably due to the high dipole moment of the solute, and the subsequent decrease is attributed to increase in anomalous dispersion with increasing viscosity.   The dielectric-constant contributions of the other large solute molecules are presumably lowered in these solutions by large molecular relaxation times.   Clark[4] has briefly summarized the measurements of several other investigators.

The dielectric constant–composition isotherms[5] for aqueous hydrogen peroxide solutions show a broad maximum at intermediate concentrations, the maximum becoming more pronounced and appearing at higher peroxide concentrations as the temperature decreases.   The Kirkwood correlation factor g is smaller for hydrogen peroxide than for water at 0°, indicating that the extent of short-range order is less in hydrogen peroxide than in water.[5]

6. Dielectric Constants of Solutions of Electrolytes.   So many measurements of the dielectric constants of solutions of electrolytes have been

[2] Cf. W. P. Conner, R. P. Clarke, and C. P. Smyth, *J. Am. Chem. Soc.*, **64**, 1379 (1942).

[3] R. Fürth, *Ann. Physik*, **70**, 63 (1923).

[4] C. H. D. Clark, "The Fine Structure of Matter," Wiley, New York, 1938, vol. II, pt. II, sec. 27.

[5] P. M. Gross, Jr., and R. C. Taylor, *J. Am. Chem. Soc.*, **72**, 2075 (1950).

subject to large errors that it would be difficult to determine from a survey of the early literature[1] whether the dielectric constants really increase or decrease with increasing concentration. Fairly accurate measurements were possible upon very dilute solutions, the dielectric constants of which differed so little from that of pure water that the errors in the differences were very large, while the high conductivities greatly limited the accuracy of measurement of concentrated solutions.

Sack[2] concluded that the electric fields of the ions should hinder the orientation of neighboring water molecules in an externally applied field and thus lower the dielectric constant, the decrease being proportional to the ionic concentration as long as this was small. His measurements on solutions of eight different salts at concentrations between 0.00017 and 0.00132 molar (M) gave rough agreement with his theory, but the results are quantitatively inconsistent with those of microwave measurements discussed later in this section. Wien,[3] measuring dilute solutions of magnesium sulfate and barium ferricyanide, reported increases of dielectric constant with increase in concentration up to 0.05 normal (N) and found no evidence of the decreases of dielectric constant up to 10 per cent observed by Fürth[4] and his co-workers.[5,6] The small increases in dielectric constant, which were proportional to the square root of the concentration, agreed well with the predictions of the Debye-Falkenhagen theory.[7] The accurate measurements of Drake, Pierce, and Dow[8] on $N/270$ and $N/70$ solutions of potassium chloride showed that, when the correction for the effect of conductivity upon the measurement was properly made so as to give the true dielectric constant, the value differed from that of distilled water by less than 1 per cent. The investigators could not decide whether even this small difference was due to errors introduced by the high attenuation resulting from the conductivity. The careful measurements of Wyman[9] by a resonance method upon very dilute potassium chloride solutions showed an apparent increase of dielectric constant with concentration amounting to as much as 4 per cent for an 0.034 per cent solution. However, Wyman regarded this apparent increase as due to errors arising from the effects of conductivity and considered the dielectric constant in this range of concentrations to be actually indistinguishable from that of pure water.

[1] See footnote 4, Sec. 5.
[2] H. Sack, *Physik. Z.*, **27**, 206 (1926); *ibid.*, **28**, 199 (1927).
[3] M. Wien, *Ann. Physik*, **11**, 429 (1931).
[4] R. Fürth, *Z. Physik*, **22**, 98 (1924); *ibid.*, **44**, 256 (1927).
[5] R. Pechold, *Ann. Physik*, **83**, 427 (1927).
[6] O. Milicka and A. Slama, *Ann. Physik*, **8**, 663 (1931).
[7] H. Falkenhagen, "Electrolytes," Oxford, London, 1934, chap. IX.
[8] F. H. Drake, G. W. Pierce, and M. T. Dow, *Phys. Rev.*, **35**, 613 (1930).
[9] J. Wyman, Jr., *Phys. Rev.*, **35**, 623 (1930).

Elle,[10] using a free-wave method with damped 4-cm. waves from a herzian oscillator, and Cooper,[11] using a transmission-line reflection method with wavelengths down to 7 cm., obtained results on concentrated solutions. Cooper's results, though not so interpreted, were in rough agreement with the results of the comprehensive investigations of Hasted, Ritson, and Collie,[12] who measured the dielectric constants and loss factors of 0.5 to 5.0 N solutions of sodium chloride at wavelengths of 1.27, 3, and 10 cm. at temperatures between 0 and 40° and of 0.25 to 2.0 N solutions of hydrogen chloride, sodium hydroxide, and eleven salts at 3 and 10 cm. at 25°C. These measurements on the concentrated solutions are so far removed from the region of the measurements upon the very dilute solutions that the decrease observed in the concentrated

TABLE 6.1. STATIC DIELECTRIC CONSTANTS AND CRITICAL WAVELENGTHS OF
SOLUTIONS OF ELECTROLYTES AT 25°C.

Salt	Normality	ϵ_0	λ_m, cm.	Salt	Normality	ϵ_0	λ_m, cm.
LiCl	0.5	71.2	1.55	RbCl	0.5	73.5	1.54
	1.0	64.2	1.52		1.0	68.5	1.50
	1.5	57.0	1.49		1.5	63.5	1.47
	2.0	51.0	1.45		2.0	58.5	1.43
KCl	0.5	73.5	1.54	BaCl$_2$	1.0	64.0	1.50
	1.0	68.5	1.50		2.0	51.0	1.42
	1.5	63.5	1.47	LaCl$_3$	0.52	71.0	1.54
	2.0	58.5	1.43		1.04	64.0	1.50

region is not necessarily inconsistent with a possible increase in the very dilute region. They are qualitatively consistent with the decreases observed by Sack in very dilute solutions, which are, however, much too large to be quantitatively consistent with the results of the microwave measurements.

The experimental errors in the measurements of Hasted, Ritson, and Collie were 2 to 4 per cent in the measurements of ϵ' and 1 to 3 units in ϵ'', the values of the latter being from 15 to 27 at 3 cm. and 8 to 10 at 10 cm. Because both pure water and the solutions show anomalous dispersion of the dielectric constant at these microwave frequencies, the static dielectric constant ϵ_0 was obtained by fitting Eqs. II(2.34) and (2.35) to the values of ϵ' and ϵ'' for each solution. Consistent results were obtained with a single value of the critical wavelength λ_m for each solution.

[10] D. Elle, *Ann. Physik*, **30**, 355 (1937).
[11] R. Cooper, *J. Inst. Elec. Engrs. (London)*, **93**, 69 (1946).
[12] J. B. Hasted, D. M. Ritson, and C. H. Collie, *J. Chem. Phys.*, **16**, 1 (1948).

Some of the measurements are reproduced in Table 6.1, where the error in ϵ_0 is ± 2 and that in λ_m, ± 0.04 cm.

It is clear from these and other measurements not reproduced in Table 6.1 that the dielectric constants of concentrated solutions of a variety of typical electrolytes decrease with increasing concentration. Within the error of the observation, the decrease is linear up to a concentration slightly less than 2 M, above which it becomes gradually less pronounced. The critical wavelength also decreases with increasing concentration, the curve being similar in appearance to that for the dielectric constant. For a 0.66 N sodium chloride solution, the percentage depression of the dielectric constant increases with rising temperature, while the percentage depression of the critical wavelength decreases. For concentrations less than 2 M, Hasted, Ritson, and Collie represent the static dielectric constant by an equation which may be written

$$\epsilon = \epsilon_{H_2O} - (\delta^+ + \delta^-)c \tag{6.1}$$

where ϵ_{H_2O} is the static dielectric constant of water, c is the concentration in moles per liter, and δ^+ and δ^- are the contributions of the cation and anion, respectively. The sum of these two contributions is obtained directly from the experimental data by means of Eq. (6.1). By a theoretical treatment, Hasted, Ritson, and Collie divide the sum 11 for sodium chloride into $\delta^+ = 10$ and $\delta^- = 1$, but conclude that better values are

$$\delta^+ = 8 \pm 1 \qquad \text{and} \qquad \delta^- = 3 \pm 1$$

With these approximate values as a basis, they calculate the individual ionic contributions given in Table 6.2. These are the values of the lowering of dielectric constant per mole of ion per liter of solution.

TABLE 6.2. IONIC LOWERING OF DIELECTRIC CONSTANT

H^+	17	Mg^{++}	24	F^-	5
Li^+	11	Ba^{++}	22	Cl^-	3
Na^+	8	La^{+++}	35	I^-	7
K^+	8			OH^-	13
Rb^+	7			SO_4^-	7

The ions may be pictured as attracting sheaths of water molecules, each sheath, according to Hasted, Ritson, and Collie, consisting of several layers of molecules. The cation should attract the negative end of the H_2O dipole rendering rotation of the water molecule possible only about the molecular dipole axis. As orientation around this axis would not give any dipole contribution to the dielectric constant, the contribution of the molecules thus fixed would drop to a low value corresponding approximately to the optical dielectric constant. The anion should attract one of the two protons of the water molecule, leaving the axis of the molecular dipole at an angle to the line between the center of the ion

and that of the molecule. The component of the dipole moment perpendicular to the axis of permissible rotation is able to contribute to the
dielectric constant, but its contribution is less than that of an unattached
water molecule. It is evident that the hydration of the anion should
reduce the dielectric constant less than does that of the cation. The
innermost layer of bound H_2O molecules should conform most closely to
this rough picture, while the conformation of subsequent layers to the
model should be increasingly approximate. When the ionic concentration is increased to a point where all the water molecules are appreciably
affected by the binding forces of the ions, further increase of concentration
should lower the dielectric constant less than in the more dilute solutions.
The average values of δ should then decrease, and the curve for the
dependence of dielectric constant upon concentration should depart from
linearity. It is evident in Table 6.2 that, as would be expected, the
cationic lowering of the dielectric constant tends to increase with decreasing ionic size and increasing ionic charge, that is, with increasing field
intensity. The large effect of OH^- somewhat parallels that of H^+ in
attracting and fixing water molecules. It should be pointed out that in
the most concentrated solutions so many water molecules are replaced by
ions making much lower contributions to the dielectric constant that a
detectable effect upon the dielectric constant should result quite apart
from the more important effects of hydration.

Hasted, Ritson, and Collie believed that molecular orientation took
place at the moving boundaries of broken pieces of the rough molecular
lattice existing in liquid water and attributed the shortening of the relaxation time or critical wavelength to the creation of more boundaries by the
rupture of the lattice by the addition of ions. This work gives reliable
experimental evidence of the lowering of the dielectric constants of concentrated solutions below that of water, a lowering in semiquantitative
agreement with the predictable effects of hydration of the ions.

Haggis, Hasted, and Buchanan[13] made extensive microwave measurements on a wide variety of aqueous solutions of ions and organic molecules, finding that, while the water relaxation time is shortened by
positive ions, it is lengthened by hydrogen bond-forming molecules.
They treated the properties of water statistically in terms of the numbers
of molecules in states having four, three, two, one, and zero hydrogen
bonds per molecule and calculated dielectric-constant values for ice and
liquid water in fair agreement with the experimental values in the literature. A dielectric theory of mixtures was used to estimate the number
of molecules prevented by the ion or organic molecule from turning in the
electric field. The number was found to be zero for uncharged solute
molecules but finite for organic or inorganic ions. However, the effect

[13] G. H. Haggis, J. B. Hasted, and T. J. Buchanan, *J. Chem. Phys.*, **20**, 1452 (1952).

of hydrogen bonding to an uncharged molecule is shown by the 70 per cent increase in the relaxation time of an aqueous solution containing 45 per cent dioxane above that of pure water.[14]

Lane and Saxton[15] have measured the refractive indices and absorption coefficients [see Eq. II(2.43)] of 0.68 to 2.74 N solutions of sodium chloride in water at 0.62, 1.24, and 3.21 cm. wavelength and of solutions of lithium chloride, sodium bromide, potassium iodide, calcium nitrate, strontium bromide, and barium bromide in methyl alcohol. Their results show depressions of the static dielectric constant and of the relaxation time which are linear functions of the effective ionic concentration in the sodium chloride solution as required for the dielectric constant by Eq. (6.1). In the methyl alcohol solutions the relative depression of the static dielectric constant is greater than in the water solutions, while some electrolytes produce an increase in the absorption coefficient, others a decrease. The value obtained for $\delta^+ + \delta^-$ in the aqueous sodium chloride solutions was 12.5 ± 1 as compared to 11 obtained by Hasted, Ritson, and Collie.

The dielectric behavior of water is discussed further in connection with its dielectric loss (Sec. IV.5).

7. Colloidal Solutions. The dielectric behavior of colloidal solutions may involve many factors. A solution or dispersion of a high polymer in a nonpolar solvent may have the dielectric constant calculable for it as a mixture. If the solute particles have dipole moments, the solution should show anomalous dispersion and loss at low frequencies, provided that the dipole orientation involves orientation of the entire particle. If there is a considerable difference in dielectric constant or conductivity between the dispersoid and the dispersing medium, interfacial polarization causes dielectric loss and frequency dependence of the dielectric constant in the low-frequency region. In aqueous colloidal solutions, the presence of electrolyte, even in small amounts, in the water should commonly cause sufficient conductivity difference to give rise to interfacial polarization. In addition, there is the complicating effect of the electric double layer at the particle surfaces even in the absence of an externally applied electric field. The influence of these factors must be taken into account in the interpretation of dielectric-constant measurements upon colloidal systems. An obscuring factor is the large error often occurring in dielectric-constant measurements on materials of appreciable conductance. At the high frequencies, where the effects of conductivity and interfacial polarization are unimportant, orientation of the colloidal particles is commonly prevented by their long relaxation times.

In view of the number of factors evidently influencing the dielectric

[14] J. B. Hasted, G. H. Haggis, and P. Hutton, *Trans. Faraday Soc.*, **47**, 577 (1951).
[15] J. A. Lane and J. A. Saxton, *Proc. Roy. Soc. (London)*, **214A**, 531 (1952).

behavior of colloidal solutions, in addition to the variables of preparation and aging, it seems best for the purposes of this book to discuss the results of important or typical investigations and refer to summaries,[1-3] two of them[1,3] very brief, for additional literature references. Proteins and organic high polymers will be discussed from the structural point of view subsequently under separate headings.

Gold sols and aluminum oxide sols appear to have dielectric constants a little smaller than those of water.[1] Thorium oxide sols show high dielectric constants, a solution of 16.2 g. of ThO_2 in 1,000 g. of water being reported to have a dielectric constant of 102. A 3 per cent sol of vanadium pentoxide has been reported[4] to have a dielectric constant of 1,280. The dielectric constant increases with concentration and decreases with increasing temperature.[5] It increases at room temperature with increasing wavelength up to about 80 km., where anomalous dispersion ceases, the relaxation time for the orientation of the particles being about 10^{-7} sec. A decrease of dielectric constant at a somewhat longer wavelength was attributed to energy absorption in the migration of the particles. The dielectric constant of a solution of 0.38 g. of V_2O_5 per 1,000 g. of water aged from a dielectric constant of 112.4 after 20 days to one of 173.4 after 134 days. In view of the many factors involved, it would seem that the calculation of a dipole moment of 415×10^{-18} for the vanadium pentoxide particles[6] may best be interpreted merely as indicating the presence of a high polarization during the measurement.

Kruyt and Kunst[7] have found that the dielectric constants of sodium arabinate and silver iodide sols increase with concentration, the latter almost linearly in the range from 0.7 to 3 volume per cent with the ratio of the sol dielectric constant to that of water lying between 1.05 and 1.4. The sodium arabinate was prepared by repeated solution of gum arabic in sodium nitrate solution and precipitation with alcohol. These sols and also silver bromide and arsenic trisulfide sols show rapid increase of dielectric constant with increase in wavelength from 150 to about 400 m., with a somewhat diminishing increase up to 1,930 m., the longest wavelength used. From measurements on sols containing different amounts of salt up to $\frac{2}{3}$ meq., Kruyt and Kunst concluded that electrolytes influ-

[1] H. Freundlich, "Kapillarchemie," Akademische Verlagsgesellschaft m.b.H., Leipzig, 1932, vol. II, pp. 62 and 333.

[2] E. Heymann, *Kolloid-Z.*, **66**, 229, 258 (1934).

[3] C. H. D. Clark, "The Fine Structure of Matter," Wiley, New York, 1938, vol. II, part II, p. 240.

[4] J. Errera, "Colloid Chemistry" (J. Alexander), Chemical Catalog, New York, 1926, vol. I, pp. 507–514.

[5] J. Errera, *Bull. soc. chim. Belgique*, **33**, 422, 432 (1924).

[6] J. Errera, *J. phys. radium*, [VI]**9**, 307 (1928).

[7] H. R. Kruyt and H. Kunst, *Kolloid-Z.*, **91**, 1 (1940).

ence the dielectric constants of sols and that not all hydrophilic sols possess high dielectric constants.   A 0.9 per cent amylum sol, for example, had at 25°C. a dielectric-constant ratio to that of water of 1.002 at 300 m. and 1.013 at 1,930 m. wavelength.   The surfaces of the micelles of amylum carry very little charge,[8] while the surfaces of the micelles of the sodium arabinate sols, which have high dielectric constants, are strongly ionized.   Sodium ions, which lower the viscosity of sodium arabinate, do not change the dielectric constant of the sol.   These and other facts led Kruyt and Kunst to the hypothesis that the polarization of the double layer is responsible for the high dielectric constant of the sol, the dipole moment acquired in an electric field by a particle with a double layer being greater, the greater the dimensions of the particle. Hydration affected the dielectric constant by changing the particle size, and adsorption altered it by changing the structure of the double layer. Support for the idea that the polarization of the double layer is the cause of the high dielectric constants of sols is given by the fact that hydrophobic sols investigated by Kruyt and Kunst[7] had dielectric constants of the same order of magnitude as hydrophilic sols.   Arsenic trisulfide sols were found by conductimetric titration to have the largest densities of charge, and silver bromide sols the smallest, while the arsenic trisulfide sols had the highest dielectric constants and the silver bromide sols the lowest.   Fricke and Havestadt[9] attributed the high dielectric constants which they found for different hydroxide sols to the conductivity of the particle surfaces.

Kruyt and Overbeek[10] used a resonance method with a wavelength of 85.7 cm. to measure the dielectric constants of several hydrophilic sols, sodium arabinate, sodium agar, amylum, egg albumen, and gelatine, and critically examined measurements of earlier investigators.   In all the sols investigated the dielectric constant was lower than that of water, the lowering being proportional to the concentration of the colloid. With the use of an approximation based on an equation of Wiener[11] for heterogeneous mixtures, the ratio of the dielectric constant ϵ of the sol to that of water ϵ_{H_2O} was calculated as

$$\frac{\epsilon}{\epsilon_{H_2O}} = 1 - 1.48v$$

the dielectric constant of water being taken as 80, that of the colloid being assumed to be 4, and v being the volume fraction of the colloid.

[8] H. G. Bungenberg de Jong and P. van der Linde, *Biochem. Z.*, **262**, 390 (1933).

[9] R. Fricke, *Kolloid-Z.*, **56**, 166 (1931); L. Havestadt and R. Fricke, *Z. anorg. allgem. Chem.*, **188**, 357 (1930); **196**, 120 (1931).

[10] H. R. Kruyt and J. T. G. Overbeek, *Kolloid-Z.*, **81**, 257 (1937).

[11] O. Wiener, *Abhandl. Sächs. Ges. Math.-physik. Kl.*, **32**, 507 (1912).

These calculated values were lower than those observed for volume fractions not far from 0.01 except in the case of sodium agar at 24°C. and egg albumen at 21.6 and 48.6°, the latter solutions showing no change in the dielectric-constant ratio with temperature. The increase of the dielectric-constant ratios of the other solutions with temperature showed that they were at the beginning of a region of anomalous dispersion. This was consistent with the dispersion curve obtained by Errera[12] for a white of egg sol between 2 and 17,000 m. At the shortest wavelengths, the sol had a low dielectric constant, which then rose rapidly with increasing wavelength and leveled off at about 4,000 m. in a typical dispersion curve. Kruyt and Overbeek[10] found that the transition from sol to gel in the cases of gelatine and agar produced no change in the dielectric constant. They attributed to errors of measurement any previous indications that hydration caused a lowering of the dielectric constants of hydrophilic colloids.

Fricke and Curtis[13] have measured what might perhaps be called the "apparent dielectric constants" of suspensions, such as 0.5 μ diameter particles of kaolin in 1 per cent sodium oleate solution, in 0.00005 M sodium carbonate solution, and in gelatine solutions; 1.0 μ diameter spherules of Pyrex glass in 0.00005 M sodium carbonate solution; and 1.7 μ spherules in potassium chloride solutions of various concentrations. They obtained values from 200 to 20,000, which decreased rapidly with increasing frequency in the range from 0.25 to 64 kc. They found similarly high values for colloidal solutions of ferric oxide, vanadium pentoxide, aluminum oxide, soap, and potato starch and cited measurements[14] on soil containing 25 per cent moisture, which decreased from 10,000 to about 200 in the frequency range 0.5 to 100 kc. They considered the differences between their measured values and the nearly constant values observed at high frequency and calculated them fairly successfully in terms of "interphasial" conductivities and capacities. They concluded that the dielectric properties of dielectrics dispersed in water were derived to an important extent from the interphases—the layers at the particle surfaces—a fact essential in determining the dielectric behavior of systems such as living cells, soil, and hygroscopic insulating materials, like paper and fabrics.

It is evident that the dielectric behavior of a colloidal material is often determined far less by the dielectric constants of its components than by the other factors enumerated at the beginning of this section.

[12] J. Errera, *J. chim. phys.*, **29**, 577 (1932).
[13] H. Fricke and H. J. Curtis, *J. Phys. Chem.*, **41**, 729 (1937).
[14] R. L. Smith-Rose, *J. Inst. Elec. Engrs.* (*London*), **75**, 221 (1934).

CHAPTER IV

DIELECTRIC LOSS AND STRUCTURE IN LIQUIDS

Ordinary dielectric measurements upon liquids involve such low frequencies and viscosities that the product of the frequency by the relaxation time is negligibly small, with the result that the measured dielectric constant is indistinguishable from the static value measured at zero frequency and the dielectric loss is indistinguishable from zero, as indicated in Chap. II. Thus, the dielectric constant of a liquid measured at a frequency as high as a megacycle is commonly referred to as the static dielectric constant. The difficulty of measuring at very high frequencies limited the early studies of the variation of the dielectric constant of liquids with frequencies to liquids of abnormally high viscosity, solutions of very large molecules, or colloidal solutions. However, the development of microwave techniques extended the range of dielectric-constant measurements to frequencies as high as 30,000 megacycles, where even the smallest polar molecules in the liquid state show some dependence of dielectric constant upon frequency.

1. Early Measurements in Meter-wavelength Region. The early measurements of Cole[1] and Drude[2] gave evidence of anomalous dispersion, that is, decrease in the dielectric constants of some liquids at high frequencies. Because of their viscosities, which become very high at low temperatures, the alcohols were particularly suitable for dispersion investigations when very short waves were not available for the measurements. Mizushima[3] measured several at wavelengths of 58 cm. and 3.08, 9.5, and 50 m. over a wide range of temperature. The dielectric constants and loss factors behaved approximately according to the requirements of the Debye equations II(2.38) and (2.39). Application of Eq. II(2.36) to the relaxation times calculated from the data for n-propyl alcohol at different temperatures and wavelengths gave a surprisingly

---

[1] A. D. Cole, *Ann. Physik*, **57**, 290 (1896).

[2] P. Drude, *Ann. Physik*, **58**, 1 (1896); *ibid.*, **60**, 1, 500 (1897); *ibid.*, **61**, 466 (1897); *Z. physik. Chem.*, **23**, 267 (1897).

[3] S. Mizushima, *Sci. Papers Inst. Phys. Chem. Research (Tokyo)*, **5**, 201 (1927); *ibid.*, **9**, 209 (1928).

constant value, 2.2 ± 0.2 A., for the radius of the molecule. The extensive investigations of glycerol show some discrepancies, attributable in part to inaccuracies in the methods of measurement and in part to inadequate removal of water from the material measured. The agreement with the Debye theory is qualitatively satisfactory, but the value calculated for the molecular radius is only about 0.1 of what it should be according to known atomic dimensions. Morgan's[4] and Mizushima's[5] measurements at frequencies from 0.03 to 98,000 kc show (Fig. 1.1) the

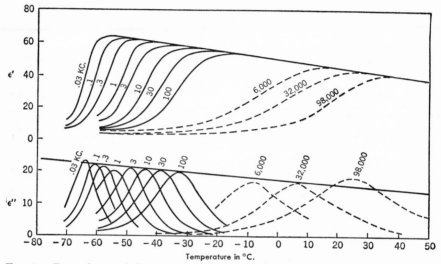

FIG. 1.1. Dependence of dielectric constant of glycerol upon frequency and temperature. [S. O. Morgan, Trans. Am. Electrochem. Soc., **65**, 109 (1934).]

required falling off of dielectric constant in successively lower temperature regions at successively lower frequencies as the increasing viscosity caused by decreasing temperature brings the liquid into a region of anomalous dispersion for a given frequency. The corresponding loss-factor curves show sharper and higher maxima as the temperature decreases. White and Morgan[6] obtained similar curves for propylene glycol, trimethylene glycol, and 2-methylpentandiol-2,4. The values of ϵ' and ϵ'' for pure 2-methylpentandiol-2,4 lay so close to the curves calculated with the Debye equation as to suggest a distribution of relaxation times hardly distinguishable from zero, but a solution containing 0.83 mole fraction of the substance in dioxane showed a very considerable flattening out of the curves below those calculated, thus indicating a considerable distribution of relaxation times.

[4] S. O. Morgan, *Trans. Am. Electrochem. Soc.*, **65**, 109 (1934).
[5] S. Mizushima, *Bull. Chem. Soc. Japan*, **1**, 47 (1926).
[6] A. H. White and S. O. Morgan, *Physics*, **2**, 313 (1932).

The maximum loss-factor value for glycerol increases[4] with decreasing temperature as required by the increase in static dielectric constant [cf. Eq. II(2.25)], but it is in the vicinity of 20 instead of 28, as calculated from ϵ_0 and ϵ_∞, indicating a distribution of relaxation times. Halowax, a predominantly solid mixture of chlorinated naphthalenes, showed[4] a rapid decrease in the maximum loss factor with decreasing temperature, which was attributable to the presence of Maxwell-Wagner effect.

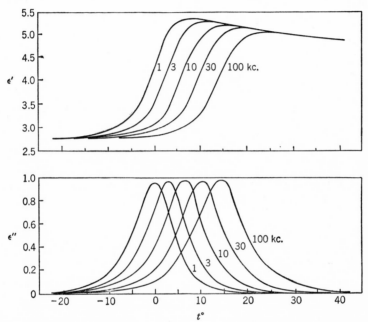

FIG. 1.2. Dependence of dielectric constant of chlorinated diphenyls upon frequency and temperature. [*A. H. White and S. O. Morgan, J. Franklin Inst.*, **216**, 635 (1933).]

Analogous behavior was observed for a sample of condenser paper.[4] This complicating influence of Maxwell-Wagner effect, pointed out by Morgan, must be borne in mind when considering the behavior of materials which may contain more than one phase. Commercial mixtures of chlorinated diphenyls gave[7] curves (Fig. 1.2) similar to those for glycerol except that the values ϵ''_m of the loss-factor maxima were independent of the temperature over the ranges of 15 to 25°C. within which they were observed. The distribution of relaxation times evidenced by the somewhat low values of ϵ''_m may so reduce their temperature dependence that it is not evident in the short range observed. More or less similar dielectric behavior has been observed for many insulating materials such as rosin,[8]

[7] A. H. White and S. O. Morgan, *J. Franklin Inst.*, **216**, 635 (1933).
[8] D. W. Kitchen and H. Müller, *Phys. Rev.*, **32**, 979 (1928).

rosin oils,[9] insulating oils,[10] and mixtures of rosin and transformer oils.[11] Müller[12] tabulated a number of values for the critical wavelength λ_m calculated from measurements[13–18] at different frequencies and frequently obtained from loss measurements carried out by a thermal method.

TABLE 1.1. APPARENT MOLECULAR RADII[12] CALCULATED FROM RELAXATION TIMES

Solute	Solvent	t, °C.	λ_0, m.	Viscosity, poises	a, A.
$C_6H_5NO_2$	Mineral oil[19]	25	34–300	7.7–23	2.4
	Shell BL3[20]	20	0.5–300	10–12	0.37–0.35
	Shell BL3[21]	0	0.6	52	0.25
		10	0.6	18	0.31
		20	0.6	7.4	0.37
		30	0.6	3.2	0.42
	Hexane[22]	24	3.7	0.00326	1.26
	Benzene[22]	24	3.7	0.00654	1.29
	Cyclohexane[22]	24	3.7	0.00810	1.05
	Decalin[22]	24	3.7	0.0240	0.87
	Hexane[23]	21	7.2	0.00510	1.88
	Benzene[23]	19	7.2	0.00966	1.55
C_6H_5Cl	C_6H_6, C_6H_{14}, CCl_4[23]		7.2		1.83
m-$C_6H_4Cl_2$	C_6H_6, C_6H_{14}, CCl_4		7.2		1.93
o-$C_6H_4Cl_2$	C_6H_6, C_6H_{14}, CCl_4		7.2		1.94
	C_6H_6[22]		3.7		1.3
n-C_3H_7OH	C_6H_6[22]		3.7		1.1
n-C_4H_9OH	Paraffin oil[24]		0.72		0.9
	Shell BL3[20]		0.5–300		0.2
$(CH_3)_2CO$	C_6H_6[25]		3.8		1.26

[9] S. O. Morgan and A. H. White, *J. Franklin Inst.*, **213**, 313 (1932).

[10] H. H. Race, *Phys. Rev.*, **37**, 430 (1931).

[11] E. Kirch and W. Riebel, *Arch. Elektrotech.*, **24**, 355 and 533 (1930).

[12] F. H. Müller, *Ergeb. Exakt. Naturw.*, **17**, 164 (1938); F. H. Müller and C. Schmelzer, *Ergeb. Exakt. Naturw.*, **25**, 359 (1951).

[13] A. Esau and G. Bäz, *Physik. Z.*, **38**, 774 (1937).

[14] M. von Ardenne, O. Groos, and G. Otterbein, *Physik. Z.*, **37**, 533 (1936).

[15] S. Mizushima, *Sci. Papers Inst. Phys. Chem. Research (Tokyo)*, **9**, 209 (1928).

[16] C. Schmelzer, *Physik. Z.*, **37**, 162 (1936).

[17] C. Schmelzer, *Ann. Physik*, **28**, 35 (1937).

[18] W. Hackel, *Physik. Z.*, **37**, 160 (1936); *ibid.*, **38**, 195 (1937).

[19] J. H. L. Johnston and J. W. Williams, *Phys. Rev.*, **34**, 1483 (1929).

[20] R. Luthi, *Helv. Phys. Acta*, **6**, 139 (1933).

[21] W. Müller, *Ann. Physik*, **24**, 99 (1935).

[22] P. Debye, *Physik. Z.*, **35**, 101 (1934); *Trans. Faraday Soc.*, **30**, 679 (1934).

[23] J. Henrion, *Rev. universelle mines*, [8]8 (1937); *Bull. soc. roy. sci. Liège*, **7**, 229 (1938); *ibid.*, **8**, 333 (1939).

[24] R. Goldammer, *Physik. Z.*, **33**, 361 (1932).

[25] W. Holzmüller, *Physik. Z.*, **38**, 574 (1937).

Table 1.1 gives results compiled by Müller[12] from measurements on solutions. The measurements on solutions in viscous oils were in the region of high loss, while those on solutions in liquids of low viscosity, such as benzene and hexane, were far from the region of maximum dispersion and involved a long extrapolation to the region of the critical wavelength. Instead of the critical wavelength or relaxation time, the value of the radius a calculated from it by means of Eq. II(2.36) is given in the last column of the table.

From the density of liquid nitrobenzene, the molecular radius is calculated[12] as 2.4 A., which should be an upper limit for the average value obtained by treating the molecule as a sphere, which it is not. Similar calculations give 2.3 A. for n-butyl alcohol and 2.5 for acetone.[12] The chlorobenzenes should be close to nitrobenzene in size. Henrion[23] calculated radii for these remarkably close to the values in Table 1.1 obtained from the critical wavelengths or relaxation times, but these cannot be correct if the value 2.05 A. calculated[26] for the benzene molecule from the viscosity of the vapor is to be believed. Other dimensional considerations also would give larger values for the radii. The molecular radius involved in the relaxation phenomenon is that along the axis in which the molecular dipole lies. The tables of electron-diffraction results prepared by Allen and Sutton[27] give 6.18 A. as the chlorine-chlorine internuclear distance in p-dichlorobenzene. If we subtract from this the carbon-chlorine internuclear distance[26] 1.69 A. and add the carbon-hydrogen internuclear distance[27] 1.04 A. and the kinetic-theory radii[26] of bound hydrogen 0.7 A. and of bound chlorine 1.4 A., we obtain 7.6 A. as the kinetic-theory diameter of the chlorobenzene molecule along the axis in which the dipole lies. The corresponding radius 3.8 A. is about twice as large as the values for the chlorobenzenes in Table 1.1. All the radii values in Table 1.1 are too low, but it is apparent that they tend to be lower, the higher the viscosity of the medium in which they are measured. It is thus evident that Eq. II(2.36) does not adequately represent the relation between relaxation time, molecular radius, and the macroscopic viscosity of the medium.

If this equation is written

$$\tau = \frac{4\pi a^3}{k} \frac{\eta}{T}$$

it is evident that for a given liquid the relaxation times at different temperatures should be in the same ratios as the values of η/T. Müller[12] showed this to be approximately true of Mizushima's values for propyl alcohol, the ratios of the values of τ at 35, -15, and $-45°C$. being

[26] H. A. Stuart, "Molekülstruktur," Springer, Berlin, 1934, chap. II.
[27] P. W. Allen and L. E. Sutton, *Acta Cryst.*, **3**, pt. 1, 46 (1950).

1:5.45:16.5, as compared to 1:4.9:17.7 for the corresponding values of
η/T. For an 8 per cent solution of o-dichlorobenzene in benzene, the
ratio of the values of τ at 16° and at 24° was 1.15 and that for the values
of η/T was 1.17. Jackson's measurements[28] on permitol, a mixture of
chlorinated diphenyls, showed a close parallelism between the temperature dependence of τ and that of η. Measurements by Martin[29] on
solutions of o-dichlorobenzene in hexane, benzene, carbon tetrachloride
and decahydronaphthalene showed an increase in relaxation time with

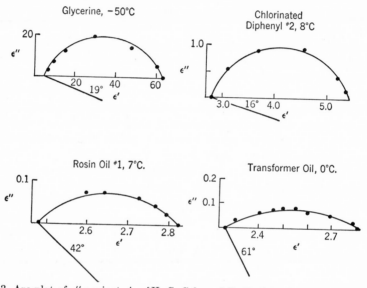

Fig. 1.3. Arc plot of ϵ'' against ϵ'. [K. S. Cole and R. H. Cole, J. Chem. Phys., **9**, 341
(1941).]

increase in viscosity, the rate of increase diminishing with increasing
viscosity as far as could be evidenced by four liquids covering an approximately fivefold range of viscosity.

The data for several liquids by the semicircular-arc method [see Eq.
II(5.22)] are plotted in Fig. 1.3 taken from the paper of Cole and Cole,[30]
who tabulated the results of many measurements. It is evident that the
arc plot gives a good semiempirical representation of the relation between
ϵ' and ϵ''. There is some uncertainty as to the rather small extent of the
distribution times in the short-chain alcohols because of discrepancies in
the data, but a considerable distribution is evident in glycerine and very

[28] W. Jackson, *Proc. Roy. Soc. (London)*, **153A**, 158 (1935); A. Gemant and W. Jackson, *Phil. Mag.*, **23**, 960 (1937).
[29] G. Martin, *Physik. Z.*, **37**, 665 (1936).
[30] K. S. Cole and R. H. Cole, *J. Chem. Phys.*, **9**, 341 (1941).

large distributions are apparent in the mixed insulating liquids, as would be expected from the variety of molecules of which they consist.

2. Centimeter-wave Measurements on Alcohols.   The modern development of microwave techniques has made possible the extension of dielectric-constant measurements over the entire dielectric dispersion region of many liquids without the necessity of using low temperatures or solutions in viscous liquids.   Girard and Abadie[1,2] have measured n-propyl and n-octyl alcohol in the meter- and centimeter-wavelength region and have found some flattening out of both the dielectric-constant and the loss-factor curves, corresponding to an apparent effect of distribution of relaxation times.   However, the dielectric-constant curves showed a plateau between 10 and 4 cm. for n-propyl alcohol and between 30 and 10 cm. for n-octyl alcohol with a dispersion region on each side.   An analogous plateau occurred in the values for solutions of n-octyl alcohol in three different solvents, but for these solutions Girard and Abadie thought to observe three distinct dispersion regions and relaxation times. They observed two such apparent regions in liquid nitrobenzene and, for all these liquids, associated each dispersion region with rotation around a single molecular axis.

Earlier measurements by Luthi (see Table 1.1) indicated two dispersion regions for dilute solutions of nitrobenzene, butyl alcohol, and amyl alcohol in a viscous mineral oil.   The region in the vicinity of 100-m. wavelength was attributed to the orientation of single polar molecules

TABLE 2.1. CRITICAL WAVELENGTHS (CM.) OF ALCOHOLS[3] AT 20°C.

CH_3OH	13
C_2H_5OH	27
$n\text{-}C_3H_7OH$	100
$n\text{-}C_4H_9OH$	125
$n\text{-}C_8H_{17}OH$	330

surrounded by molecules of the oil, while the second region, in the vicinity of 1 m., was attributed to the relaxation of the polar molecules within clusters, which were supposed to possess nearly the properties of the pure polar liquids.

The measurements of Girard and Abadie and other investigators on several straight-chain alcohols have been collected and analyzed, together with their own measurements, by Dalbert, Magat, and Surdut.[3]   Their tabulated critical-wavelength values are presented above in Table 2.1. The dielectric-constant and loss-factor curves[3] (Fig. 2.1) for methyl alcohol at 20°C. based on the measurements of nine different investi-

[1] P. Girard and P. Abadie, *Trans. Faraday Soc.*, **42A**, 40 (1946).

[2] P. Abadie, *Trans. Faraday Soc.*, **42A**, 143 (1946).

[3] Mme Dalbert, M. Magat, and A. Surdut, *Bull. soc. chim. France*, D345 (1949); "Polarisation de la Matière," Centre Nat. Recherche Sci., Paris, 1949, p. 14.

gators are fairly typical of the behavior of the alcohols. The dielectric-constant points lie satisfactorily close to the curve which has been calculated from the Debye equation II(2.34) with $\epsilon_0 = 32.2$, $\epsilon_\infty = 1.95$, and $\lambda_m = 13.0$ cm. The loss-factor values deviate more widely from the curve calculated with Eq. II(2.35), the experimental points seeming to require a narrower and perhaps slightly higher maximum than that calculated.

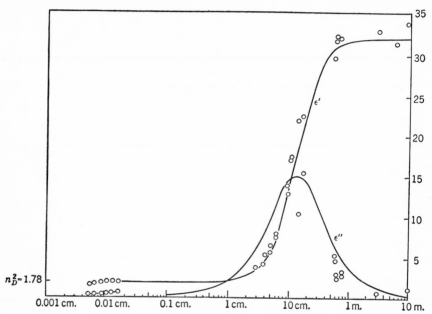

FIG. 2.1. Dependence of dielectric constant and loss factor of methyl alcohol at 20° upon wavelength. [*Mme Dalbert, M. Magat, and A. Surdut, Bull. soc. chim. France,* D435 (1949); *"Polarisation de la Matière," Centre Nat. Recherche Sci., Paris,* 1949, p. 14.]

It has been suggested that the far-infrared dispersion may be associated with the rotation of the ellipsoidal molecule around its long axis, while the principal dispersion is associated with the rotation around the short axis [cf. Eq. II(5.1)]. However, the infrared dispersion is too small and at too high a frequency to be associated with molecular orientation and is just that to be expected from atomic polarization. Moreover, the large dispersion at centimeter wavelengths is in the general region to be expected for orientation of the entire molecule.

The ϵ' and ϵ'' curves for ethyl alcohol at 20°, calculated with $\epsilon_0 = 25.0$, $\epsilon_\infty = 2.2$, and $\lambda_m = 27$ cm., are very similar to those for methyl alcohol, except that the ϵ'' points show no systematic deviation from the Debye curve. The experimental points for *n*-propyl and *n*-butyl alcohol at 20° are in satisfactory agreement with the Debye curves calculated with

$\lambda_m = 100$ cm. and 125 cm., respectively.   In Fig. 2.2, for n-octyl alcohol at 20°, Dalbert, Magat, and Surdut have calculated two curves each for ϵ' and ϵ'', the solid lines with $\lambda_m = 4.30$ m. and the dashed lines with $\lambda_m = 3.30$ m., and have concluded that neither set of curves alone satisfactorily represents the points of Girard and Abadie.   Three dispersion regions appear in the ϵ' curve, two of them obviously analogous to the two observed for methyl alcohol (Fig. 2.1).   The apparent dispersion region in the vicinity of 10 cm. was associated according to Girard and Abadie

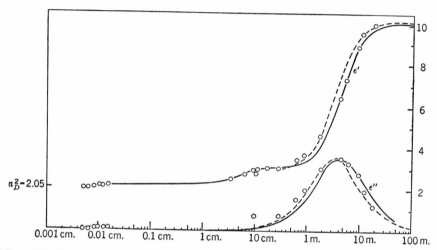

FIG. 2.2. Dependence of dielectric constant and loss factor of n-octyl alcohol upon wavelength. [*Mme Dalbert, M. Magat, and A. Surdut, Bull. soc. chim. France,* D345 (1949); *"Polarisation de la Matière," Centre Nat. Recherche Sci., Paris,* 1949, p. 14.]

with orientation of the molecule around its long axis, while that in the vicinity of 4 m. was associated with orientation around the short axis, although, in order to account for the separation of the two regions, the Perrin equation II(5.1) would require that the ratio of the length of the molecule to its width should be more than twenty times that given by the fairly well-known dimensions of the molecule in its extended form.   Such a departure from the Perrin extension of the Debye theory is to be expected according to Girard[4] because rotation of the molecules around the long axes involves the overcoming of only weak intermolecular forces, while rotation of the molecule around its short axis requires the overcoming of very strong hindrance.   A serious objection to this explanation of the centimeter and meter dispersion regions arises when it is considered

[4] P. Girard, *Bull. soc. chim. France,* D351 (1949); "Polarisation de la Matière," Centre Nat. Recherche Sci., Paris, 1949, p. 20.

that, as will be shown later (Sec. IX.8), the axis of the molecular dipole makes, on an average, a considerable angle with the long axis of the alcohol molecule. The contribution to the dielectric constant of orientation around the long axis should, therefore, be as large as and probably larger than that of orientation around the short axis, which would require a correspondingly large drop in dielectric constant in the centimeter dispersion region instead of the very small change observed. In Fig. 2.2, the ϵ' points can be represented without very serious deviations by a single curve drawn with no plateau between the large meter dispersion and the small apparent centimeter dispersion, in other words, a curve which eliminates the centimeter dispersion as a separate region. Moreover, the experimental points at 1.5 and 20°C. lie satisfactorily on semicircular-arc plots, corresponding to Debye behavior with a single dispersion region. In spite of this, the three dispersion regions for n-octyl alcohol are consistent with the results of Häfelin and of Cole and Davidson on other alcohols to be discussed shortly.

There is no more reason to expect rotation around two different molecular axes to give two distinct dispersion regions in the alcohols than there is in the case of the alkyl bromides, where it will presently be shown that different modes of orientation may give some distribution of relaxation times but only one dispersion region. If the association of the alcohols resulted in the formation of fairly large complexes, all of one size, in equilibrium with monomeric molecules, the presence of two distinct dispersion regions could be accounted for. However, association should result in the coexistence of monomeric, dimeric, trimeric, and larger molecules with a single widely spread dispersion region corresponding to a distribution of relaxation times. Dalbert, Magat, and Surdut have suggested that the critical wavelength of the principal dispersion region may correspond to the length of life of the complexes. This leaves the orientation mechanism in rather vague terms, which might be made more definite by saying that only those molecules contribute to the dipole orientation which break off from the complex and that the rate of breaking off is the determining factor. It is evident then from Sec. II.3 that the number of times per second a molecule will thus break off is $k = 1/\tau = 2\pi c/\lambda_m$. If the whole complex were orienting, variation in the size of the complex would give a distribution of relaxation times. The curve[3] for the increase in critical wavelength of the alcohols with increasing molecular length is roughly similar in form to those found for the alkyl bromides (Sec. 4). An alternation between the values for odd- and even-numbered chains is interesting, although it would appear to be well within the experimental uncertainty of the values.

Lane and Saxton[5] have measured the absorption coefficient and refrac-

[5] J. A. Lane and J. A. Saxton, *Proc. Roy. Soc. (London)*, **213A**, 400 (1952).

tive index of methyl and ethyl alcohols at 0.62, 1.24, and 3.21 cm. wavelength over the temperature range -10 to $50°$, finding indication of high atomic polarization, corresponding to ϵ_∞ values of 6 for methyl alcohol and 4.4 for ethyl alcohol, much higher than the seemingly accurate values of Dalbert, Magat, and Surdut.[3] Their results are shown[6] to be consistent with those of previous workers in that dispersion corresponding to dipole rotation can be represented in terms of a single relaxation time. However, Saxton suggests that the behavior observed near 1 cm. is the consequence of resonance absorption, with natural frequencies of oscillation corresponding to 2.5 mm. wavelength for methyl alcohol and 5 mm. for ethyl alcohol.

Häfelin[7] has measured the dielectric constants at wavelengths from 9 cm. to 300 m. of pure isobutyl alcohol and of solutions of it in benzene and in two very viscous oils at $20°$. The critical wavelengths decrease with increasing dilution of the alcohol in benzene from 145 cm. for 100 per cent alcohol to 6.45 cm. at 2.52 per cent alcohol. The Debye equations give apparent radii values calculated from the critical wavelengths for the most concentrated and the most dilute solutions in satisfactory agreement with the usual value 2.5A. The results for the 100 to 90 per cent and 10 to 2.5 per cent ranges are 2.3 to 2.5A., but those in between are higher, reaching 3.08A. at 49.88 per cent. Ten per cent solutions in the more viscous solvents give two dispersion regions and much lower radii values, as low as 0.39A. in one oil. Häfelin attributes one dispersion region to rotation of the entire molecule and the other to rotation of the —CH_2OH group, and he attempts to reconcile the existence of the two distinct dispersion regions by reasoning not unlike that involved in the explanation proposed by Girard.[4] If the restriction upon orientation of the molecule as a whole is small, that is, if the potential energy barrier to be surmounted is low, the only orientation is that of the whole molecule, and only one dispersion region is observed, as in the benzene solutions. If, however, the potential energy barrier is high, as in the viscous oils, the CH_2OH rotation is supposed to occur more readily than that of the molecule as a whole and give rise to a second dispersion region at a higher frequency than that corresponding to molecular rotation.

Further evidence[8] for the existence of more than one relaxation mechanism in alcohol solutions has been obtained from loss measurements over a range of temperature at 10 cm. and 3 cm. wavelength. For solutions of n-amyl alcohol in n-heptane, in addition to the peak which was to be expected at high temperatures, the loss rose again as the temperature was decreased, the effect becoming more pronounced for the more dilute solu-

[6] J. A. Saxton, *Proc. Roy. Soc. (London)*, **213A**, 473 (1952).

[7] J. Häfelin, *Arch. sci. phys. et nat.*, [5]**28**, 19 (1946).

[8] Private communication from Dr. G. N. Roberts.

tions. Similar results were found for solutions of n-propyl and n-butyl alcohol in n-heptane.

The suggestion of the rotation of the CH_2OH group is reminiscent of earlier work on alcohols.[9,10] For four pure alcohols, Fischer[9] found the ratio τ/η to have values from 5 to 8 in contrast to values 0.1 to 0.5 for several unassociated liquids, while the values of the ratio decreased with rising temperature, which, presumably, reduced the association. Keutner and Potapenko,[10] by means of measurements of the dispersion and absorption of 18- to 130-cm. waves, obtained critical wavelengths for pure methyl, ethyl, propyl, and butyl alcohol of the same magnitude as the values found by Schmelzer,[11] Hackel,[12] and Dalbert, Magat, and Surdut,[3] the discrepancies amounting sometimes to as much as 60 per cent in either direction. They divided their critical-wavelength value for each alcohol by an association factor of very dubious significance and calculated a molecular radius from the corresponding relaxation time. As the radii thus obtained—2.12A. for the methyl alcohol molecule and 2.22 to 2.24A. for the other three molecules—were very close to the effective radius of the hydroxyl group, they concluded that the hydroxyl group and not the whole molecule was the orienting unit in all four molecules. Fischer,[9] on the other hand, found that the observed relaxation time for methyl alcohol in dilute benzene solution was only slightly smaller than that calculated for the molecule as a whole, while the increase in relaxation time with increasing molecular size was much smaller than that which would occur if the larger molecules were orienting as a whole. He therefore concluded that the CH_2OH group was the principal orienting unit.

By cooling to the temperature range -120 to $-156°$, Cole and Davidson[13,14] brought the dispersion of n-propyl alcohol into the region of audio and radio frequencies, where more points could be obtained with greater accuracy than in the microwave region. In addition to the usual primary dispersion region, two dispersion regions were found which made small but significant contributions to the dielectric constant. The variations of both were those to be expected for orientation rather than induced polarization. The relaxation times for the intermediate dispersion were 200 times smaller than those for the primary one. Their origin was attributed to rearrangements of the molecules in their local environment. The single relaxation process for the low-frequency dispersion evidently involved the orientation of a single unit rather than

[9] E. Fischer, *Physik. Z.*, **40**, 645 (1939).
[10] E. Keutner and G. Potapenko, *Physik. Z.*, **40**, 100 (1939).
[11] C. Schmelzer, *Ann. Physik*, **28**, 35 (1937).
[12] W. Hackel, *Physik. Z.*, **38**, 195 (1937).
[13] D. W. Davidson and R. H. Cole, *J. Chem. Phys.*, **19**, 1484 (1951).
[14] R. H. Cole and D. W. Davidson, *J. Chem. Phys.*, **20**, 1389 (1952).

that of a polymer with a variety of modes of orientation. This could result from the breaking and reforming of intermolecular hydrogen bonds in such a way that each molecule spent most of its time having two neighbors in positions consistent with bond angles. Two dispersion regions were found for glycerol and propylene glycol.

It would appear that the dielectric relaxation process in the liquid alcohols might involve as orienting units the OH group, the CH_2OH group, or, in large molecules, larger segments—the monomeric molecules and polymeric molecules—and might even depend on the length of life of molecular complexes. Indeed, the formation and breaking of hydrogen bonds may be an important factor. The evidence for segment orientation as the entire process is not wholly implausible but is far from convincing. The apparent absence of a distribution of relaxation times argues against the orientation of a variety of polymeric molecules or of a variety of molecular segments as the relaxation process in the pure liquid alcohols, but the observation[8] of some distribution in solutions makes molecular orientation the probable mechanism in this case, as would be expected for dilute solutions.

3. Loss Measurements and Molecular Structures. Fischer and Frank,[1] using a thermal method to measure loss at a wavelength of 4.3 m., obtained relative values for the relaxation times of some aromatic halides. In terms of the relaxation time of the rigid o-dichlorobenzene molecule as unity, the larger molecule of p-xylylene chloride, $p\text{-}C_6H_4(CH_2Cl)_2$, was found to have a relaxation time of only 0.475, and, while the rigid o-dibromobenzene molecule had a value of 1.24, p-xylylene bromide had one of only 0.907. Chlorobenzene had a value of 0.915. The short relaxation times of the larger molecules were explained as being associated with the orientation of the —CH_2X groups by rotation around their bonds to the ring, in contrast to the rotation of the entire molecule in the cases of the two rigid molecules. The results of other measurements of this type have been considered with reference to molecular structure.[2-5] Budó, Fischer, and Miyamoto,[3] with a 4.3-m. wavelength and a temperature of 23°, obtained relaxation times for o-dichlorobenzene, 2,3-dichloroanthraquinone, and 1,8-dichloroanthraquinone in dilute benzene solutions, the two latter substances at concentrations below 0.07 molar per cent. They treated all three molecules as rigid ellipsoids with the molecular dipole lying in one of three principal axes of symmetry and transformed the Perrin equation II(5.1) to give the ratio of the relaxation time of the

[1] E. Fischer and F. C. Frank, *Physik. Z.*, **40**, 345 (1939).

[2] A. Budó, *Physik. Z.*, **39**, 706 (1938).

[3] A. Budó, E. Fischer, and S. Miyamoto, *Physik. Z.*, **40**, 337 (1939).

[4] E. Fischer, *Physik. Z.*, **40**, 645 (1939).

[5] E. Fischer, *Naturwissenschaften*, **33**, 368 (1946).

ellipsoid to that of a sphere of equal volume as a function of the axis ratios. From molecular dimensions calculated from bond radii, the ratio of the relaxation time of the 2,3- to that of the 1,8-dichloroanthraquinone was 1.43 as compared to 1.46 observed experimentally, while the ratio of the value for 2,3-dichloroanthraquinone to that of o-dichlorobenzene was 3.75 as compared to 4.60 observed. When the effective molecular radii, obtained by adding 0.5 A. to the values given by the bond radii, were used, the calculated ratios were less satisfactory, being 1.36 and 3.12, respectively.

Fischer[6] has tabulated the relaxation times of several molecules in dilute solution in benzene calculated from loss measurements by a thermal method at 23°. As the measurements were carried out at a single wavelength in the meter region remote from that of the critical wavelength, their significance may be different from that of values determined directly in the region of the critical wavelength, but, relative to one another, they lend themselves to interpretation.

TABLE 3.1. RELAXATION TIMES AT 23°C. OF DILUTE BENZENE SOLUTIONS BY THERMAL METHOD

Solute	τ, 10^{-11} sec.	Solute	τ, 10^{-11} sec.
Chloroform	0.84	Aniline	0.67
Chlorobenzene	1.06	p-Phenylenediamine	<0.15
α-Chloronaphthalene	1.57	4,4'-Diaminodiphenyl	<0.15
1-Chloroanthraquinone	1.92	Di-n-butylamine	0.54
		Diphenylamine	0.80
Di-n-butylketone	0.81	Di-n-butyl ether	0.48
Benzophenone	2.04	Diphenyl ether	0.28

The first four molecules, with rigidly bound dipoles, in Table 3.1, chloroform, chlorobenzene, α-chloronaphthalene, and 1-chloroanthraquinone, show the expected increase in relaxation time with increase in molecular size. The somewhat lower relaxation time of the aniline molecule was attributed by Fischer to its possession of two orientational modes, the rotation of the molecule as a whole and the rotation of the —NH₂ group around its C—N bond to the ring. The much lower values for p-phenylenediamine and 4,4'-diaminodiphenyl might then arise simply from rotation of the —NH₂ groups. However, the molecules are not so large as to prevent some orientation of the molecule as a whole. Fischer also considered the possibility that orientation might occur by inversion of the molecule as in the umbrellalike vibration of the ammonia molecule and suggested that a partial inversion might occur in the amines by the jumping of the proton from its bonding electron pair to the unshared

[6] E. Fischer, *Z. Elektrochem.*, **53**, 16 (1949).

electron pair of the nitrogen.   He also suggested that the low value for diphenyl ether might be due to orientation by internal motion of the molecule, in particular, of the oxygen atom, which might occur in the other ethers as well.   These suggestions must be regarded as highly speculative.

Fischer also investigated the ratio of the value of τ/η for the pure polar liquids to that for the dilute solution and found it to be from about 0.1 to 0.5 for several unassociated liquids, remaining constant or increasing with rising temperature.   For four associated alcohols, the ratio was from 5 to 8 and decreased with rising temperature.   For the highly associated acetic acid, the value was about 8 and independent of temperature from 20 to 50°. τ/η is a quantity which at constant temperature is corrected for the effect of viscosity and is, therefore, more useful for some comparisons than τ itself.   The hypothetical volume V_D [Eq. II(2.49)] is a somewhat more general quantity of more evident physical significance.

From similar thermal measurements Fischer[4] has calculated the relaxation times of several ketones, alkyl halides, and alcohols (see Sec. 2) in benzene solutions at concentrations from about 0.2 to 1.7 molar per cent. For the ketones and alkyl halides, the dielectric losses increased linearly with concentration, but, for the alcohols, the rate of increase increased with concentration, presumably because of the increase in association. Fischer determined the relaxation time of o-dichlorobenzene with an estimated accuracy of about 8 per cent and, by comparison, calculated the relaxation times for the other substances with a relative accuracy of 2 to 3 per cent.   For each homologous series the relaxation times increased regularly with increase in the number of carbon atoms in the molecule.

Instead of the Debye equation, Fischer,[4] in calculating the relaxation time to be expected of an ellipsoidal molecule, used the expression

$$\tau = \frac{4\pi\eta^*fabc}{kT}$$

in which f is a molecular structure factor, a, b, and c are the half axes of the molecular ellipsoid, and η^* is an empirical viscosity value

$$\eta^* = 0.36\eta$$

The empirical factor 0.36 was obtained as the value necessary to bring agreement between the relaxation time calculated from loss measurements and that calculated from molecular dimensions.   With the exception of the alcohols and the diphenyls, these relationships gave rough agreement between the relaxation times calculated from loss measurements and those calculated from molecular dimensions.   It may be noted that the use of this empirical factor 0.36 increases by a factor 1.4 the molecular radii calculated from the critical wavelengths.   With a static dielectric-constant value 9.7 for the liquid the same increase would be effected by setting the Debye factor $(\epsilon_\infty + 2)/(\epsilon_0 + 2)$ equal to 1, as was done in Chap. II [cf. Eqs. II(2.30) and (2.41)]. Fischer and Klages[7] concluded that the relaxation times for acetone, nitrobenzene, and chlorobenzene in the pure liquid were lower than those in dilute benzene solutions. The application of Eq. II(2.28) instead of II(2.41) to the subsequent microwave measurements (cf. Sec. 4) gives higher values for the pure liquids. Dielectric-constant measurements between 10 and 150 cm. on octyl, decyl, dodecyl, and hexadecyl chlorides as pure liquids showed a much more gradual decrease of ϵ' with increasing frequency than that required by the Debye equation. The measurements at different wavelengths were not mutually consistent, since the value obtained for the relaxation time of a given liquid was shorter, the shorter the wavelength employed in the measurement, and it was much shorter than that calculated from molecular dimensions, the discrepancy increasing with increasing molecular length. It was suggested that the unexpectedly short relaxation times were due to orientation of the molecules around their long axes, the molecules in the pure liquid being packed in extended form in a quasi-crystalline structure.

These results are at least qualitatively consistent with the results of later, more extensive measurements on long-chain bromides.[8] However, the loss measurements of Henrion[9] on 0.05 mole fraction solutions of alkyl bromides in benzene by a thermal method with a wavelength of 7 m. gave molecular radii values in fair agreement with the estimated molecular dimensions.

4. Critical Wavelength, Structure, and Viscosity. The microwave measurements by Heston, Hennelly, Laquer, Branin, and Smyth[1-4] gave dielectric constant and loss factors at 1.27-, 3.22-, and 10.00-cm. wavelengths over a range of temperature for twenty-seven organic halides in the pure liquid state. The results for each liquid at a given temperature fitted satisfactorily on an arc plot, as shown for i-butyl bromide and n-octyl bromide in Figs. 2.2 and 2.3, Chap. II, and the values of the distribution constant α showed fair consistency in decreasing with rising temperature and increasing with increasing molecular length. However,

[7] E. Fischer and G. Klages, *Physik. Z.*, **40**, 721 (1939).

[8] E. J. Hennelly, W. M. Heston, Jr., and C. P. Smyth, *J. Am. Chem. Soc.*, **70**, 4102 (1948).

[9] J. Henrion, *Bull. soc. roy. sci. Liège*, **8**, 333 (1939).

[1] W. M. Heston, Jr., E. J. Hennelly, and C. P. Smyth, *J. Am. Chem. Soc.*, **70**, 4093 (1948).

[2] H. L. Laquer and C. P. Smyth, *J. Am. Chem. Soc.*, **70**, 4097 (1948).

[3] E. J. Hennelly, W. M. Heston, Jr., and C. P. Smyth, *J. Am. Chem. Soc.*, **70**, 4102 (1948).

[4] F. H. Branin, Jr., and C. P. Smyth, *J. Chem. Phys.*, **20**, 1121 (1952).

values of the critical wavelength or relaxation time calculated by means of Eq. II(5.23) from a single point on the arc plot, that is, from single corresponding values of ϵ' and ϵ'', sometimes differ markedly from one another and from those obtained by plotting log (v/u), calculated by means of Eq. II(5.24), against log λ according to Eq. II(5.26). They are, however, much more dependable than those calculated by means of the Debye equations without allowance for distribution of relaxation

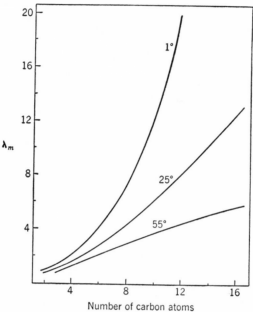

FIG. 4.1. Critical wavelengths (cm.) of n-alkyl bromides as functions of chain length. [E. J. Hennelly, W. M. Heston, Jr., and C. P. Smyth, J. Am. Chem. Soc., **70**, 4102 (1948).]

times and should be much closer to the correct absolute values than the previously cited determinations based upon a single loss measurement some distance from the region of maximum dispersion or than the preliminary measurements of Conner and Smyth[5] of dielectric constant and loss at 10 cm. only.

In the case of the alkyl bromides, the curves (Fig. 4.1) for the critical wavelength against the number of carbon atoms in the molecular chain show an increasing upward slope with increasing size at the lower temperatures. On the basis of Eq. II(2.36), τ and hence λ_m should, if the viscosity and temperature remained constant, increase linearly with a^3, which is proportional to the number of carbon atoms in the molecule.

[5] W. P. Conner and C. P. Smyth, J. Am. Chem. Soc., **65**, 382 (1943).

Since the viscosity[6] increases rapidly with increasing molecular size, the upward swing of the 1 and 25°C. curves in Fig. 4.1 is to be expected. The decrease in the rate of change of the slope of the curves from positive to zero or slightly negative at 55° with increasing chain length shows that the effective a^3 is not a linear function of the number of carbon atoms. This would seem to indicate dipole orientation not only by orientation of the molecule as a whole but also by rotation around the carbon-carbon bonds of the chain.   This latter type of orientation becomes increasingly possible as the number of carbon-carbon bonds increases with increasing chain length and as the temperature rises.   The twisting of a portion of the molecule by rotation around a bond is hindered by neighboring molecules and may require some displacement of these molecules.   Consequently, λ_m should still increase with the viscosity of the liquid even if dipole orientation were occurring wholly through internal rotation in the molecule.   A parallelism between λ_m and viscosity is shown when the two quantities are plotted against number of carbon atoms on such scales as to make the curves at each temperature as nearly coincident as possible.[3]

The hypothetical molar volume V_D, given by Eq. II(2.49), may be used as a convenient function for describing the behavior of the dielectric relaxation time and the viscosity.   Values previously obtained[5] for it were commonly only 10 to 20 per cent of the directly measured molar volume $V = M/d$ and, in some cases, even smaller.   Comparison of the values of V_D plotted in Fig. 4.2 with the measured molar volumes shows a similar relation between the two quantities, with the ratio decreasing for the long-chain molecules to less than 0.03 for hexadecyl bromide.   If the liquid were a system of close-packed molecular spheres, the ratio of the actual volume of the spheres to the total volume of the liquid would be 0.74.   In Fig. 4.2 the values of V_D for the straight-chain alkyl bromides rise to a maximum for the six-carbon chain instead of showing a continuous increase with increasing number of carbon atoms as would be the case if the values of V_D represented true volume.   Although the critical wavelengths and relaxation times increase with increasing chain length for all the straight-chain molecules investigated, it appears that the previously mentioned increasing internal orienting power of the molecular chains causes their increase with increasing chain length to fall further and further behind the increase in viscosity.   A second factor in shortening the relaxation time below the expected value is probably the orientation of the extended molecule around its long axis, as discussed earlier in the chapter.   For the almost spherical t-butyl bromide molecule, for which Eq. II(2.36) should be at its best, the radius value obtained is

[6] W. M. Heston, Jr., E. J. Hennelly, and C. P. Smyth, *J. Am. Chem. Soc.*, **72**, 2071 (1950).

1.4 A. as compared to an approximate van der Waals radius of 3.7 A. calculated from the bond radii and van der Waals radii of the atoms.[7]

Branching of the chain in the shorter molecules shortens the critical wavelength.[3] Thus, at 25° the critical wavelength for *i*-propyl bromide is 0.1 cm. shorter than that for *n*-propyl bromide, and for the butyl bromides the values decrease from 1.64 for the normal compound to 1.56 for the iso, 1.34 for the secondary, and 1.17 for the tertiary. The values of V_D also decrease. This decrease in the critical wavelength, which

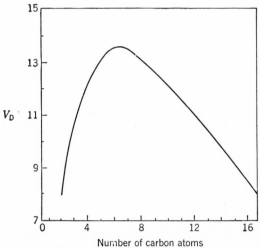

Fig. 4.2. Dependence of hypothetical molar volume V_D of *n*-alkyl bromide upon chain length at 25°. [*E. J. Hennelly, W. M. Heston, Jr., and C. P. Smyth, J. Am. Chem. Soc.,* **70**, 4102 (1948).]

indicates an increase in the ease of orientation with change in molecular shape from that of a rod toward that of a sphere, is not accompanied by a consistent decrease in the viscosity of the liquid. It would appear that while molecular orientation, which occurs merely through rotation, is facilitated by approach toward sphericity, translational motion, which is required for viscous flow in addition to rotation, may be hindered by the increase in the smallest molecular dimension caused by branching of the chain.

Ring formation increases both the viscosity and the critical wavelength. The difference between the critical wavelength at 25° of *n*-decyl bromide (6.32 cm.) and that of α-bromonaphthalene (16.20 cm.) is relatively greater than the difference in viscosities, in accordance with the increased opportunity for intramolecular orientation in the long, straight-chain molecule, in contrast to the rigidity of the α-bromo-

[7] C. P. Smyth, *Record Chem. Progr. (Kresge-Hooker Sci. Lib.)* **11**, 1 (1950).

naphthalene molecule, and with the facility of orientation around the long axis of the extended molecule.

Values of the distribution constant α decrease with rising temperature showing an increase in uniformity of the potential barriers hindering molecular orientation throughout the liquid. The curves in Fig. 4.3 for the dependence of α for the straight-chain alkyl bromides upon the number of carbon atoms in the chain show a rapid rise from a small value for the ethyl bromide molecule with a flattening out at 1° in the vicinity

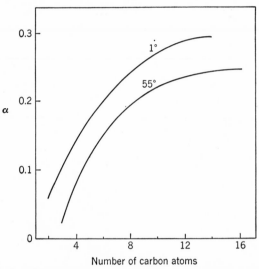

Fig. 4.3. Dependence of the distribution constant α for n-alkyl bromides upon chain length. [*E. J. Hennelly, W. M. Heston, Jr., and C. P. Smyth, J. Am. Chem. Soc.,* **70,** 4102 (1948).]

of a fourteen-carbon chain and a flattening at 55° in the vicinity of a ten-carbon chain. The increase in α with increase in chain length could be attributed to increase in the number of shapes which the molecules can acquire by twisting around the carbon-carbon bonds. Although this increase in the variety of molecular shapes may contribute somewhat to the increase, it does not account for the flattening out of the curve for the longer chains. If, as the number of bonds increases, dipole orientation occurs to an increasing extent by twisting around the bonds of the molecule instead of by orientation of the molecule as a whole, the maximum rotating unit may rarely exceed the segment of chain extending ten to twelve carbon atoms from the dipole, in which case α would increase little, if at all, with increase in the chain beyond the length of this segment.

Branching of the chain in the propyl and butyl bromides lowers α so that in s-butyl bromide and t-butyl bromide, the molecule of which is almost spherical, it is indistinguishable from zero. The cyclic molecules have lower values of α than the straight-chain molecules containing the same number of carbon atoms since they possess less variety of modes of orientation.   The decrease in the distribution of relaxation times with rising temperature causes a number of somewhat unsymmetrical molecules to conform fairly well to the Debye equations at 55°, although they do not do so at lower temperatures.

The approximately linear relationship between the logarithm of the relaxation time and the reciprocal of the absolute temperature required by Eq. II(3.9) is shown by the data for the alkyl bromides[3] and by the measurements of Whiffen and Thompson[8] over a wide range of temperature on o-xylene, p-cymene, and solutions in heptane of chloroform, camphor, methyl benzoate, and α-bromonaphthalene.   Plotting $\ln T\tau$ or $\ln T\lambda_m$ instead of $\ln \tau$ [see Eq. II(3.11)] gives no better linearity, since in both types of plot any departure from linearity is less than the experimental error.

The analogy between the molecular motion occurring in dipole orientation and that involved in the process of viscous flow is shown[3] by the similarity in appearance of the plots for viscosity against $1/T$ to those for $\ln \tau$ against $1/T$.   Viscous flow may be pictured as the movement of one layer of molecules with respect to another layer, involving translational as well as rotational motion of the molecules, with an activation energy required to pass over a hindering potential energy barrier.   The equation derived[9] for the viscosity in terms of this mechanism is

$$\eta = \frac{hN}{V}\, e^{\Delta F_v \ddagger / RT} \qquad (4.1)$$

where $\Delta F_v^{\ddagger}$ is the free energy of activation for viscous flow, and V is the molar volume. ΔF_v, as before, may be rewritten as $\Delta F_v = \Delta H_v - T\,\Delta S_v$, or

$$\eta = \frac{hN}{V}\, e^{\Delta H_v \ddagger / RT} e^{-\Delta S_v \ddagger / R} \qquad (4.2)$$

Combination of Eq. II(3.9) and Eq. (4.2) gives

$$\frac{\eta V}{\tau RT} = e^{(\Delta F_v \ddagger - \Delta F_\epsilon \ddagger)/RT} \qquad (4.3)$$

an expression which is useful in comparing the processes of dipole rotation and viscous flow.

The temperature dependence of the relaxation time is used, according to Eq. II(3.10), to calculate the values of the heat of activation for dielectric relaxation $\Delta H_\epsilon^{\ddagger}$ from the slopes of the straight lines.   Similarly, the values

[8] D. H. Whiffen and H. W. Thompson, *Trans. Faraday Soc.*, **24A**, 114, 122 (1946).
[9] S. Glasstone, K. J. Laidler, and H. Eyring, "The Theory of Rate Processes," McGraw-Hill, New York, 1941, chap. IX.

of the heat of activation for viscous flow $\Delta H_v^{\ddagger}$ are obtained approximately from the slopes of the curves for the logarithms of the viscosities against the reciprocals of the absolute temperatures. The values of the free energy of activation for dielectric relaxation $\Delta F_{\epsilon}^{\ddagger}$ are calculated by means of Eq. II(3.8), and those of the free energy of activation for viscous flow $\Delta F_v^{\ddagger}$ are similarly calculated by means of Eq. (4.1). The entropies of activation for the two processes follow directly from these values. Because of the considerable uncertainties in the values of these thermodynamic quantities, no positive conclusions can be drawn from them, but

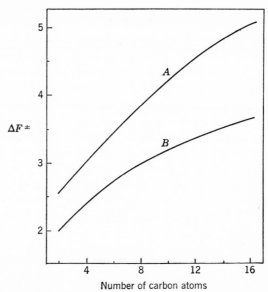

Fig. 4.4. Dependence of the free energies of activation (kcal. per mole) of the n-alkyl bromides upon chain length: (A) viscous flow, (B) dielectric relaxation. [$E.\ J.\ Hennelly,\ W.\ M.\ Heston,\ Jr.,\ and\ C.\ P.\ Smyth,\ J.\ Am.\ Chem.\ Soc.,$ **70**, 4102 (1948).]

the indications given by them are not without interest. In Fig. 4.4 the curve[3,4] for the free energy change of activation for dielectric relaxation at 25°C. plotted against the number of carbon atoms in the molecular chain is rather similar in form but somewhat lower than the corresponding curve for viscous flow. The ratio $\Delta F_{\epsilon}^{\ddagger}/\Delta F_v^{\ddagger}$ remains close to 0.6 over the range from two to sixteen carbon atoms, a difference probably attributable to the fact that dielectric relaxation primarily requires only molecular rotation, while viscous flow requires translation in addition to rotation. Both curves show some tendency to level off, which could arise from increased internal rotation with increasing chain length. The curves for the entropies of activation for the two processes are similar in shape. The values for viscous flow are all negative, and, in the case of dielectric relaxation, the values are certainly negative for the smaller molecules and probably negative for the larger as well. From this it follows that the activated state is one of greater order than the normal state, interpreted as indicating the existence of cooperative orientation of the molecules, decreasing with increasing molecular size.

The critical wavelengths, distribution parameters, α, and viscosities of a variety of esters[10] are given in Table 4.1.

TABLE 4.1. VALUES OF VISCOSITY, CRITICAL WAVELENGTH, AND DISTRIBUTION PARAMETER

Substance	t, °C.	η, centipoises	λ_m, cm.	α
Ethyl acetate	3	. . . . . .	0.90	0.09
	20	0.457	0.82	0.06
	40	0.372	0.68	0.04
	60	0.331	0.58	. . . .
Isoamyl acetate	20	0.805	1.6	0.10
	50	0.590	1.2	0.08
Cetyl acetate	35	4.79	2.5	0.29
	55	3.10	2.1	0.26
	75	2.09	1.7	0.24
Octadecyl acetate	35	6.39	2.8	0.29
	55	4.05	2.2	0.24
	75	2.76	1.8	0.19
Decyl stearate	40	10.9	5.8	0.34
	60	6.94	4.5	0.26
	80	4.21	3.5	0.14
Tetradecyl palmitate	60	. . . . . .	4.5	0.24
	70	. . . . . .	3.6	0.19
Cetyl stearate	60	9.87	3.8	0.28
	80	6.23	2.7	0.13
Monostearin	80	27.3	8.3	0.22
	90	18.3	6.9	0.24
Distearin	80	15.1	6.6	0.31
	90	11.4	4.7	0.30
Tristearin	80	14.6	7.8	0.47
	90	11.1	7.8	0.47
Ethylene dimyristate	70	5.95	2.5	0.21
	80	5.16	. . . .	. . . .
Ethylene dipalmitate	75	6.40	3.0	0.22
Ethylene distearate	80	8.04	3.4	0.22

The viscosities of the esters are slightly lower than those of alkyl bromides of approximately the same molecular length, and the critical wavelengths are only about half as large. The points give no evidence of increase or decrease resulting from moving the molecular dipole from a location near the end of the molecule to one near the middle, although a

[10] P. L. McGeer, A. J. Curtis, G. B. Rathmann, and C. P. Smyth, *J. Am. Chem. Soc.*, **74**, 3541 (1952).

small effect may well be obscured by the experimental errors.   In both locations segment orientation by twisting around the C—C bonds presumably contributes largely to the orientation polarization.   The correlation of the critical wavelengths with viscosity is shown in Fig. 4.5 for both the bromides and the esters.   In the bromides, the orienting C—Br dipole is at the extreme end of the molecular chain, while in the acetates the polar COOC group is separated from the end by a methyl group, and in the longer ester molecules it is remote from the end.   Possibly, the frictional forces on the bromine atom are responsible for the slightly higher viscosities and the much higher critical wavelengths of the alkyl bromides.

The distribution parameter α, which has been shown to increase with increasing chain length and viscosity, tends to increase as the size of the ester molecule increases and to decrease with increasing temperature. The latter effect indicates that the manner of orientation is becoming more uniform.   It may be that the expansion of the liquid has reduced the effect of the arrangement of the neighboring molecules in the orientation process.

In Table 4.2[11] the second and third columns give the viscosities and critical wavelengths of the pure, liquid solutes listed in the first column and the subsequent columns give the critical wavelengths of the solutions in the solvent listed at the top of each column, the viscosity of each solvent being given below its formula.

TABLE 4.2. CRITICAL WAVELENGTHS AND VISCOSITIES AT 20°C.

Solute	Pure solute		λ_m, cm., for solutions in					
	η, centipoises	λ_m, cm.	C_7H_{16} $\eta = 0.42$	$C_{16}H_{34}$ $\eta = 3.6$	Nujol $\eta = 108$	C_6H_{12} $\eta = 0.97$	C_6H_6 $\eta = 0.65$	CCl_4 $\eta = 0.97$
t-C_4H_9Cl	0.53	0.90	0.3		0.5	0.3		0.65
CH_3CCl_3	1.12	1.1	0.45		0.8			
$CHCl_3$	0.56	1.4	0.58			0.60	1.34	.94
C_2H_5Br	0.40	0.8	0.3	0.4		0.4	0.6	
$C_8H_{17}Br$	1.65	4.6	2.1	3.6		3.1		
$C_{14}H_{29}Br$	4.67	12.3	4.1		19			6.7
C_6H_5Cl	0.80	2.1				1.47	1.56	
C_6H_5Br	1.16	3.4				2.0	2.0	
$C_6H_5CH_3$	0.59	1.4						
$C_6H_5NO_2$	2.01	9	1.3			1.8	2.4	2.9
α-$C_{10}H_7Cl$	3.33	11.0	2.0		12			
α-$C_{10}H_7Br$	4.98	17.6	2.7					
$CH_3COOC_2H_5$	0.457	0.82	0.42					

It has been suggested previously that, if the shape of the molecule undergoing dipole orientation departs little from that of a sphere, it can

[11] A. J. Curtis, P. L. McGeer, G. B. Rathmann, and C. P. Smyth, *J. Am. Chem. Soc.*, **74**, 644 (1952).

rotate without any considerable displacement of the surrounding molecules. In this case, its relaxation time should be relatively insensitive
to the macroscopic viscosity of the medium measured by the usual methods. If, however, the molecule is unsymmetrical in shape, its rotation,
around at least one axis, must involve the displacement of neighboring
molecules, and the corresponding relaxation time should depend markedly
upon the viscosity of the medium.

For the almost spherical molecule of t-butyl chloride, the critical wavelength at 20°C. is only $\frac{2}{3}$ greater in the viscous nujol than in heptane,

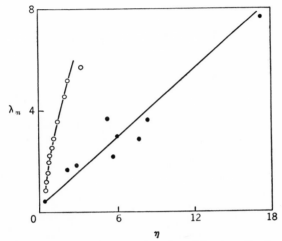

FIG. 4.5. Correlation of the critical wavelengths with viscosity for alkyl bromides
(hollow circles) at 55° and esters (filled circles) at 75°. [*P. L. McGeer, A. J. Curtis,
G. B. Rathmann, and C. P. Smyth, J. Am. Chem. Soc.*, **74**, 3541 (1952).]

although the viscosity of the nujol is 257 times that of heptane. At 40°,
the critical wavelength in nujol is $\frac{1}{3}$ greater, although the viscosity of
the nujol is 112 times that of heptane. For the methylchloroform molecule, which is similar in size and shape to the t-butyl chloride molecule, the
critical wavelength is slightly higher in heptane and increases a little more
from heptane to nujol than does t-butyl chloride. The small differences
between the values for the two solute molecules may be due to the slightly
greater polarizability of the methylchloroform molecule with consequently greater intermolecular attraction and frictional forces.

The long, flexible molecule of n-tetradecyl bromide in heptane has a
much longer critical wavelength than the two smaller, nearly spherical
molecules just considered and shows a nearly fivefold increase from
heptane to nujol at 20°, much larger than the relative increase for the
two nearly spherical molecules. Although the longer molecule of
n-docosyl bromide, n-$C_{22}H_{45}Br$, gives dipole orientation in the crystal,

presumably by rotation about the long axis in a cylindrical volume,[12] the molecules of the long-chain bromides in the liquid state are probably less regular in form.   Consequently, dipole orientation by rotation either of the entire molecule or of a molecular segment about a carbon-carbon bond should involve some displacement of the surrounding molecules and, hence, the greater dependence upon viscosity which has been noted. The somewhat flattened, rigid molecule of α-chloronaphthalene shows a critical wavelength in heptane at 20° half as long as that of n-tetradecyl bromide, but the value in nujol is six times that in heptane, a relative increase slightly larger than that in the case of the long, flexible molecule and much larger than those for the nearly spherical molecules.   This sixfold increase would seem to indicate a considerable amount of trans-lational displacement of the surrounding molecules when the polar mole-cule orients, but the sixfold increase in relaxation time is still very small in comparison to the 257-fold increase in viscosity, the relaxation time being supposed to be proportional to the internal viscosity.   In spite of the parallelism between the mechanism of dipole orientation and that of viscous flow as indicated by the dependence of both upon temperature and molecular size, there would still appear to be considerable quantita-tive differences between the two processes.

The measurements in the viscous paraffin (nujol) solutions already discussed seem to provide strong confirmation of the hypothesis that the critical wavelengths or relaxation times of nearly spherical molecules are much less dependent upon the viscosity of the medium than are those of unsymmetrical molecules, the rotation of which requires displacement of the surrounding molecules.   This is shown also in Table 4.2 by the greater viscosity dependence of the critical wavelength for n-octyl bromide than of that for ethyl bromide.

While both viscous flow and dipole orientation in liquids are dependent upon the van der Waals forces acting between the molecules, the differ-ences between the mechanisms of the two processes may result in rela-tively different effects of the van der Waals forces.   Since the medium surrounding the dipolar molecule is not continuous but consists of other molecules with fluctuating gaps of various sizes between them, the effects of the van der Waals forces upon dipole orientation will depend somewhat upon the type of force involved.   Of the three types of interaction, in terms of which van der Waals attractive forces may be described, the dispersion or London forces act in all liquids; the dipole-induced dipole forces act between the dipolar molecule and the molecules surrounding it; and, if the latter are dipolar, as in a pure polar liquid, dipole-dipole forces also act.   Since the potential energy of a dipolar molecule due to these latter forces should change rapidly as the dipole is rotated, they should

---

[12] J. D. Hoffman and C. P. Smyth, *J. Am. Chem. Soc.*, **72**, 171 (1950).

contribute considerably to the potential barrier hindering rotation and thus increase the critical wavelength. As the other two types of van der Waals force are dependent upon molecular polarizability, this quantity, which is proportional to the refraction, should be an important factor in determining the relaxation time or critical wavelength.

The tendency of the critical wavelength of the pure polar liquid to be longer than that of the solution of about the same viscosity may be attributed[7,11,13] to hindrance of molecular rotation by dipole-dipole interaction, which is present in the pure liquid and largely absent in the dilute solution. This hypothesis receives strong support from Table 4.2, in which only the very viscous nujol solutions show critical wavelengths longer than those of the corresponding pure polar liquids. Indeed, the nearly spherical t-butyl chloride molecule, whose orientation is relatively independent of the viscosity of the medium, shows almost twice as great a critical wavelength in the pure liquid state as it does in solution in nujol, which has 200 times the viscosity.

The data for the four monosubstituted benzenes in Table 4.2 give further evidence in support of these views. The small increases in molecular volume and polarizability from the chloro to the bromo compound in both the substituted benzenes and naphthalenes cause increases in viscosity and critical wavelength somewhat larger than would be expected. The toluene molecule is identical in size and shape with that of bromobenzene, but its dipole moment is only $\frac{1}{4}$ as large. The viscosity of bromobenzene is twice as large, but the critical wavelength is 2.4 times as great, presumably because of greater dipole-dipole forces. Nitrobenzene has a dipole moment about 2.7 times that of bromobenzene and a viscosity about 1.7 times as great, but its critical wavelength is about 2.6 times that of bromobenzene. The high critical wavelength of nitrobenzene in the pure liquid state is evidently due to dipole-dipole forces, since in cyclohexane and benzene solutions, where dipole-dipole forces are unimportant, its values are close to those of bromobenzene. The apparent effect of dipole-dipole forces upon molecular relaxation time is reduced when the latter is calculated by means of Eq. II(2.42) instead of II(2.28), but seems to be still present.[14]

These results are consistent with those of Whiffen and Thompson,[8] who find for a dilute solution of chlorobenzene in a mixed cyclohexane-paraffin solvent of viscosity about eighty times that of cyclohexane a critical wavelength about four times that in cyclohexane and, therefore, about three times that in the pure polar liquid. For both ethyl benzoate and chlorobenzene solutions, successive additions of the viscous paraffin

[13] A. D. Franklin, W. M. Heston, Jr. and C. P. Smyth, *J. Am. Chem. Soc.*, **72**, 3447 (1950).
[14] C. P. Smyth, *J. Phys. Chem.*, **58**, 580 (1954).

to the dilute solution in cyclohexane increase the viscosity some eighty-fold, while increasing the critical wavelength four- to sevenfold. Similarly, Jackson and Powles[15] have found a relaxation time or critical wavelength for benzophenone in dilute solution in medicinal liquid paraffin 18 times that in benzene, while the viscosity of the paraffin is 298 times that of the benzene.

The measurements[1-3] upon ethylene chloride, ethylene bromide, and tetramethylene chloride do not show any lowering of critical wavelength as compared to the monohalogenated molecules of equal size. The critical wavelength of ethylene bromide at 25°C. is 2.2 cm. as compared to 1.3 for ethylene chloride—corresponding to its possession of a viscosity[6] of 1.60 centipoises as compared to 0.79 for ethylene chloride at 25°, as well as a slightly larger molecular radius. n-Propyl bromide, with a molecule of the same size as that of ethylene bromide, has a critical wavelength of 1.1 cm. at 25° and a viscosity of only 0.495 centipoises. Tetramethylene chloride has a critical wavelength of 1.8 cm. at 25° and a viscosity of 1.31 as compared to 2.3 for n-amyl bromide, which has a very slightly smaller molecule and a viscosity of 0.755. These molecules containing two dipoles show no evidence of a shortening of the critical wavelength or relaxation time by segment orientation such as was indicated (Sec. 3) for molecules containing a CH_2X group attached to a ring. Since, however, the monohalogenated molecules have equal opportunities for segment orientation, the effect would not appear in a comparison of the critical wavelengths for the mono- and dihalogenated molecules.

An excellent example of the intramolecular orientation of dipoles without any orientation of the molecule as a whole was observed by two investigators[16,17] independently in benzene solutions of the polyesters of ω-hydroxydecanoic acid, $HO[(CH_2)_9COO]_{n-1}(CH_2)_9COOH$. Bridgman found no loss at wavelengths of 79 and 180 m. for polymers of molecular weights 905 to 13,900 ($n = 5$ to 82), and Wyman found none at 4.8×10^7 cycles (6.4 m.), 2.547×10^5 cycles (1,178 m.), and 1,000 cycles for polymers of molecular weights 1,715 to 28,650 ($n = 10$ to 168). The absence of any dispersion for these large molecules over the wide range of frequency employed showed clearly that the molecule as a whole could not be orienting in the field. The polarization per gram was found to be independent of polymer size and equal to the sum of the polarizations of the individual polar groups. If the dipoles within the molecules have the freedom necessary to give orientational equilibrium with the field, the effective moment μ per molecule is given, as shown by Bridgman by a

[15] W. Jackson and J. G. Powles, *Trans. Faraday Soc.*, **42A**, 101 (1946).

[16] W. B. Bridgman, *J. Am. Chem. Soc.*, **59**, 1579 (1937); *ibid.*, **60**, 530 (1938).

[17] J. Wyman, Jr., *J. Am. Chem. Soc.*, **60**, 328 (1938).

method to be discussed in a subsequent chapter, by

$$\mu^2 = m^2_{-COOH} + (n - 1)m^2_{-COOC-} + m^2_{-CH_2OH} \qquad (4.4)$$

where the group moment $m_{-COOH} = 1.4$, $m_{-COOC-} = 1.8$, and

$$m_{-CH_2OH} = 1.7$$

The moment values calculated by means of this equation were found by Bridgman to be in satisfactory agreement with the effective molecular moments calculated in the usual way from the polarization values obtained by extrapolating the solution measurements to infinite dilution. This would seem to establish clearly the possession of orientational freedom by the polar segments of the molecules.

5. Dispersion of Water. The many dielectric-constant and loss-factor values of water measured at different frequencies and temperatures have been collected by Dr. A. D. Franklin in the writer's laboratory and interpolated to obtain comparable values at 0, 20, 25, 40, and 55°. At wavelengths longer than 20 cm. at 20°, the values of ϵ' differ from the static value 80.3 by less than the error of measurement, but the value of ϵ'' is still not far from 6 at 20 cm. and a value 0.6 is reported at 246 cm. The values lie very satisfactorily on semicircular-arc plots for each temperature, showing the absence of any distribution of relaxation times. The values of ϵ_∞ required by the arc plots for satisfactory representation of the data are approximately 5.5 to 6.2, values markedly higher than that found[1-3] for ice, 3.0, and somewhat higher than the value 4.1 used by Magat[4] on the basis of refraction and infrared-absorption measurements. Saxton[5] found 5.5 and later[6] lowered the value to 4.9. The many points available for a plot of log (v/u) against log λ [see Eq. II(5.26)] do not deviate much from the best straight line drawn at each temperature. The values of the critical wavelength calculated from these lines are given in Table 5.1. They agree so closely with the values obtained by Collie, Hasted, and Ritson[7] that the values of these investigators at 10, 30, 50, 60, and 75° are added. Although a tabulation of the results of ten different observers at 20° shows values as low as 1.50

[1] C. P. Smyth and C. S. Hitchcock, *J. Am. Chem. Soc.*, **54**, 4631 (1932).

[2] J. Lamb, *Trans. Faraday Soc.*, **42A**, 238 (1946).

[3] J. Lamb and A. Turney, *Proc. Phys. Soc. (London)*, **62**, 272 (1948).

[4] M. Magat, *J. chim. phys.*, **45**, 93 (1948).

[5] J. A. Saxton, "Meteorological Factors in Radio-wave Propagation," The Physical Society, London, 1946, p. 292.

[6] J. A. Saxton, *Proc. Roy. Soc. (London)*, **213A**, 473 (1952); J. A. Lane and J. A. Saxton, *Proc. Roy. Soc. (London)*, **213A**, 400 (1952).

[7] C. H. Collie, J. B. Hasted, and D. M. Ritson, *Proc. Phys. Soc. (London)*, **60**, 145 (1948).

and as high as 2.00, the values in Table 5.1 are probably accurate to within ± 0.03.

TABLE 5.1. CRITICAL WAVELENGTHS OF WATER

t, °C.	λ_m, cm.	t, °C.	λ_m, cm.
0	3.37	40	1.10
10	2.39	50	0.91
20	1.78	55	0.84
25	1.56	60	0.76
30	1.39	75	0.61

In water, as in the alcohols, the association of the molecules into polymers of various sizes should result in a distribution of relaxation times if the polymeric molecules are the orienting units. The striking absence of such distribution, even in n-octyl alcohol, in contrast to the distribution observed in the unassociated n-octyl bromide, suggests that some mechanism other than mere molecular or molecular-segment rotation may enter into the process. If water is, for the moment, treated as the first member of the alcohol series, the critical wavelength of 1.78 cm. at 20° appears small in comparison to the value 13 for methyl alcohol, since, although the molecule is about half the size of the methyl alcohol molecule, the viscosity of 10.05 millipoises for the liquid is almost twice the value 5.93 for methyl alcohol. It has been suggested[8] that polarization may arise by the jump of a proton from the oxygen to which it is covalently bonded to that to which it is hydrogen bonded in the polymeric molecule or quasi-crystalline liquid structure, the change being from O—H$\cdots$O to O$\cdots$H—O. There is a good deal of evidence in support of such a change in ice, accompanied by partial molecular rotation, but its occurrence in liquid water is less probable. The close parallelism between viscous flow and the dielectric relaxation process is indicated by the difference by less than 2 per cent over a considerable temperature range of the ratios $\lambda_m(H_2O)/\lambda_m(D_2O)$ and $\eta(H_2O)/\eta(D_2O)$ observed by Collie, Hasted, and Ritson,[7] although the critical wavelengths of H_2O and D_2O at 10° are 2.39 and 3.12 cm. The relaxation time 0.85×10^{-11} sec. calculated[7] by means of Eq. II(2.36) on the basis of a molecular radius $a = 1.38$ A. is in fortuitously good agreement with the observed value 0.9×10^{11}. However, these facts seem to point to a polarization mechanism dominated by molecular rotation in the liquid, a conclusion consistent with the evidence given by the dielectric constants of aqueous solutions (Sec. III.6).

[8] See S. Glasstone, K. J. Laidler, and H. Eyring, "The Theory of Rate Processes," McGraw-Hill, New York, 1941, chaps. IX and X.

6. Anomalous Dispersion of Binary Mixtures of Polar Liquids.

Schallamach[1] measured as a function of temperature the dielectric constants and loss factors at one or more frequencies between 134 kilocycles and 268 megacycles of several binary mixtures of the polar liquids geraniol, di-dihydrocitronellyl ether, n-propyl alcohol, glycerol, n-butyl ether, isoamyl bromide, citral, and geranic acid. He found that the curve of dielectric constant showed a single dispersion region and the dielectric loss showed a single maximum if both components of the mixture were associated liquids or if both were unassociated. In his interpretation, Schallamach suggested that the dielectric relaxation process is not directly connected with individual molecules, but is a disturbance of an appreciable region in the liquid, a concept similar to that previously put forward by Bauer[2] and Magat.[3] On this basis, any liquid which was microscopically homogeneous, even if a mixture, would be characterized by only one relaxation time. Schallamach concluded that a mixture of an associated and a nonassociated liquid was not microscopically homogeneous and, therefore, showed two relaxation processes. More recently, Phillips and Roberts[4] have employed microwave techniques to investigate mixtures of simpler liquids of both low and high loss under various conditions. They found agreement with Schallamach in the case of high-loss mixtures of nonassociated liquids in that the dielectric loss–temperature curve showed only a single peak. Where the mixtures were of low loss, however, such as a dilute solution of α-bromonaphthalene in toluene, two peaks were obtained. Moreover, it was found that the loss-temperature curve for a high-loss mixture of two nonassociated liquids (α-bromonaphthalene and chlorobenzene), which normally consisted of a single peak, showed a gradual changeover to two separate peaks as the mixture was successively diluted in a nonpolar solvent (n-heptane). Although these workers have been able to interpret their results qualitatively in terms of the picture of quasi-crystalline regions in the liquid put forward by Schallamach and Bauer, Ritson[5] has pointed out that even with the molecular mechanism previously assumed the relaxation of a mixture need not be the sum of the relaxation effects which each component would have if independent of the other. The modification by one component of the potential barriers hindering the orientation of molecules of the other component can be such as to interfere little with the additivity of relaxation effects or such as to modify it greatly. Clearly, more quantitative measurements over a wide range of frequency are required,

[1] A. Schallamach, *Trans. Faraday Soc.*, **42A**, 180 (1946).

[2] E. Bauer, *Cahiers phys.*, **20**, 1 (1944); *ibid.*, **21**, 37 (1944).

[3] M. Magat, *J. chim. phys.*, **45**, 93 (1948).

[4] Private communication.

[5] D. M. Ritson, *Trans. Faraday Soc.*, **42A**, 193 (1946).

but there appears to be no necessity, as yet, to depart from the molecular mechanism in order to account for the behavior of these mixtures.

7. Loss in Nonpolar Liquids. A very small loss, too small to affect the dielectric constant by a measurable amount, has been observed[1-3] at microwave frequencies in a number of pure liquids for whose molecules no permanent dipole moments have been found. The losses found for benzene, cyclohexane, *trans*-decalin, carbon disulfide, carbon tetrachloride, tetrachloroethylene, and a mixture of benzene and carbon tetrachloride increase approximately linearly with frequency between 10 and 0.8 cm. wavelength[2] and correspond[2,3] to dipole moments of about 0.04 to 0.10 $\times 10^{-18}$ and relaxation times of about 10^{-12} sec. It has been suggested[2] that the dipole moment may be induced in a molecule by a neighboring molecule and that the induced dipole will change direction, not by rotation of the molecule containing it, but because of a new distortion produced at a later instant by another neighbor. The very short relaxation and the very small moment are thus qualitatively accounted for, but more work is necessary for confirmation of both the experimental observations and the interpretation.

8. Conclusions. The frequency dependence of the dielectric constant and loss factor is well represented by the Debye equations with the introduction frequently necessary of a distribution function, such as that of Cole and Cole. The molecular radii calculated from the relaxation times are of more reasonable magnitudes if the relaxation time is taken as the reciprocal of the critical frequency ω_m, that is,

$$\tau = \frac{1}{\omega_m}$$

as given by Eq. II(2.28), instead of $\tau = \frac{\epsilon_\infty + 2}{\epsilon_0 + 2}\frac{1}{\omega_m}$ as given by II(2.41) as derived by Debye. Single loss measurements upon dilute solutions of low viscosities at frequencies considerably removed from the critical frequency corresponding to a maximum loss have been used, through the relaxation times, to calculate molecular radius values in fair agreement with those obtained by other means. Indeed, variations in relaxation time have been observed in approximate correspondence with variations in the position of the dipole in the molecule as well as of the orientational freedom of the dipole. Relative to one another such measurements are not without significance, but it must be remembered that the cube-root extraction involved in the calculation of the apparent molecular radius does much to smooth

[1] B. Bleaney, J. H. N. Loubser, and R. P. Penrose, *Proc. Phys. Soc. (London)*, **59**, 185 (1947).

[2] D. H. Whiffen, *Trans. Faraday Soc.*, **46**, 124 (1950).

[3] W. M. Heston, Jr., and C. P. Smyth, *J. Am. Chem. Soc.*, **72**, 99 (1950).

out otherwise large discrepancies. Measurements at different frequencies which lie well on a Cole and Cole plot often give poor agreement in the critical wavelengths calculated from them. Although the relaxation time tends to increase with increasing viscosity, it is far from being proportional to the macroscopic viscosity and its dependence upon viscosity is influenced by the size and shape of the polar molecule and the position of the molecular dipole. Thus, if dipole orientation involves merely the rotation of a sphere or of a cylinder around its long axis, little or no displacement of the surrounding molecules should be involved and the relaxation process should be much less dependent upon viscosity than in the case of an orientation involving extensive displacement or viscous flow of the surrounding molecules.

CHAPTER V

THE DIELECTRIC CONSTANTS AND LOSSES OF SOLIDS

1. Molecular Orientational Freedom and Rotation. The principal difference in the dielectric behaviors of solids and liquids arises from the restriction of the orientation of polar molecules usually caused in the solid state by lattice forces.[1] This restriction normally reduces or eliminates the orientation polarization and, consequently, reduces the dielectric constant, commonly to a value between 2 and 3, and alters or eliminates the dielectric loss. For pure nonpolar solids, the dielectric constant differs from that of the liquid mainly because of the difference in density. In some solids, dipolar molecules have been found to possess sufficient orientational freedom to give dielectric constants comparable to those in the liquid state. Under these circumstances, the molecules have sometimes been described as rotating or as possessing rotational freedom, or the solid has been said to be a rotator phase. These descriptions should not be taken to mean that the molecules are rotating freely as in a gas, but merely that they are possessed of sufficient energy to permit a fairly frequent passage over the potential energy barriers hindering rotation. If the orientation process involved quantum-mechanical tunneling through a hindering potential barrier, it also would be classed under this general description as rotation. Although the disorder resulting from this occasional molecular rotation is evident in the entropy values found for the solids, the rotation would appear to be too occasional and irregular to give rise to a rotation spectrum.

Structural investigations by means of nuclear magnetism[2,3,4] have given information concerning hindered molecular rotation in solids. The magnetic dipolar broadening of nuclear resonance absorption lines is reduced by molecular motion in the crystal lattice. In some cases, it has

[1] C. P. Smyth, *Chem. Revs.*, **19**, 329 (1936).

[2] H. S. Gutowsky, G. B. Kistiakowsky, G. E. Pake, and E. M. Purcell, *J. Chem. Phys.*, **17**, 972 (1950).

[3] H. S. Gutowsky and G. E. Pake, *J. Chem. Phys.*, **18**, 162 (1950).

[4] E. R. Andrew, *J. Chem. Phys.*, **18**, 607 (1950).

been possible to relate observed line structure and transitions in the line width to the existence and frequency of certain types of hindered rotational motion in the solid state.   Relatively low-frequency motion of the order of 10^5 cycles suffices to narrow the width of an absorption line from its value in the absence of that motion.   1,2-Dichloroethane, 1,1,1-trichloroethane, and perfluoroethane were found to have line-width transitions coinciding with changes in crystal form and anomalies in the heat capacity.[3]   In 1,2-dichloroethane and perfluoroethane, these transitions were interpreted as corresponding to rotational motion about the long axis of the molecule.   1,1,1-Trichloroethane, or methyl chloroform, has a line-width transition corresponding to similar molecular rotation, but the heat-capacity anomaly and change in crystal form coincide with a further small decrease in the line width to that characteristic of the liquid. It is this transition which dielectric-constant measurements[5] indicate as corresponding to the setting in of rotational motion around the axes perpendicular to the axis of symmetry of the molecule.   The band envelopes in the infrared spectra[6] of the solid forms above and below this transition temperature are so similar as to give no evidence of the existence of this additional rotational freedom above the transition.

Several molecules,[3] including acetonitrile, methyl iodide, nitromethane, mercury dimethyl, and ammonia, have absorption lines at 90°K., corresponding to molecular rotation about the axis of symmetry, in which the molecular dipole, if any, lies.   As discussed later in this chapter, the ammonium ion also shows a low-frequency hindered rotation in crystalline salts.   Except for a possible slight discontinuity due to change of density, the commencement of such rotation would not make itself apparent in the dielectric-constant values.   Rotation of molecules or of intramolecular groups containing hydrogen has also been observed[3] in solid 2,2-dimethyl propane, methyl alcohol, ethyl alcohol, acetone, methylamine, and the ethyl halides.   A similar investigation[4] of four dimorphous solids, n-octadecane, n-octacosane, dicetyl, and dodecyl alcohol indicates that in the lower-temperature modification the molecules are rigid at the lowest temperatures, while with rising temperature an increasing number of molecules begin to rotate around their long axes.   In the upper-temperature modification, all the molecules are indicated as rotating. Benzene shows a sharp line-width transition at about 110°K., which is attributed to tunneling or rotation of the molecules around their hexagonal axes.   The naphthalene crystal lattice is found to be rigid up to its melting point.   Anthracene was, at first, thought to show molecular rotation, but the apparent transition was subsequently shown to be caused by the presence of an impurity.   The xylenes, mesitylene, and

[5] A. Turkevich and C. P. Smyth, *J. Am. Chem. Soc.*, **62**, 2468 (1940).
[6] R. Karplus and R. S. Halford, *J. Chem. Phys.*, **18**, 910 (1950).

hexamethylbenzene show rotation of the methyl groups at all temperatures above 95°K. In addition, hexamethylbenzene has a line-width transition over the range 135 to 210°K., which is attributed to tunneling or rotation of the molecules around their hexagonal axes. This is consistent with the dielectric-constant observations on polar penta- and hexasubstituted benzenes to be discussed later.

It is evident that the description of dielectric behavior in terms of rotating or nonrotating molecules is consistent with the indications of nuclear resonance absorption investigations.

In ionic solids, the dielectric constant arises from shift of charge as in nonpolar molecular solids, but the shift of ionic charge may play a more important part than the electronic shift and give rise to a high dielectric constant.

2. Nonpolar Molecular Crystalline Solids. For a solid consisting of nonpolar molecules, that is, of molecules with no permanent dipole moment, the dielectric constant is very close to the square of the refractive index for visible light and differs from the dielectric constant of the liquid only because of the difference in the number of molecules in unit volume. Thus, in the case of the nonpolar substance benzene, $n_D{}^2$ for the liquid at 20°C. is 2.25 and ϵ is 2.29,[1] while at 5° the dielectric constant of the supercooled liquid is 2.34[2] and that of the solid 2.46. The failure of the dielectric constant–temperature curves for such solids to show any rise with increasing density at low temperatures is due to the fact that the material is usually frozen between the fixed plates of a condenser, so that increasing density does not alter the amount of material between the plates. The total polarization P is 27.01 for the vapor,[3] 26.62 for the liquid[1] at 10°, and 26.70 for the solid[4] at 5° and 28.5 at 0°.[5] As the electronic polarization P_E is 25.1, the atomic polarization P_A may be taken as 1.5. The difference in polarization between the solid and the liquid is evidently within the experimental error, as would be expected in view of the smallness of the effect which the environment of a group has upon its polarizability.[6,7] The case of n-dodecane[8] (lower curve, Fig. 2.1) is typical of a large class of substances without dipole moment, such as the paraffins, whose dielectric constants depend upon the induced displacement of electrons and, to a very small extent, of atoms or groups in the molecules. These dielectric constants are almost independent of physical

[1] C. P. Smyth and W. N. Stoops, *J. Am. Chem. Soc.*, **51**, 3312 (1929).
[2] C. P. Smyth and C. S. Hitchcock, *J. Am. Chem. Soc.*, **54**, 4631 (1932).
[3] K. B. McAlpine and C. P. Smyth, *J. Am. Chem. Soc.*, **55**, 453 (1933).
[4] J. Errera, *Bull. classe sci. Acad. roy. Belg.*, **12**, 327 (1926).
[5] S. O. Morgan and H. H. Lowry, *J. Phys. Chem.*, **34**, 2385 (1930).
[6] C. P. Smyth, *Phil. Mag.*, **50**, 361 (1925).
[7] C. P. Smyth, E. W. Engel, and E. B. Wilson, *J. Am. Chem. Soc.*, **51**, 1736 (1929).
[8] C. P. Smyth, *Record Chem. Progr. (Kresge-Hooker Sci. Lib.)*, **11**, 1 (1950).

state and temperature, except in so far as these factors determine the number of molecules in unit volume, or, in other words, the number of charges present to undergo displacement.

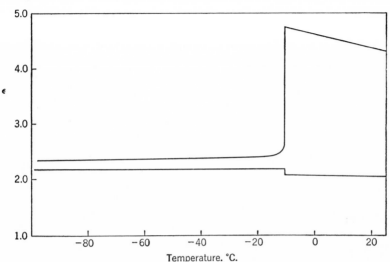

FIG. 2.1. Temperature dependence of the dielectric constants of n-dodecane (lower curve) and n-undecyl bromide (upper curve). [$C. P. Smyth, Record Chem. Prog.$, **11**, 1 (1950).]

3. Ionic Solids. In ionic solids, the dielectric constant still arises only from shift of charge, as in the nonpolar molecular solids, but the shift of ionic charge, which gives rise to P_A, may be more important than the electronic shift. Table 3.1 gives for the cubic-latticed and therefore

TABLE 3.1. DIELECTRIC CONSTANTS AND SQUARES OF REFRACTIVE INDICES
OF ALKALI METAL HALIDES

Substance	F		Cl		Br		I	
	ϵ	n_∞^2	ϵ	n_∞^2	ϵ	n_∞^2	ϵ	n_∞^2
Li	9.2	1.91	11.05	2.68	12.1	3.04	11.03	3.55
Na	4.9	1.74	5.77	2.32	5.99	2.60	6.60	2.96
K	6.05	1.83	4.76	2.17	4.78	2.35	4.94	2.64
Rb	5.91	1.93	5.20	2.18	4.70	2.34	4.81	2.58

isotropic alkali metal halides, except those of cesium, the values of the dielectric constant ϵ and the squares of the refractive indices n_∞ extrapolated from the visible region to infinite wavelength by means of a classical dispersion formula, and Table 3.2 gives the total and the atomic polarizations calculated from these values.[1] The considerable differences between ϵ and n_∞^2 are due to the displacements of the ions in the lattices. Both the total polarization P and the electronic P_E increase with increase in the size of either ion.   The same trend is evident in the values of P_A, but it is only approximate.   The larger one ion is, the smaller is the effect of the size of the other ion upon P_A.   For ordinary field strengths, the actual ionic displacement is very small.   As the displacement of the ions in the externally applied field depends upon the interionic forces, Errera[1] has applied the Born theory of the lattice[2] to these dielectric-constant values to calculate the infrared wavelengths corresponding to the characteristic vibration frequencies in the lattices.   From consideration of the fraction of the dielectric constant which is due to ionic displacement, expressed as $(\epsilon - n_\infty^2)/(\epsilon - 1)$, Errera and Brasseur[3] conclude that for solids of one family the fraction of the total polarization dependent upon ionic displacement is greater, the smaller the ionic radius, the smaller the interionic distances, and the smaller the electronic polarizability.   At first glance, this statement appears to be a direct contradiction of the evidence given by the P_A values in Table 3.2, which tend to increase

TABLE 3.2. TOTAL AND ATOMIC POLARIZATIONS OF ALKALI METAL HALIDES

Substance	F		Cl		Br		I	
	P	P_A	P	P_A	P	P_A	P	P_A
Li	7.20	4.90	15.80	8.44	19.74	9.60	25.38	10.24
Na	8.45	5.48	16.58	8.30	20.05	8.90	26.60	10.44
K	14.63	9.57	20.83	10.29	25.10	11.65	30.18	11.45
Rb	17.32	10.73	25.21	13.02	27.25	12.06	33.41	12.82

with ionic size.   Increasing ionic size and separation lessen the binding forces between ions of opposite charge and, therefore, cause increasing P_A. The conclusion of Errera and Brasseur is based upon the effect per cc. of substance, while the polarization values are based upon the number of molecules per mole.   The greater number of ionic charges present per cc. in the substances formed of small ions more than compensates for the stronger binding forces and thus gives higher dielectric constants.

In anisotropic solids, the different forces in different directions cause differences in the dielectric constants in these directions.   Thus, in the orthorhombic sulfates of strontium, barium, and lead—celestite, barite, and anglesite[3]—the refractive index of each is about the same along its

[1] J. Errera, Z. Elektrochem., **36**, 818 (1930).

[2] M. Born, "Atomtheorie des festen Zustandes," Teubner Verlagsgesellschaft, Leipzig, 1923.

[3] J. Errera and H. V. Brasseur, Physik. Z., **34**, 368 (1933).

three crystal axes, but the dielectric constant along the b axis is approximately double those along the a and c axes, which are nearly equal. ϵ_0 for anglesite has the unusually high value 54.6, more than ten times that due to electronic displacement alone. In a group of six rhombohedral carbonates, the refractive index along the equal a and b axes is larger than that along the c axis. The dielectric constant along the a and b axes is slightly larger than that along the c axis except in magnesite, where it is 15 per cent smaller than that along the c axis. A group of four orthorhombic carbonates has almost equal refractive indices along the a and b axes, with somewhat lower values along the c axis. The same is approximately true of the dielectric constants except in aragonite, which has a value along the a axis 60 per cent higher than that along the b axis. Titanium dioxide,[4,5] in the form of brown rutile, which is tetragonal, is a particularly striking example of the effect of ionic displacement, having a dielectric constant of 167 parallel to its optic axis and a value 83 perpendicular to this axis (see Sec. 9).

Rising temperature tends to decrease the dielectric constant of an ionic solid by decreasing the number of molecules per cubic centimeter as in the case of the nonpolar molecular solids. At the same time, however, the greater separation of the ions produced by the increasing volume weakens the forces between them and thus increases their ease of displacement. In the cases of calcium fluoride and sodium chloride examined by Bretscher,[6] the calculated increase of dielectric constant due to weakening of the interionic forces is nearly three times as large as the decrease caused by decreasing density.

Fröhlich[7] has derived an equation for the static dielectric constant of an ionic crystal with one infrared frequency for this type of polarization:

$$\epsilon_0 = n^2 + \frac{4\pi(n^2 + 2)^2}{9} \frac{e^{*2}N_D}{M\omega_t{}^2} \tag{3.1}$$

in which n is the optical refractive index, e^* the effective ionic charge, N_D the number of unit cells per unit volume, M the reduced mass, and ω_t the transverse angular vibration frequency. For a crystal of the NaCl type $1/M = 1/M^+ + 1/M^-$. As the effective ionic charge is not known, Fröhlich calculates it from experimental values of the other quantities for a number of salts with univalent ions and for three bivalent metallic oxides, obtaining values which bear ratios between 0.6 and 1.1 to the charges of the isolated ions. Most of the ratios lie between 0.7 and 0.9.

[4] W. Schmidt, *Ann. Physik*, **9**, 919 (1902).

[5] T. Liebisch and H. Rubens, *Sitzber. preuss. Akad. Wiss. Physik.-math. Kl.* 211 (1921).

[6] E. Bretscher, *Trans. Faraday Soc.*, **30**, 684 (1934).

[7] H. Fröhlich, "Theory of Dielectrics," Oxford, London, 1949, sec. 18.

Since the resonance frequencies of the electronic motions are in the visible or ultraviolet region and those for the ionic motions are in the infrared, both remote from the range of ordinary electrical measurements, the dielectric constants of ionic crystals normally vary little with frequency and the losses are correspondingly small. The presence of appreciable d.c. conductance will, of course, modify the dielectric behavior according to Eqs. II(6.7) and (6.8), as shown for rubbers in Sec. 8 of the present chapter. High temperature will give rise to this conductance, but, for most salts, the d.c. conductance at room temperature is too small to cause appreciable loss.

In ionic crystals that have been treated to introduce a relatively large number of lattice defects, small loss maxima have been observed in the kilocycle region.[8] The maximum values of the loss tangent thus observed for the alkali metal halides and silver chloride lie between 0.0003 and 0.03. These losses were, for the most part, observed at a frequency of 1 kc. (in a few cases, a range of 0.160 to 40,000 kc. was used) at temperatures between 80 and 200°, but, in silver chloride, a maximum was observed at −153° and a second maximum at −124°, the frequency being 1 kc. The contribution to the loss tangent from the dispersion effect of the ions was superimposed on a loss due to conductivity, which was subtracted from the total to obtain the absorption peak. The effect was attributed by Breckenridge to a jumping of the positive ions to vacant lattice sites under the influence of the applied field. The change in dielectric constant produced by the jumping was small and frequently within the error of the measurement, but the loss-tangent peak was used as a function of frequency and temperature to calculate the number of lattice defects present in the sample and the activation energy for diffusion of the positive ion in the crystal. This work was extended[9] by measurements of dielectric loss at 1 kc. as a function of temperature on four salts with a variety of foreign ions at several concentrations below 0.2 per cent. A number of loss maxima observed were found to depend, in height, on the concentration of the foreign ion and the heat treatment of the crystal and, in position on the temperature scale, upon the nature of the salt and of the foreign ion.

In measurements on a series of alkali metal halides with and without impurities, these anomalous loss peaks were not observed by Henvis, Davisson, and Burstein,[10] although special effort was made to find them. Haven[11] also was unable to reproduce the peaks found by Breckenridge, but found Debye-type losses attributable to pairs of associated lattice defects, involving Ca^{++} or Mn^{++} ions paired with Na^+ vacancies in a

[8] R. G. Breckenridge, *J. Chem. Phys.*, **16**, 959 (1948).

[9] R. G. Breckenridge, *J. Chem. Phys.*, **18**, 913 (1950).

[10] B. W. Henvis, J. W. Davisson, and E. Burstein, *Phys. Rev.*, **82**, 774 (1951).

[11] Y. Haven, *J. Chem. Phys.*, **21**, 171 (1953).

sodium chloride lattice.   A pair of defects was considered a dipole which could orient in an externally applied field.

An increase in the dielectric constants of impurity-activated phosphors when excited has been studied extensively.   According to Garlick,[12] dielectric-constant increases are shown only by phosphors which also show photoconductivity during luminescence.   For some zinc sulfide phosphors, the dielectric constants may increase to as much as double the normal value of about 8.   The dielectric-constant and loss changes are approximately proportional to the logarithm of the excitation intensity.   The changes may be represented[12] by equations analogous to Eqs. II(2.22) and (2.23), and the relaxation times calculated' from dielectric-constant change and from loss change are in satisfactory agreement with each other, being of the order of 10^{-7} sec.   The relaxation process is associated with the electron traps in the phosphor, and the time does not change much with temperature or from one phosphor to another.[12]

4. Polar Molecular Crystalline Solids.   Solids consisting of polar molecules, that is, molecules possessing permanent dipole moments, commonly behave like those consisting of nonpolar molecules, because solidification usually fixes the molecules with such rigidity in the lattice that little or no orientation of the dipoles in an externally applied field is possible.   The orientation polarization P_M is therefore zero, and the dielectric constant depends simply upon the displacement of charges inside the molecule.   The values of the electronic polarization P_E are unaffected by the presence of the dipole moments, and the values of P_A are little, if any, larger than those of the nonpolar molecules.[1]   The dielectric constant of the solid thus depends upon the same factors as in the nonpolar molecular solid.   The dielectric constant–temperature curve shows a great difference at the melting point, for, in the case of the nonpolar molecular solid, the small change produced by melting is usually a slight drop caused by decrease in the number of molecules per cc., while the polar molecules acquire freedom of rotation on melting and P_M changes abruptly from zero to a value often many times that of $P_E + P_A$.   Nitromethane,[2] which has a large dipole moment and, consequently, a large value of P_M in the liquid, affords a particularly striking example of this change at the melting point (Fig. 4.1).   The effect of the dipole is also well shown by the curve for n-undecyl bromide (upper curve, Fig. 2.1), which has a molecule almost identical in size and shape with that of n-dodecane.   The very slight increase in dielectric constant with temperature at low temperature and the more pronounced rise just below the melting point are typical.   An impure sample of a polar sub-

[12] G. F. J. Garlick, "Luminescent Materials," Oxford, London, 1949, chap. V.

[1] C. P. Smyth, *J. Am. Chem. Soc.*, **51**, 2051 (1929); *J. Chem. Phys.*, **1**, 247 (1933).

[2] C. P. Smyth and W. S. Walls, *J. Chem. Phys.*, **3**, 557 (1935).

stance may show a considerable increase in dielectric constant and in apparent conductance as the melting point is approached, presumably because of the separation of a small amount of a liquid phase and consequent interfacial polarization. A slight increase in carefully purified solids may be due to the acquisition by an occasional molecule of sufficient freedom to orient in an externally applied field or to the effect of increasing conductance upon the apparent value of the dielectric constant. A carefully purified solid nitrobenzene of melting point 5.67° showed an increase in dielectric constant from 3.25 at 0° to 3.62 at 5°, while pure solid benzene of melting point 5.4° increased by only 0.009 from 0° to 5°, and benzene saturated with water (0.01 to 0.05 per cent) before freezing increased by only 0.01 from 0° to 5°.[3] It seems probable, however, that loosening of the molecular lattice as the melting point is approached gives sufficient freedom to an occasional molecule to permit its orientation in the externally applied field. This effect is often termed "premelting."[4]

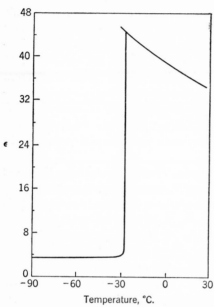

FIG. 4.1. Dielectric constant–temperature curve (at 70 kc.) of nitromethane. [*C. P. Smyth and W. S. Walls, J. Chem. Phys.*, **3**, 557 (1935).]

In considering the possibility of high dielectric constant through molecular rotation in solids it is necessary to weigh other types of evidence also. The thermal energy of solids as evidenced by their specific heats is due mainly to the translational vibrations of the atoms, ions, or molecules about fixed points in the crystals or in the molecules, although rotational vibration or, very occasionally, free rotation of a molecule or polyatomic ion may play a part. Instead of the perfectly random translational motion and complete freedom of rotation which was formerly attributed to the molecules of a liquid, Debye has suggested[5] that the molecules are vibrating about points which themselves move relatively slowly through the liquid. Each molecule is, of course, acted upon by strong electric forces due to the surrounding molecules. Unless the molecule has spherical symmetry, one or more of its orientations in the

[3] C. P. Smyth and C. S. Hitchcock, *J. Am. Chem. Soc.*, **54**, 4631 (1932).

[4] C. P. Smyth, *Trans. Faraday Soc.*, **42A**, 175 (1946).

[5] P. Debye, *Physik. Z.*, **36**, 100 (1935).

field of force surrounding it are more stable than the others.   Pauling[6] gave an approximate theoretical treatment of the problem, showing that the commencement of molecular rotation with rising temperature could account for a number of transitions which specific-heat measurements had revealed in certain solids, and predicting that dielectric-constant measurements would show freedom of rotation above these transitions. Fowler[7] used partition functions to represent the effect of molecular rotation upon the specific heats and dielectric constants of these substances which show transitions.   The equations thus obtained show that the transitions should occur, but require the changes to be more gradual than those actually observed and are not successful in predicting where they should occur.   Frenkel, Todes, and Ismailow[8] based an approximate treatment on the assumption that the transition from nonrotation to rotation is very sharp, so that a rotating phase and a nonrotating phase are in equilibrium at a definite transition temperature.   They were unable, however, to obtain much support of their treatment from the experimental facts.   This type of transition is sometimes called a second-order transition or lambda point,[9,10] but involves the discontinuity of properties characteristic of a first-order transition.   As molecular rotation or a disordered arrangement of the molecules tends to lower the internal field, it is apt to give symmetry to a lattice.   If the rotating molecule is fairly symmetrical in form, the lattice is usually one which could be formed of close-packed spheres, commonly cubic or hexagonal.   From the opposite point of view, if the crystal is isotropic, the potential energy of a molecule will tend to vary less with its orientation in the lattice, which means that the molecule is more apt to be able to rotate.   It is obviously desirable to correlate the lattice structure as revealed by X-ray analysis with the evidence of molecular rotation.   The mechanism of dipole orientation will be examined after the experimental results have been surveyed.

Table 4.1 summarizes the information in regard to crystal structure and rotation or nonrotation in a large number of solids which either show rotation or might be expected to show it but do not.   A number of substances concerning which dielectric measurements give no evidence are included in order to show the influence of their molecular shapes upon their rotational freedom.   The numbers in parentheses after the formula or name of the substance refer to the list of references at the end of the table.   These references will normally not be repeated in the subsequent discussion. T_t is the transition temperature.   The table is a somewhat

(*Text continues on page* 153)

[6] L. Pauling, *Phys. Rev.*, **36**, 430 (1930).
[7] R. H. Fowler, *Proc. Roy. Soc. (London)*, **149**, 1 (1935).
[8] Y. Frenkel, O. Todes, and S. Ismailow, *Acta Physicochim. U.R.S.S.*, **1**, 97 (1934).
[9] P. Ehrenfest, *Communs. Kamerlingh Onnes Lab. Univ. Leiden*, Suppl. 75b (1933).
[10] J. E. Mayer and S. F. Streeter, *J. Chem. Phys.*, **7**, 1019 (1939).

142   DIELECTRIC BEHAVIOR AND STRUCTURE

TABLE 4.1. MOLECULAR ORIENTATIONAL FREEDOM AND CRYSTAL STRUCTURE

Molecule	Below transition	T_t, °K	Above transition
H_2 (1)	Rot. at very low temperature		Hexagonal
Cl_2 (2)	No rot.		
Br_2 (3)	No rot.		
I_2 (1, 4)	Orthorhombic. No rot.		
O_2 (5, 6, 7, 8)	Orthorhombic	23.8	Orthorhombic
	Orthorhombic	43.5	Rot. Hexagonal
N_2 (5, 7, 8, 9)	Cubic	35.4	Rot. Hexagonal
CO (5, 8)	Cubic	61.5	Rot. Hexagonal
NO (2, 10)	No rot. indicated		
N_2O (11, 12)	Cubic. No rot.		
CO_2 (5, 12)	Cubic. No rot.		
SO_2 (104)	No rot.		
CH_4 (7, 13)	Cubic	20.4	Cubic. Probable rot.
CH_3D (14)		15.9	Probable rot.
	Probable rot.	23.2	Probable rot.
CD_4 (14)		22.3	Probable rot.
	Probable rot.	27.1	Probable rot.
SiH_4 (14)		63.4	Rot. Higher symmetry
NH_3 (2, 11, 16, 89)	Cubic. Probable rot. around axis of symmetry		
PH_3 (17)		30	Rot.
	Rot.	89	Rot. Cubic (103°)
AsH_3 (18)		20–32.1	Rot. Cubic (103°)
	Rot. Cubic	106.6	Rot.
H_2O (19, 20, 90, 106)	Hexagonal. Probably hindered rot. and proton transfer		
H_2S (16, 17, 21)		103.5	Rot. Cubic
	Rot. Cubic	126.3	Rot.
D_2S (22)		107.8	Rot.
	Rot.	132.8	Rot.
H_2Se (18, 22)		89	Rot. Cubic (103°)
	Rot. Cubic (103°)	172.5	Rot.
D_2Se (22)		90	Rot.
	Rot.	176.0	Rot.
HF (11, 17)	No rot.		
HCl (2, 23, 24, 25, 104)	Orthorhombic	98.7	Cubic. Rot.
DCl (104)		103	Resembles HCl
HBr (2, 24, 26, 27, 28, 29, 30, 103, 105)	Orthorhombic. Dispersion	89	Dispersion. Cubic. Rot.
	Cubic. Rot.	113	Cubic. Rot.
	Cubic. Rot.	117	Cubic. Rot.

TABLE 4.1. MOLECULAR ORIENTATIONAL FREEDOM AND CRYSTAL STRUCTURE
(*Continued*)

Molecule	Below transition	T_t, °K	Above transition
DBr (30, 103)	Dispersion	92	Dispersion. Rot.
	Rot.	120	Rot.
HI (2, 24, 31, 104, 107)	Tetragonal (f.c.). Dispersion	70.1	Dispersion. Tetragonal (f.c.)
	Rot. Tetragonal (f.c.)	125.7	Tetragonal (f.c.). Rot.
DI (104, 107)		77.3	Similar to HI
		128.3	
HCN (18)	No rot.		
CH$_3$Br (32)	No rot. around axis perpendicular to axis of symmetry		
CH$_3$Cl (32)	No rot. around axis perpendicular to axis of symmetry		
CH$_3$I (32, 89)	Probable rot. around axis of symmetry		
CH$_2$Cl$_2$ (32)	No rot. around axis perpendicular to axis of symmetry		
CHCl$_3$ (32)	No rot. around axis perpendicular to axis of symmetry		
CH$_3$NO$_2$ (33, 89)	Probable rot. around axis of symmetry		
CH$_3$OH (16, 34, 35, 36, 89)	No rot.	159	Limited rot.
CH$_3$NH$_2$ (37, 89)	Probably no molecular rot.		
CH$_2$ClCH$_2$Cl (16, 38, 39, 40, 89)	No rot.	177	Rot. around chain axis with chlorines in trans position
CH$_2$ClCH$_2$Br (41, 42)	No rot.	177	Rot. around chain axis with halogens in trans position
CH$_2$BrCH$_2$Br (38, 39)	No rot.	249.5	Rot. around chain axis with bromines in trans position
CHCl$_2$CHCl$_2$ (42)	No rot.		
(CH$_3$)$_2$ClC·CCl(CH$_3$)$_2$ (43)	No rot.	263–277	Rot.
(CH$_3$)$_2$BrC·CBr(CH$_3$)$_2$ (43)	No rot.	348–383	Rot.
CH$_2$CNCH$_2$CN (38)	No rot.	232.8–235.2	Rot.
CH$_2$BrCH$_2$CH$_2$Br (44)	No rot.		
(C$_2$H$_5$)$_2$O (37)	No rot.		

TABLE 4.1. MOLECULAR ORIENTATIONAL FREEDOM AND CRYSTAL STRUCTURE
(*Continued*)

Molecule	Below transition	T_t, °K	Above transition
$(CH_3)_2CO$ (37, 89)	Apparent gradual onset of rot.		
$CH_2ClCHCl_2$ (44)	No rot.		
CH_3CCl_3 (44, 45, 89, 95)	Anisotropic. No rot.	224.3	Cubic. Rot.
$(CH_3)_2CCl_2$ (45, 95)	Anisotropic. No rot.	188.1	Cubic. Rot.
$(CH_3)_3CCl$ (46, 47, 48, 95)	No rot.	183.0	No rot. around axis perpendicular to axis of symmetry
	No rot. around axis perpendicular to axis of symmetry	219.7	Isotropic. Rot.
$(CH_3)_3CBr$ (46, 47, 95)	Anisotropic. No rot.	208.7	Isotropic. Limited rot.
	Isotropic. Limited rot.	231.6	Isotropic. Rot.
$(CH_3)_3CI$ (46)	No rot.	193.8	Rot. with some difficulty
$(CH_3)_3COH$ (36)	No rot.		
$(CH_2)_2(COOH)_2$ (49)	No rot.		
$CH_3CCl(NO_2)CH_3$ (44, 95)	No rot.	215.7	Rot.
$CH_3CBr(NO_2)CH_3$ (44)	No rot.	239	Rot.
$(CH_3)_2SO_4$ (19)	No rot.	203	Limited rot.
$(C_2H_5)_2SO_4$ (19)	No rot.		
$(CH_3)_3CNO_2$ (44)	No rot.	257.8	Rot.
$(CH_3)_2C(CH_2NO_2)_2$ (44)	No rot.	276.0	Rot.
$(CH_3)_2C(NO_2)_2$ (44, 95)	No rot.	268.1	Rot.
Cyclohexane (92)		186.4	Rot.
Cyclopentanol (43)	No rot.	203	Rot.
Cyclohexanol (49, 50, 51, 92)	No rot. Anisotropic	265.3	Cubic. Rot.
Cyclohexanone (43, 50, 52, 92)	No rot. Anisotropic	220.6	Cubic. Rot.
Chlorocyclohexane (43, 50, 52, 92)	No rot. Anisotropic	220.6	Cubic. Rot.
Bromocyclohexane (43, 50)	No rot.		
Cyclohexylamine (43)	No rot.		
Cyclohexyl fluoroform (43)	No rot.	164–167	Limited rot.
1,3-Cyclohexadiene (43)	No rot.	159–164	Rot.

TABLE 4.1. MOLECULAR ORIENTATIONAL FREEDOM AND CRYSTAL STRUCTURE
(*Continued*)

Molecule	Below transition	T_t, °K	Above transition
1,4-Cyclohexadione (43)	No rot.	321–324	Partial rot.
d-Camphor (49, 53, 111)	Hexagonal (rhombohedral)	233–236	Rot. Hexagonal (rhombohedral)
	Rot. Hexagonal (rhombohedral)	370	Rot. Cubic
dl-Camphor (49, 53)		125–208	Rot.
Borneol (49, 53)		173–223	Limited rot.
	Limited rot.	343–348	Rot.
Isoborneol (49, 53)		173–223	Limited rot.
	Limited rot.	285–319	Rot.
Bornyl chloride (53)		130–165	Rot.
d-Camphoric anhydride (53)		408	Rot.
C_6H_6 (54)		(110)	Possible rot. around hexagonal axis
C_6H_5OH (55)	No rot.		
$C_6H_5NH_2$ (19)	No rot.		
$C_6H_5NO_2$ (19)	No rot.		
$C_6H_5OCH_3$ (55)	No rot.		
p-$CH_3OC_6H_4OCH_3$ (55)	No rot.		
$C_6H_5COC_6H_5$ (37)	No rot.		
Methylpentachlorobenzene (56)	Rot. with anomalous dispersion in solid		
Tetrachloro-m-xylene (56)	Rot. with anomalous dispersion in solid		
Tetrachloro-o-xylene (56)	Rot. with anomalous dispersion in solid		
1,2,3-Trimethyl-4,5,6-trichlorobenzene (56)	Rot. with anomalous dispersion in solid		
1,2,4-Trimethyl-3,5,6-trichlorobenzene (56)	Rot. with anomalous dispersion in solid		
1,2,3,4-Tetramethyl-5,6-dichlorobenzene (56)	Rot. with anomalous dispersion in solid		
1,2,3,5-Tetramethyl-4,6-dichlorobenzene (56)	Rot. with anomalous dispersion in solid		
Pentamethylchlorobenzene (56)	Rot. with anomalous dispersion in solid		
Trichloro-m-xylene (56)	No rot.	293–295	Rot.
3,4,5-Trichloro-o-xylene (56)	No rot.	288–293	Rot.

TABLE 4.1. MOLECULAR ORIENTATIONAL FREEDOM AND CRYSTAL STRUCTURE
(Continued)

Molecule	Below transition	T_t, °K	Above transition
Pentamethylnitrobenzene (56)	No rot.		
2,4,6-Trimethylnitrobenzene (56)	No rot.		
1,2,3,4-Tetramethyl-5,6-dinitrobenzene (56)	No rot.	423	Limited rot.
2,4,6-Trimethyldinitrobenzene (56)	No rot.		
5-Nitro-3,4-dichloro-o-xylene (56)	No rot.	338	Rot.
3-Nitro-4,5-dichloro-o-xylene (56)	No rot.		
Ethylpentachlorobenzene (56)	No rot.		
1,2,3,4-Tetraethyl-5,6-dinitrobenzene (56)	No rot.		
1,2,3,4-Tetrachlorobenzene (56)	No rot.		
4,5-Dichloro-o-xylene (56)	No rot.		
i-C_3H_7Br (57)	Premelting in crystal. Tends to vitrify		
i-C_4H_9Br (58)	No rot. in crystal. Tends to vitrify		
i-C_4H_9Cl (59)	No rot. in crystal. Tends to vitrify		
i-$C_5H_{11}Br$ (58)	No rot. in crystal. Tends to vitrify		
n-$C_5H_{11}Br$ (47, 57, 60)	Two crystalline forms. No rot.		
i-$C_5H_{11}Cl$ (59)	No rot.		
$CH_3CH_2CHClCH_2Cl$ (59)	Vitrifies		
n-$C_7H_{15}Br$ (55, 61)	Two crystalline forms. No rot.		
n-$C_8H_{17}Br$ (61)	No rot.		
n-$C_9H_{19}Br$ (61, 62)	Two crystalline forms. No rot.		
n-$C_{10}H_{21}Br$ (61)	No rot.		
n-$C_{11}H_{23}Br$ (61)	No rot.		
n-$C_{12}H_{25}Br$ (63)	No rot.		
n-$C_{13}H_{27}Br$ (61)	No rot.		
n-$C_{15}H_{31}Br$ (61)	No rot.		
n-$C_{18}H_{37}Br$ (63)	No rot.		

TABLE 4.1. MOLECULAR ORIENTATIONAL FREEDOM AND CRYSTAL STRUCTURE
(*Continued*)

Molecule	Below transition	T_t, °K	Above transition
n-$C_{22}H_{45}Br$ (63, 108, 109)	Very restricted. Two absorption regions	303.5 (Monotropic)	Rot. around chain axis
n-$C_{30}H_{61}Br$ (108, 109)	Very restricted rot. Two absorption regions	330	Rot.
n-$C_8H_{17}OH$ (36, 101)	No rot.		
n-$C_{10}H_{21}OH$ (101)			
n-$C_{12}H_{25}OH$ (54, 64, 65, 66, 101)	No rot.	289 (Monotropic)	Unstable. Observed in impure samples. Rot. and probable proton transfer
n-$C_{14}H_{29}OH$ (64, 101)	No rot.	307.6 (Monotropic)	Rot. with probable proton transfer.
n-$C_{16}H_{33}OH$ (67, 68, 69, 70, 71, 98, 101, 102)	No rot.	317 (Monotropic)	Rot. and probable proton transfer.
n-$C_{18}H_{37}OH$ (64, 70, 71, 96, 100)	No rot.	326.6 (Monotropic)	Rot. and probable proton transfer
n-$C_{22}H_{45}OH$ (64, 96, 98, 100)	No rot.	337.7 (Monotropic)	Rot. and probable proton transfer
n-$C_{26}H_{53}OH$ (98, 100)			
dl-$CH_3CHOHC_{18}H_{37}$ (97)	Slight dispersion		
dl-$C_3H_7CHOHC_{16}H_{33}$ (97)	Dispersion		
dl-$C_5H_{11}CHOHC_{14}H_{29}$ (97)	Dispersion		
dl-$C_7H_{15}CHOHC_{12}H_{25}$ (97)	Dispersion		
dl-$C_9H_{19}CHOHC_{10}H_{21}$ (97)	Dispersion		
$C_9H_{19}CHOHC_8H_{19}$ (97, 100)	Dispersion		
$C_{13}H_{27}CHOHCH_{13}H_{27}$ (100)	Dispersion		
$C_{17}H_{35}CHOHC_{17}H_{35}$ (100)	Dispersion		
$C_{14}H_{29}SH$ (94)	α-Phase, dipole orientation with dispersion.		
$C_{18}H_{37}SH$ (94)	α-Phase, dipole orientation with dispersion		
$(C_{12}H_{25})_2O$ (94)	No rot.		

TABLE 4.1. MOLECULAR ORIENTATIONAL FREEDOM AND CRYSTAL STRUCTURE
(*Continued*)

Molecule	Below transition	T_t, °K	Above transition
$(C_{14}H_{29})_2O$ (94)	No rot.		
$(C_{16}H_{33})_2O$ (94)	Dipole orientation with dispersion		
$(C_{18}H_{37})_2O$ (94)	Dipole orientation with dispersion		
$n\text{-}C_8H_{17}NH_2$ (72)	Apparent proton transfer		
$n\text{-}C_{12}H_{25}NH_2$ (72)	Apparent proton transfer		
$n\text{-}C_{14}H_{29}NH_2$ (72)	No rot.		
$n\text{-}C_{16}H_{33}NH_2$ (72)	No rot.		
$n\text{-}C_{16}H_{34}$ (63, 73)	No rot.		
$n\text{-}C_{18}H_{38}$ (54, 73, 74)	No rot.	300.0 (Monotropic)	Hexagonal symmetry. Probable rot. around chain axis
$n\text{-}C_{20}H_{42}$ (73, 74)	No rot.	305.2 (Monotropic)	Hexagonal symmetry. Probable rot. around chain axis
$n\text{-}C_{22}H_{46}$ (73, 74)	No rot.	313.2 (Monotropic)	Hexagonal symmetry. Probable rot. around chain axis
$n\text{-}C_{24}H_{50}$ (73, 74, 109)	No rot.	321.2	Hexagonal symmetry. Probable rot. around chain axis
$n\text{-}C_{26}H_{54}$ (73, 74, 75, 109)	No rot.	325.6	Hexagonal symmetry. Probable rot. around chain axis
$n\text{-}C_{27}H_{56}$ (74)	No rot.	322	Hexagonal symmetry. Probable rot. around chain axis
$n\text{-}C_{28}H_{58}$ (54, 73, 109)	No rot.	330.0	Hexagonal symmetry. Probable rot. around chain axis
$n\text{-}C_{29}H_{60}$ (73, 74)	No rot.	330	Hexagonal symmetry. Probable rot. around chain axis
$n\text{-}C_{30}H_{62}$ (73, 74, 75, 109)	No rot.	334.3	Hexagonal symmetry. Probable rot. around chain axis
$n\text{-}C_{31}H_{64}$ (74)	No rot.	335.0	Hexagonal symmetry. Probable rot. around chain axis
$n\text{-}C_{32}H_{66}$ (73, 54)	No rot.	336.7	Hexagonal symmetry. Probable rot. around chain axis

TABLE 4.1. MOLECULAR ORIENTATIONAL FREEDOM AND CRYSTAL STRUCTURE
(Continued)

Molecule	Below transition	T_t, °K	Above transition
$n\text{-}C_{34}H_{70}$ (73, 74, 75)	No rot.	341	Hexagonal symmetry. Probable rot. around chain axis
$n\text{-}C_{35}H_{72}$ (75)	No rot.	341.1	Hexagonal symmetry. Probable rot. around chain axis
$n\text{-}C_{44}H_{90}$ (73, 74)	No rot.	359	Hexagonal symmetry. Probable rot. around chain axis
$(n\text{-}C_8H_{17})_2CO$ (76)	Premelting		
$(n\text{-}C_{11}H_{23})_2CO$ (76)	Premelting		
$C_{17}H_{35}COOH$ (93)	No rot.		
$C_{17}H_{35}CONH_2$ (94)	No rot.		
$C_{10}H_{21}COOC_2H_5$ (67)	No rot. Premelting		
$C_{15}H_{31}COOCH_3$ (99, 110)	Rot. of molecule and of polar group with dispersion		
$C_{15}H_{31}COOC_2H_5$ (67)	No rot.	292.8	Transition from α to β at solidification point. Rot. during transformation
$C_{17}H_{35}COOCH_3$ (99)	Rot. of molecule and of polar group with dispersion		
$C_{17}H_{35}COOC_2H_5$ (67, 93)	No rot.	295.8 (Monotropic)	Restricted rot. probably around chain axis
$CH_3COOC_{18}H_{37}$ (93)	β-Form, no rot.		α-Form, some orientational freedom
$C_{21}H_{43}COOCH_3$ (99)	Rot. of molecule and of polar group with dispersion		
$C_{21}H_{43}COOC_2H_5$ (77)	No rot.	316.2	Limited rot. probably around chain axis
$C_{15}H_{31}COOC_{10}H_{21}$ (93)	Rot. with anomalous dispersion		
$C_{15}H_{31}COOC_{12}H_{25}$ (93)	No rot.		
$C_{15}H_{31}COOC_{14}H_{29}$ (93)	Rot. with anomalous dispersion		
$C_{15}H_{31}COOC_{16}H_{33}$ (93)	Rot. with anomalous dispersion		
$C_{17}H_{35}COOC_{12}H_{25}$ (93)	Anomalous dispersion	249.6	Rot. around chain axis
$C_{17}H_{35}COOC_{14}H_{29}$ (93)	No rot.		
$(C_{13}H_{27}COO)_2C_2H_4$ (93)	No rot.		

TABLE 4.1. MOLECULAR ORIENTATIONAL FREEDOM AND CRYSTAL STRUCTURE
(*Continued*)

Molecule	Below transition	T_t, °K	Above transition
$(C_{15}H_{31}COO)_2C_2H_4$ (93)	No rot.		
$(C_{17}H_{35}COO)_2C_2H_4$ (93)	No rot.		
Cholesteryl stearate (94)	No rot. in solid or in mesomorphic state		
1-Monopalmitin (79, 80, 81)	Segment orientation in sub-α form. No rotation in β and β' forms	312	Rot. around chain axis in α form with possibility of proton transfer
1-Monostearin (79, 80, 81, 82)	Segment orientation in sub-α form. No rotation in β and β' forms	322	Rot. around chain axis in α form with possibility of proton transfer
1-Monomyristin (80, 82	No rot.	297	Rot. around chain axis in α form
1,3-Dipalmitin (78, 83, 84)	Two crystalline forms. No rot.		
1,3-Distearin (78, 83, 84)	Two crystalline forms. No rot.		
Tripalmitin (78, 85, 86)	Three crystalline forms. Segment orientation in α form only		
Tristearin (78, 85, 86, 87)	Three crystalline forms. Segment orientation in α form only		
1-Oleyldipalmitin (94)	Segment orientation in α form		
1-Oleyldistearin (94)	Segment orientation in α form		
2-Palmityldistearin (88)	Two crystalline forms		Rot. in α form only
2-Stearyldipalmitin (88)	Two crystalline forms		Rot. in α form only
2-Lauryldistearin (88)	Four crystalline forms		Rot. in α form only
2-Oleyldipalmitin (88)	Four crystalline forms		Rot. in α form only
2-Oleyldistearin (88)	Four crystalline forms		Rot. in α form only

REFERENCES FOR TABLE 4.1

1. L. Pauling, *Phys. Rev.*, **36**, 430 (1930).
2. A. Eucken and E. Karwat, *Z. physik. Chem.*, **112**, 467 (1924).
3. W. M. Latimer and H. D. Hoenshel, *J. Am. Chem. Soc.*, **48**, 19 (1926).
4. W. F. Giauque, *J. Am. Chem. Soc.*, **53**, 507 (1931).
5. A. Eucken, *Verhandl. deut. physik. Ges.*, **18**, 4 (1916).
6. W. F. Giauque and H. L. Johnston, *J. Am. Chem. Soc.*, **51**, 2300 (1929).
7. K. Clusius, *Z. physik. Chem.*, **3B**, 41 (1929).
8. B. Ruhemann, *Z. Physik*, **76**, 368 (1932).
9. W. H. Keesom and H. K. Onnes, *Proc. Acad. Sci. Amsterdam*, **18**, 1247 (1916).
10. H. L. Johnston and W. F. Giauque, *J. Am. Chem. Soc.*, **51**, 3194 (1929).
11. K. Clusius, K. Hiller, and J. V. Vaughen, *Z. physik. Chem.*, **8B**, 427 (1930).
12. A. Eucken and F. Hauck, *Z. physik. Chem.*, **134**, 161 (1928).
13. K. Clusius and A. Perlick, *Z. physik. Chem.*, **24B**, 313 (1934).
14. K. Clusius and L. Popp, *Z. physik. Chem.*, **46B**, 63 (1940).
15. K. Clusius, *Z. physik. Chem.*, **23B**, 213 (1933).
16. C. P. Smyth and C. S. Hitchcock, *J. Am. Chem. Soc.*, **55**, 1296 (1933); **56**, 1084 (1934).
17. K. Clusius, *Z. Elektrochem.*, **39**, 598 (1933).
18. C. P. Smyth and S. A. McNeight, *J. Am. Chem. Soc.*, **58**, 1723 (1936).
19. C. P. Smyth and C. S. Hitchcock, *J. Am. Chem. Soc.*, **54**, 4631 (1932).
20. E. J. Murphy, *Trans. Am. Electrochem. Soc.*, **65**, 133 (1934).
21. J. D. Kemp and G. H. Denison, *J. Am. Chem. Soc.*, **55**, 251 (1933).
22. K. Clusius and A. Kruis, *Z. physik. Chem.*, **38B**, 156 (1937).
23. R. M. Cone, G. H. Denison, and J. D. Kemp, *J. Am. Chem. Soc.*, **53**, 1278 (1931).
24. C. P. Smyth and C. S. Hitchcock, *J. Am. Chem. Soc.*, **55**, 1830 (1933).
25. W. F. Giauque and R. Wiebe, *J. Am. Chem. Soc.*, **50**, 101 (1928).
26. W. F. Giauque and R. Wiebe, *J. Am. Chem. Soc.*, **50**, 2193 (1928).
27. B. Ruhemann and F. Simon, *Z. physik. Chem.*, **15B**, 389 (1932).
28. G. Natta, *Gazz. chim. ital.*, **63**, 425 (1933).
29. J. G. Powles, *Nature*, **165**, 686 (1950).
30. J. G. Powles, *Compt. rend.*, **230**, 836 (1950).
31. W. F. Giauque and R. Wiebe, *J. Am. Chem. Soc.*, **51**, 1441 (1929).
32. S. O. Morgan and H. H. Lowry, *J. Phys. Chem.*, **34**, 2385 (1930).
33. C. P. Smyth and W. S. Walls, *J. Chem. Phys.*, **3**, 557 (1935).
34. G. S. Parks, *J. Am. Chem. Soc.*, **47**, 338 (1925).
35. K. K. Kelley, *J. Am. Chem. Soc.*, **51**, 180 (1929).
36. C. P. Smyth and S. A. McNeight, *J. Am. Chem. Soc.*, **58**, 1597 (1936).
37. S. A. McNeight and C. P. Smyth, *J. Am. Chem. Soc.*, **58**, 1718 (1936).
38. A. H. White and S. O. Morgan, *J. Chem. Phys.*, **5**, 655 (1937).
39. K. S. Pitzer, *J. Am. Chem. Soc.*, **62**, 331 (1940).
40. H. S. Gutowsky and G. E. Pake, *J. Chem. Phys.*, **18**, 162 (1950).
41. W. E. Railing, *J. Am. Chem. Soc.*, **61**, 3349 (1939).
42. M. Kubo, *Sci. Papers Inst. Phys. Chem. Research (Tokyo)*, **35**, 462 (1939).
43. A. H. White and W. S. Bishop, *J. Am. Chem. Soc.*, **62**, 8 (1940).
44. R. W. Crowe and C. P. Smyth, *J. Am. Chem. Soc.*, **72**, 4009 (1950).
45. A. Turkevich and C. P. Smyth, *J. Am. Chem. Soc.*, **62**, 2468 (1940).
46. W. O. Baker and C. P. Smyth, *J. Am. Chem. Soc.*, **61**, 2798 (1939).

47. L. M. Kushner, R. W. Crowe, and C. P. Smyth, *J. Am. Chem. Soc.*, **72**, 1091 (1950).
48. W. P. Conner and C. P. Smyth, *J. Am. Chem. Soc.*, **63**, 3424 (1941).
49. A. H. White and S. O. Morgan, *J. Am. Chem. Soc.*, **57**, 2078 (1935).
50. O. Hassel and A. M. Sommerfeldt, *Z. physik. Chem.*, **40B**, 391 (1938).
51. L. Deffet, *Bull. soc. chim. Belges*, **49**, 223 (1940).
52. L. O. Fischer, *Bull. soc. chim. Belges*, **49**, 129 (1940).
53. W. A. Yager and S. O. Morgan, *J. Am. Chem. Soc.*, **57**, 2071 (1935).
54. E. R. Andrew, *J. Chem. Phys.*, **18**, 607 (1950).
55. S. E. Kamerling and C. P. Smyth, *J. Am. Chem. Soc.*, **55**, 462 (1933).
56. A. H. White, B. S. Biggs, and S. O. Morgan, *J. Am. Chem. Soc.*, **62**, 16 (1940).
57. W. O. Baker and C. P. Smyth, *J. Am. Chem. Soc.*, **61**, 1695 (1939).
58. W. O. Baker and C. P. Smyth, *J. Am. Chem. Soc.*, **61**, 2063 (1939).
59. A. Turkevich and C. P. Smyth, *J. Am. Chem. Soc.*, **64**, 737 (1942).
60. R. F. Deese, *J. Am. Chem. Soc.*, **53**, 3673 (1931).
61. R. W. Crowe and C. P. Smyth, *J. Am. Chem. Soc.*, **72**, 1098 (1950).
62. B. J. Mair, *Bur. Standards J. Research*, **9**, 457 (1932).
63. J. D. Hoffman and C. P. Smyth, *J. Am. Chem. Soc.*, **72**, 171 (1950).
64. J. D. Hoffman and C. P. Smyth, *J. Am. Chem. Soc.*, **71**, 431 (1949).
65. E. Ott, *Z. physik. Chem.*, **193**, 218 (1944).
66. J. D. Bernal, *Nature*, **129**, 870 (1932).
67. W. O. Baker and C. P. Smyth, *J. Am. Chem. Soc.*, **60**, 1229 (1938).
68. K. Sano and Y. Kakiuchi, *J. Phys. Soc. Japan*, **4**, 178 (1949).
69. Y. Kakiuchi and T. Sakurai, *J. Phys. Soc. Japan*, **4**, 365 (1949).
70. K. Higasi and M. Kubo, *Sci. Papers Inst. Phys. Chem. Research (Tokyo)*, **36**, 286 (1939).
71. D. A. Wilson and E. Ott, *J. Chem. Phys.*, **2**, 231 (1934).
72. J. D. Hoffmann and C. P. Smyth, *J. Am. Chem. Soc.*, **71**, 3591 (1949).
73. W. F. Seyer, R. F. Patterson, and J. L. Keays, *J. Am. Chem. Soc.*, **66**, 179 (1944).
74. A. Müller, *Proc. Roy. Soc. (London)*, **138A**, 514 (1932).
75. W. E. Garner, K. van Bibber and A. M. King, *J. Chem. Soc.*, 1533 (1931).
76. A. Müller, *Proc. Roy. Soc. (London)*, **158A**, 403 (1937).
77. R. Buckingham, *Trans. Faraday Soc.*, **30**, 377 (1934).
78. R. W. Crowe and C. P. Smyth, *J. Am. Chem. Soc.*, **72**, 5280 (1950).
79. R. W. Crowe and C. P. Smyth, *J. Am. Chem. Soc.*, **72**, 4427 (1950).
80. T. Malkin and M. R. Shurbagy, *J. Chem. Soc.*, 1628 (1936).
81. E. S. Lutton and F. L. Jackson, *J. Am. Chem. Soc.*, **70**, 2445 (1948).
82. B. V. Bhide and R. D. Bhide, *J. Univ. Bombay*, **8**, 220 (1939).
83. T. Malkin, M. R. Shurbagy, and M. L. Meara, *J. Chem. Soc.*, 1409 (1937).
84. F. J. Baur, F. L. Jackson, D. G. Kolp, and E. S. Lutton, *J. Am. Chem. Soc.*, **71**, 3363 (1949).
85. C. E. Clarkson and T. Malkin, *J. Chem. Soc.*, 666 (1934).
86. E. S. Lutton, *J. Am. Chem. Soc.*, **67**, 524 (1945).
87. B. V. Bhide and R. D. Bhide, *J. Univ. Bombay*, **7**, 97 (1938).
88. R. W. Crowe and C. P. Smyth, *J. Am. Chem. Soc.*, **73**, 2040 (1951).
89. H. S. Gutowsky and G. E. Pake, *J. Chem. Phys.*, **18**, 162 (1950).
90. J. Errera, *J. phys.*, (6)**5**, 304 (1924).
91. H. Wintsch, *Helv. Phys. Acta*, **5**, 126 (1932).
92. R. W. Crowe and C. P. Smyth, *J. Am. Chem. Soc.*, **73**, 5406 (1951).
93. R. W. Crowe and C. P. Smyth, *J. Am. Chem. Soc.*, **73**, 5401 (1951).

94. A. Di Giacomo and C. P. Smyth, Unpublished measurements.
95. J. G. Powles, D. E. Williams, and C. P. Smyth, *J. Chem. Phys.*, **21**, 736 (1953).
96. R. J. Meakins and R. A. Sack, *Australian J. Sci. Research*, **4A**, 213 (1951).
97. R. J. Meakins and H. K. Welsh, *Australian J. Sci. Research*, **4A**, 359 (1951).
98. R. J. Meakins and J. W. Mulley, *Australian J. Sci. Research*, **4A**, 365 (1951).
99. J. S. Dryden and H. K. Welsh, *Australian J. Sci. Research*, **4A**, 616 (1951).
100. J. S. Dryden, *Australian J. Sci. Research*, **5A**, 661 (1952).
101. B. V. Hamon and R. J. Meakins, *Australian J. Sci. Research*, **A5**, 671 (1952).
102. K. Sano and Y. Kakiuchi, *J. Phys. Soc. Japan*, **4**, 178 (1949).
103. J. G. Powles, *Nature*, **165**, 686 (1950); *Compt. rend.*, **230**, 836 (1950); J. Physique, **13**, 121 (1952).
104. C. S. E. Phillips, *J. phys.*, **13**, 216 (1952).
105. N. L. Brown and R. H. Cole, *J. Chem. Phys.*, **20**, 196 (1952).
106. R. P. Auty and R. H. Cole, *J. Chem. Phys.*, **20**, 1309 (1952).
107. K. Clusius and G. Wolf, *Z. Naturforsch.*, **2A**, 495 (1947).
108. J. D. Hoffman, *J. Chem. Phys.*, **20**, 541 (1952).
109. J. D. Hoffman and B. V. Decker, *J. Chem. Phys.*, **22**, (1954).
110. H. F. Cook and T. J. Buchanan, *Nature*, **165**, 358 (1950).
111. J. G. Powles, *J. Chem. Phys.*, **20**, 1648 (1952).

enlarged version of one prepared by Dr. R. W. Crowe,[11] which, in turn, was an extensively revised and enlarged version of one published previously.[12] The term "rot." (rotation) is used in the sense of molecular orientational freedom as discussed in Sec. 1. Where no rotation or anomalous dispersion is indicated, it may occasionally be due to the absence of measurements at exceptionally low frequencies. The substances are frequently arranged more according to similarities in size and shape than according to chemical character.

Although the change of dielectric constant produced by freezing or melting is for the most part an exceedingly sharp one, the dielectric constant of the solid just before melting or just after freezing is higher than it is at temperatures well below the melting point and decreases at a decreasing rate, sometimes with anomalous dispersion, as the temperature decreases below the freezing point.[13] A portion of this effect, at least in many cases, is attributable to the presence of impurities, which may spread the last part of the process of solidification or the first part of the process of fusion over a considerable range of temperature, with the possibility of a small Maxwell-Wagner effect to give a slight dielectric absorption. However, the effect appears to be of too general occurrence and often of too large a size to be generally explicable in terms of impurities. Specific-heat measurements near the melting point give evidence of a similar loosening of the solid structure, or premelting. This premelting was evident, for example, to a small extent in carefully purified nitro-

[11] R. W. Crowe, Ph.D. Thesis, Princeton University, Princeton, N.J., 1951.
[12] C. P. Smyth, *Chem. Revs.*, **19**, 329 (1936).
[13] C. P. Smyth, *Trans. Faraday Soc.*, **42A**, 175 (1946).

benzene over a temperature range of nearly 40°; in isopropyl bromide, where impurities may have contributed somewhat to the effect; and in ethyl undecylate, where the dielectric constant increased at a uniform rate for about 25° from the lowest measurement at $-58.8°$C. and then at an increasing rate as the temperature of melting, $-22.5°$, was approached. A similar loosening of structure is often apparent in the temperature region below a sharp rotational transition and may be termed "prerotation." Premelting and prerotation are evident in several of the accompanying figures. The effects of prerotation and premelting upon dielectric constant are small in comparison with that of rotational freedom of the molecules as in a liquid. They cause a usually small rise in a low dielectric constant with rising temperature as loosening of the lattice structure permits increase in molecular orientation, while rotational freedom of the molecules as in a liquid causes a large decrease with rising temperature in a relatively high dielectric constant, the polarization often varying inversely as the absolute temperature, as in the case of hydrogen chloride.

In solid hydrogen, which crystallizes in the hexagonal system corresponding to the closest possible packing of spheres, the H_2 molecule apparently possesses rotational freedom. On the other hand, the equally symmetrical diatomic molecule of iodine shows no rotation in its orthorhombic lattice, because the spacing of the molecules is so close in this lattice that they have no room to turn over. The specific-heat curves for solid chlorine and bromine also give no evidence of rotation. The upper of the two transitions listed for oxygen is indicated by the specific-heat curve as due to a great increase in any freedom of rotation possibly existing below it and above the lower transition. The rotational freedom of the nitrogen molecule sets in at a slightly lower temperature, while that of the less-symmetrical carbon monoxide molecule, which has a small dipole moment, 0.11×10^{-18}, requires an appreciably higher temperature. The linear triatomic molecules of nitrous oxide and carbon dioxide show no rotation in their cubic lattices because there is not sufficient space for end-over-end rotation.

Methane crystallizes in a cubic lattice and undergoes a sharp transition at 20.4°K., as shown by the specific heat–temperature curve, without any apparent change in the lattice structure. The molecule has the form of a regular tetrahedron with rounded corners and an indentation in the middle of each edge. Its symmetry is such that there should be little variation in the energy of its orientation. Rotation can thus set in at the low temperature found for its transition. CH_3D and CD_4 have two transitions instead of the single one of methane, but the two upper transitions of HBr are replaced by a single one in DBr. Monosilane, SiH_4, undergoes a transition at 63.4°K., with a change to a more symmetrical lattice above the transition.   Although the monosilane molecule should be similar in form to that of methane, the larger silicon atom, which has a bond radius 50 per cent larger than that of carbon, gives a longer edge to the tetrahedron and a greater variation in the energy of molecular orientation, requiring a higher temperature to produce rotation.

The ammonia molecule, a flattened tetrahedron with a dipole moment of 1.46×10^{-18}, crystallizes in the cubic system.   Neither specific-heat nor dielectric-constant measurements show molecular rotation in the crystal, but nuclear magnetism investigations indicate rotation around an axis of symmetry.   The considerable dipole moment of the molecule, the lower symmetry of its form, and probable hydrogen bonding cause a

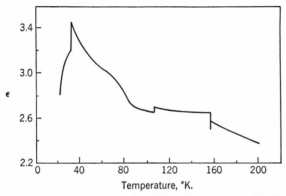

FIG. 4.2. Temperature dependence of the dielectric constant (at 50 kc.) of arsine. [C. P. Smyth and S. A. McNeight, J. Am. Chem. Soc., **58**, 1723 (1936).]

greater hindering by the potential energy barrier than in methane and monosilane.

Phosphine, which should resemble ammonia in molecular shape as monosilane does methane, has a dipole moment of 0.55×10^{-18} and exists in a cubic lattice at 103°K.   Below this temperature, two or more transitions are shown by the specific heats, which are indicative of molecular rotation above them.   The dielectric constant of arsine (Fig. 4.2) is higher at 20.5°K. than that of the liquid and rises rapidly with temperature up to 32.1°K., where the rotational transition is complete.   From this point up, the dielectric constant behaves like that of a liquid, the lattice being reported cubic at 103°K.   The second transition, at 106.6°K., produces a very slight rise in the dielectric constant, which then falls off much more slowly than before.   This is similar to the effect of the upper transition in hydrogen bromide, hydrogen iodide, and hydrogen sulfide, indicating, probably, a change in lattice dimensions with consequent change in internal field but no fundamental alteration in lattice structure.

The ammonium ion in ammonium chloride, bromide, and iodide was once regarded as an almost classic example of the ion rotating in its crystal lattice, but subsequent thermodynamic evidence[14] seemed to indicate that the phase transition in ammonium chloride involved a change from ordered to disordered orientation of the ammonium ion rather than one from a state of nonrotation to a state of free rotation. Beck's grating studies[15] of the infrared spectra of ammonium chloride and bromide showed fine structure, which was taken as evidence of rotation, but Wagner and Hornig[16] attributed this observation to the presence of water vapor and, from their own measurements, concluded that the phase transition was a simple order-disorder transition. Hornig[17] suggested that free rotation would be a particular case of such disorder but questioned whether free rotation had been definitely demonstrated in a single case. As pointed out at the beginning of this chapter, the rotational freedom necessary for dipole orientation is not the same as the free rotation sought in these earlier spectroscopic investigations. In later work Plumb and Hornig[18] concluded that the infrared spectrum strongly indicated a structure for phase I of ammonium iodide in which one hydrogen bond was formed to the iodide ion and the ammonium ion rotated freely about this bond. This conclusion was consistent with neutron-diffraction studies[19] of ND_4Br and ND_4I and with the interpretation of heat-capacity measurements.[20]

As the result of nuclear magnetism studies[21] on eleven ammonium salts, Gutowsky and Pake account for the line width just above an observed transition region by assuming hindered rotation or quantum-mechanical tunneling of the ammonium tetrahedrons at frequencies of the order of 100 kc. Such a frequency would contribute negligibly to the infrared spectrum.

Hydrogen fluoride resembles ammonia in that its specific heat-temperature curve shows no transition in the solid above liquid air temperature. The zigzag chains of hydrogen-bonded molecules shown[22] by X-ray analysis to exist in the solid should be sufficiently strong to prevent turning of the molecules to give dipole orientation or an order-disorder transition. The specific heats of the other hydrogen halides suggested the existence of molecular rotation, and this was confirmed by dielectric-constant measurements. Each of these molecules may be regarded as a

[14] A. W. Lawson, *Phys. Rev.*, **57**, 417 (1940).

[15] C. Beck, *J. Chem. Phys.*, **12**, 71 (1944).

[16] E. L. Wagner and D. F. Hornig, *J. Chem. Phys.*, **17**, 105 (1949).

[17] D. F. Hornig, *J. Chem. Phys.*, **17**, 1346 (1949).

[18] R. C. Plumb and D. F. Hornig, *J. Chem. Phys.*, **21**, 366 (1953).

[19] H. A. Levy and S. W. Peterson, *J. Chem. Phys.*, **21**, 366 (1953).

[20] C. C. Stephenson, L. A. Landers, and A. G. Cole, *J. Chem. Phys.*, **20**, 1044 (1952).

[21] H. S. Gutowsky and G. E. Pake, *J. Chem. Phys.*, **16**, 1164 (1948).

[22] P. Günther, K. Holm, and H. Strunz, *Z. physik. Chem.*, **43B**, 229 (1939).

sphere with a bulge on one side created by the hydrogen. At low temperature, the hydrogen chloride lattice, for example, is shown by X-ray analysis to be orthorhombic, but, as the temperature rises to 98.7°K., the orthorhombic lattice undergoes a sharp transition to a cubic lattice, absorbs heat, and shows a jump in dielectric constant (Fig. 4.3) like that shown by a typical dipolar solid on melting. Above the transition, the linear change of the molar polarization as a function of $1/T$ agrees qualitatively with the requirements of the Debye equation. When the solid melts, the dielectric constant drops because of the decrease in density, instead of rising because of increase in molecular freedom. The natural conclusion is that between the transition and the melting point the molecules possess rotational freedom in the solid like that which they possess in the liquid. Phillips observed a slight dispersion just below the transition point and a considerable dispersion for some distance below the melting point. Hydrogen bromide (Fig. 4.4) resembles the chloride in showing rotational freedom but differs from it in that the shape of the dielectric constant–temperature curve in the region of the transition has the lambda form found in the specific-heat curves for such transitions. It also differs in possessing two additional transitions above that at which the lattice probably changes from orthorhombic to cubic

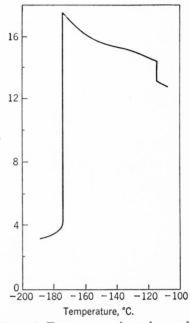

FIG. 4.3. Temperature dependence of the dielectric constant (at 60 kc.) of hydrogen chloride. [C. P. Smyth and C. S. Hitchcock, J. Am. Chem. Soc., **55**, 1830 (1933).]

with the acquisition of rotational freedom. Because of disagreement between investigators the crystal structure is not certain, but the orthorhombic modification reported by Natta in the neighborhood of the lowest transition probably corresponds to the lattice of nonrotating molecules, and the cubic lattice reported by him in the vicinity of the two upper transitions presumably consists of rotating molecules. Ruhemann and Simon, however, believed that the lattice is face-centered rhombic throughout. The two additional transitions are so close together that it can only be said that the dielectric constant is slightly lower between them, but above them the dielectric constant–temperature curve is much flatter, showing a marked change in the internal field of the crystal. The lowest of the three transitions differs from the others in that the dielectric constant rises very high and depends upon the frequency of the field in the immediate neighborhood of the transition.

Powles's measurements show that there are two dispersion regions for hydrogen bromide, for both of which the critical frequency increases with rising temperature. The low-frequency dispersion, below 100 kc. and 90°K., disappears abruptly at the transition, 90°K., or within less than 3° of this temperature. The second dispersion, in the megacycle region,

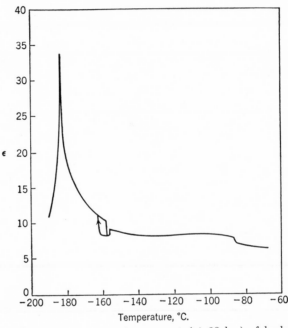

FIG. 4.4. Dielectric constant–temperature curves (at 60 kc.) of hydrogen bromide. [C. P. Smyth and C. S. Hitchcock, J. Am. Chem. Soc., **56**, 1084 (1934).]

appears to be not greatly affected by passage through the transition. The existence of a third dispersion region at higher frequencies is indicated by the fact that the limiting value of ϵ' above the second dispersion is about 3.1, as compared to the value 2.05 for n_D^2. The curves for hydrogen bromide and deuterium bromide resemble each other in form and show hysteresis in the low-temperature transition, the hysteresis being greater in the deuterium bromide. The second transition in hydrogen bromide shows an appreciable hysteresis, but the uppermost transition does not. These two upper transitions in hydrogen bromide are replaced by a single transition in deuterium bromide. It would appear that the two dispersion regions correspond to two different proc-

:sses, the precise nature of which is not clear, although hindered molecular
·otation is indicated.

Powles applied constant fields between 0 and 3 kv. per cm. to hydrogen
)romide and found no variation of dielectric constant exceeding the
)ossible error of 3 per cent, from which he concluded that the peculiar
)ehavior at the lowest transition was not a ferroelectric effect.   He
ittributed the two dispersion regions which he observed to a rotational
·unneling effect.   The excellent measurements of Brown and Cole on
1ydrogen bromide give a peak value of 200 for the dielectric constant
tt the transition at 89°K. and a value of 33.4 at 70°K.   The lower of the
·wo dispersion regions is described by a series of arc plots at different
.emperatures, and the temperature dependence of the relaxation time is
;iven by a rate law with an activation energy of 2.7 kcal. per mole.   The
1igher-frequency relaxation process appears to be qualitatively similar
vith a much smaller total dispersion.   Brown and Cole consider very
.arge dielectric constants near second-order transitions to be a reasonable
·esult of cooperative effects as pointed out by Tisza,[23] but find the change
nuch greater than that predicted by theories such as that of Kirkwood.[24]
They regard the two dispersion regions as explicable in terms of the
lifferent dielectric constants parallel and perpendicular to the c axis of
;he nearly tetragonal structure.

The behavior of solid hydrogen iodide and deuterium iodide is rather
similar to that of hydrogen bromide and deuterium bromide.   There is
;trong dispersion over a very wide range of frequency on each side of the
.ow-temperature transition.   Even at 3.23 cm. wavelength, ϵ' rises from
3.0 to 4.4 on passing through the transition, with ϵ'' reaching a peak value
of 0.6.

In all three halides and in the methanes, the deuterium compound has
the higher rotational transition temperature, as would be expected.   The
temperature necessary to produce rotational freedom decreases with
increasing size of the halogen in this group of compounds, as it does in
the ammonium halides.   Increasing molecular size also facilitates rotation in the groups consisting of water, hydrogen sulfide, and hydrogen
selenide and ammonia, phosphine, and arsine.   The reverse is true in the
case of methane and monosilane, where the first member of the group
also rotates, in contrast to the other three groups in which the first member shows no rotational transition, presumably because of hydrogen
bonding.   All these rotators, except the ammonium ion, methane, and
monosilane, have dipoles, which decrease in size with increasing size of the
molecule and are at the same time farther separated from one another the
larger the molecule.   In both these ways, therefore, increasing size of the

[23] L. Tisza, *MIT Research Lab. Electronics Tech. Rept.* 127 (1949).
[24] J. G. Kirkwood, *J. Chem. Phys.*, **8**, 205 (1940).

molecule should facilitate rotation by decreasing the height of the potential energy hump which tends to prevent molecular rotation. In the ammonium halides the field due to the negative charge of the halide ion decreases with increasing ionic size, and the potential hump is thereby reduced.

Behavior similar to that of hydrogen chloride is shown by the molecules of hydrogen sulfide, the dielectric constant–temperature curve of which is reproduced in Fig. 4.5. The hydrogen sulfide molecule should differ

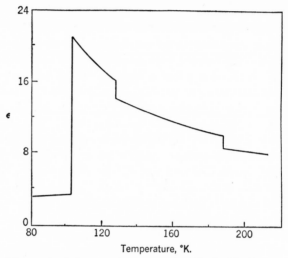

Fig. 4.5. Dielectric constant–temperature curve (at 5 kc.) of hydrogen sulfide. [C. P. Smyth and C. S. Hitchcock, J. Am. Chem. Soc., **56**, 1084 (1934).]

from that of hydrogen chloride in having two bulges on the sphere instead of one. The curve also differs from that for hydrogen chloride in showing a small transition in the cubic lattice at a temperature higher than that of the rotational transition, a phenomenon often observed. At a temperature as low as 20.5°K., the dielectric constant of solid arsine, as previously mentioned, gives evidence of some rotational freedom, which increases to a rotational transition at 32.1°K. It is characteristic of these small molecules, not far from spherical in form, that their lattices are anisotropic below the rotational transitions and isotropic, like those of closely packed spheres, above the transitions.[12] The heats of fusion of these solids are usually abnormally small, smaller than the heats of transition, and the corresponding entropies of fusion are often[25,26] close to the 2 e.u. calculated[27] for a substance already possessing rotational freedom.

[25] W. O. Baker and C. P. Smyth, J. Am. Chem. Soc., **61**, 1695 (1939).

[26] R. W. Crowe and C. P. Smyth, J. Am. Chem. Soc., **72**, 4009 (1950).

[27] J. Hirschfelder, D. Stevenson, and H. Eyring, J. Chem. Phys., **5**, 896 (1937).

In the early work on possible molecular rotation in solids, it was thought that rotational freedom might be limited to small molecules or to cylindrical structures of small radius, the possible rotation occurring around the long axis of the cylinder. However, it was soon found that the large molecules of camphor and of some of its derivatives, which were not very far from spherical in form, showed molecular rotation. The tertiary butyl halides were found to resemble hydrogen sulfide in general behavior, although marked differences in detail were observed. These molecules may be regarded as having the form of a tetrahedron with large spheres at the corners, the sizes of the halogen atoms and the methyl groups being sufficiently similar to give structures of high symmetry approximating a sphere considerably distorted in form. *t*-Butyl chloride, bromide, and iodide, 2,2-dichloropropane, 1,1,1-trichloroethane, 2-methyl-2-nitropropane, 2-chloro-2-nitropropane, 2-bromo 2-nitropropane, and 2,2-dinitropropane have been found to show molecular rotation, but 1,1,2-trichloroethane, which is less symmetrical, does not show it.

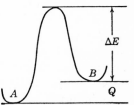

Fig. 4.6. Rotational potential energy curve for a molecule in a crystal lattice. [*J. G. Powles, D. E. Williams, and C. P. Smyth, J. Chem. Phys.,* **21**, 136 (1953).]

Measurements on several of these substances at a wavelength of 3.22 cm. make possible further consideration of the factors determining orientational freedom of the molecules in the lattice.[28] The interactions of a molecule with its neighbors in the crystal result in a variation of its potential energy with angular position having the general form shown in Fig. 4.6. *A* is the more populated equilibrium position and *B*, a second equilibrium position higher than *A* by an amount *Q*, is separated from it by an energy barrier ΔE. It may be shown that *Q* is very approximately proportional to the transition temperature, while ΔE determines the order of magnitude of the dielectric relaxation time or critical wavelength by the following approximate relation:

$$\tau \propto \lambda_m \propto e^{\Delta E/kT}$$

The actual potential energy curve is much more complicated, and it is possible that the representation of the molecular interaction by an average potential energy curve for a single molecule is not valid, especially when the motion of the molecules in a rotator phase is highly cooperative. Nevertheless, this representation makes it possible to form some picture of the dielectric relaxation process in these materials. It is not likely that *Q* and ΔE are simply related. At a transition, *Q* is very much reduced and ΔE is probably reduced at the same time, if only because of the lattice expansion which occurs. This is in accord with the

[28] J. G. Powles, D. E. Williams, and C. P. Smyth, *J. Chem. Phys.,* **21**, 136 (1953).

observation of a fall in critical wavelength at the transition from the lower to the upper rotator phase in t-butyl bromide. It is impossible to predict, in general, the relation of Q and ΔE in the present state of our knowledge. However, if the molecule is very symmetrical and the intermolecular forces are small, both ΔE and Q will be small, which is exemplified by the very low transition temperature of methane.

In the case of polar and less-spherical molecules the values of Q and ΔE depend on both the magnitude and the asymmetry of all the intermolecular forces involved. The van der Waals radii of the methyl group, 2.0 A., and chlorine, 1.80 A.,[29] are sufficiently close to give molecular symmetry permitting rotational orientation of the molecules of the methyl chloromethanes in the solid state, but the rotational transition temperatures do not show a consistent variation with molecular structure. This absence of consistent variation of transition temperature and of Q can be accounted for by the presumable differences in molecular packing in the anisotropic lattices existing below the transitions.

Again in the series of the t-butyl halides the rotational transition temperature of t-butyl bromide is 11° lower than that of the chloride, but the critical wavelength is longer. The transition temperature of t-butyl iodide is 15° lower than that of the bromide, and the critical wavelength of the rotator phase is greater by a factor of about 10^7. Evidently, in the t-butyl halides, increase in the height of the potential barrier hindering rotation does not substantially raise the transition temperature or the value of Q. The increase in radius from that of bromine to that of iodine, 2.15A., increases both the molecular asymmetry and the intermolecular attraction, thus raising the hindering potential barrier. The great increase in the critical wavelength is less surprising when it is recalled that the change of a methyl group in t-butyl chloride to an ethyl to give t-amyl chloride appears to prevent rotation entirely. The results for t-butyl chloride, 2,2-dichloropropane, and methyl chloroform show that the potential barrier to rotation increases with successive replacement of the methyl groups by chlorine atoms and consequent increase in the number of strong local dipoles. This increase in the hindering potential barriers parallels an apparent effect of dipole-dipole forces observed in the liquid state (Sec. IV.4).[30]

The replacement of a chlorine atom in 2,2-dichloropropane by a nitro group increases the dipole moment considerably and the volume slightly, and decreases the molecular symmetry slightly, all of which factors should contribute to the large increase observed in the hindering potential

[29] L. Pauling, "The Nature of the Chemical Bond," Cornell University Press, Ithaca, New York, 1940, p. 189.

[30] A. J. Curtis, P. L. McGeer, G. B. Rathmann, and C. P. Smyth, *J. Am. Chem. Soc.*, **74**, 644 (1952).

barrier.   The replacement of the remaining chlorine atom by a second nitro group further increases the dipole moment without greatly altering the spatial symmetry of the molecule or the consequent potential barrier. In view of the prevention of molecular rotation by the insertion of a CH_2 group in the t-butyl chloride molecule, it is at first surprising to find a rotator state in dinitroneopentane, $(CH_3)_2C(CH_2NO_2)_2$, but examination of a model of the molecule shows that it can take up a shape which does not differ greatly from a sphere.

It is, perhaps, remarkable to find that the critical wavelength in the crystal is shorter than that in the liquid in some cases.   In terms of our simple picture, this means that the energy barrier is lower in the crystal than in the liquid.   Another example of the short critical wavelength in the solid state is found in n-docosyl bromide.   The similarity in some respects between the solid rotator phase and the liquid gives added interest to the fact that these materials just considered are soft or waxy in the rotator phase.

An interesting rotation has been found in solid penta- and hexasubstituted benzenes, in which the substituents are chlorine, nitro, and methyl groups.   Replacement of a methyl group by an ethyl apparently builds a projection on the molecule which blocks its rotation.   Reduction of the number of substituents below five also prevents the rotation of the molecules.   These molecules may be tentatively pictured as very much flattened spheres capable of rotation in the solid only in the plane of the benzene ring.   Of the substituted benzenes which show molecular rotation, the less symmetrical cease rotating abruptly at transitions, while the more symmetrical exhibit reduced frequency of rotation but not transitions as the temperature declines.   A case of rotation about one molecular axis only has been clearly established in n-docosyl bromide, n-$C_{22}H_{45}Br$, the dielectric constant of which drops sharply on solidification to a value considerably below that of the liquid but well above that of ϵ_∞.   A second sharp drop at a transition temperature lowers the dielectric constant almost to ϵ_∞ as the rotational freedom of the molecules around their long axis disappears.   In contrast to the great majority of rotational transitions, this one is monotropic and is not observed with rising temperature. Molecular rotation is absent in the shorter, straight-chain alkyl bromides thus far studied, although nonrotational transitions have been observed in some of the odd members of the series.[31]

n-Tetradecyl, n-hexadecyl, n-octadecyl, and n-docosyl alcohols show rotation around the long molecular axis in an unstable phase which forms initially on solidification (Fig. 4.7), but pure dodecyl and the somewhat shorter alcohols do not show it.   Methyl alcohol shows a solid rotator

[31] R. W. Crowe and C. P. Smyth, *J. Am. Chem. Soc.*, **72**, 1098 (1950).

phase, but *t*-butyl and *n*-octyl alcohol do not. A high electric conductivity and dielectric loss found in this rotator phase were attributed by Hoffman and Smyth[32] to proton transfer from one hydroxyl oxygen to another facilitated by the molecular rotation since the loss exceeded that which could arise from dipole relaxation alone. A similar but somewhat less pronounced effect was found by them in long-chain primary amines. It is to be noted that this conductivity effect has been observed only in the cases of molecules capable of hydrogen bonding. It is not

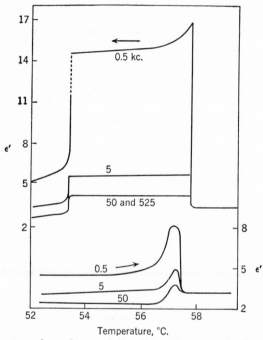

Fig. 4.7. Temperature dependence of the dielectric constant of octadecyl alcohol. [*J. D. Hoffman* and *C. P. Smyth*, *J. Am. Chem. Soc.*, **71**, 432 (1949).]

present, for example, in the long-chain bromides. Evidence supporting the hypothesis of proton transfer was obtained[33] by spectroscopic examination of a small quantity of gas evolved when current was flowing through solid *n*-hexadecyl alcohol. In the temperature region of the abnormally conducting rotator phase, electrolysis produced a quantity of hydrogen sufficient to indicate that the greater part of the current was carried by protons, while in the region of low conductivity the hydrogen evolved was found to be small in quantity.

A broad loss maximum was found at 20°C. by Meakins and Sack[34] (see

[32] J. D. Hoffman and C. P. Smyth, *J. Am. Chem. Soc.*, **71**, 431 (1949).
[33] Y. Kakiuchi, H. Komatsu, and S. Kyoya, *J. Chem. Phys.*, **19**, 132 (1951).
[34] R. J. Meakins and R. A. Sack, *Nature*, **164**, 798 (1949).

also other long-chain alcohols in Table 4.1) for 14-heptacosanol, $C_{13}H_{27}$-CHOHC$_{13}H_{27}$, and for 16-hentriacontanol, $C_{15}H_{31}CHOHC_{15}H_{31}$, between 0.1 and 2 megacycles, and similar dielectric behavior was observed for several other crystalline secondary alcohols. Since the dielectric absorption was not displaced to lower frequencies with increasing chain length, it was suggested that the absorption might be associated, not with the orientation of the molecule as a whole, but merely with that of the hydroxyl group by rotation around the C—O bond with two positions of equilibrium stabilized by hydrogen bonding. The wide frequency range of the absorption was attributed to the varying numbers of hydroxyl groups forming continuous chains, the orientation being a cooperative effect. The absence of absorption in this frequency region when these alcohols were dissolved in dilute solid solution in hydrocarbons containing one more atom in the chain was attributed to displacement of the absorption to ultra-high frequencies because of the isolation of the hydroxyl groups and consequent absence of hydrogen bonding. The losses observed in the pure secondary alcohols, although large, were much smaller than the maximum losses observed by Hoffman and Smyth in the long-chain primary alcohols. In these same strongly hydrogen-bonded primary alcohols, preliminary measurements by Dr. P. J. McGeer and Dr. G. B. Rathmann in the writer's laboratory indicate that dipole orientation is still occurring at microwave frequencies. Measurements by Hamon and Meakins[35] led them to conclude that high dielectric loss at low frequencies and d.c. conductivity in oxidized long-chain compounds was due to the presence of small proportions of alcohols of comparatively short chain length.

Tetradecyl and octadecyl mercaptan, in which any hydrogen bonding should be very weak, do not show[36] the abnormally high losses shown by most of the long-chain alcohols but form a metastable phase, in which a region of anomalous dispersion for kilocycle frequencies extends over a temperature range of about 65°.

Dodecyl and tetradecyl ether do not show molecular rotation or dipole orientation in the solid state, but hexadecyl and octadecyl ether show a considerable rise in dielectric constant on solidification and a much more rapid rise with decreasing temperature than is shown by the liquid. Neither the solid hexadecyl ether nor the solid octadecyl ether shows any transition above −40°, but both show anomalous dispersion in the kilocycle region with disappearance of all or most of the dipole orientation, presumably made possible by molecular rotation. The dielectric behavior of each substance in its region of anomalous dispersion is represented accurately by an arc plot at each temperature with a wide distribution

[35] B. V. Hamon and R. J. Meakins, *Nature*, **166**, 29 (1950).
[36] A. Di Giacomo and C. P. Smyth, Unpublished measurements.

of relaxation times. As commonly observed for liquids, the value of the distribution parameter α decreases with rising temperature, for hexadecyl ether from 0.54 at 17.8° to 0.32 at 28.3°, and for octadecyl ether from 0.46 at 18.6° to 0.39 at 34.7°.

Dryden and Welsh have found two distinct absorption regions in methyl palmitate, methyl stearate, and methyl behenate. An absorption with a maximum between 10^3 and 10^4 megacycles almost independent of chain length but dependent upon temperature is attributed by them to rotation of the polar group at the end of the molecule from one equilibrium position to another, while an absorption with a maximum between 1 and 100 megacycles, dependent upon both chain length and

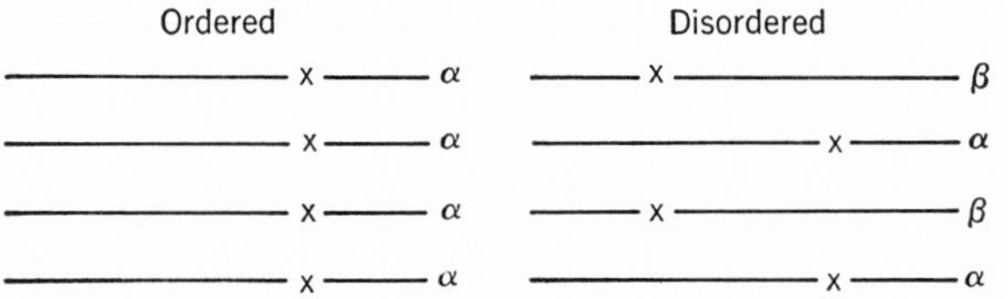

Fig. 4.8. Longitudinally ordered and disordered phases in crystalline long-chain esters. [R. W. Crowe, J. D. Hoffman, and C. P. Smyth, J. Chem. Phys., 20, 550 (1952).]

temperature, is attributed to rotation of the entire molecule from one position of equilibrium in the crystal lattice to another.

Like other long-chain molecules containing twenty or more carbon atoms, most of the ester molecules showed evidence of hindered molecular rotation about their long axes in the crystal lattice. It was also found that higher dielectric constants resulted when the samples were rapidly frozen than when they were allowed to solidify gradually, the effect being more pronounced as the chain length was increased. In order to explain this behavior, it has been assumed by Crowe, Hoffman, and Smyth[37] that the esters may crystallize in an ordered lattice in which the dipoles are in a plane, or in a longitudinally disordered lattice in which some of the chains are reversed as shown in Fig. 4.8.[37] In the latter case, the dipoles may or may not form two planes, depending upon the position of the polar group in the chain. It has also been assumed that the degree of longitudinal disorder increases with increase in freezing rate. Once frozen in, however, it remains fixed until the sample is remelted.

The potential barrier hindering rotation has been assumed to be much higher in the ordered state than in the disordered state because separation of the dipoles should lower steric and dipole interaction in the latter. Since the rotational transition temperature is proportional to a potential energy difference related to the barrier against rotation, the transition temperature should increase with increase in longitudinal order. In a

[37] R. W. Crowe, J. D. Hoffman, and C. P. Smyth, J. Chem. Phys., 20, 550 (1952).

completely ordered ester or a nearly symmetrical disordered ester, the barrier may be sufficiently high to raise the transition point to a temperature near or above that of fusion.

1-Monopalmitin (Fig. 4.9) and 1-monostearin showed molecular orientational freedom in their α and sub-α forms. As these two latter compounds contained hydroxyl groups capable of hydrogen bonding, the α forms showed strong frequency dependence of the dielectric constant and abnormally high conductivity similar to that observed in the long-chain alcohols, a behavior attributed to proton transfer facilitated by

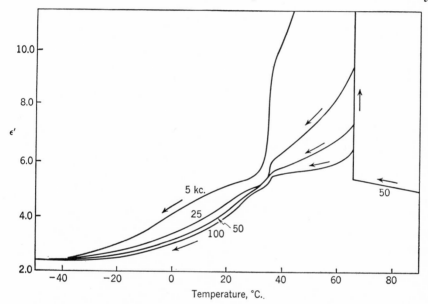

FIG. 4.9. Temperature dependence of the dielectric constant of 1-monopalmitin at different frequencies. [R. W. Crowe and C. P. Smyth, J. Am. Chem. Soc., **72**, 4427 (1950).]

rotation of the chains about their long axes. The diglycerides, 1,3-dipalmitin and 1,3-distearin, were found to show no appreciable amount of dipole orientation, since their molecular shapes were such as to prevent rotation in the crystal lattice. However, the triglycerides, tripalmitin and tristearin, showed dipole orientational freedom in their α forms down to relatively low temperatures with exceptionally wide dispersion regions, which indicated a wide distribution of relaxation times for the orientational process. As the shapes of these molecules were such as to prevent rotation of the molecule as a whole in the lattice, the orientation was attributed to the movement of molecular segments.

The fundamental reason for the presence of molecular orientational freedom in the solid states of some members of an homologous series and not in others is not obvious. It requires the acquisition by the molecules of sufficient rotational energy for passage over the restricting potential energy barriers before the energy of translational vibration has become sufficient to break down the lattice and convert the solid to the liquid state. The regular increase in transition (T.P.) and melting (M.P.) points of the even members of several homologous series with increase in the chain length is shown in Fig. 4.10. It is evident that for any given

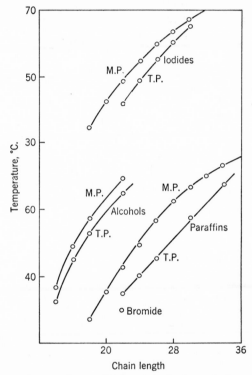

FIG. 4.10. Melting points and transition points in long-chain compounds. [*J. D. Hoffman and C. P. Smyth, J. Am. Chem. Soc.*, **72**, 178 (1950).]

series the transition-point and the melting-point curves are not parallel and that intersection of the two curves will mean the disappearance of the transition. Müller[38] attributed the sudden appearance of a rotational transition at a given chain length to the overcoming of end-group forces, which, however, would seem to be only one of the factors involved.

Kirkwood[24] has given a treatment of phase transitions in solids due to hindered rotation which is able to predict the dielectric constant near the lambda point in hydrobromic acid at 89°K. with fair accuracy. If a two-minima potential between neighboring molecules had been used,

[38] A. Müller, *Proc. Roy. Soc. (London)*, **138A**, 514 (1932).

first-order transitions could have been obtained.   Kirkwood also sur-
mises that first-order transitions could arise from the sensitivity of barrier
height to lattice parameters.

Frank[39] has developed a theory for a rotator with one frozen position.
Employing an expression of the form $N_{rot}/N_{\text{frozen}} = ge^{-E/kt}$, where N_{rot} is
the number of rotating molecules and N_{frozen} the number fixed, and applying the Bragg-Williams[40] cooperative approximation to the energy E, he
obtains the fraction rotating, r vs. T curves for different values of g
indicating first-order transitions.   When the statistical weight g of the
rotators is arbitrarily set equal to 13, the results are nearly identical with
those of Hoffman and Smyth (see below).

Fröhlich[41] has developed an interesting theory of the dielectric properties of long-chain compounds based on order-disorder in the dipole array,
in which it is assumed that the interaction energy is due solely to dipolar
forces.   As pointed out in the addendum to his paper, the calculations
suggest a transition of the second order and do not agree with experiment.
Fröhlich's theory, as he apparently realized, does not explain the transitions in the paraffins since they possess no dipole array and could therefore have no solid transition.   Actually, the close parallelism between
the transitions in paraffins, bromides, alcohols, and iodides (Fig. 4.10)
with such varying polar nature strongly suggests that the dipole interactions are quite weak in comparison to the London forces at the end
groups and along the chain.

Hoffman and Smyth[42] have calculated the dielectric constant of
n-docosyl bromide in the solid rotator phase, applying the Onsager
equation I(14.23) and modifying extensively the previously mentioned
theory of Fowler,[7] which assumed a fraction of the molecules to be
rotating.   Hoffman[43] has further treated the problem of rotation of the
chain molecules about their long axes in the crystal lattice by assuming
that rotation is hindered by potential energy barriers which give one deep
minimum and a number of relatively shallow minima.   Molecular models
suggest that the number of shallow minima lies between eight and eighteen.   When the number is taken as twelve, the calculated static dielectric
constant agrees closely with the observed value.   The two absorption
regions observed for n-docosyl bromide and n-tricontyl bromide are
explicable in terms of the two kinds of potential minima, the low-frequency absorption arising from rotational jumps between the deep
minimum and the shallow minima and the high-frequency absorption

[39] F. C. Frank, *Trans. Faraday Soc.*, **42A**, 32 (1946).
[40] W. L. Bragg and E. J. Williams, *Proc. Roy. Soc. (London)*, **145A**, 699 (1934).
[41] H. Fröhlich, *Proc. Roy. Soc. (London)*, **185A**, 399 (1946).
[42] J. D. Hoffman and C. P. Smyth, *J. Am. Chem. Soc.*, **72**, 171 (1950).
[43] J. D. Hoffman, *J. Chem. Phys.*, **20**, 541 (1952).

arising from jumps between two shallow minima. The two absorption regions observed by Dryden and Welsh for long-chain methyl esters could be qualitatively accounted for similarly in terms of two kinds of molecular rotational jumps instead of a polar-group jump and a molecular jump. The theory is consistent with the observed rise of transition temperatures with increasing chain length. In a later paper,[44] it is concluded that, if the molecular dipole has three or more accessible sites (potential minima) and one is more stable than the others, a distribution of relaxation times should occur, while, if the sites are all equivalent, only a single relaxation time should occur.

The acquisition by the molecules of rotation or disorder involves a considerable increase of entropy, an increase frequently larger than that of fusion. For a substance already possessed of rotational freedom and in the absence of a change in the intramolecular vibrations, the entropy of fusion should be 2 e.u.,[27] as previously mentioned. The possession by a substance of this entropy of rotation or disorder tends to postpone to a higher temperature the acquisition of further entropy by liquefaction,[45] and the substance, consequently, will possess an abnormally short range of existence as a liquid. This is illustrated by the properties of n-butyl bromide and t-butyl bromide selected from an extensive tabulation by Baker and Smyth[45] and completed by later measurements:[46]

Substance	M.P., °K.	ΔS (fusion)	ΔS (transition)	Liquid range
n-C$_4$H$_9$Br	160.4	13.5	...	214.3°
t-C$_4$H$_9$Br	256.1	1.8	7.6	90.9°

The sum of the entropy changes of the two transitions in solid t-butyl bromide is more than four times the entropy of fusion, which is close to the theoretical value for a solid possessing rotation. The abnormally short liquid range of the t-butyl bromide is typical. Conversely, the possession of an abnormally low entropy of fusion and, to some extent, a short liquid range may be regarded as an indication of the probable existence of molecular orientational freedom in the solid and high dielectric constant if the molecules are polar.

In accordance with this relation between molecular rotation in the solid and the melting point, an investigation of tetrachloro-, pentachloro-, hexachloro-, and methylsubstituted benzenes has shown[47] that the solu-

[44] J. D. Hoffman and H. G. Pfeiffer, *J. Chem. Phys.*, **22**, 132 (1954).

[45] W. O. Baker and C. P. Smyth, *J. Am. Chem. Soc.*, **61**, 1695 (1939); *Ann. N.Y. Acad. Sci.*, **40**, 447 (1940).

[46] L. M. Kushner, R. W. Crowe, and C. P. Smyth, *J. Am. Chem. Soc.*, **72**, 1091 (1950).

[47] C. P. Smyth and G. L. Lewis, *J. Am. Chem. Soc.*, **62**, 949 (1940).

bilities of the solids and the entropies of fusion of these compounds tend to be low and the melting points high when the molecules possess freedom of rotation in the solid.

The dielectric behavior of ice[48] (Fig. 4.11) is different from that of the long-chain alcohols in the solid state since no transition occurs from a rotator to a nonrotator phase and the loss does not exceed that which could arise from dipole relaxation.

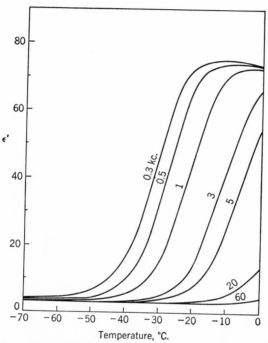

FIG. 4.11. Variation of the dielectric constant of ice with temperature at different frequencies (kc.). [C. P. Smyth and C. S. Hitchcock, J. Am. Chem. Soc., **54,** 4631 (1932).]

The great effect of ionic impurities upon the dielectric constant of ice is shown by Fig. 4.12, in which the solid lines represent the dielectric constants of frozen conductivity water and the broken lines the values for a frozen 0.0002 M solution of potassium chloride which contained 278,000 water molecules for each potassium ion and chloride ion.[48] The curves for each frequency are connected by a bracket, which is marked with the frequency in cycles. At low frequencies the dielectric constants of the frozen solution were much higher on first cooling down slowly from the freezing point than on warming up. Arrows pointing downward and upward distinguish the curves for falling and rising temperatures. With

[48] C. P. Smyth and C. S. Hitchcock, J. Am. Chem. Soc., **54,** 4631 (1932).

increasing frequency, the difference between the falling-temperature and the rising-temperature curves becomes small and actually reverses, and the difference between the pure ice and the frozen solution almost disappears.   The large effect of the small number of ions at low frequencies suggests a large displacement of the ions in the field, very different from the small elastic displacements in ionic crystals, or an influence of lattice imperfections resulting from the presence of the ions.

Because of the large effects of voids in the solid and of very small quantities of ionic impurities just discussed, considerable discrepancies

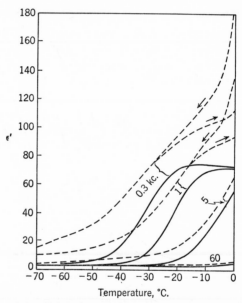

Fig. 4.12. Variation of the dielectric constant of frozen 0.0002-M potassium chloride solution with temperature and frequency (kc.).   [*C. P. Smyth and C. S. Hitchcock, J. Am. Chem. Soc.*, **54**, 4631 (1932).]

occur among the values obtained by the different investigators listed under Table 4.1, but the agreement as to general behavior is excellent. The values[48] in Fig. 4.11 are somewhat low, presumably because of voids. The values of ϵ' and ϵ'' give good semicircular plots indicating the absence of any distribution of relaxation times.   Auty and Cole,[49] whose results appear to be the most accurate, found that the relaxation times of ice and of solid deuterium oxide could be represented by rate expressions of the form

$$\tau = Ae^{B/RT}$$

with $A = 5.30 \times 10^{-6}$ sec. and $B = 13.25$ kcal. per mole for ice, and

[49] R. P. Auty and R. H. Cole, *J. Chem. Phys.*, **20**, 1309 (1952).

$A = 7.7 \times 10^{-6}$ sec. and $B = 13.4$ kcal. per mole for solid deuterium oxide. For ice, they found ϵ_0 and ϵ_∞ to be 91.5 and 3.10 at $-0.1°$, and 133 and 3.1 at $-65.8°$.

At first glance, one might expect the H_2O molecule to show rotational freedom in the solid state like that observed in solid hydrogen sulfide. If the dielectric constant is measured with a current of very low frequency, the dielectric constant of ice rises with decreasing temperature from a value at the freezing point not far from that of liquid water. With continued decrease in temperature, the change of the dielectric constant at a given frequency becomes negative so that it decreases rapidly toward ϵ_∞. At the same time, there is a large apparent conductivity or dielectric loss qualitatively resembling that in the long-chain alcohols and amines. With a frequency as high as 60,000 cycles, the dielectric constant of the solid is little higher than ϵ_∞ even just below the freezing point, at a given frequency. Two principal explanations have been advanced for the dielectric behavior of ice. The obvious one is that the dipolar H_2O molecules are capable of rotation in the highly viscous solid medium,[50] whose dielectric behavior is represented almost quantitatively by Eqs. II(2.22) and (2.23). The other suggested mechanism depends upon the hydrogen bonds binding the H_2O molecules together in the ice lattice. A proton covalently bonded to one oxygen in the lattice and forming a hydrogen bond with a neighboring oxygen may be represented as $O\!-\!H\cdots O$ and is pictured as capable of passing over a potential energy barrier and jumping from the first oxygen to the second to give $O\cdots H\!-\!O$. This transfer of charge would give rise to polarization, with consequent high dielectric constant and loss. It may be treated as a rate process, as may that of molecular rotation, so that both processes are capable of representation by the same type of rate equation.[51,52]

Powles[53] has calculated the dielectric constant of ice by applying Fröhlich's general theory[54] of the static dielectric constant (see Chap. I) to Pauling's[55] model for ice, which was used to explain the residual entropy at low temperatures. It was supposed that the crystal could take up, with equal probability, any of a number of configurations consistent with the conditions that there be only one proton between any two oxygen atoms nearer the one than the other and that, at any instant, there be two protons near each oxygen atom. Powles's calculation was

[50] P. Debye, "Polar Molecules," Chemical Catalog, New York, 1929, sec. 20.

[51] S. Glasstone, K. Laidler, and H. Eyring, "Theory of Rate Processes," McGraw-Hill, New York, 1941.

[52] W. Kauzmann, Revs. Mod. Phys., 14, 12 (1942).

[53] J. G. Powles, J. Chem. Phys., 20, 1302 (1952).

[54] H. Fröhlich, Trans. Faraday Soc., 44, 238 (1949); "Theory of Dielectrics," Oxford, London, 1949, p. 36.

[55] L. Pauling, J. Am. Chem. Soc., 57, 2680 (1935).

not concerned with the mechanism by which one configuration changed to another, whether by molecular rotation or by proton transfer or by both, but merely required that the configurations be taken up with a probability depending on their energies. A calculation assuming that all configurations were of equal probabilities gave values slightly higher than those in Fig. 4.11, but considerably lower than those of Murphy and of Cole and Auty. A calculation including the effect of electrostatic interaction on the probabilities of the configurations gave results considerably higher than those of Murphy and of Cole and Auty. The calculated values of the static dielectric constant at 0° were 77.3 by the first method and 103 by the second method. Powles concluded that refinement of the calculation was likely to lead to calculated values in good agreement with the experimental, but the difficulty of taking proper account of the electrostatic interactions makes the calculations necessarily somewhat approximate.

The proton shifts which have been proposed as the source of the polarization of ice either have improbable energy requirements or lead to no net polarization.[49] A critical discussion of the various proposed mechanisms has been given by Schellman[56] and Kauzmann,[57] who conclude that the proton transfer mechanism is not consistent with experimental fact and propose a consecutive rotation of individual molecules made possible by lattice defects.[58] This would account qualitatively for the abnormally high dielectric constant produced by the trace of potassium chloride (Fig. 4.12), which could cause additional lattice defects. The lattice defects cause bonds to be missing between a few of the oxygen atoms, and propagation of the missing bonds through the lattice makes possible molecular reorientation.

Errera and his coworkers[59,60] have found that the dielectric behavior of a number of salt hydrates is very similar along at least one crystal axis to that of ice. Single crystals of $MgPt(CN)_4 \cdot 7H_2O$ and $Y_2Pt_3(CN)_{12} \cdot 21H_2O$ show dielectric constants along the a and b axes almost independent of temperature and frequency, while along the c axis the dielectric constant is much higher and dependent upon temperature and frequency. Dipole orientation appears possible in the corresponding calcium and strontium compounds, in $BaPt(CN)_4 \cdot 4H_2O$, which has a dielectric constant of 9.5 along the c axis, and also in the pentahydrates of copper sulfate and sodium thiosulfate.

[56] J. A. Schellman, Ph.D. Thesis, Princeton University Princeton, N.J.

[57] J. A. Schellman and W. Kauzmann, *Phys. Rev.*, **82**, 315 (1951).

[58] See also N. Bjerrum, *Kgl. Danske Videnskab. Selskab, Mat.-fys. Medd.*, **27**(1) (1951); *Science*, **115**, 385 (1952).

[59] J. Errera and H. V. Brasseur, *Physik. Z.*, **34**, 368 (1933).

[60] J. Errera and H. Sack, *Trans. Faraday Soc.*, **30**, 687 (1934).

5. Binary Systems.   The effect of molecular orientation as shown by the changes of dielectric constant with phase has been used[1] to work out the phase diagram of the binary system t-butyl chloride–carbon tetrachloride, in which both molecules possess rotational freedom over considerable ranges of temperature.   The method obviously is not universally applicable, but it is capable of giving very useful information about a system to which it can be applied.

Jackson[2,3] found that the dielectric behavior of dilute solid solutions of long-chain esters in paraffin wax and in polystyrene could be accounted for in terms of the Debye theory if a viscosity like that of a moderately viscous liquid was assumed.

Similar measurements were made by Sillars[4] and Pelmore.[5,6]   Fröhlich[7] developed a theoretical treatment of a model consisting of a crystalline paraffin hydrocarbon in which a small proportion of the molecules was assumed to be replaced by shorter molecules of a polar compound, such as an ester or a ketone.   The assumption of two equilibrium positions having opposite dipole directions and separated by a potential barrier of height proportional to the chain length led to an equation for the relationship between the chain length and the relaxation time for the dipole orientation process.   For a rigid, planar, zigzag chain[8]

$$\log \tau = \text{constant} + \frac{H_m}{T} \tag{5.1}$$

where H_m is the total energy required to lift a whole molecule possessing a chain of m carbon atoms over the barrier.   For the rigid chain,

$$H_m = mH_1 \tag{5.2}$$

where H_1 is the energy required to lift a single link of the chain over the barrier.   Flexibility of the chain lowers the barrier so that

$$H_m = H_1 m_0 \tanh \frac{m}{\bar{m}} \tag{5.3}$$

where $\bar{m}$ is a constant which separates short chains ($m < \bar{m}$, little torsion) from long chains ($m > \bar{m}$, appreciable torsion).   Comparison with the previously mentioned experimental data gave H_1 as about 0.033 electron

[1] W. P. Conner and C. P. Smyth, *J. Am. Chem. Soc.*, **63**, 3424 (1941).

[2] W. Jackson, *Proc. Roy. Soc. (London)*, **150A**, 197 (1935).

[3] W. Jackson and F. C. Frank, *Trans. Faraday Soc.*, **36**, 440 (1940).

[4] R. W. Sillars, *Proc. Roy. Soc. (London)*, **169A**, 66 (1939).

[5] D. R. Pelmore, *Proc. Roy. Soc. (London)*, **172A**, 502 (1939).

[6] D. R. Pelmore and E. L. Simons, *Proc. Roy. Soc. (London)*, **175A**, 253 (1940).

[7] H. Fröhlich, *Proc. Phys. Soc. (London)*, **54**, 422 (1942).

[8] H. Fröhlich, "Theory of Dielectrics," Oxford, London, 1949, p. 128.

volt, or 770 cal., $\bar{m}$ as 26, and the third necessary constant such that an equation could be written

$$\log 2\pi\tau = -50.4 + \frac{13,800}{T} \tanh \frac{m}{26} \qquad (5.4)$$

Since paraffin wax consists of a mixture of hydrocarbons of different molecular lengths and is therefore not a simple crystalline structure, Fröhlich's theory does not apply exactly to the measurements of Jackson, Sillars, and Pelmore. For this reason, Meakins[9] made a more rigorous test of the equation by using pure crystalline hydrocarbons as solvents for symmetrical long-chain ketones. The variation of dielectric constant and loss tangent with frequency was found to be in approximate agreement with the Debye theory. For ketones of chain length shorter than that of the hydrocarbon solvent, the relationship between relaxation time and chain length conforms qualitatively to Fröhlich's theory, but it was necessary to determine new constants in the equation for each type of polar molecule and for each solvent. Measurements[9] on the system laurone-n-hexacosane ($C_{11}H_{23}COC_{11}H_{23}$-$C_{26}H_{54}$) at concentrations from 6.8 to 90 per cent laurone within the frequency range 60 kilocycles to 50 megacycles showed that the dielectric absorption at first increased with increasing concentration of the polar substances and then decreased, pure laurone giving negligible loss in this frequency range. The initial increase in loss was obviously due to increase in the number of polar molecules. However, increasing concentration of polar molecules was thought[9] to result in increasing dipole interaction with consequent increase in the heights of the restricting potential barriers and ultimate decrease in the number of dipoles undergoing orientation and producing the loss. Although the situation in this system is complicated by the existence of two different solid solutions, the indication of the effect of polarity in restricting rotation is extremely interesting.

Metastable solid solutions of the ketone $C_6H_{13}COC_{11}H_{23}$ in $C_{17}H_{36}$ have been found[10,11] to show a transition from a high-temperature form with free dipole rotation to a low-temperature form in which dipolar rotation is restricted. A large difference in dielectric properties was found to result from a small difference in structure between the two forms.

An attempt was made[12] to prepare dilute solid solutions of tetradecyl alcohol and hexadecyl alcohol in dicetyl, $C_{32}H_{66}$, and in hexadecyl ether, $(C_{16}H_{33})_2O$, by the fusion and subsequent cooling of the binary mixtures, but the resultant mixtures evidently contained the two components as

[9] R. J. Meakins, *Nature*, **162**, 994 (1948); *Australian J. Sci. Research*, **2**, 405 (1949).
[10] V. Daniel, *Nature*, **163**, 725 (1949).
[11] V. Daniel and K. H. Stark, *Trans. Faraday Soc.*, **48**, 685 (1952).
[12] A. Di Giacomo and C. P. Smyth, Unpublished measurements.

separate solid phases, each of which showed the dielectric behavior of the pure substance.

Plessner and Richards[13] have investigated solutions of dibutyl, dihexyl, and dioctyl phthalates, tricresyl phosphate, and propyl stearate in polyisobutene, polythene, and polystyrene, observing relaxation times for the dipole orientation process of 10^{-8} to 10^{-9} sec. and calculating a dipole moment 2.5 to 2.6 $\times$ 10^{-18} for dioctyl phthalate in agreement with the values for the methyl and ethyl esters in dilute liquid solution. The dipole orientation process in at least some of these solutions probably resembles that examined in the subsequent section in high polymers and involves intramolecular twisting.

6. Organic Glasses. If the Debye equations applied exactly to solids, the very high viscosities of crystalline solids would eliminate dipole orientation at the frequencies ordinarily used in measurement. The many cases of molecular orientation in crystalline solids show that the effective viscosity may be quite different from the macroscopic viscosity measured by ordinary methods. Indeed, it has been shown that even in liquids the relaxation time changes much less rapidly with viscosity than is expected. Equations II(2.22) and (2.23) represent qualitatively the behavior of an organic glass, about the nature of which dielectric-constant measurements give very interesting information.[1-4] Some branched-chain organic halides have been found to form glasses when the liquids are cooled. It is difficult for these molecules to crystallize, since they can fit in only one way into their anisotropic crystal lattices. Molecules which pack efficiently in the liquid, but which do not form isotropic lattices, should tend to vitrify. The behavior of i-butyl chloride[3] may be cited as typical (Fig. 6.1). The liquid does not crystallize on cooling, but vitrifies at some distance below the freezing point, the cooling curves closely resembling those found for i-butyl bromide and i-amyl bromide. The glass behaves like a very viscous liquid. The relaxation time of the molecules increases with falling temperature and increasing viscosity of the material until the orientation of the molecules lags behind the alternating electric field used in the measurement. The consequent anomalous dispersion of the dielectric constant causes the dielectric constant–temperature curve to separate into branches, which unite again when the molecules are entirely unable to orient in the field even of the 0.5-kc. current. The dielectric constant–temperature curves in the

[13] K. W. Plessner and R. B. Richards, *Trans. Faraday Soc.*, **42A**, 206 (1946).

[1] W. O. Baker and C. P. Smyth, *J. Am. Chem. Soc.*, **61**, 2063 (1939); *J. Chem. Phys.*, **7**, 574 (1939).

[2] W. O. Baker and C. P. Smyth, *Ann. N.Y. Acad. Sci.*, **40**, 447 (1940).

[3] A. Turkevich and C. P. Smyth, *J. Am. Chem. Soc.*, **64**, 737 (1942).

[4] W. Kauzmann, *Chem. Revs.*, **43**, 219 (1948).

lower half of Fig. 6.1 were obtained on warming a specimen of the *i*-butyl chloride glass which had been kept between −180° and −190° for 27 hours. Another run, after the glass had been kept at this low temperature for 25 hours, duplicated this behavior exactly. After the glass had been kept at the low temperature for 100 hours, the behavior was very similar, crystallization becoming apparent at about the same temperature, −170°, but occurring at a noticeably faster rate, probably because

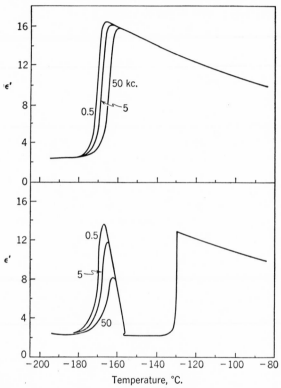

FIG. 6.1. Temperature dependence of the dielectric constant of *i*-butyl chloride. (Upper curves, cooling; lower curves, heating after 27 hours at −185°C.) [*A. Turkevich and C. P. Smyth, J. Am. Chem. Soc.*, **64,** 737 (1942).]

more crystal nuclei had formed in the longer period of time. The dielectric-constant curves obtained on warming the glass up from −185° are identical with the cooling curves up to about −168°, above which the dielectric-constant values begin to fall below those obtained at the same temperatures on cooling. This change in the curves is due to crystallization of the glass, which proceeds faster and faster. The sample heats up above the temperature of the thermostat, and the dielectric constant goes through a maximum and then drops to a low value characteristic of a crystalline solid having molecules unable to rotate. A small drop in temperature occurs on the completion of crystallization, when the solid, which has been heated by its heat of crystallization, cools down to the temperature of its environment. At $-130.5°$, the now crystalline solid melts and the dielectric constant rises sharply to the value for the dipolar liquid at that temperature. The experiment shows the nature of the mechanically rigid glass to be that of a highly viscous liquid, which undergoes nucleation on prolonged standing at low temperature. The rate of crystallization, which has occurred to an almost negligible extent in 100 hours at $-185°$, is increased so rapidly by rising temperature that most of the process occurs in the temperature interval from $-167°$ to $-157°C$.

Polyhydroxy molecules in the liquid state show strong hydrogen bonding, presumably forming structures of irregular shape, with consequent tendency toward supercooling and vitrification. Glycerol,[5,6] propylene glycol[7], trimethylene glycol,[7] and glucose[8] thus supercool to glasses which show the dielectric behavior of very viscous liquids. Similar behavior has been reported[9] also for propyl alcohol, isobutyl alcohol, and phenolphthalein.

7. Inorganic Glasses. As in the case of ionic crystals, the dielectric constants of inorganic glasses depend primarily upon the electronic and ionic polarization, and the observed loss commonly depends mainly on the relaxation of the latter. For most glasses, as for the majority of ionic crystals, the dielectric constants lie between 4 and 9. They tend to increase as rising temperature increases the amplitude of the ionic displacement and to decrease very slowly with increasing frequency over a wide range. The loss is commonly small and subject to only a small change over a wide range of frequency. As the temperature rises, usually above 80° or so, the rapid increase in d.c. conductivity causes a strong frequency dependence and rapid increase in the dielectric loss and apparent dielectric constant[1] as required by Eqs. II(6.7) and (6.8). It appears that at the lower temperatures the loss is a true dielectric loss with very little effect due to the ohmic resistance of the glass, but, at higher temperatures, the effect of d.c. conductivity is predominant.[1-4]

[5] S. Mizushima, *Physik. Z.*, **28**, 418 (1927).

[6] S. O. Morgan and W. Yager, *Ind. Eng. Chem.*, **32**, 1523 (1940).

[7] A. H. White and S. O. Morgan, *Physics*, **2**, 312 (1932).

[8] B. Thomas, *J. Phys. Chem.*, **35**, 2103 (1931).

[9] E. Kuvshinsky and P. Kobeko, *Tech. Phys. U.S.S.R.*, **5**, 401 (1938).

[1] G. W. Morey, "The Properties of Glass," Reinhold, New York, 1938, chap. XVIII.

[2] E. Schott, *Jahrb. Z. drahtl. Tel.*, **18**, 82 (1921).

[3] L. S. McDowell and H. L. Begeman, *Phys. Rev.*, **33**, 55 (1929).

[4] M. J. O. Strutt, *Archiv. Elektrotech.*, **25**, 715 (1931).

The logarithm of the loss tangent increases linearly with temperature, the increase being more rapid for low frequencies than for high. High content of heavy metals, such as lead and barium, in glasses with low alkali content gives high dielectric constants and low loss tangents, while high alkali content gives high loss tangent.[1,2]

Strutt[4] has proposed an empirical formula for the dependence of the loss tangent of glasses upon temperature T:

$$\tan \delta = K e^{\alpha T} \tag{7.1}$$

in which K and α depend upon the composition of the glass and the frequency ω, α decreasing with increasing ω. The following picture has been suggested for the mechanism of the relaxation in glasses.[5,6] In the absence of an external field, each alkali metal ion in the glass is vibrating around an equilibrium position in its interstice with a frequency of the order of 10^{12}. If an external alternating field is applied, the equilibrium position changes periodically with the frequency of the applied field. This change of equilibrium position is closely connected with small deformations of the oxygen network around the alkali metal ions, and in this process after-effects occur, which involve a series of excitation energies q, giving rise to the relaxation times τ, such that

$$\tau = \tau_0 e^{q/kT} \tag{7.2}$$

in which τ_0 is of the order of 10^{-14} sec. The empirical constant α in Eq. (7.1) is then given by

$$\alpha = -\beta k \ln \omega \tau_0 \tag{7.3}$$

in which β is a quantity depending on a Gaussian distribution of the excitation energies. The presence of cations other than those of the alkali metals may contribute somewhat to the dielectric constant and loss, and, in particular, some loss is attributed to the silicon-oxygen network of the glass. Because the rigid structures of the continuous networks of SiO_2 and B_2O_3 glasses do not oscillate readily, these glasses have low losses in the microwave region, but, as at lower frequencies, interstitial cations give rise to losses, which are larger the more loosely bound the cations.[7] The maximum in the loss curve required by theory and normally observed in dielectric measurements is not observed in inorganic glasses at the frequencies used in measuring the dielectric properties. Because of the complexity of the composition of most inorganic glasses and the resultant empirical and detailed nature of

[5] M. Gevers and F. K. du Pré, *Philips Tech. Rev.*, **9**, 91 (1947).

[6] J. M. Stevels, "Progress in the Theory of the Physical Properties of Glass," Elsevier, New York, 1948, chap. IV.

[7] L. Navias and R. L. Green, *J. Am. Ceramic Soc.*, **29**, 267 (1946).

the treatment required, their behavior does not lend itself to general discussion.

8. High Polymers. Dielectric relaxation in high polymers involves the factors which have already been discussed for simpler materials. Electronic and atomic polarization always contribute to the dielectric constant. If ionic materials are present, there is ionic polarization. If there are two or more phases of different conductivities present, as in many rubbers and plastics, interfacial polarization occurs with corresponding loss, usually at low frequencies. High polymers containing polar groups show more or less orientation polarization, with dipole loss due to change in the orientation of molecular segments in an externally applied field without change in the orientation of the whole macromolecule. The relaxation times of this orientation process commonly have a wide distribution of values, and the corresponding dielectric loss is therefore smaller and of much wider frequency range than in the case of small molecules. The dielectric behavior of high polymers has been effectively treated by Fuoss and his collaborators,[1-11] and many measurements have been published. The previously discussed dipole orientation in the molecules of the ω-hydroxydecanoic acid polymers (Sec. IV.4) and in the long-chain alkyl bromide molecules (Sec. IV.4), the moments found for the polymethylene bromides as the result of rotation around the bonds of the chain, and the dielectric behavior of the organic glasses (Sec. 6) give evidence of the type of dipole orientation to be found in high polymers.

The considerable resemblance of the dielectric behavior of plastics to that of viscous liquids and organic glasses is shown by the curves in Figs. 8.1 and 8.2 for the dielectric constants and loss factors at 60 cycles of a series of polyvinyl chloride plastics containing various amounts of diphenyl as plasticizer, the number on each curve in Fig. 8.1 giving the percentage by weight of diphenyl in the plastic. The dielectric constant of the 80:20 polyvinyl chloride–diphenyl system goes through a sigmoid increase as rising temperature decreases the viscosity and thus facilitates dipole orientation. With less plasticizer and consequent higher viscosity,

[1] R. M. Fuoss, *J. Am. Chem. Soc.*, **59**, 1703 (1937); **60**, 451, 456 (1938).
[2] R. M. Fuoss, *Ann. N.Y. Acad. Sci.*, **40**, 429 (1940).
[3] R. M. Fuoss, *J. Am. Chem. Soc.*, **61**, 2329, 2334 (1939).
[4] R. M. Fuoss, *J. Am. Chem. Soc.*, **63**, 369, 378 (1941).
[5] R. M. Fuoss and J. G. Kirkwood, *J. Am. Chem. Soc.*, **63**, 385 (1941).
[6] J. G. Kirkwood and R. M. Fuoss, *J. Chem. Phys.*, **9**, 329 (1941).
[7] R. M. Fuoss, *J. Am. Chem. Soc.*, **63**, 2401, 2410 (1941).
[8] D. J. Mead and R. M. Fuoss, *J. Am. Chem. Soc.*, **63**, 2832 (1941).
[9] D. J. Mead, R. L. Tichenor, and R. M. Fuoss, *J. Am. Chem. Soc.*, **64**, 283 (1942).
[10] D. J. Mead and R. M. Fuoss, *J. Am. Chem. Soc.*, **64**, 2389 (1942); *ibid.* **65**, 2067 (1943); *ibid.* **67**, 1566 (1945).
[11] R. M. Fuoss, "The Chemistry of Large Molecules" (R. E. Burk and O. Grummitt editors), Interscience, New York, 1943, chap. VI.

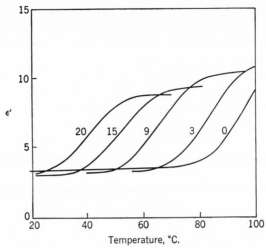

Fɪɢ. 8.1. Dielectric constants (at 60 cycles) of polyvinyl chloride plastics as functions of temperature (the number on each curve gives the weight per cent of diphenyl in the mixture).   [*R. M. Fuoss, J. Am. Chem. Soc.*, **63**, 378 (1941).]

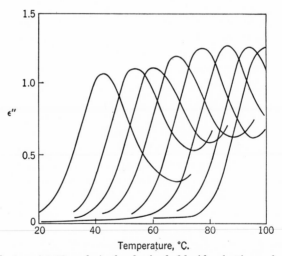

Fɪɢ. 8.2. Loss factors (at 60 cycles) of polyvinyl chloride plastics as functions of temperature (left to right: 20, 15, 12, 9, 6, 3, 1, 0% diphenyl).   [*R. M. Fuoss, J. Am. Chem. Soc.*, **63**, 378 (1941).]

the dielectric-constant increase occurs at higher temperatures, where the viscosity is lower.   The low-temperature values of the dielectric constant are considerably larger than the squares of the refractive indices, and the static dielectric constant given by the high temperature limit at fixed frequency is much larger than the dielectric constant of the corresponding monomer.   Qualitatively, the loss-factor curves in Fig. 8.2 have the position and shape which would be expected in view of the nature of the dielectric-constant curves. However, the maximum loss factor is less than half of $(\epsilon_0 - \epsilon_\infty)/2$, indicating a distribution of relaxation times. The minima at higher temperatures on the curves are an effect of d.c. conductance due to the presence of electrolytic impurities. In general, the static dielectric constants of polar polymers increase as the moments of the polar groups increase[5,8] and decrease as the amount of nonpolar plasticizer increases.[9] In polystyrene containing p-chlorodiphenyl and in poly-p-chlorostyrene containing diphenyl, it was found[4] that the absorption was approximately proportional to the content of chlorine, regardless of whether it was on the small molecules or the larger ones. In a series of cross-linked phenol-formaldehyde resins, it was similarly found[12] that the loss-factor maxima were proportional to the content of polar groups. From data on solid plastics containing polyvinyl chloride, a value 2.0×10^{-18} was calculated[5] for the C—Cl dipole moment in good agreement with the values found for simple alkyl chloride molecules. The method of calculation employed was that outlined in Sec. II.5. These facts show that the dielectric behavior of polar plastics is determined largely by dipole orientation, a behavior in harmony with the large body of information as to dipole orientation in crystalline solids and intramolecular dipole orientation which has been discussed.

The extent of the distribution of relaxation times in several plastics[4] is shown graphically in Fig. 8.3, in which the ratio of the loss factor to its maximum value ϵ_m'' is plotted against the logarithm of the ratio of the frequency to f_m. Pure polyvinyl chloride shows the widest distribution, and polyvinyl chloroacetate shows the least departure from the theoretical Debye curve calculated for a single relaxation time. Although plots of ϵ'' against ϵ' at different temperatures for polyvinyl chloride–diphenyl (6 per cent) showed some departure from arc form, several plastics containing about 19 per cent diphenyl gave points lying exactly on arcs according to the Cole and Cole distribution. The most probable value about which the relaxation times were distributed was, in general, found to be proportional to the degree of polymerization as required by the Debye theory and to an internal viscosity, which was several decades smaller than the macroscopic viscosity, a behavior consistent with that observed in the microwave measurements on liquids. These relaxation times also showed the normal linear dependence of their logarithms upon the reciprocal of the absolute temperature. For polyvinyl chloride–diphenyl systems at temperatures from 35° to 70°, plots of $\cosh^{-1}[H(0)/H(X)]$ against $\log f$ according to the method outlined in Sec. II.5 were found[5] to be linear. The distribution parameter α was found to increase

[12] L. Hartshorn, N. J. L. Megson, and E. Rushton, *Proc. Phys. Soc. (London)*, **52**, 796 (1940).

with increasing diphenyl content between 0 and 20 per cent and with increasing temperature. The moment value calculated per monomer unit by the method outlined in Sec. II.5 decreased with increasing concentration of diphenyl and increasing temperature.

Oakes and Richards[13] investigated chlorinated polythenes containing up to 60 per cent chlorine and found an increase in relaxation time with increasing chlorine content corresponding to a change from a flexible or

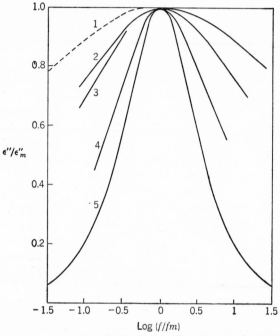

Fɪɢ. 8.3. Frequency curves: 1, polyvinyl chloride; 2, polyvinyl chloride–diphenyl 80:20; 3, polychlorostyrene-diphenyl 80:20; 4, polyvinyl acetate; 5, Debye absorption curve. [*R. M. Fuoss, J. Am. Chem. Soc.*, **63**, 369 (1941).]

rubbery to a rigid state. The fact that the average dipole moment calculated per C—Cl bond was lower than the values in ethyl chloride, neoprene, or plasticized polyvinyl chloride was attributed to the presence of —CCl_2— or —CHCl—CHCl— groups.

The curves for the dielectric constants and loss factors of polyvinyl acetate[8] at frequencies from 60 to 10,000 cycles in Fig. 8.4 show the normal shift of the maximum absorption to higher temperatures as the frequency is increased, with accompanying broadening of the loss-factor maxima and decrease in the inflexion slopes of the dielectric constant–temperature curves. The much narrower distribution found

[13] W. G. Oakes and R. B. Richards, *Trans. Faraday Soc.*, **42A**, 197 (1946).

for polyvinyl acetate as compared to polyvinyl chloride was attributed
by Fuoss[11] to the attachment of the polar carbonyl group to the polymeric
chain of the acetate by a flexible oxygen hinge, which made the dipole
orientation much less dependent on the convolutions of the chain than
in the case of the chloride, where the C—Cl dipole is attached directly
to the chain.   Polyvinyl chloroacetate gives a narrower distribution of
relaxation times than the acetate because of the greater freedom of the

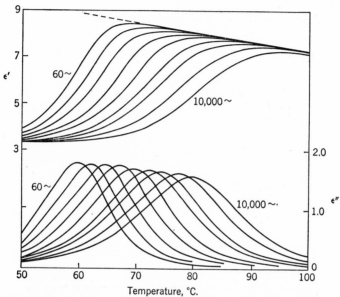

Fig. 8.4. Dielectric constants and loss factors of polyvinyl acetate (Gelva 60) at 60,
120, 240, 500, 1,000, 2,000, 3,000, 6,000, and 10,000 cycles. [D. J. Mead and R. M.
Fuoss, J. Am. Chem. Soc., 63, 2832 (1941).]

C—Cl dipole from restraints imposed by the chain.[11]   The static dielectric constant is double that of the monomer.
   The high static dielectric constants of polymeric systems as compared
to the corresponding monomers were attributed by Fuoss[11] to less mutual
cancellation of the dipoles in the polymers than in the corresponding
monomers because of suppression of the translational freedom of the
dipoles by their bonds to the polymeric chains and consequent prevention
of mutual cancellation by motion due to field interaction alone.   The
average moment per monomer unit calculated from data on the plastic
is generally higher than the value calculated from direct determinations
on the monomer but approaches this value as the polymer is diluted with
nonpolar plasticizer.
   When a liquid polymer is cooled, local crystallization occurs over a
temperature region of several degrees, leaving amorphous regions

between crystalline regions.[11] In the high-temperature range, the coefficient of thermal expansion is about double that in the low-temperature range, where the material is brittle.   The transition temperature or "brittle point" between the two regions is an internal melting range, in which the crystallites disappear on heating.   For pure polyvinyl chloride[4] (Fig. 8.5), the loss factor at 60 cycles goes through a minimum at 70°, the brittle point, and, at lower temperatures, through a very low, broad maximum with ϵ''_m only about 0.06 as compared to the value 1.2 at the upper maximum at 100°.   When diphenyl is added as plasticizer, the

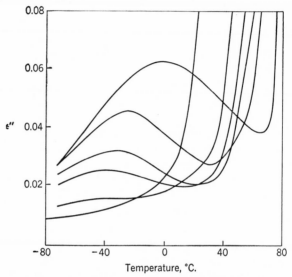

FIG. 8.5. Low-temperature loss factors of polyvinyl chloride at 0, 1, 3, 6, 12, and 20% diphenyl. [R. M. Fuoss, J. Am. Chem. Soc., **63**, 378 (1941).]

maximum shifts to lower temperatures and becomes lower, disappearing entirely when 20 per cent diphenyl is present.[4]   According to Fuoss, this low absorption peak is dependent on interaction between the chains, and the plasticizer molecules dissolve in the polymer and separate the chains sufficiently to prevent crystallization.   Crystallization can be similarly prevented by attaching to the chain substituents which interfere with the proper alignment of the molecules.   Thus, polymethyl acrylate behaves like polyvinyl chloride, but polymethyl methacrylate does not. This would appear to be analogous to the effect of branching of the carbon chain in producing vitrification instead of crystallization, as discussed in Sec. 6.

When a polar plasticizer, such as dimethylthianthrene, is used, the dielectric dispersion is the result of dipole orientation both of the plasticizer molecule and of the chain segments of the polymer.[14]   Fitzgerald and Ferry[15,16] have measured the complex shear modulus for a polyvinyl chloride–dimethylthianthrene gel (10 per cent polymer by volume) and for polyvinyl chloride plasticized with dimethylthianthrene (40 per cent polymer by volume) and have found that the dynamic mechanical results give roughly the same type of temperature-frequency dispersion.   The maximum loss tangent for the mechanical case is much larger than that for the electrical, but, for each concentration, the slopes of the curves obtained by plotting the logarithm of maximum loss tangent against $1/T$ are identical for the two cases, indicating that the activation energies for the two relaxation processes are the same.

The considerable orientational freedom possessed by polar groups in linear polymers such as those which have been discussed is reduced or eliminated by the cross linking in the three-dimensional networks of primary valence bonds found in many important polymers, such as vulcanized rubber and the phenol-formaldehyde condensation resins. Pure rubber is a hydrocarbon containing no groups with polarity other than the slight polarity found associated with an unsymmetrically located carbon-carbon double bond, like that in propylene.[17]   That the total amount of such polarity in pure rubber is very small is shown[18] by the low value of its dielectric constant, 2.36 at 25° and 60 cycles, and its substantial independence of frequency, as well as by the very low value of the loss factor.   When rubber is vulcanized, the reaction of sulfur with the double bonds gives cross linking between the chains.   The considerable dipole moments associated with the carbon-sulfur bonds tend to increase the dielectric constant, while the increased binding reduces orientational freedom and thus tends to reduce the dielectric constant.   The result of these effects is shown[18] in the curves for the dielectric constant and power factor or loss tangent as functions of sulfur content in Fig. 8.6.   As the small values of power factor found for these rubbers are indistinguishable from those of the loss tangent ϵ''/ϵ', the curve is labeled as the latter.   The increase in dielectric constant due to the carbon-sulfur dipoles is ultimately more than compensated by the increased restriction of orientation.   The slight, gradual rise with increasing sulfur content after a shallow minimum in the vicinity of 21 per cent sulfur may be attributed to the high electronic polarizability of sulfur.

---

[14] E. R. Fitzgerald and R. F. Miller, *J. Colloid Sci.*, **8**, 148 (1953).

[15] E. R. Fitzgerald and J. D. Ferry, *J. Colloid Sci.*, **8**, 1 (1953).

[16] J. D. Ferry and E. R. Fitzgerald, *J. Colloid Sci.*, **2**, 224 (1953).

[17] K. B. McAlpine and C. P. Smyth, *J. Am. Chem. Soc.*, **55**, 453 (1933).

[18] A. H. Scott, A. T. McPherson, and H. L. Curtis, *Bur. Standards J. Research*, **11**, 172 (1933).

In bakelite and similar polycondensation products, such dipole orientation as may occur is largely that of unreacted hydroxyl groups, since cross bonding practically prevents rotation of large groups. The dielectric constant and loss factor are then not very dependent on frequency and temperature.

Most rubbers and many other high-polymeric materials in actual use are mixtures, which frequently consist of more than one phase. The coexistence of two phases may give rise to interfacial polarization with large effects upon dielectric constant and loss. Mere impurities may have sufficient influence to make necessary the correction of the measured conductance used in calculating the loss factor by subtracting from it the

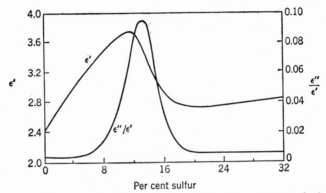

FIG. 8.6. Relation of the dielectric constant and loss tangent (at 1 kc.) of rubber-sulfur compounds to sulfur content at 25°. [*A. H. Scott, A. T. McPherson, and H. L. Curtis, Bur. Standards J. Research,* **11,** 191 (1933).]

d.c. conductance of the material. The behavior of the rubbers is illustrated by the results of measurements on vulcanized gum and tread stocks of Neoprene,[19] of natural rubber,[20] and of Butaprene N and Butaprene S elastomers[20] differing in butadiene-styrene ratio and degree of conversion. The results are typical of plastic materials, that is, the dielectric dispersion is quite broad, much broader than that predicted by the Debye theory, and the maximum losses are lower than those predicted by theory [$\epsilon_m'' = \frac{1}{2}(\epsilon_0 - \epsilon_\infty)$]. In the low-frequency range (1 kc.), the dielectric constants ϵ' for Butaprene NM and Neoprene are high, 14.7 and 7.35, respectively, because of their C≡N and C—Cl dipoles, while the values for natural rubber and the Butaprene S rubbers are low, around 3.00, due to their nonpolar structure. The decrease in ϵ' with increasing temperature is small. This can be attributed to the combina-

[19] W. C. Schneider, W. C. Carter, M. Magat, and C. P. Smyth, *J. Am. Chem. Soc.,* **67,** 959 (1945).

[20] W. C. Carter, M. Magat, W. C. Schneider, and C. P. Smyth, *Trans. Faraday Soc.,* **42A,** 213 (1946).

tion of three effects: the decrease in density, the increase in the kinetic energy of the moving segments leading to a greater randomness of motion and thus to a falling off of dipole orientation, and a loosening up of a rigid structure causing an increase in dipole orientation.

The value of ϵ' at low frequencies, which is close to the static dielectric constant, decreases with increasing styrene content, as does also ϵ_m''. The losses for polystyrene are so small that there is no maximum. For Neoprene and Butaprene NM, the values are ten to fifteen times greater. The behavior of the Butaprene S rubbers as well as natural rubber indicates the presence of groups containing dipoles which orient in an externally applied electric field. These are carbon-sulphur bonds, which give rise to a relatively small number of good-sized dipoles, and the conjugated or hyperconjugated side chains which give rise to a large number of small dipoles. Sharp increase in the dielectric loss ϵ'' at low frequencies is attributed to d.c. conductivity and is in no way connected with the dipole relaxation process.

The critical frequencies are determined from the inflection point in the ϵ' vs. log f plots, the point of maximum loss, and Cole and Cole plots. At 20° the critical frequencies for all the samples are the same, about 4 megacycles, indicating that their inner viscosities are nearly equal. A critical-frequency increase with temperature is presumably due to the decrease in the viscosity of the polymer. Butaprene NM has a lower critical frequency, 1.0 megacycle, and thus a more rigid structure or higher inner viscosity. Other Butaprene N rubbers for which no modifier was added showed still lower critical frequencies.

For all these rubbers, the plots of the function [Eq. II(5.10)] proposed by Fuoss and Kirkwood against the logarithm of the frequency gave linearity in conformity with their theory. The slopes of these plots were used to calculate, by the method of Fuoss and Kirkwood, the dipole moment per monomer unit. These calculated values are not far from the measured values for the moments of small molecules similar to the monomer units. The monomer moment calculated for natural rubber was 0.63×10^{-18} as compared to values measured[21] in the vapor state, 0.38×10^{-18} for 2-methylbutadiene, 0.52 for 2,3-dimethylbutadiene, and 0.68 for 1-methylbutadiene (*trans*). For Neoprene GN, with a monomer unit $-CH_2-CCl=CH-CH_2-$, the calculated moment was 1.99 as compared to vapor values[22] 1.69 for 2-chloropropylene, 1.71 for *cis*-1-chloropropylene, and 1.97 for *trans*-1-chloropropylene. For Butaprene NM, the calculated moment was 5.61 as compared to vapor values 3.88 for acrylonitrile,[23] 4.50 for *trans*-crotononitrile,[23] and 3.90 for 4-cyano-

[21] N. B. Hannay and C. P. Smyth, *J. Am. Chem. Soc.*, **65**, 1931 (1943).

[22] N. B. Hannay and C. P. Smyth, *J. Am. Chem. Soc.*, **68**, 1005 (1946).

[23] E. C. Hurdis and C. P. Smyth, *J. Am. Chem. Soc.*, **65**, 89 (1943).

butadiene-1,3.[24]   In view of the small quantities of other substances present in the rubber as well as of the approximation necessary in the treatment, any better agreement between the calculated moments for the monomer units and the measured moments for the gas molecules would be fortuitous.

In the case of the synthetic, Neoprene, there is a loss maximum at 5 megacycles at 20°, which is associated with the Debye dispersion.   In addition there is another maximum at 7 kc. quite independent of temperature.   For nonpolar elastomers, the small losses in the region of Debye dispersion observed for the gum stocks are completely obscured by the high losses due to the presence of carbon black.   The presence of a maximum at 7 kc. in the loss curve for Neoprene as well as the presence of inflections in the ϵ' curves for natural rubber and Butaprene S led to an analysis of the data in terms of Maxwell-Wagner effect.

For these tread stocks, because of the high conductivity of the carbon black which makes up nearly one-third of their very assorted composition, the observed loss factor must be regarded as the sum of three distinct effects, that is,

$$\epsilon''_{obs} = \epsilon''_{dc} + \epsilon''_{MW} + \epsilon''_{D} \tag{8.1}$$

where ϵ''_{dc}, the loss factor due to d.c. conductance, is given by Eq. II(6.15) as

$$\epsilon''_{dc} = \frac{1.8 \times 10^{12} k'}{f} \tag{8.2}$$

ϵ''_{MW}, the Maxwell-Wagner or interfacial-polarization loss factor, is given by Eq. II(6.24), and ϵ''_{D} is the usual dipole orientation or Debye loss factor.

Figure 8.7 shows the observed loss-factor values for a sample of Butaprene NM (tread) together with curves for their three component parts calculated from the equations given or referred to above.   It is evident that for this material, at the lowest frequencies, only the loss due to d.c. conductance is significant; in a narrow region near 10 kc. the Maxwell-Wagner loss is most important; and, above 100 kc., the dipole loss becomes all-important.

As far as the dipole loss is concerned, it is interesting that the critical frequencies are nearly identical for the gum and the tread stocks of Neoprene.   Carbon black is known to reinforce Neoprene only slightly. The negligible shift in critical frequency suggests that there is no interaction between carbon black and Neoprene.   For natural rubber and Butaprene S $^{85}/_{15}$ treads, there seems to be a definite shift in the critical frequency with the addition of carbon black, suggesting strong interaction with the carbon black in these elastomers.   A small shift in the

[24] N. B. Hannay and C. P. Smyth, *J. Am. Chem. Soc.*, **68**, 1357 (1946).

critical frequency for Butaprene NM indicates interaction intermediate between that for the nonpolar rubber and that for Neoprene.

These rubbers give good examples of the problems to be encountered in the examination of the dielectric behavior of commercial insulating materials, which may be inhomogeneous and may acquire a conducting phase through absorption of water and presence of electrolytic impurities.

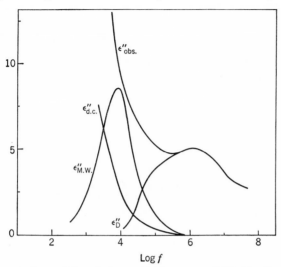

Fig. 8.7. The analysis of dielectric losses in Butaprene NM (tread) at 20°. [*W. C. Carter, M. Magat, W. C. Schneider, and C. P. Smyth, Trans. Faraday Soc.*, **42A**, 213 (1946).]

9. Ferroelectric Effect. The electric analog of the Curie point in ferromagnetism, the temperature below which spontaneous alignment of permanent magnetic dipoles can occur, is rarely observed in dielectric behavior, but, in a small number of materials, it has great importance. If we combine Eqs. I(5.17), I(5.18), and I(6.10), we obtain for the dipole moment per unit volume due to orientation of the permanent dipoles

$$P = N_1 \bar{m} = \frac{N_1 \mu^2}{3kT} \left(E + \frac{4\pi}{3} P \right) = \frac{3}{4\pi} \frac{T_c}{T - T_c} E \qquad (9.1)$$

where [cf. Eq. I(11.2)]
$$T_c = \frac{4\pi N_1 \mu^2}{9k} \qquad (9.2)$$

Substitution from Eq. I(5.3) gives

$$\epsilon - 1 = \frac{3 T_c}{T - T_c} \qquad (9.3)$$

which is the dielectric equivalent of the Curie-Weiss law of ferromagnetism. If this equation were correct, it would require the dielectric constant to approach infinity as the absolute temperature was lowered to approach a critical or Curie temperature T_c. For water, this temperature would be in the vicinity of 1,140°K., and for many other substances it should be a readily observable phenomenon. However, intermolecular action and the resultant inadequacy of the treatment of the internal field upon which the derivation of Eq. (9.3) is based renders it of no quantitative significance. Apparently, very special conditions must exist before the predicted spontaneous polarization can occur. It was first observed in Rochelle salt,[1] then in primary potassium phosphate and arsenate,[2] and more recently in barium titanate.[3,4] The very extensive literature on Rochelle salt and the relatively few investigations on primary potassium phosphate and arsenate and the rather similar ammonium salts have been extensively treated by Cady[5] and will be only briefly summarized here.

Rochelle salt, sodium potassium tartrate tetrahydrate, $NaKC_4H_4O_6 \cdot 4H_2O$, forms rhombic crystals and shows a large piezoelectric effect. Its dielectric constants in the y and z directions are normal, having values in the neighborhood of 10 with small temperature coefficients. For electric fields of certain strengths parallel to the x axis, the dielectric constant rises to tremendously high values over a certain range of temperature. At temperatures well outside this range, the dielectric behavior is normal, but within the range the dielectric polarization shows saturation and hysteresis. A spontaneous polarization parallel to x, together with a spontaneous strain, exists between -18 and $+24°$, the lower and upper Curie points, maxima being found at about 5°. For small fields the dielectric constant of the free crystal tends toward infinite values at the Curie points with a minimum at about 6° (Fig. 9.1).[6] The linear relation required by Eq. (9.3) between the dielectric constant and $1/(T - T_c)$ exists outside the Curie points and over small ranges between these points.

The behavior of Rochelle salt was first explained in terms of rotational orientation of the dipolar molecules of the water of crystallization.[7,8]

[1] J. Valasek, *Phys. Rev.*, **16**, 475 (1921).

[2] G. Busch and P. Scherrer, *Naturwissenschaften*, **23**, 737 (1935).

[3] E. Wainer and A. N. Salomon, *Titanium Alloy Manufacturing Co. Elect. Repts.* 8 (1942), 9, 10 (1943).

[4] A. von Hippel and co-workers, *N.D.R.C. Rept.* 300, August, 1944. cf. A. von Hippel, R. G. Breckenridge, F. G. Chelsey, and L. Tisza, *J. Ind. Eng. Chem.*, **38**, 1097 (1946).

[5] W. G. Cady, "Piezoelectricity," McGraw-Hill, New York, 1946, chaps. XX–XXVII.

[6] H. Mueller, *Phys. Rev.*, **58**, 565, 585 (1940); *Ann. N.Y. Acad. Sci.*, **40**, 321 (1940).

[7] P. Kobeko and I. Kurchatov, *Z. Physik*, **66**, 192 (1930); *J. Russ. Phys.-Chem. Soc.*, **62**, 251 (1930).

[8] R. H. Fowler, *Proc. Roy. Soc. (London)*, **149A**, 1 (1935); "Statistical Mechanics," 2d ed., Cambridge, 1936, p. 864.

Mueller's first theory[9] related the dielectric and piezoelectric effects to the strong internal field associated with the dipoles without explicit introduction of the dipole moments and rotation.   His later work[6] disregarded the internal field and related the dielectric properties to a nonlinear dependence of field strength upon polarization, his equations being more or less empirical.   Mason has proposed[10] a plausible mechanism for the behavior of Rochelle salt based on the crystal structure determination

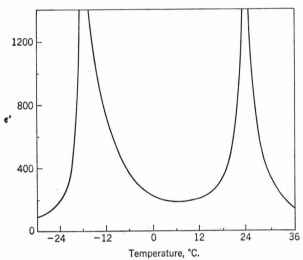

Temperature, °C.

Fig. 9.1. Dielectric constant for small fields of Rochelle salt in the ferroelectric range. [*H. Mueller, N.Y. Acad. Sci.*, **40**, 321 (1940).]

of Beevers and Hughes.[11]   Of three possible hydrogen bonds in the structure, the shortest, 2.59 A. in length between an oxygen and a water molecule, was taken as responsible for the ferroelectric effect.   As in the case of the solid alcohols discussed earlier in the present chapter, the proton of the hydrogen bond was treated as capable of passing from one potential energy minimum over a barrier to a second minimum

$$O—H \cdots O \rightleftharpoons O \cdots H—O$$

Such passage may give rise to polarization in the manner described in Sec. I.4.   For the "clamped" dielectric constant, that is, the dielectric constant measured in the absence of strain, Mason derived an expression for the case of small applied fields

$$\epsilon = \epsilon_\infty + \frac{(4\pi A/\beta)[1 - (P_s/N\mu)^2]}{1 - A[1 - (P_s/N\mu)^2]} + \frac{i\omega e^{\Delta U/kT}}{\Gamma \cosh (AP_s/N\mu)} \qquad (9.4)$$

[9] H. Mueller, *Phys. Rev.*, **47**, 175 (1935).
[10] W. P. Mason, *Phys. Rev.*, **72**, 854 (1947).
[11] C. A. Beevers and W. Hughes, *Proc. Roy. Soc. (London)*, **177A**, 251 (1941).

where ϵ_∞ is the dielectric constant corresponding to electronic and atomic polarization,

$$A = \frac{edN\mu_A\beta \cos^2 25°}{2(1 - \beta\gamma)kT} \qquad (9.5)$$

where e = electronic charge, 4.80×10^{-10} e.s.u.

d = distance separating two energy minima

ΔU = potential barrier between them

N = total number of dipoles per unit volume

μ = dipole moment along x axis, given by $\mu = \mu_A \cos 25°$ (where μ_A = value of dipole moment along bond, which is at an angle of 25° to x axis)

β = internal field constant, $4\pi/3$ for an isotropic medium

γ = polarizability per unit volume due to all polarization except that of hydrogen dipole

k = gas constant per molecule

T = absolute temperature

P_s = spontaneous dipole polarization contained in the expression

$$\tanh (AP_s/N\mu) = P_s/N\mu \qquad (9.6)$$

ω = angular frequency

Γ = constant which may be taken as kT/h (where h = Planck constant)

Mason has calculated $P_s/N\mu$ as a function of A, the potential barrier ΔU and the distance of the proton from the center of the bond as functions of the oxygen separation, and the value of β as 4.07, very close to the theoretical value $4\pi/3$ for an isotropic substance. He was thus able to calculate the curve for the temperature dependence of ϵ in rough agreement with the course of the observed values, but the theory failed to account for the finite values observed for the clamped dielectric constant at the Curie points. Equation (9.4) also accounted for the measurements of W. A. Yager, quoted by Mason, which showed that from -40 to $+26°$ the dielectric constant at 2.5×10^{10} cycles was practically independent of temperature, having the value 8, because the frequency was so high that the hydrogen-bond dipoles could not follow the field.

When all the hydrogens in Rochelle salt are replaced by deuterium to give heavy-water Rochelle salt, the lower Curie point is lowered to $-22°$, the upper one is raised to 35°, and a considerably larger spontaneous polarization occurs.[12,13] This behavior was quantitatively accounted for by Mason on the assumption that the separation of the oxygens was increased in the heavy-water salt over that in the ordinary salt.

[12] J. Hablutzel, *Helv. Phys. Acta*, **12**, 489 (1939).
[13] A. N. Holden and W. P. Mason, *Phys. Rev.*, **57**, 54 (1940).

No other pure tartrates have been found to show the ferroelectric effect, but mixed crystals of $NaNH_4C_4H_4O_6 \cdot 4H_2O$, $NaRbC_4H_4O_6 \cdot 4H_2O$, and $NaTlC_4H_4O_6 \cdot 4H_2O$ with Rochelle salt have been found to show it.[5] Curie points (°K.) have been found for primary potassium and ammonium phosphates and arsenates as follows:[5] KH_2PO_4, 122.0°; KD_2PO_4, 213°; KH_2AsO_4, 95.6°; $NH_4H_2PO_4$, 147.9°; $NH_4H_2AsO_4$, 216.1°. In Rochelle salt the ferroelectric range is narrow, and in the phosphates and arsenates it is limited to low temperatures.   The effect is presumably attributable to the hydrogen bond in all these crystals.

The theory of the transition in primary potassium phosphate was treated by Slater[14] in terms of the occupation by the acid hydrogens of one or the other of two potential minima along the hydrogen bonds between the oxygens of adjacent phosphate ions.   An interesting study[15] of proton nuclear resonance in these primary potassium and ammonium phosphates and arsenates showed two minima in the relaxation time vs. temperature curves for the ammonium salts, one minimum corresponding to a temperature at which the acid hydrogens were regarded as the most effective relaxation agent and the other to a temperature where the ammonium-ion hydrogens were most effective.

Barium titanate, $BaTiO_3$, is ferroelectric below 120°C., although it contains no hydrogen.   It crystallizes in the simple perovskite structure and may be employed not only as a single crystal but as a rugged ceramic material.   It is thus particularly suitable for practical application. Much of the following account of the dielectric behavior of barium titanate is based upon the report of von Hippel.[16]

When a multicrystalline sample of barium titanate is cooled from 135° down, its dielectric constant passes through a sharp maximum with a value of over 6,000 at a field strength of 2.29 volts per cm.[4,16]   Its loss tangent, correspondingly, passes through a minimum (Fig. 9.2),[4,16] the slope of the thermal expansion coefficient changes, ferroelectric hysteresis loops appear,[4] and the cubic structure is progressively transformed into a tetragonal structure.[16,17]   The loss tangent (Fig. 9.2) and thermal-expansion curves indicate another phase transition near 0°, and the dielectric-constant curve (Fig. 9.2) indicates this as occurring between 0 and 20° with a third transition not far from −60°.   When the initial dielectric constants for various field strengths are plotted against tem-

[14] J. C. Slater, *J. Chem. Phys.*, **9**, 16 (1941).

[15] R. Newman, *J. Chem. Phys.*, **18**, 669 (1950).

[16] A. von Hippel, Ferroelectricity, Domain Structure and Phase Transitions of Barium Titanate, *MIT Lab. Insulation Research Tech. Rept.* 28 (1950); see also *ibid.* 51 (1952); *Revs. Mod. Phys.*, **22**, 221 (1950).

[17] H. D. Megaw, *Trans. Faraday Soc.*, **42A**, 224 (1946); *Proc. Roy. Soc. (London)*, **189A**, 261 (1947).

perature, these two transition points become clearly evident near 0 and −70°. They become more pronounced with increasing voltage from 59 to 4,800 volts per cm., but the material remains ferroelectric throughout this region. The barium titanate, cubic above the Curie point, changes by a second-order transition at the Curie point into a tetragonal form, by a first-order transition near 5° to an orthorhombic form, and by a first-order transition near −70° to a trigonal form.[18] The Curie

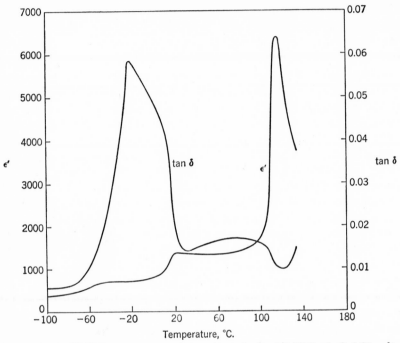

FIG. 9.2. Dielectric constant and loss tangent (at 1 kc. and field strength 2.29 volts per cm.) of barium titanate ceramic. [*A. von Hippel, MIT Lab. Insulation Research Tech. Rept.* 28 (1950).]

point is lowered as a linear function of pressure from 120° at 1 atm. to 100° at about 3,400 atm. and is similarly lowered by replacement of barium ions in the lattice with strontium ions, the value being −190° when the composition of the mixed crystal is about 0.75 $SrTiO_3$. The temperature dependence of the dielectric constant above the Curie point corresponds to the Curie-Weiss law at low field strengths, but at high field strengths the dielectric constant decreases rapidly with increase in the strength of the applied field. The constant in the Curie-Weiss law is much larger than the $3T_c$ required by Eq. (9.3), having a value 88,000 for a $(Ba-Sr)TiO_3$ sample, which has $T_c = 281°K$.[16]

[18] H. F. Kay and P. Vousden, *Phil. Mag.*, (7)**40**, 1019 (1949).

The dependence of the dielectric constant and loss tangent of barium titanate upon frequency is shown in Fig. 9.3.[16] Although there is some loss throughout the entire frequency range shown, the major portion of the decrease in dielectric constant and increase in loss tangent occurs between 10^8 and 3×10^{10} cycles, at which latter frequency the dielectric constant has decreased to about 150, while the loss tangent has not yet attained its maximum value. In correspondence to this decrease of the ferroelectric response, the effect of a biasing voltage decreases and seems to disappear in the 1-cm. region. Under the action of a biasing field, very

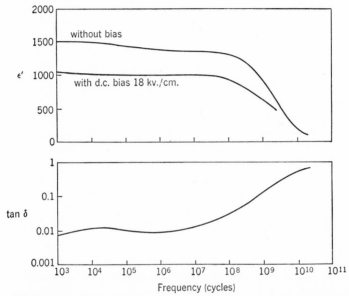

FIG. 9.3. Relaxation spectrum of the ferroelectric state of barium titanate (thin sheet material) at 25° (a.c. field strength <40 volts per cm.). [*A. von Hippel, MIT Lab. Insulation Research Tech. Rept.* 28 (1950).]

strong resonance effects (not shown in Fig. 9.3) occur just below and in the megacycle range.

In the perovskite structure of the cubic barium titanate, the symmetry is such that there is no permanent dipole moment. Each Ti^{4+} ion is at the center of a regular octahedron, which has an $O^=$ ion at each of its six corners. Titanium dioxide, and calcium, strontium, and barium titanates contain this octahedral group and have high dielectric constants, which increase in the order indicated, while magnesium titanate, in which the titanium ion shares only three oxygen ions in a corundum structure, has the much lower dielectric constant characteristic of normal ionic crystals.[16] For the rutile form of titanium dioxide, the refractive indices for sodium light parallel and perpendicular to the optical axis of the crystal are 2.6 and 2.9, but the refractive indices for 300μ are 9.1 and 12.9, in good agreement with the dielectric constants ($\epsilon = n^2$) 83 and 167 measured in the electrical range.   These large dielectric-constant and infrared refractive-index values must arise from the dipole moments produced by the displacement of the titanium cations relative to the oxide anions.   It is reasonable, therefore, to attribute the very high dielectric constants of the titanates to the same displacement of the Ti^{4+} ions from the centers of the $O^=$ octahedra.   For the displacement to be large, the octahedra must have the proper size and spatial arrangement. Thus, reduction of the lattice parameter of barium titanate by high pressure or by replacement of barium ions by strontium ions lowers the Curie point linearly.[16,19]   In the cubic form of barium titanate the octahedra share corners only, but in the hexagonal form, two-thirds of the octahedra occur in groups of two which share one face.   The smaller separation of the Ti^{4+} ions in the hexagonal form and consequent greater mutual forces hinder the concerted action required for ferroelectric behavior, which is therefore absent in the hexagonal form, its dielectric constant being only about 100 at room temperature.   The mechanism for the creation of the very high polarization in barium titanate is slightly different from that in Rochelle salt, where the polarization is pictured as arising from the displacement of a proton from one potential minimum to another.   The titanium ion may be pictured as vibrating in a broad, shallow minimum, where considerable displacement with consequent large dipole moment may easily occur.   When several dipole moments are pointed in the same direction, either by an external field or by thermal fluctuation, the resulting local field increases the polarization and displaces the potential minima, giving rise to permanent polarization.

Since the preparation of this brief account of the subject, other surveys have been published.[20-22]

10. Electrets.   Electrets have been known for many years but have only recently become a subject of considerable interest.   Heaviside used the word "electret" to denote a permanently electrified material having electric charges of opposite sign at its extremities.[1]   Eguchi,[2] who was the first to report the preparation of an electret, melted equal parts of carnauba wax and resin with a little beeswax and permitted the liquid mixture to solidify in a strong electric field.   Disks thus prepared had a

[19] R. D. Burbank and H. T. Evans, Jr., *Acta Cryst.*, **1**, 330 (1948).

[20] C. J. F. Böttcher, "Theory of Electric Polarisation," Elsevier, Houston, 1952, sec. 66.

[21] E. T. Jaynes, "Ferroelectricity," Princeton University Press, Princeton, N.J., 1953.

[22] A. R. von Hippel, "Dielectrics and Waves," Wiley, New York, 1954, pp. 202–213.

[1] F. Gutmann, *Revs. Mod. Phys.*, **20**, 457 (1948).

[2] M. Eguchi, *Phil. Mag.*, **49**, 178 (1925).

strong negative charge on the face which had been against the anode and a strong positive charge on the face which had been in contact with the cathode. The initial charges decayed within a few days and were followed by the building up of charges of opposite sign, in other words, by charges of the same sign as those of the adjacent forming electrodes. No measurable decay of these charges was observed over a period of 3 years. Gemant[3] has termed a charge on the electret of the same sign as that on the adjacent electrode a "homocharge" and a charge of sign opposite to that on the adjacent electrode a "heterocharge." The heterocharge always forms initially, and it is only in certain materials that it decays and is followed by the building up of a permanent homocharge. The electret is in many respects the electric analog of a permanent magnet. If an electret is cut between its poles, two complete electrets are formed. For permanency, an electret is kept with its faces short-circuited just as a magnet is kept with a soft iron bar across its poles. Eguchi[2] observed that the electrification disappeared on irradiation of the electret with X rays but reappeared after cessation of the radiation, while melting destroyed the electret. He concluded that the electrification was not merely a surface phenomenon but was a volume effect.

Thiessen, Winkel, and Herrmann[4] found that an electret could be made by allowing the resin-wax mixture to solidify between tin electrodes without the application of any external field. A heterocharge two-thirds the magnitude of the electret charge prepared with a polarizing field was thus obtained and found to show no decay in 6 months. Rubbing the same material with a hair brush was found to produce more or less permanent surface electrification. This latter electrification was, however, not that of a true electret, which is a volume effect extending throughout the whole mass of the material.

The first investigators used fields of more than 10 kv. per cm. in forming electrets, but later workers[4,5] found that lower fields, even down to 100 volts per cm., could be used. However, electrets prepared with fields of less than 10 kv. per cm. were reported to carry only a heterocharge, which decayed in 10 to 20 days to a permanent value.[2] The size of this charge is proportional to the polarizing field,[4,6] while, in the high-field electrets, increase of the applied field above 10 to 12 kv. does not produce a proportionate increase in the resulting electret charges, presumably because the charge on the surface of the electrets reaches the maximum value which can exist without leading to breakdown of the adjoining layer

[3] A. Gemant, *Phil. Mag.*, **20**, 929 (1935).

[4] P. A. Thiessen, A. Winkel, and K. Herrmann, *Physik. Z.*, **37**, 511 (1936).

[5] O. J. Johnson and P. H. Carr, *Phys. Rev.*, **42**, 912 (1932).

[6] B. Gross and L. F. Denard, *Phys. Rev.*, **67**, 253 (1945).

of air.   In the low-field electrets, the distribution of space charge is very
different from that in electrets formed in high fields.   Surface charges
up to 10 e.s.u. per cm.[2] have been observed,[3,4,7] and fields up to 30 kv. per
cm. at or near the surface have been reported.[4,8]

Groetzinger,[9] in seemingly careful work, observed a 71 per cent increase
in the thermal conductivity of beeswax on the formation of an electret,
but similar investigations by Sharbaugh[10] failed to reveal any change in
thermal conductivity larger than the possible error of observation.
Piezoelectric properties have been reported by some investigators[1,11] but
have not been found by others.   Some indication has been obtained of
the development of crystalline structure in the interior of an electret.[1]

Remelting destroys the electret, as previously mentioned, and liberates
the stored electricity.   Frei and Groetzinger[12] found that the quantity
of electricity obtained by remelting was proportional to the polarizing
field and independent of the time elapsed between polarization and
remelting.   Groetzinger and Kretsch[13] reported that the depolarization
current began to flow at temperatures below the melting point, but that
depolarization became complete only if the highest temperature attained
during the polarization was exceeded or if complete liquefaction occurred.
They also observed an increase in the rate of decay of the charge when the
electret was exposed to a strong radio-frequency field.

Mikola[14] divided electrets into (1) those of comparatively high conductivity yielding only heterocharges and (2) those of much lower conductivity capable of yielding homocharges.   Materials capable of electrification have been classified[1] as follows:

Permanent volume polarization		Surface charges only	No permanent charges
Heterocharges only	Homocharges also		
Glass	Carnauba wax	Cetyl alcohol	Paraffin wax
Resin	Beeswax	Cetyl palmitate	Palmitic acid
Sulfur	Polar hydrocarbons	Nonpolar hydrocarbons	Stearic acid
Substances containing	Esters	Stearanilide	1,8-Dinitro-
acid groups	Alcohols	Seekay wax	naphthalene
	Asphaltos		

[7] G. E. Sheppard and J. D. Stranathan, *Phys. Rev.*, **60**, 360 (1941).
[8] A. Gemant, *Rev. Sci. Instr.*, **11**, 65 (1940).
[9] G. Groetzinger, *Physik. Z.*, **37**, 720 (1936).
[10] A. H. Sharbaugh, Paper presented to National Research Council Conference on
Electrical Insulation, Pocono Manor, Pa., November, 1950.
[11] E. P. Adams, *J. Franklin Inst.*, **204**, 469 (1927).
[12] H. Frei and G. Groetzinger, *Physik. Z.*, **37**, 720 (1936).
[13] G. Groetzinger and H. Kretsch, *Z. Physik*, **103**, 337 (1936).
[14] S. Mikola, *Z. Physik*, **32**, 476 (1925).

This is obviously not a satisfactory classification according to chemical composition or molecular polarity but a résumé of materials which have been observed to show certain electrification phenomena. Most of these materials are mixtures, and the purity of many, at least, of the single substances is open to doubt.

The foregoing experimental observations have been much more fully summarized by Gutmann, together with some discussion of the causes of the observed behavior.[1]

Gross,[15] in further work on carnauba wax, points out that all effects produced by the application of low or medium polarizing voltage at room temperature are attributable to dielectric absorption, which, according to the accepted theories, may involve (a) hindered dipole orientation, (b) displacement of ions over microscopic distances in a microscopically heterogeneous structure giving rise to Maxwell-Wagner effect, and (c) ionic conduction associated with the formation of space charges. When the applied voltage is at temperatures sufficiently above room temperature or even when a very high voltage is applied at room temperature, transfer of charge from the electrode to the surface of the dielectric occurs. The result of this transfer of charge is the formation of a homocharge on the dielectric, while the result of the dielectric absorption is the formation of a heterocharge. A homocharge may also arise from the adsorption on the dielectric surface of ions of charge opposite in sign to the heterocharge. The subsequent behavior of the electret will depend upon the rate of decay of the heterocharge and that of the homocharge. Swann[16] has given an extensive mathematical treatment to the problem of electrets and their decay of charge.

[15] B. Gross, *Phys. Rev.*, **66**, 26 (1944); *J. Chem. Phys.*, **17**, 866 (1949).
[16] W. F. G. Swann, *J. Franklin Inst.*, **250**, 219 (1950).

CHAPTER VI

MEASUREMENT OF DIELECTRIC CONSTANT AND LOSS

1. Introduction. This chapter aims to survey briefly the methods of measuring dielectric constant and loss which are described more fully in various books on electrical measurements and in papers in the literature. To a considerable extent, it follows a fuller treatment given by the author elsewhere.[1,2]

The measurement of dielectric constant by the determination of the force between electric charges separated by a dielectric and the calculation of the dielectric constant from it by means of the inverse-square law is little used at the present time. It has been described in summary fashion elsewhere.[3] A method for conducting liquids employs[4] a metallic ellipsoid of revolution hung on a filament between two vertical plates. When a difference of potential is applied to the plates, the turning moment acting upon the ellipsoid depends upon the potential difference and upon the dielectric constant of the liquid in such a way that the latter can be calculated. This method will not be described here, since for most purposes it seems to be less satisfactory than the methods now available with modern equipment. It has, however, been employed by G. Jungner[5] in measurements on protein solutions with an accuracy of about 0.2 per cent and, in a further improved form giving an accuracy of about 0.1 per cent, by I. Jungner[6] and Allgén.[7]

The most generally used methods for measuring dielectric constant ϵ'

[1] C. P. Smyth, The Determination of Dipole Moments, in "Physical Methods of Organic Chemistry" (A. Weissberger editor), Interscience, New York, 2d ed., 1949, vol. I, pt. II, chap. XXIV.

[2] J. G. Powles and C. P. Smyth, Measurement of Dielectric Constant and Loss, in "Physical Methods of Organic Chemistry" (A. Weissberger editor), Interscience, New York, 2d ed., 1954, vol. I, part III, chap. XXXV.

[3] C. P. Smyth, "Dielectric Constant and Molecular Structure," Chemical Catalog, New York, 1931, chap. III.

[4] R. Fürth, Z. Physik, **22,** 98 (1924); Physik. Z., **25,** 676 (1924).

[5] G. Jungner, Acta Physiol. Scand., **10,** Suppl. 32 (1945).

[6] I. Jungner, Acta Physiol. Scand., **20,** Suppl. 69 (1950).

[7] L. Allgén, Acta Physiol. Scand., **22,** Suppl. 76 (1950).

and loss ϵ'' consist of the measurement of the capacitance C_0 of an empty condenser and the capacitance C and the resistance R of the condenser filled with the dielectric material in question.   The measurement commonly involves the determination of the impedance (voltage/current) of the circuit element formed by a cell containing the dielectric.   This impedance is

$$Z = \frac{1}{i\omega C + 1/R} = \frac{1}{i\omega C_0 \epsilon^*} \tag{1.1}$$

where

$$\epsilon^* = \epsilon' - i\epsilon'' \tag{1.2}$$

Substitution of (1.2) in (1.1) and solution of the real and the imaginary parts gives

$$\epsilon' = \frac{C}{C_0} \qquad \text{and} \qquad \epsilon'' = \frac{1}{\omega R C_0} \tag{1.3}$$

The two principal methods of measuring the capacitance of a condenser are the capacitance-bridge method and the method of adjusting the capacitance of a circuit until the alternating current flowing in the circuit has a certain characteristic or desired frequency.   The bridge method is capable of the accuracy required for any ordinary measurements on liquids or solids and has even been applied occasionally to gases.   The resonance methods are extensively used, and the heterodyne beat-frequency method gives great accuracy when the loss is negligibly small.

The development of microwaves has greatly increased the importance of the methods in which the length of an electromagnetic wave is measured in air and then in the dielectric material.   The change in wavelength depends mainly on the dielectric constant, while the loss is largely determined by the damping or attenuation of the wave in the dielectric.

2. Dielectric Cell or Sample Holder.   This section will not describe the cell or sample holder for very-short-wave measurements, since this is so integral a part of the entire apparatus that it can best be treated in Sec. 11.   The dielectric-constant measuring apparatus for lower frequencies is generally so constructed that one side of the condenser to be measured, the side most subject to variation in environment, can be grounded.   The condenser is sometimes constructed of parallel plates, adjacent plates being insulated from one another and alternate plates being connected in parallel.   Such sets of plates have been used for liquids and for gases.   The capacitance of each pair of neighboring plates is given by Eq. I(2.1) and the total capacitance of the condenser is the sum of the capacitances for each pair, N similar and equally spaced plates giving a capacitance $(N - 1)$ times that of a pair.

A condenser consisting of a pair of metal disks is suitable for measurements on solids which can be shaped into reproducible disks.   Such a condenser has been described by Yager and used to measure the dielectric constants and losses of plastics.[1,2] A uniform disk of solid dielectric, perhaps 5 cm. in diameter and 2 or 3 mm. in thickness, is stamped or cut out. Disks of tinfoil of the same diameter are stuck to the faces of the sample disk with a very thin film of pure vaseline,[3] and the sample is inserted between the electrodes of the condenser, which are then pressed firmly against the sample by springs. The separation of the plates d_s, which is indistinguishable from the thickness of the sample, is read with a micrometer built into the cell. The cell is attached to a bridge or other measuring apparatus, which is then balanced. The sample is removed from the measuring apparatus, which is then rebalanced by reducing the distance between the plates to d_0. The dielectric constant of the sample is $\epsilon = d_s/d_0$. In the measurements described the sample disk is of the same diameter as the condenser plates. Variations of the technique may be employed to reduce the effect of edge capacitance.[3] Temperatures other than room temperature can be maintained by circulating liquid through a coil of copper tubing surrounding the cell, the whole being enclosed in a Dewar tube.[2]

In condensers of this type, a source of error is the lack of uniformity of the electric field at the edges of the plates, because the lines of electric force curve out into the space outside that between the plates. The error due to this edge capacitance may be eliminated or reduced by the use of a guard ring, which lies in the plane of one of the two disk electrodes, separated from it by a narrow annular space and connected to the measuring apparatus in such a way that, when the latter is balanced, the ring is brought to the same potential as the electrode which it encloses.[4] It is evident that calibration of the cell with a liquid of known dielectric constant will reduce or eliminate the effect of edge capacitance.

A simple cell to construct consists of concentric metal cylinders insulated from one another. The detailed construction of a three-cylinder condenser and containing vessel has been described elsewhere.[5,6] The capacitance in micromicrofarads of a condenser consisting of two coaxial cylinders of length l is

$$C = \frac{0.2416l}{\log_{10}(r_1/r_2)} \tag{2.1}$$

where r_1 is the internal radius of the outer cylinder and r_2, the external radius of the inner cylinder. A separation of at least 0.5 mm. is desirable

[1] W. A. Yager, *Trans. Am. Electrochem. Soc.*, **74**, 117 (1938).

[2] W. C. Schneider, W. C. Carter, M. Magat, and C. P. Smyth, *J. Am. Chem. Soc.*, **67**, 959 (1945).

[3] L. Hartshorn, "Radiofrequency Measurements," Wiley, New York, 1941, p. 192.

[4] L. Hartshorn, *op. cit.*, pp. 104, 193, and 225.

[5] C. P. Smyth, "Dielectric Constant and Molecular Structure," Chemical Catalog, New York, 1931, chap. 3.

[6] C. P. Smyth and S. O. Morgan, *J. Am. Chem. Soc.*, **50**, 1547 (1928).

to facilitate the escape of possible gas bubbles from the space between the cylinders. A length of 5 to 8 cm. and a diameter of 1 to 2 cm. are convenient dimensions, while an air capacitance of 50 to 200 $\mu\mu f$ is suitable for most solution measurements. For small quantities of material, much smaller condensers may be constructed for use with precision measuring condensers. The use of a shorter middle cylinder largely eliminates stray capacities between it and objects outside the condenser. Brass, plated or unplated, gold, platinum, nickel, stainless steel, monel metal, silver, copper, etc., may be used in the tubes. Glass tubes with a film of platinum or silver on the inside of the outer tube and on the outside of the inner tube have been used. The metal tubes are held apart by forcing small strips of mica, glass, quartz, micalex, Teflon, etc., 5 to 6 mm. long and 2 to 3 mm. wide, between them at three points at the top and at the bottom. Mica cannot be used in very accurate measurements on liquids because of its tendency to absorb. The cylinders are enclosed in a glass tube, to which a smaller tube leads from above for the admission of liquid. Two platinum lead wires fused or soldered to the condenser cylinders are brought up through glass tubes sealed to either side of the top of the vessel and terminating in small cups filled with mercury, into which brass rods are dipped to connect the condenser to the measuring apparatus. The two leads should be as widely separated as possible to reduce the capacitance and inductance between them.

The concentric-cylinder type of cell may be used for solids which can be melted and allowed to freeze between the cylinders. A thermocouple or platinum resistance thermometer may be placed in the dielectric material while still liquid in the interior of the innermost cylinder, while the whole cell is immersed in a bath or surrounded by a block of metal for temperature control. This type of cell lends itself particularly well to measurement over a wide range of temperature. It has been used down[7] to −253°C. and on liquids up[8] to 200°. To prevent the formation of bubbles in the sample, the liquid should be boiled, usually under reduced pressure, before solidification. The liquid should be frozen slowly from the bottom up to prevent as far as possible the formation of gaps between it and the electrodes. Some error due to the presence of gaps is always possible. If the process of freezing, melting, and refreezing is repeated three or four times, dielectric-constant values reproducible to about 1 per cent are obtainable.

A concentric-cylinder type of cell with guarded electrode has been described by Cole and Gross[9] and used in connection with a bridge in the

---

[7] C. P. Smyth and S. A. McNeight, *J. Am. Chem. Soc.*, **58**, 1723 (1936).

[8] C. P. Smyth, R. W. Dornte, and E. B. Wilson, Jr., *J. Am. Chem. Soc.*, **53**, 4242 (1931).

[9] R. H. Cole and P. M. Gross, Jr., *Rev. Sci. Instr.*, **20**, 252 (1949).

frequency range from 50 cycles to 5 megacycles.   Cell capacitances vary-ing from 1 to 10 $\mu\mu$f or more are obtained by varying the size of a central rod which forms the innermost cylinder.

A liquid-jacketed cell of very low inductance for use at megacycle frequencies has been described by Conner, Clarke, and Smyth.[10]

A measuring cell has a certain fixed capacitance C_L through the insula-tion of the plates or cylinders from one another and between the leads. Its capacitance, when measured with air in it and neglecting the small deviation of the dielectric constant of air from 1, is therefore $C_0 + C_L$, and, when measured with a liquid of dielectric constant ϵ in it, is $\epsilon C_0 + C_L$. By using a pure liquid of known dielectric constant, such as benzene, C_0 and C_L may be determined and used for the measurement of the dielectric constant of an unknown material.   The dielectric constant of benzene at $t°C$. between 15 and 30°C. is given in a list of ten standard liquids[11] as

$$\epsilon = 2.274 - 0.0020(25 - t)$$

with a probable accuracy of 0.1 per cent.   An absolute measurement[12] by the resonance cell method of Wyman[13] has given 2.2747 $\pm$ 0.0003 for the dielectric constant of benzene at 25°.   Absolute measurements with microwaves of 1.277, 3.22, and 10.00 cm. wavelength have given[14]

$$\epsilon = 2.325 - 0.0020t$$

with a probable accuracy of about 0.1 per cent for benzene between 10 and 60°C.   The values of Brown, Levin, and Abrahamson and Heston and Smyth agree well with the value of Maryott and Smith based on a critical survey, but differ by more than the error attributed to it from the value 2.2821 $\pm$ 0.0011 of Treiber, Schurz, and Koren[15] at 20°, which gives 2.2722 at 25°.   The evidence would appear to favor the Bureau of Standards value.   Attention must be called to the importance of thor-ough drying of the benzene before use as a calibrating liquid.

Cells for the measurement of gases are similar in type to those used for liquids but are usually of higher capacitance, 200 to 500 $\mu\mu$f being suffi-cient.   Resistance of the metal to corrosion is even more important than in the case of cells for liquid measurements.   Detailed descriptions of gas cells may be found in the references given in Sec. 6.

[10] W. P. Conner, R. P. Clarke, and C. P. Smyth, *J. Am. Chem. Soc.*, **64**, 1379 (1942).

[11] A. A. Maryott and E. R. Smith, Table of Dielectric Constants of Pure Liquids, *Nat. Bur. Standards Circ.* 514, August 10, 1951.

[12] A. S. Brown, P. M. Levin, and E. W. Abrahamson, *J. Chem. Phys.*, **19**, 1226 (1951).

[13] J. Wyman, *Phys. Rev.*, **35**, 623 (1930).

[14] W. M. Heston, Jr., and C. P. Smyth, *J. Am. Chem. Soc.*, **72**, 99 (1950).

[15] E. Treiber, J. Schurz, and H. Koren, *Monatsh. Chem.*, **82**, 32 (1951).

3. Precision Condenser.   The dielectric cell to be measured is usually compared by a substitution method with the capacitance of a portion of a calibrated precision condenser.   Precision condensers have been constructed in which a plate of insulating material such as glass is moved forward or backward between the two parallel metal plates of the condenser, the capacitance of which is a linear or nearly linear function of the position of the plate of insulator as read on a scale.   In another type, the capacitance is varied by moving one cylinder into another concentric cylinder, both cylinders being shielded by a third which is large and usually grounded.   The use of a worm drive and vernier scale makes both these instruments capable of high precision.   The precision condenser commonly used, resembling the ordinary variable radio condenser, consists of two sets of interlocking plates; the two sets carefully insulated one from the other, the one fixed and the other movable, its position read on a scale giving the capacity.   Instruments (type 722 Precision Condenser, General Radio Company, Cambridge, Mass.) are obtainable in which the use of a worm drive makes possible a scale which can be set and read to one part in 25,000 of full scale.   Maximum capacitances of 110, 500, 1,000, and 1,100 $\mu\mu$f are available.   Although calibration curves may be supplied with the instruments, the investigator of dielectric constants and loss will probably find it more satisfactory to carry out his own calibration with the instrument in place in the apparatus to be used for the measurement.   Since the dielectric constant is obtained as the ratio between two capacitance readings, the unit in which the capacitance is expressed is immaterial.   A convenient method of calibration is to measure a small fixed capacitance, the exact value of which does not need to be known, step by step over the entire portion of the precision-condenser scale which is to be used in the dielectric-constant measurements.

4. Resonance Method for Dielectric Constant and Loss.   In the resonance method, a high-frequency alternating current is set up in a primary circuit which is loosely coupled to a secondary circuit containing capacitance and inductance.   The current flowing in this secondary circuit can be altered by change in the capacitance or the inductance of the circuit, a maximum value being reached when the frequency f equals $\frac{1}{2}\pi \sqrt{LC}$, a condition called resonance.   Resonance is obtained by adjusting the capacitance of a precision condenser in the secondary circuit until the current reaches a maximum, as shown by a detector circuit coupled to it. When this adjustment has been made, the cell to be measured is connected in parallel with the precision condenser, which is lowered until the detector again shows a maximum current.   The difference between the two condenser readings gives the capacitance of the cell.   The method has been used rather widely for the dielectric constants of liquids and is of such accuracy that it has been applied to measurements of gases.

Hartshorn and Ward[1] developed a resonance apparatus which has been used for the dielectric constants and losses of solids and liquids of rather low loss at frequencies up to 100 megacycles. The effect of inductance is reduced to a minimum by building the test condenser directly into the apparatus. A capacitance balance with the condenser filled and empty is used to obtain the dielectric constant, as in the case of the Yager cell described in Sec. 2. The dielectric loss is obtained from the widths of the resonance curves for the cell empty and filled and the known capacitance of the system. If there are no other losses,

$$Q = 2\pi f C R \qquad (4.1)$$

obtained for the test condenser gives the loss tangent, since

$$\tan \delta = \frac{\epsilon''}{\epsilon'} = \frac{1}{Q} \qquad (4.2)$$

A rather widely used instrument, the "Q meter," manufactured by the Boonton Radio Corporation, Boonton, N.J., consists of a radio-frequency oscillator, a measuring circuit formed by a coil and tuning condensers, a vacuum-tube voltmeter which reads the voltage across the tuning condenser, and a means of introducing a known amount of the oscillator voltage in series in the measuring circuit. The value of Q in Eq. (4.1), where C is the capacitance and R is the equivalent parallel resistance corresponding to the dissipation in the circuit, is measured by adjusting the oscillator to a predetermined frequency and tuning the measuring circuit to resonance, or, with a predetermined capacitance, adjusting the oscillator until resonance is attained. At resonance, the voltmeter gives directly the Q of the circuit. The measuring cell or test condenser is substituted for part of the capacitance of the precision tuning condenser, and the change in setting of the latter gives the capacitance of the cell. The percentage change in the Q of the circuit is used to compute the Q of the cell and hence the loss tangent of the dielectric material in it. Q meters may be employed over a frequency range from 1 kilocycle to about 200 megacycles. The accuracy of the direct-reading measurement of circuit Q is about 5 per cent and decreases with increasing frequency above 30 megacycles. The capacitance measurement by substitution is considerably more accurate than this. The instrument has general utility because of its wide frequency range, but is less accurate than most of those designed specifically for dielectric-constant or dielectric-constant and loss measurements.

A resonance method developed by Wyman,[2] particularly valuable for

[1] L. Hartshorn and W. H. Ward, *J. Inst. Elect. Engrs.* (*London*), **79**, 597 (1936); L. Hartshorn, "Radio-frequency Measurements," Wiley, New York, 1941, p. 196.

[2] J. Wyman, *Phys. Rev.*, **35**, 623 (1930).

liquids of appreciable conductivity, consists of the determination of the frequency ω_0 of a resonator surrounded by air and the frequency ω when immersed in the liquid, the dielectric constant of the liquid being $\epsilon = \omega_0^2/\omega^2$.   The resonators were spirals or concentric cylinders of metal connected by a short loop of metal rod.   To determine the frequency of the resonator, which was between 10 and 700 megacycles, an oscillator of variable frequency was adjusted to resonance with it, as indicated by the current in the plate circuit of the variable oscillator.   If the product of the natural period of the resonator and the conductivity of the liquid is not sufficiently small, the method cannot be used to determine the dielectric constant of the liquid.   With the smallest resonators used by Wyman, dielectric constants were measured for liquids having conductivities 100 times that of water.   Further descriptions of the use of the method are contained in subsequent papers.[3-5]   Although the special merit of the method would appear to be its applicability with accuracy to liquids of appreciable conductance, it has been applied with great precision to pure benzene.[5]

5. Heterodyne Beat Method for Dielectric Constant.[1]   This method depends upon the control of the frequency of a vacuum-tube oscillator by adjustment of the capacitance of its circuits, the resistance and inductance remaining constant.   Essentially, the apparatus consists of two separate oscillators, one of which is usually held at constant frequency by the vibration of a quartz crystal while the other is adjusted by varying its capacitance to give a frequency different by a constant amount from that of the fixed oscillator.   The frequencies of the oscillators are far above the audible range, but the difference between them is a frequency audible as a distinct musical note in a telephone connected to an amplifier to which the two oscillators are coupled.   The precision of the frequency balance can be increased by the addition to the apparatus of a 1,000-cycle tuning-fork oscillator against which the beat note is balanced.   This frequency setting is considerably better than 1 cycle per sec., which means, if the frequency of the variable oscillator is 10^6 cycles, an accuracy greater than 1 part in 10^6.   A cathode-ray oscilloscope instead of the telephone as an indicating device facilitates the balancing of the circuits.   Accounts of apparatus without any tuning fork have been given elsewhere.[2,3]   The fixed oscillator is occasionally replaced by a signal received from a radio broadcasting station.[2]   An

[3] G. S. Hooper and C. A. Kraus, *J. Am. Chem. Soc.*, **56**, 2265 (1934).
[4] J. A. Geddes and C. A. Kraus, *Trans. Faraday Soc.*, **32**, 585 (1936).
[5] A. S. Brown, P. M. Levin, and E. W. Abrahamson, *J. Chem. Phys.*, **19**, 1226 (1951).
[1] See footnote 1, Sec. 1.
[2] See footnote 3, Sec. 1.
[3] F. Daniels, J. H. Mathews, and J. W. Williams, "Experimental Physical Chemistry," 4th ed., McGraw-Hill, New York, 1949, chap. XIII.

apparatus with tuning fork originally described by Stranathan[4] has been used for many years in much the same form[5] in the writer's laboratory and has been described in detail elsewhere.[1]

An apparatus described by Jen-Yuan[6] and used with minor modifications in the writer's laboratory for measuring gases[7] has also been described in detail elsewhere.[1] Two other experimental set-ups, that of Coop and Sutton[8] and that of Hudson and Hobbs,[9] should be particularly mentioned.

6. Measurement of Dielectric Constant of Gases. Gas measurements are discussed at this point because the losses involved are negligible and the heterodyne beat method is the one most frequently employed. A precision must be obtained in gas measurements much greater than that in liquid measurements, since the capacitance of a condenser filled with air at atmospheric pressure is less than 0.06 per cent greater than that of the evacuated condenser. The error in the dielectric-constant value of the gas should not be more than 1 in the fifth place and should preferably be reduced to the sixth place. To obtain the necessary precision in the capacitance reading, the precision condenser used in measurements on liquids is placed in series with a small fixed condenser, or a condenser of large scale and capacitance of the order of 5 $\mu\mu$f is used. The necessary circuit stability and reproducibility is obtained with the heterodyne beat apparatus by enclosing it in an air bath maintained a few degrees above room temperature and constant to about 0.2°. A metal or metal-covered box used for electric shielding may serve simultaneously as the air bath. The cell to be measured should be immersed in an oil bath kept constant to about 0.02°, and the cell leads should be shielded from the bath liquid to prevent large errors caused by small changes in the dielectric constant or in the height of the oil in the bath, changes which naturally accompany change in temperature. The dielectric constant value ϵ at 760 mm. pressure is given by

$$\epsilon - 1 = \frac{760}{C_0} \frac{dC}{dp} \tag{6.1}$$

where C_0 is the vacuum capacitance of the measuring cell and dC/dp is the rate of change of the capacitance of the cell condenser with change of the pressure of the gas in it. If the readings of the balancing precision condenser expressed in the same units as C_0 are plotted against the gas

[4] J. Stranathan, *Rev. Sci. Instr.*, **5**, 334 (1934).

[5] G. L. Lewis and C. P. Smyth, *J. Chem. Phys.*, **7**, 1085 (1939).

[6] Jen-Yuan, *J. Chem. Educ.*, **24**, 494 (1947).

[7] J. H. Gibbs and C. P. Smyth, *J. Am. Chem. Soc.*, **73**, 5115 (1951).

[8] I. E. Coop and L. E. Sutton, *J. Chem. Soc.*, 1269 (1938).

[9] B. E. Hudson and M. E. Hobbs, *Rev. Sci. Instr.*, **13**, 140 (1942).

pressure in millimeters of mercury, the slope of the resulting curve gives the value dC/dp.

Further details and variations of technique may be found in the original papers.[1-11] For the measurement of gases by means of micro waves, see Sec. 11.

7. Bridge Method for Dielectric Constant and Loss.[1-6] This is the most generally useful method for the measurement of dielectric loss and of the dielectric constant of materials possessing appreciable loss. The balance of the bridge is obtained by reducing to zero the voltage between two opposite corners, a condition which occurs when the ratio of the impedances of two adjacent bridge arms is equal to the ratio of the impedances of the other pair of arms. The capacitance bridges commonly used for the measurement of dielectric constant and loss contain two resistance arms, the so-called ratio arms, and two capacitance arms. In such bridges inductance is kept to a minimum and, by symmetrical construction of the bridge parts, is made to cancel out. Since, however, the material to be measured has an effective conductance if it possesses any loss, and since small inequalities in resistance may occur elsewhere in the system, small, noninductively wound resistances are placed in series with the capacitances or large, noninductively wound resistances are placed in parallel with them. If R_1 is the resistance in parallel with the precision measuring condenser and the measuring cell of resistance R_m,

[1] J. Stranathan, *J. Chem. Phys.*, **6**, 395 (1938).

[2] See footnote 9, Sec. 5.

[3] C. T. Zahn, *Phys. Rev.*, **24**, 400 (1924); *Rev. Sci. Instr.*, **1**, 299 (1930).

[4] H. A. Stuart, *Z. Physik*, **47**, 457 (1928).

[5] K. B. McAlpine and C. P. Smyth, *J. Am. Chem. Soc.*, **55**, 453 (1933).

[6] R. H. Wiswall and C. P. Smyth, *J. Chem. Phys.*, **9**, 352 (1941).

[7] E. C. Hurdis and C. P. Smyth, *J. Am. Chem. Soc.*, **64**, 2829 (1942).

[8] See footnote 8, Sec. 5.

[9] H. E. Watson, *Proc. Roy. Soc. (London)*, **143A**, 558 (1934).

[10] H. E. Watson, G. G. Rao, and K. L. Ramaswamy, *Proc. Roy. Soc. (London)*, **132A**, 569 (1931).

[11] J. G. Jelatis, *MIT Lab. Insulation Research Tech. Rept.* 7 (1947).

Footnotes for Sec. 7.

[1] F. A. Laws, "Electrical Measurements," McGraw-Hill, New York, 1938, chap. VII.

[2] E. W. Golding, "Electrical Measurements and Measuring Instruments," Sir Isaac Pitman & Sons, London, 1940, chap. VI.

[3] L. Hartshorn, "Radio-frequency Measurements," Wiley, New York, 1941, chap. XI.

[4] B. Hague, "Alternating Current Bridge Methods," Sir Isaac Pitman & Sons, London, 1946.

[5] F. K. Harris, "Electrical Measurements," Wiley, New York, 1952, chap. 15.

[6] F. E. Terman and J. M. Pettit, "Electronic Measurements," McGraw-Hill, New York, 1952, chap. 3.

and R_2 is the resistance in parallel with the other capacitance arm of the bridge, then, at balance, $1/R_m = 1/R_2 - 1/R_1$. The specific conductance k of the dielectric under measurement in the cell is then

$$k = \frac{0.0885}{C_0 R_m} \qquad (7.1)$$

where C_0 is the geometrical capacitance (in $\mu\mu$f) of the empty cell. The loss factor of the material under measurement can be calculated as

$$\epsilon'' = \frac{1.8 \times 10^{12} k}{f} \qquad (7.2)$$

where f is the frequency.

Many commercial bridges are so designed that the capacitance to be measured forms an entire arm of the bridge. The absolute accuracy of such an instrument can often be greatly improved by substituting a precision measuring condenser in this arm of the bridge, balancing the bridge, attaching the cell to be measured in parallel with the precision condenser, and turning down the latter until the bridge is balanced again. The difference between the two condenser readings usually gives the unknown capacitance with an accuracy unobtainable with an instrument in another arm of the bridge.

A bridge designed[7] for use with a cell containing a guard ring achieves automatic adjustment of the potential of the guard electrode and thus shortens the balancing process when a guard ring is used.

In place of the conventional bridge, the "twin-T" instrument is particularly useful for measurements at frequencies from 0.5 to 40 megacycles on weakly conducting solutions with specific conductances below 10^{-4} mho cm.$^{-1}$, for which the heterodyne beat method and many bridges cannot be used. Because of the magnitude of the frequency in the upper range, inductive effects may cause very large errors unless proper precautions are observed, and a lower frequency is preferable in the absence of appreciable conductance. The use of the apparatus has been described in detail elsewhere.[8]

8. Measurements at Very Low Frequencies. For measurements on solids having long dielectric relaxation times, very low frequencies may be desirable. Bridges for measurement at 60 cycles are available commercially, and the bridge of Cole and Gross (Sec. 7), is usable in a frequency range down to 50 cycles. However, at low frequencies, the conventional bridge circuits described in Sec. 7 become increasingly difficult to operate because of the inconvenient size of the components and the duration of the induced transients, which may be effective for several

[7] R. H. Cole and P. M. Gross, Jr., *Rev. Sci. Instr.*, **20**, 252 (1949).

[8] W. P. Conner, R. P. Clarke, and C. P. Smyth, *J. Am. Chem. Soc.*, **64**, 1379 (1942). See also footnote 1, Sec. 1.

tens of cycles of the applied voltage. Low-frequency methods, in particular with a ballistic galvanometer,[1] have been described elsewhere.[1-5] If a voltage V_0 is applied suddenly to a perfect condenser, in which there is no dissipation of energy, the condenser will be charged instantaneously with a charge q as the result of an infinitely brief pulse of current. From the definition of dielectric constant in Sec. I.1, it is evident that

$$q = \epsilon C_0 V_0$$

The sudden application of V_0 to a condenser filled with a real dielectric results in a flow of current and a gradual, rather than an instantaneous, build-up of charge. The process can be followed with a ballistic galvanometer. Instead of the sudden application of voltage, a linearly rising potential may be applied.[6] The resulting current is amplified and its value recorded on an oscillograph in combination with a moving film camera. Alternatively, a saw-tooth voltage may be applied to the condenser. The apparatus described by Davidson, Auty, and Cole[6] has a lower frequency limit of about 1 cycle per sec., which could be considerably lowered by suitable modifications.

9. Effects of Conductance and Electrode Polarization. The combined effect of d.c. conductance and electrode polarization may cause considerable errors in the apparent values of dielectric constant and absorption conductance. Johnson and Cole* have been able to represent apparent dielectric-constant values e of liquid formic acid measured with the bridge of Cole and Gross (Sec. 7) by the equation

$$e = \epsilon + \frac{G^2}{\omega^2 C_0 C_{el}} \tag{9.1}$$

in which ϵ is the true dielectric constant, ω the angular frequency, C_0 the air capacitance of the cell, C_{el} a pure capacitance corresponding to an electrode impedance in series with the dielectric, and G a reduced conductance given by the expression for the specific conductance,

$$k \ (\mu\text{mho/cm.}) = \frac{0.0885G \ (\mu\text{mho})}{C_0 \ (\mu\mu\text{f})} \tag{9.2}$$

[1] F. A. Laws, "Electrical Measurements," McGraw-Hill, New York, 1938, chap. II.

[2] E. Giebe, "Handbuch der Physik" (H. Geiger and K. Scheel), Springer, Berlin, 1927, vol. XVI, pp. 508–511.

[3] A. W. Smith, "Electrical Measurements in Theory and Application," McGraw-Hill, New York, 1948, pp. 272–275.

[4] R. F. Field in "Digest of the Literature on Dielectrics," National Research Council, Washington, 1950, vol. XIV, p. 26.

[5] See, however, E. J. Murphy, *Trans. Am. Electrochem. Soc.*, **65**, 133 (1934).

[6] D. W. Davidson, R. P. Auty, and R. H. Cole, *Rev. Sci. Instr.*, **22**, 678 (1951).

* J. F. Johnson and R. H. Cole, *J. Am. Chem. Soc.*, **73**, 4536 (1951).

For a given cell and sample of liquid, Eq. (9.1) may be written

$$e = \epsilon + \frac{\text{constant}}{\omega^2} \tag{9.3}$$

The formic acid had a specific conductance 6×10^{-5} ohm^{-1} cm.$^{-1}$ at 25°. At frequencies above 10^4 cycles, the apparent dielectric constant did not differ from ϵ, but at 20 cycles it was approximately ten times as great. The magnitude of the electrode impedance C_{el} varied considerably with the sample and with the electrodes, which means that the constant in Eq. (9.3) would have to be determined empirically for each sample.

The dielectric loss is calculated as

$$\epsilon'' = \frac{G - G_0}{\omega C_0} \tag{9.4}$$

on the assumption that the limiting value of G/C_0 at low frequencies results from a d.c. conductance G_0/C_0 [cf. Eq. V(8.1)].

10. High-frequency (10^8 to 3×10^9 cycles) Methods. The resonance method developed by Wyman for liquids in a frequency range extending from 10^7 to 7×10^8 cycles has been described in Sec. 4. The frequency range of this section is treated separately because neither the lumped-circuit methods which have been described in the preceding sections nor the typical microwave techniques (Sec. 11) are applicable.[1] Some discussion of measurements in this frequency range has been given by Hartshorn.[1]

An apparatus for the measurement of dielectric constant by the determination of wavelength in air and in the liquid to be measured has been described in some detail.[2] The apparatus uses a "standpipe" oscillator with a frequency range of 3 to 7.5×10^8 cycles and a plunger mechanism for the determination of resonance lengths in concentric tubes. The dielectric constants of aqueous solutions with specific conductivities up to 10^{-3} ohm^{-1} cm.$^{-1}$ were measured with an apparent probable error less than 0.2 per cent, while, with a specific conductivity of 10^{-2}, the probable error increased to 0.5 per cent.

A resonant-cavity method for measurement of dielectric constant and loss in the frequency range 10^8 to 10^9 cycles has been described in detail.[3,4] The application of the susceptance-variation method to both fixed and variable-length re-entrant cavities yields a rapid measuring technique and simple expressions for calculating the values of the dielectric constant

[1] L. Hartshorn, "Radio-frequency Measurements," Wiley, New York, 1941, chap. XII.

[2] W. P. Conner and C. P. Smyth, *J. Am. Chem. Soc.*, **64**, 1870 (1942).

[3] C. N. Works, T. W. Dakin, and F. W. Boggs, *Trans. Am. Inst. Elec. Engrs.*, **63**, 1092 (1944); *Proc. Inst. Radio Engrs.*, **33**, 245 (1945).

[4] C. N. Works, *J. Appl. Phys.*, **18**, 605 (1947).

and loss tangent.   The empirically calibrated apparatus is so sensitive that very small disk-shaped samples of solid can be used.*

11. Measurements in the Microwave Region.[1-4] The microwave region is variously defined, but is approximately the frequency spectrum in which the free-space wavelength corresponding to the frequency of oscillation lies between 1 mm. and 30 cm.   The wavelengths are thus comparable in magnitude to the dimensions of laboratory apparatus. Microwave measurements may be made with cavities by determining the field distribution within the system rather than the voltage or current as in low-frequency measurements.   The two conducting leads used in low-frequency measurements are replaced even at moderately high frequencies by a coaxial line consisting of a central conductor enclosed in a hollow conducting tube.[5]   At very high frequencies, the central conductor is eliminated and only the hollow tube is left to form a "wave guide."   The wave guide, circular or rectangular in cross section, conveys electric energy so as to act as a transmission line.

The various modes of oscillation[5] in a cavity are described by reference to an axis and designated by integers.   If the axis of a short cylinder is taken as the reference axis and if the electric field is along this axis, the magnetic field is transverse to it and the mode is a transverse magnetic, or TM, mode.   If the electric field is along radial lines, the mode is called a transverse electric or TE mode.   Numbers pertaining to the solution of the field equations are added as subscripts.

In order that electric energy may be transmitted along a wave guide, the wavelength must be less than a certain critical value, the cutoff wavelength,[6] given for a rectangular guide[7] in terms of the guide cross-sectional dimensions a and b by

$$\lambda_c = \frac{2}{(m^2/a^2 + n^2/b^2)^{1/2}} \tag{11.1}$$

which holds for both TE and TM modes. m and n are integers designating the particular mode.   In a round guide,[8,9] the cutoff wavelength

* See footnote 4 on page 214.

[1] C. G. Montgomery, "Technique of Microwave Measurements," MIT Radiation Laboratory Series, McGraw-Hill, New York, 1947, vol. 11, particularly chap. 10 (R. M. Redheffer).

[2] L. G. H. Huxley, "Waveguides," Macmillan, New York, 1947.

[3] E. C. Pollard and J. M. Sturtevant, "Microwaves and Radar Electronics," Wiley, New York, 1948.

[4] A. Hund, "Short-wave Radiation Phenomena," McGraw-Hill, New York, 1952.

[5] S. Ramo and J. R. Whinnery, "Fields and Waves in Modern Radio," Wiley, New York, 2d ed., 1953, chap 8; also L. G. H. Huxley, *op. cit.*, chap. 2.

[6] E. C. Pollard and J. M. Sturtevant, *op. cit.*, chap. 2.

[7] W. Gordy, *Revs. Mod. Phys.*, **20**, 668 (1948).

[8] G. L. Southworth, *Bell System Tech. J.*, **15**, 284 (1936).

[9] W. L. Barrow, *Proc. I.R.E.*, **24**, 1298 (1936).

λ_c for the lowest-order waves is 1.71 times the diameter, and, in a coaxial line, $\lambda_c = \infty$.

Many methods for the measurement of dielectric constant or loss tangent in the microwave region have been tabulated by Redheffer,[1] and others are described in the literature. Typical or particularly useful methods will be summarized or referred to here.

Resonance Methods. Resonance methods are generally unsuitable for dielectric measurements on materials of high loss. In the resonance method of measurement at lower frequencies, the sample of dielectric is placed between the plates of a condenser. An analogous procedure is followed in the microwave region, the resonant cavity being wholly or partially filled with the material to be measured. An oscillator supplies energy to the resonant cavity via a coaxial line or wave guide and an attenuator, which reduces the reaction of the load on the oscillator. Coupling between the coaxial line and the cavity may be obtained by means of a loop or probe protruding into the cavity. A second loop or probe of similar design to the first and well removed from it has induced in it a current proportional to the field strength in the cavity. It is connected by a coaxial line to a crystal detector[10,11] connected to a galvanometer or to an amplifier and meter. The empty cavity may be brought to resonance by adjustment of the oscillator frequency, and the Q of the cavity is measured by frequency variation as at lower frequencies (Sec. 4). If the cavity is completely filled with a dielectric whose loss is not large, the resonance frequency is reduced by the factor $(\epsilon')^{-\frac{1}{2}}$ and the decrease in Q, caused by the dissipation of energy in the lossy dielectric, may be used to calculate tan δ. The resonance cavity is completely filled with the dielectric only for measurements on very-low-loss liquids or on gases. Excessive reduction in Q may be avoided by filling the cavity only partially. The sample of material may then take the form of a rod placed at the center and of the same height as the resonator.[12–14]

As it is often inconvenient or impossible to vary the frequency of a microwave oscillator over any considerable range, the cavity may be brought to resonance by varying its length by means of a moving piston.[13,15,16] For this purpose, a cavity 5 cm. in diameter is suitable at a 3-cm. wavelength,[13] while for measurement at 1.2 cm. wavelength a

---

[10] E. C. Pollard and J. M. Sturtevant, *op. cit.*, p. 86.

[11] H. C. Torrey and A. C. Whitmer, "Crystal Rectifiers," MIT Radiation Laboratory Series, McGraw-Hill, New York, 1948, vol. 15.

[12] W. Jackson, *Trans. Faraday Soc.*, **42A**, 91 (1946).

[13] F. Horner, T. A. Taylor, R. Dunsmuir, J. Lamb, and W. Jackson, *J. Inst. Elec. Engrs. (London)*, **93**, III, 53 (1946).

[14] J. G. Powles and R. Dunsmuir, *Phil. Mag.*, **37**, 747 (1946).

[15] R. P. Penrose, *Trans. Faraday Soc.*, **42A**, 108 (1946).

[16] M. Bruma, *Compt. rend.*, **232**, 42 and 219 (1951).

resonator of 1.9 cm. diameter has been used.[12]   The relations between the dielectric properties of the material and the movement of the piston or plunger may be somewhat complicated.   Detailed descriptions have been given of methods designed to keep resonators and specimens of convenient size at various wavelengths.[17–19]   Accurate measurements of vapor dielectric constant have been made with a resonance apparatus at 3 cm. wavelength,[20,21] by means of the relation

$$\frac{f_0}{f} = \epsilon^{\frac{1}{2}} \quad \text{or} \quad \frac{f_0 - f}{f} = \epsilon^{\frac{1}{2}} - 1 \tag{11.2}$$

in which f_0 is the resonance frequency when the resonance cavity is evacuated and f is the frequency when it is filled with the gas in question.

Transmission Methods.   Several important methods of measurement involve the determination of the transmission properties of a dielectric-filled wave guide or coaxial line.   The previously considered resonant cavity may be regarded as a length of wave guide short-circuited at both ends, but for the purpose of the present discussion the propagation of energy down an infinitely long, dielectric-filled wave guide will be considered.   The electric field at a given point in the wave guide varies sinusoidally with the angular frequency ω, so that it may be represented by the real part of $E_0 e^{i\omega t}$.   It may be shown that the field strength at a distance x down the guide is given by

$$E_x = E_0{}^{i\omega t} e^{-\gamma x} \tag{11.3}$$

where

$$\gamma = \alpha + i\beta \tag{11.4}$$

or

$$E_x = E_0 e^{i(\omega t - \beta x)} e^{-\alpha x} \tag{11.5}$$

Thus, the phase of the propagated wave changes by βx and its amplitude decreases by the factor $e^{-\alpha x}$ as it traverses a length x of the wave guide. Consequently, β is called the phase constant and α the attenuation constant.   These quantities are found in the well-known optical relations involving the index of refraction n and the absorption index κ,

$$\epsilon^* = (n^*)^2 = [n(1 - i\kappa)]^2 \tag{11.6}$$

$$\epsilon' = n^2(1 - \kappa^2) \tag{11.7}$$

$$\epsilon'' = n^2(2\kappa) \tag{11.8}$$

where $\kappa = \alpha/\beta$ and $n = \lambda_0/\lambda_d$, the ratio of the wavelength in free space to the wavelength in the dielectric.   Substitution for κ and n gives

[17] W. Jackson and J. G. Powles, *Trans. Faraday Soc.*, **42A**, 101 (1946).

[18] C. H. Collie, J. B. Hasted, and D. M. Ritson, *Proc. Phys. Soc. (London)*, **60**, 71 (1948).

[19] G. Birnbaum and J. Franeau, *J. Appl. Phys.*, **20**, 817 (1949).

[20] G. Birnbaum, S. J. Kryder, and H. Lyons, *J. Appl. Phys.*, **22**, 95 (1951).

[21] G. Birnbaum and S. K. Chatterjee, *J. Appl. Phys.*, **23**, 220 (1952).

$$\epsilon' = \frac{\lambda_0{}^2}{\lambda_d{}^2}\left(1 - \frac{\alpha^2}{\beta^2}\right) \tag{11.9}$$

$$\epsilon'' = \frac{\lambda_0{}^2}{\lambda_d{}^2}\frac{2\alpha}{\beta} \tag{11.10}$$

These equations apply not only to plane waves but also to the principal or TEM mode of propagation in a coaxial transmission line. However, for wave-guide propagation and for higher modes of propagation in a coaxial line, Eq. (11.9) must be modified as follows:

$$\epsilon' = \frac{\lambda_0{}^2}{\lambda_d{}^2}\left(1 - \frac{\alpha^2}{\beta^2}\right) + \frac{\lambda_0{}^2}{\lambda_c{}^2} \tag{11.11}$$

where λ_c is the cutoff wavelength. Since

$$\lambda_d = \frac{2\pi}{\beta} \tag{11.12}$$

Eqs. (11.11) and (11.10) may be written

$$\epsilon' = \lambda_0{}^2\left(\frac{\beta^2 - \alpha^2}{4\pi^2} + \frac{1}{\lambda_c{}^2}\right) \tag{11.13}$$

$$\epsilon'' = \lambda_0{}^2\frac{\alpha\beta}{2\pi^2} \tag{11.14}$$

The empty-guide wavelength λ_g, which is the wavelength in an air-filled wave guide, is given by

$$\frac{1}{\lambda_g{}^2} = \frac{1}{\lambda_0{}^2} - \frac{1}{\lambda_c{}^2} \tag{11.15}$$

In a wave guide whose dimensions are large compared with the free-space wavelength λ_0, $\lambda_c \to \infty$, and, as previously mentioned, in a coaxial line, $\lambda_c = \infty$. In these cases, the wave is evidently propagated just as in free space, or as in an infinite dielectric medium if the wave guide is filled with a dielectric.

Conner and Smyth[22] have described an apparatus for determining the dielectric constants and losses of liquids at 9.72 cm. wavelength by measuring the wavelength and attenuation of standing waves in a coaxial tube filled with the liquid under investigation. The apparatus gave ϵ' values accurate to about 1 per cent and ϵ'' values which appeared to be reproducible to about 2 per cent but were actually of a somewhat lower absolute accuracy. Improvements in available equipment and techniques have led to greater accuracy in subsequently described methods.

In a frequently used method described by Roberts and von Hippel,[23] a section of circular or rectangular wave guide is closed at one end by a metal plate, which gives a short circuit. The dielectric to be measured fills the wave guide in front of the short circuit for a distance d, and an

[22] W. P. Conner and C. P. Smyth, *J. Am. Chem. Soc.*, **65**, 382 (1943).
[23] S. Roberts and A. von Hippel, *J. Appl. Phys.*, **17**, 610 (1946).

oscillator feeds energy into the system through an attenuator. When a wave from the oscillator is propagated along the wave guide, it is partly reflected and partly transmitted on arrival at the interface. The transmitted part is propagated through the dielectric in a manner dependent upon γ until it reaches the short circuit, where it is totally reflected and propagated back until it reaches the interface. Again part is transmitted and part is reflected, and the process is continued until, after a certain build-up time, the flow of energy in the air-filled portion of the guide may be regarded as consisting of two resultant waves moving in opposite directions. A sliding probe connected to a suitable detector and inserted into the air-filled portion of the wave guide through a longitudinal slot measures a quantity which is dependent upon the resultant electric field E due to the two waves. The field at the probe depends on the relative magnitudes and phases of the incident and reflected waves, which annul each other at some points and reinforce each other at others, forming a standing wave. The standing wave is defined by the ratio of maximum to minimum values of $|E|^2$ and the distance x_0 of a given minimum from a fixed point in the guide, conveniently taken as the position of the air-dielectric interface. The minima occur at $x_0 + n\lambda_g/2$, where $n = 0, 1, 2, 3, \ldots$. For the experimental details and necessary equations, the reader is referred to the original paper of Roberts and von Hippel.[23] The method, more frequently employed for solids than for liquids, uses only a weak oscillator and a small amount of the material to be measured, but requires measurements upon samples of different thicknesses and somewhat tedious calculations. The calculations may be simplified by a modification[24] of the experimental method.

Solids and liquids have been measured over a 120° range of temperature by a method[25] in which the short-circuit termination is replaced by one which prevents reflection of energy. This apparatus is designed particularly for measurements on solid samples which can be melted but cannot be shaped into the sharply defined slabs used in the previously mentioned measurements. It is probably somewhat less accurate. Several other arrangements for the measurement of solids have been described in the literature involving various combinations of open- and short-circuit terminations and probe and sample positions.

A method[26-29] especially suited to liquids of high dielectric loss is based upon the variation in the reflection coefficient of a uniform layer of dielectric as the depth of the layer is varied by means of a moving plunger.

[24] W. H. Surber, Jr., and G. E. Crouch, Jr., *J. Appl. Phys.*, **19**, 1130 (1948).

[25] J. G. Powles, D. E. Williams, and C. P. Smyth, *J. Chem. Phys.*, **21**, 136 (1953).

[26] W. M. Heston, Jr., E. J. Hennelly, and C. P. Smyth, *J. Am. Chem. Soc.*, **70**, 4093 (1948).

[27] H. L. Laquer and C. P. Smyth, *J. Am. Chem. Soc.*, **70**, 4097 (1948).

[28] W. H. Surber, Jr., *J. Appl. Phys.*, **19**, 514 (1948).

[29] G. E. Crouch, Jr., *J. Chem. Phys.*, **16**, 364 (1948).

For low-loss liquids, the variation in magnitude of the reflection coefficient with sample length is too small for accurate measurement. The apparatus is therefore changed[30] so as to measure the voltage standing-wave ratio. The probable error in these measurements is about 0.5 per cent for the dielectric constant and 3 per cent for the loss. The self-consistency of the measurements is often better than this, while the absolute error in the loss may considerably exceed 3 per cent. However, careful measurements[31] upon liquids of very low loss have given absolute dielectric-constant values with a probable error of only ±0.1 per cent. The high-loss method has been used at 1.2 and 3.2 cm. wavelength, and the low-loss method at 1.2, 3.2, and 5.6 cm. The quantity of the sample required for measurement increases inconveniently with increasing wavelength.

Methods depending upon the transmission through a layer of dielectric have been used for liquids[18,32,33] and solids,[34] attenuation or phase change of the transmitted wave being measured. A traveling-wave and a standing-wave method have been devised[35,36] for measurement at 10 cm. wavelength with a traveling probe immersed in a liquid-filled slotted line. In the traveling-wave method, absolute measurements of both wavelength and absorption index can be made simultaneously and used to calculate ϵ' and ϵ''. In the standing-wave method, the absorption index is determined graphically from the power standing-wave ratio, while the wavelength is obtained by a modified null technique. The accuracy obtained with this apparatus appears to be slightly greater than that given by the method of Heston, Hennelly, and Smyth.[26,31]

Special arrangements have been used in special cases, as in the measurement of the dielectric properties of ferroelectric materials.[37] When the wave guide is filled with a gas instead of a liquid or solid the dielectric constant of the dielectric, of course, differs very little from unity, the attenuation coefficient is measured as a function of wavelength or gas pressure, and the microwave method becomes that of the spectroscopist.[7,38,39]

[30] W. M. Heston, Jr., A. D. Franklin, E. J. Hennelly, and C. P. Smyth, *J. Am. Chem. Soc.*, **72**, 3443 (1950).

[31] W. M. Heston, Jr., and C. P. Smyth, *J. Am. Chem. Soc.*, **72**, 99 (1950).

[32] D. H. Whiffen and H. W. Thompson, *Trans. Faraday Soc.*, **24A**, 114, 122 (1946).

[33] J. G. Powles, *Trans. Faraday Soc.*, **44**, 537 (1948).

[34] J. G. Powles, *Nature*, **162**, 614 (1948).

[35] F. H. Branin, Jr., and C. P. Smyth, *J. Chem. Phys.*, **20**, 1121 (1952).

[36] F. H. Branin, Jr., *J. Appl. Phys.*, **23**, 990 (1952).

[37] J. G. Powles and W. Jackson, *J. Inst. Elec. Engrs.* (*London*), **96**, III, 383 (1949).

[38] W. Gordy, W. V. Smith, R. F. Trambarulo, "Microwave Spectroscopy," Wiley, New York, 1953.

[39] B. P. Dailey, Radio-frequency Spectroscopy, in "Physical Methods of Organic Chemistry" (A. Weissberger, editor), Interscience, New York, 2d ed., 1954, vol. I, part III, chap. XXVI.

CHAPTER VII

CALCULATION OF DIPOLE MOMENT FROM EXPERIMENTAL DATA

A few approximate values of dipole moment have been obtained by measurements of electrostriction,[1] dipole rotation effect,[1] and deflection of a molecular beam in an inhomogeneous electric field.[2]   Moment values have been obtained for a number of molecules by microwave spectroscopic measurements,[3] a method of great importance when applicable, since it may permit the determination of the moment of the molecule in a particular vibrational state. Although dipole moments have been obtained by other methods, the normal method of obtaining them is by means of the dielectric constant.   Although gaseous dielectric-constant measurements are most suitable for the determination of dipole moment, the less-exacting measurements on solutions are usually employed because of the high precision required to obtain significant dielectric-constant values for gases.

1. Determination in the Vapor. It has been shown in Chap. I that the Debye equation I(6.13) for the dielectric constant applies accurately to gases.   The best method of determining a dipole moment which is independent of temperature over the range of measurement is, accordingly, to measure the dielectric constant in the vapor state over the widest possible range of temperature and over a range of pressure extending to low enough values to permit elimination of errors due to deviations from the gas laws.   Plotting the polarization P against $1/T$ give a straight line, the slope of which is b [Eq. I(9.3)] and the intercept of which on the polarization axis is a [Eq. I(9.2)].   Insertion of the numerical values of the constants in Eqs. I(9.1) to (9.3) and rearrangement gives for the dipole moment

$$\mu = 0.01281 \times 10^{-18}\{[P - (P_E + P_A)]T\}^{\frac{1}{2}} = 0.01281b^{\frac{1}{2}} \times 10^{-18} \quad (1.1)$$

[1] C. P. Smyth, "Dielectric Constant and Molecular Structure," Chemical Catalog, New York, 1931, pp. 41–44.

[2] R. G. J. Fraser, "Molecular Rays," Macmillan, New York, 1931.

[3] W. Gordy, *Revs. Mod. Phys.*, **20**, 668 (1948); W. Gordy, W. V. Smith, and R. F. Trambarulo, "Microwave Spectroscopy," Wiley, New York, 1953.

As indicated in Chap. VI, the measurement of the capacitance C of the gas cell as a function of pressure p in millimeters at a given temperature may be used to obtain the dielectric constant or polarization from which the moment is calculated, the following equation being used:

$$\epsilon_{760} - 1 = \frac{760}{C_0} \frac{\Delta C}{\Delta p} \tag{1.2}$$

where ϵ_{760} is the dielectric constant of the gas at 760 mm. pressure, C_0 is the geometrical capacitance of the evacuated condenser, and $\Delta C/\Delta p$ is the slope at low pressure of the curve for C as a function of p, ΔC and C_0 being expressed in the same units. The total polarization may then be calculated with sufficient accuracy by means of the equation

$$P = \frac{22414}{273} T \frac{\epsilon_{760} - 1}{\epsilon_{760} + 2} \tag{1.3}$$

The two equations may be combined to give

$$P = KT \frac{\Delta C}{\Delta p} \tag{1.4}$$

where $\epsilon_{760} + 2$ has been set equal to 3, and the constant $K = \dfrac{22414}{273} \dfrac{760}{3C_0}$.

Unless the dielectric-constant measurement is very precise, a temperature range of at least 100° is necessary for the moderately accurate determination of b. If such a range is prevented by low vapor pressure of the substance or if thermal decomposition occurs to an appreciable extent or if the dipole moment of the molecule changes with temperature, it is necessary to calculate the moment at each temperature of measurement by using the best value obtainable for the induced polarization $P_E + P_A$, which is discussed in detail in Chap. XIV. It is evident from Eq. I(8.1) that the molar refraction measured with visible light is larger than the electronic polarization P_E at the frequency of the dielectric-constant measurement. The use (Sec. XIV.1) of two values of the refractive index n or of the molar refraction $(n^2 - 1)M/(n^2 + 2)d$ determined for two different wavelengths as given in refraction tables, such as those in Landolt-Börnstein, makes possible the calculation of an accurate value of P_E, which usually is about 3 or 4 per cent lower than the molar refraction R_D for the yellow D sodium line. As the atomic polarization P_A, which is dependent upon characteristic vibrations in the infrared region, cannot be determined directly for practical purposes, a value equal to 10 or 15 per cent of P_E[4,5] or, more recently, 5 per cent of R_D[6] is sometimes

[4] K. L. Wolf, Z. physik. Chem., 2B, 39 (1928).

[5] O. Fuchs and K. L. Wolf, Dielektrische Polarisation, "Hand- und Jahrbuch der chemischen Physik," A. Eucken and K. L. Wolf, Akademische Verlagsgesellschaft m.b.H., Leipzig, 1935, vol. 6, p. 300.

[6] R. J. W. LeFèvre, "Dipole Moments," Methuen & Co., London, 1948, p. 17.

assigned to it.   However, in cases where a can be reliably determined directly, the difference $a - P_E = P_A$ is usually much less than 15 per cent of P_E (see Sec. XIV.4) and sometimes no more than 3 per cent.   It seems as well, therefore, to avoid this arbitrary assignment of an often too large value to P_A and use the value of R_D, the molar refraction for the D sodium line, for a.   This procedure may lead to appreciable error in the value calculated for the moment only when the latter is below 1.0×10^{-18}, or, occasionally, when the molecule contains several large dipoles partially opposed to one another. a can be measured directly by determining the dielectric constant and density of the substance in the solid state at a temperature so low that no molecular orientation can occur, but this is a very uncertain procedure as evidenced by the considerations in Chap. V. It is sometimes possible to measure P for a nonpolar molecule or P_A for a polar molecule so similar to the molecule under consideration that its value may be used to estimate an approximate value of P_A for the substance in question (Sec. XIV.4).   It is fortunate that only in the cases of molecules with very small moments or very large P_A values do large errors in P_A materially affect the accuracy of the moment values.

2. Determination in Solution.   As shown in Chap. I, the separation of the polar molecules from one another by intervening nonpolar molecules, such as those of heptane or benzene, enables the polar molecules to conform approximately to Debye behavior.   From Eqs. I(10.6) and (10.7), for the polarization P_{12} of a binary mixture, the polarization P_2 of component 2 is obtained as

$$P_2 = \frac{P_{12} - P_1}{c_2} + P_1 \tag{2.1}$$

If P_1 is taken as the polarization of the solvent and assumed to be identical in value with that of the pure solvent and unaffected by the solute, which is only an approximation, the polarization P_2 of the solute may be calculated from the dielectric constant and density found for the solution. In a large majority of cases, the values of P_2 increase with decreasing concentration, the rate of increase tending to be greater the lower the concentration (see Sec. III.2).   The measurements are made upon four or five solutions covering concentration ranges such as $c_2 = 0.001$ to 0.01 or $c_2 = 0.02$ to 0.10, which are selected according to the accuracy of the apparatus, the size and variability of P_2, and possibly the solubility of the solute.   The resulting values of P_2 are plotted as ordinates against those of c_2 as abscissas, and the curve is extrapolated to $c_2 = 0$ to obtain a polarization value P_∞ for the solute at infinite dilution, where the solute molecules should be oriented at random in the absence of an externally applied field.   This value of P_∞ is then used as P in Eq. (1.1), and the best approximation to $P_E + P_A$ is used, as described for the gas, to calculate the dipole moment. For very dilute solutions, where the values of P_2 should be most significant, the difference $P_{12} - P_1$ is so small that the effect of any error in P_{12} is blown up tremendously by the division by the very small quantity c_2. If the P_2-c_2 curve departs much from linearity, as it commonly does, a large error may result in the extrapolation to $c_2 = 0$ to obtain P_∞. In careful work, the resultant error in moment is usually much less than the difference between the apparent value in solution and the gas value, the so-called solvent effect, which has been discussed fully in Sec. I.18. The method of calculation has been illustrated elsewhere.[1]

An alternative method of handling the solution data is the direct extrapolation[2,3] of the dielectric constant and density, rather than the polarization, as previously mentioned. Onsager's equation I(14.30) for dilute solutions shows that the dielectric constant should be a linear function of the number of polar molecules per cc., which is proportional to the weight fraction of the solute in the dilute solution. In the majority of cases the dielectric constants ϵ and the specific volumes $v = 1/d$ of the dilute solutions are found to be linear functions of the mole fractions[2-4] or weight fractions[3] w_2 of the solute, that is:

$$\epsilon = \epsilon_1 + \alpha w_2 \quad \text{and} \quad v = v_1 + \beta w_2 \tag{2.2}$$

where ϵ_1 and v_1 are the dielectric constant and the specific volume of the solvent, respectively, and α and β are the slopes of the straight lines obtained by plotting ϵ and v against w_2. Halverstadt and Kumler[3] have derived from these relations an equation for the solute polarization at infinite dilution which may be written

$$P_\infty = \frac{3\alpha v_1 M_2}{(\epsilon_1 + 2)^2} + M_2(v_1 + \beta) \frac{\epsilon_1 - 1}{\epsilon_1 + 2} \tag{2.3}$$

When ϵ is plotted against w_2, the value of ϵ_1 is given by the intercept at $w_2 = 0$, and the value of α by the slope of the line. The values of v_1 and β are obtained in similar manner. The values of these constants may also be obtained from the experimental data by the method of least squares. If, as occasionally may happen, the curves for ϵ and v are not linear, their equations become quadratic and cumbersome to handle. As compared to the previously described method of plotting P_2 against c_2 and extrapolating to $c_2 = 0$ to obtain P_∞, this method has the advantage that the

---

[1] C. P. Smyth, The Determination of Dipole Moment, in "Physical Methods of Organic Chemistry" (A. Weissberger editor), Interscience, New York, 2d ed., 1949, vol. I, pt. II, chap. XXIV.

[2] G. Hedestrand, Z. physik. Chem., 2B, 428 (1929).

[3] I. F. Halverstadt and W. D. Kumler, J. Am. Chem. Soc., 64, 2988 (1942).

[4] W. M. Heston, Jr., A. D. Franklin, E. J. Hennelly, and C. P. Smyth, J. Am. Chem. Soc., 72, 3443 (1950).

necessary extrapolations are linear.   It has an advantage also in that it reduces the error occasionally caused by contamination of the solutions, as, for example, by absorption of water vapor, with consequent change in the dielectric constant of the solvent.   Any considerable difference between the ϵ_1 obtained by the linear extrapolation and that obtained by direct measurement on the pure solvent may be taken as an indication of contamination of the solutions, the damaging effect of which is minimized by use of the extrapolated value for ϵ_1.   This method and the polarization extrapolation method lead to similar results, and both may be employed with profit, particularly when the experimental errors are large or the solutions very dilute.

Guggenheim[5] has based on the Debye equation a method of calculating the moment by plotting against the concentration C in moles of polar solute per cc. of solution a quantity

$$\Delta = (\epsilon - n^2) - (\epsilon_1 - n_1{}^2) \tag{2.4}$$

where ϵ = dielectric constant of solution
n = refractive index of solution
ϵ_1 = dielectric constant of pure solvent
n_1 = refractive index of pure solvent
The slope $(\Delta/C)_0$ of the curve at $C = 0$ is then used to calculate the moment by means of the equation

$$\mu^2 = \frac{9kT}{4\pi N} \frac{3}{(\epsilon_1 + 2)(n_1{}^2 + 2)} \left(\frac{\Delta}{C}\right)_0 \tag{2.5}$$

Since only the difference $\epsilon - n^2$ need actually be plotted, the calculation is simple.   In addition to the simplicity of calculating $\epsilon - n^2$, this method has the advantage over the polarization extrapolation method that C need normally be accurate only to 0.1 per cent and that the density necessary to calculate C need be no more accurate.   It has the disadvantage that the refractive index of each solution has to be accurately measured.   An accurate measurement of refractive index is, however, less time-consuming than one of density.   Guggenheim has recalculated the data on a few dichloronaphthalenes in benzene solution, finding that his method gives good agreement with the polarization extrapolation method of calculating.   At the time of writing this, there has not yet been time for extensive use of Guggenheim's method.

Although it is evident (Sec. I.18) that the absolute value of a dipole moment obtained from measurements in solution may, however precise the measurements, be in error by as much as 10 per cent, the errors are usually smaller and are similar for similar substances in the same or in similar solvents.   Differences as small as 2 per cent between values for

[5] E. A. Guggenheim, *Trans. Faraday Soc.*, **45**, 714 (1949).

different molecules obtained under similar conditions may have some significance, although they should be treated with discretion. Various simple formulas, empirical and otherwise, have been used to calculate the solvent effect with some success (Sec. I.18). As Eq. I(18.55) can be written in the form

$$\mu_s = \mu_0 + C\mu_0(\epsilon - 1) \qquad (2.6)$$

it is evident that a value can be obtained for the moment in the gaseous state by extrapolating to $\epsilon = 1$ the straight line obtained by plotting as ordinates the values of the moments obtained in two or more different solvents against the values of ϵ for the solvents as abscissas. The value thus obtained, although considerably less accurate than a good direct determination in the gaseous state, has greater absolute accuracy than a value determined in a single solvent. For use in rough structural considerations or more careful comparison of closely related molecules, an adequate moment value can accordingly be obtained from the dielectric constants and densities of four or five different solutions in one solvent and the molar refraction. As indicated above, better values are obtainable by the use of several solvents, but are rarely worth the effort. For the quantitative consideration of small differences in moment, measurements in the gaseous state are desirable.

3. Determination in the Pure Polar Liquid. The moderate success of the Onsager and Kirkwood equations in calculating the dipole moment from the dielectric constant, refractive index, and density of the pure polar liquid has been shown in Tables 16.1 and 16.2, Chap. I. Substituting numerical values for the universal constants in Eqs. I(16.2) and (16.3), setting $g = 1$ in the Kirkwood equation (since it is normally unknown and not far from 1), setting the optical dielectric constant $\epsilon_\infty = n_D{}^2$, where n_D is the refractive index for the D sodium line, and taking square roots, we obtain

$$\mu = 0.01281 \times 10^{-18} \left[\frac{TM}{d} \frac{(2\epsilon + n_D{}^2)(\epsilon + 2)}{3\epsilon(n_D{}^2 + 2)} \left(\frac{\epsilon - 1}{\epsilon + 2} - \frac{n_D{}^2 - 1}{n_D{}^2 + 2} \right) \right]^{1/2}$$

$$(3.1)$$

$$\mu = 0.01281 \times 10^{-18} \left[\frac{TM}{d} \left(\frac{(\epsilon - 1)(2\epsilon + 1)}{9\epsilon} - \frac{n_D{}^2 - 1}{n_D{}^2 + 2} \right) \right]^{1/2} \qquad (3.2)$$

Table 16.2, Chap. I, shows that the application of both these equations to pure polar liquids gives a fair approximation to the moment value in the vapor state, the discrepancy commonly being no greater than that between the solution moment value and the gas. The difference between the two equations is not great, but Eq. (3.1), the rearranged Onsager equation, is the only one to have been used extensively at the present time.

4. Comparison of Methods of Calculation.   A careful measurement of the dipole moment of the isolated molecule in the gaseous state should give, under normally favorable conditions, a value correct to within 0.5 to 1.0 per cent.   A similar precision is attainable in the solution measurements, where, however, solvent effect may introduce an absolute error up to 10 per cent or more.   The results obtained by the liquid methods may be illustrated by the values for the often-measured substance nitrobenzene, seemingly undependable values being omitted.   Three different sets of measurements for the moment of the molecule in the vapor state give 4.19, 4.23, and 4.24.   A large number of measurements in various solvents give values from 3.84 to 4.10 calculated by extrapolation of the polarization.   Four sets of measurements in benzene give, by polarization extrapolation, 3.97, 4.08, 3.93, and 3.94, and, by dielectric-constant and density extrapolation, 3.98, 3.98, 4.00, and 4.01, respectively.[1] Calculation by means of Eq. (3.1) from the dielectric constants and the densities of the pure liquid at temperatures ranging from the freezing point almost to the boiling point gives values varying from 4.09 to 4.26 with a mean of 4.2, in close agreement with the gas value.   The dielectric-constant and density extrapolation method reduces considerably the discrepancies among the four values calculated by the polarization extrapolation method and gives a mean value 3.99, in close agreement with the solution value 3.98, which was obtained as an average of the best values given by the polarization extrapolation method.   The polarization extrapolation method is the standard method which has been most generally used for calculating dipole moments from measurements on solutions, but the dielectric-constant and density extrapolation method provides a useful and often preferable alternative, the results of which may profitably be checked against those of the other method.   The calculation from the dielectric constant of the pure polar liquid often gives a value differing less from the gas value than do the solution values, but the difference is occasionally unexpectedly large.

[1] I. F. Halverstadt and W. D. Kumler, *J. Am. Chem. Soc.*, **64**, 2988 (1942).

CHAPTER VIII

THE RELATION OF DIPOLE MOMENT
TO MOLECULAR STRUCTURE

1. The Molecule as an Electric Dipole. The relation of the dipole moment of a molecule to the arrangement of its positive and negative charges was first considered in the era of the Lewis-Langmuir theory of atomic structure. With the electrons supposed to be located approximately at the corners of cubes or tetrahedrons, it was a relatively simple matter to estimate the locations of the centers of gravity of the positive and of the negative charges in the molecules and obtain some idea of the magnitude of the dipole moment as the product of the total positive or negative charge at either center of gravity times the distance between the two centers of gravity.[1] A simplified version of this approach gave a particularly good picture of the molecule as a dipole. The chloride ion was described as a cube with the atomic nucleus at its center and the eight electrons of the outermost shell at the corners of the cube. The center of gravity of the eighteen electrons in the ion coincided with the positive nucleus, and the ion therefore had no dipole moment, but had, effectively, a single negative charge at the center of the cube. The hydrogen chloride molecule was pictured as a similar structure with a proton opposite one edge of the ionic cube. The system of charges of the hydrogen chloride molecule was thus resolved into a negative electronic charge at the center of the chloride cube and an equal positive charge on the proton. The molecule thus formed a dipole with a moment equal to the product of the electronic charge by the distance between the hydrogen and chlorine nuclei, which latter quantity was given by infrared spectra[2] as 1.27×10^{-8} cm. The moment thus calculated for the molecule, 6.04×10^{-18}, was far larger than the experimentally determined value[3,4] 1.08×10^{-18}, because no account was taken of the displacement of the electrons by the attraction of the proton. The force necessary to produce

[1] C. P. Smyth, *Phil. Mag.*, **47**, 530 (1924).
[2] H. M. Randall, *J. Opt. Soc. Amer.*, **7**, 45 (1923).
[3] C. T. Zahn, *Phys. Rev.*, **23**, 781 (1924).
[4] R. P. Bell and I. E. Coop, *Trans. Faraday Soc.*, **34**, 1209 (1938).

unit displacement of an electron in the outer layer of the molecule was calculated from the refractive index and used to calculate the displacement of the electrons from their previously assumed locations at the corners of the cube.   The calculation of the electronic displacements was necessarily extremely approximate, but was found to be sufficient to account for the large discrepancy between the observed and calculated moment values for the hydrogen chloride molecule and for still larger discrepancies in the cases of hydrogen bromide and hydrogen iodide. These and similar considerations[1,5] applied to other molecules showed clearly that the molecular dipole moment values obtained from dielectric-constant measurements were at least fairly close to those to be expected from molecular dimensions.   A less-approximate calculation[6] of the charge distribution led to the following values: 1.15×10^{-18} for the hydrogen chloride moment as compared to 1.03×10^{-18} previously observed[3] and subsequently revised[4] to 1.08; 0.88 calculated for hydrogen bromide as compared to 0.78 observed;[3] and 0.31 calculated for hydrogen iodide as compared to 0.38 observed,[3] but the calculation was rather far off for hydrogen fluoride.

If the hydrogen chloride molecule is described merely as consisting of a symmetrical chloride ion with a proton at the distance 1.28×10^{-8} cm. now given by spectroscopic data,[7] the moment calculated for the structure is $\mu = 4.80 \times 10^{-10} \times 1.28 \times 10^{-8} = 6.14 \times 10^{-18}$, a value differing from that calculated for the Lewis-Langmuir structure only because of slight differences in the values used for the electronic charge and the internuclear distance.   The large discrepancy between this value calculated for a hypothetical undistorted distribution of negative and positive charges may then be attributed to the existence of the molecule as a structure considerably distorted by the induced shift of electronic charge toward the proton with consequent shortening of the resultant molecular dipole as previously calculated.

A different description of the structure of the molecule may be given in terms of resonance.[8]   In these terms, the wave function of the hydrogen chloride molecule is written as

$$\Psi = a\Psi_{\text{H—Cl}} + b\Psi_{\text{H}^+\text{Cl}^-} \qquad (1.1)$$

In other words, the molecule is described as a linear combination of a purely covalent structure, H—Cl, to which a zero moment is arbitrarily assigned, and the undistorted ionic structure H^+Cl^-, for which the

[5] C. P. Smyth, "Dielectric Constant and Molecular Structure," Chemical Catalog, New York, 1931, chap. IV.

[6] J. G. Kirkwood, *Physik. Z.*, **33**, 259 (1932).

[7] L. Pauling, "The Nature of the Chemical Bond," Cornell University Press, Ithaca, N.Y., 1940, p. 168.

[8] *Ibid.*, Sec. II, 9.

moment value 6.14×10^{-18} has just been calculated. In these terms, the structure of the hydrogen chloride molecule is neither H—Cl nor H^+Cl^-, but rather a combination of the two. The hydrogen-chloride bond then possesses a fractional amount of ionic character, X, given by the ratio of the observed moment to the moment calculated for the undistorted ionic structure H^+Cl^-, that is,

$$X = \frac{1.08 \times 10^{-18}}{6.14 \times 10^{-18}} = 0.176.$$

The bond is then described as 18 per cent ionic and 82 per cent covalent in character. However, it has been calculated[9] that the dipole moment of the covalent bond is of the order of -1, the hydrogen being negative, if the bond is a pure p bond, but may be increased to as much as $+2$ by s-p hybridization. On this basis, the covalent structure could have almost any reasonable dipole moment, and a calculation of amount of ionic character based upon the assumption of zero moment for the covalent structure would seem to be meaningless. There is, nevertheless, sufficient parallelism between many bond moment values and the electronegativity differences (Sec. 4) between the bonded atoms to have some qualitative, if not quantitative, significance.

For a diatomic molecule AB, Coulson[10] writes the molecular orbital

$$\Psi = N(\Psi_A + \lambda\Psi_B) \tag{1.2}$$

where N is a normalizing factor given by

$$N^{-2} = 1 + \lambda^2 + 2\lambda S \tag{1.3}$$

The constant λ, which measures the polarity of the orbital, may have any value from $+\infty$ to $-\infty$, according to the nature of atoms A and B. S is the overlap integral of the orbitals Ψ_A and Ψ_B. If the two electrons in the overlapping pair of orbitals are the only bonding electrons and if the polarization of any nonbonding electrons may be neglected, the dipole moment of the molecule is given by

$$\mu = \frac{eR(\lambda^2 - 1)}{1 + \lambda^2 + 2\lambda S} \tag{1.4}$$

where e is the electronic charge and R is the internuclear distance. Since complete a priori calculations of λ are impracticable, Coulson has assumed $S = \frac{1}{3}$ and calculated λ for the hydrogen halide and potassium chloride molecules from their observed moments, obtaining values between 1.06 for hydrogen iodide and 2.0 for potassium chloride. Hybridization of

[9] D. Z. Robinson, *J. Chem. Phys.*, **17**, 1022 (1949); see also C. A. Coulson, "Valence," Oxford, London, 1952, p. 208.

[10] C. A. Coulson, "Valence," Oxford, London, 1952, p. 103.

orbitals, which almost always occurs, and polarization of nonbonding electrons would cause error in the use of the calculation.

2. Dipole Moment as a Vector Quantity. As previously mentioned in the case of the hydrogen chloride molecule, the locations of the centers of gravity of the positive and negative charges in the molecule were calculated in order to obtain a moment value for comparison with that obtained from dielectric-constant measurements. Such considerations showed[1] the impossibility of the symmetrical linear structure H—O—H indicated for the water molecule by the Langmuir theory, and that, as between a tetrahedral and a cubical arrangement of electrons in water, hydrogen sulfide, ammonia, and the closely related molecules, the tetrahedral arrangement was the more probable.[2] From similar considerations, the ring structure proposed for sulfur dioxide was shown[1] to be much less probable than the angular structure now regarded as approximately correct, and the roughly determined[3] moment values of hydrocarbons, alcohols, ethers, sulfides, aldehydes, ketones, amines, and halogenated hydrocarbons were found[2] to be consistent with the currently accepted views of their structures.

The treatment of a molecule as containing two dipoles whose resultant moment was that of the whole molecule was proposed by J. J. Thomson[4] and applied by others to the cis and trans dihalogenated ethylenes[5] and to the problem of the structure of benzene[2,6,7] at a time when the benzene ring was regarded by many as a puckered, rather than a plane, hexagon. It had been found[2] that the replacement of the hydrogen in the hydrogen chloride molecule by an alkyl group increased the molecular moment, but that further replacement of hydrogens in the group did not as a rule greatly alter the moment, an observation consistent with the arrangement of charges indicated by the probable structures of the molecules. Since the dipole was mainly associated with the chlorine and the carbon to which it was attached, it was reasonable to treat the dipole moment as acting in the direction of the C—Cl bond.

The attachment of two dipoles to various points of the benzene ring and the determination of their resultant moments made possible the determination of the directions of the bonds of the ring. The values observed[8] for the dichlorobenzenes (Table 2.1) were compared[7] with the results to be expected on the basis of the different structures which had

[1] C. P. Smyth, *Phil. Mag.*, **47**, 530 (1924).

[2] C. P. Smyth, *J. Am. Chem. Soc.*, **46**, 2151 (1924).

[3] C. P. Smyth, *Phil. Mag.*, **45**, 849 (1923).

[4] J. J. Thomson, *Phil. Mag.*, **46**, 513 (1923).

[5] J. Errera, *J. phys. radium*, [6]**6**, 390 (1925).

[6] J. Errera, *Physik. Z.*, **27**, 764 (1926).

[7] C. P. Smyth and S. O. Morgan, *J. Am. Chem. Soc.*, **49**, 1030 (1927).

[8] C. P. Smyth, S. O. Morgan, and J. C. Boyce, *J. Am. Chem. Soc.*, **50**, 1536 (1928).

been proposed from time to time.   In the structure according to Baeyer's formula[9] (Fig. 2.1a), the dipole axes would point upward,[7] making only such angles with one another as would be caused by mutual repulsion of the chlorine atoms.   As the dipoles would thus be approximately parallel, the moments of the dichloro compounds would all be greater than

a. Baeyer's model

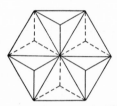

b. Körner's model

FIG. 2.1. Old models of the benzene molecule.   [C. P. Smyth and S. O. Morgan, J. Am. Chem. Soc., **49**, 1030 (1927).]

that of monochlorobenzene instead of showing the variation observed. In the formula of Koerner[10-12] (Fig. 2.1b), two dipoles in the ortho position would point in opposite directions, thus opposing and practically canceling each other, while in the meta position they would point in the

TABLE 2.1. MOMENTS OF CHLOROBENZENES MEASURED IN BENZENE SOLUTION AND CALCULATED FOR PLANE HEXAGONAL MODEL

Compound	Measured	Calculated
C_6H_5Cl	1.56	....
$o\text{-}C_6H_4Cl_2$	2.25	2.70
$m\text{-}C_6H_4Cl_2$	1.48	1.56
$p\text{-}C_6H_4Cl_2$	0	0

same direction, thus giving a moment double that of monochlorobenzene in contrast to the observed value.   If two hydrogens in the plane hexagonal structure given by the Kekulé formula were replaced by chlorine

[9] A. Baeyer, Ann. Chem., Justus Liebigs, **245**, 103 (1888).

[10] W. Koerner, Gazz. chim. ital., **4**, 304 (1874).

[11] W. Vaubel, J. prakt. Chem., [2]**49**, 308 (1894); ibid., **50**, 58 (1894).

[12] M. L. Huggins, J. Am. Chem. Soc., **44**, 1607 (1922); ibid., **45**, 264 (1923).

atoms to form o-dichlorobenzene, the angle θ between the directions of
the axes of the dipole thus formed would be 60° if the structure were not
distorted by substitution. Similarly, in the meta compound θ would
120°, and in the para 180°. The calculated resultant moment of the
molecule (Table 2.1) would be $2m \cos (\theta/2)$, where m is the moment of
chlorobenzene.

Except, of course, for the para compound, the measured values in
Table 2.1 are about 10 per cent lower, because of the solvent effect, than
those found subsequently for the molecules in the vapor state, which
makes the calculated values correspondingly lower. The agreement
between measured and calculated values for the meta and para compounds and the discrepancy for the ortho in the case of these three
disubstituted benzenes, which were originally used to prove the plane
hexagonal structure for the benzene ring, is typical of disubstituted
benzenes in general. The agreement between the observed and calculated values was sufficiently good to be regarded as proof of the plane
hexagonal structure for the benzene ring. The discrepancy between the
observed and calculated values for the ortho compound, which was so
generally recognized as to be termed the "ortho effect," was at first
attributed to widening of the angle between the two dipoles by steric
repulsion between the two substituent groups, but was later shown[13] to
be due to the inductive effects of the dipoles upon the groups. Both
these effects, which will be discussed later, will be shown to be capable
of an important influence upon molecular moments, particularly, the
inductive effect.

In general, to calculate the moment of a molecule containing several
dipoles in fixed positions, it is convenient to choose a set of reference
axes in the molecule, calculate the component of each dipole moment
along each axis, and obtain the resultant moment as the square root of
the sum of the squares of the component sums m_x, m_y, and m_z along each
axis, that is,

$$\mu = (m_x^2 + m_y^2 + m_z^2)^{1/2} \qquad (2.1)$$

When only two moments, m_1 and m_2, are involved, the expression for the
resolution of the two vectors m_1 and m_2 with an angle θ between them is

$$\mu = (m_1^2 + m_2^2 + 2m_1m_2 \cos \theta)^{1/2} \qquad (2.2)$$

The method of calculation with Eq. (2.1) or (2.2) may be illustrated
by the case of the moment of the m-chloronitrobenzene molecule in the
vapor state. Setting $m_1 = 1.70$, the vapor moment of chlorobenzene;
$m_2 = 4.21$, the vapor moment of nitrobenzene; $\theta = 120°$; and letting the
x and y axes lie in the plane of the benzene ring with the C—Cl line in

[13] H. M. Smallwood and K. F. Herzfeld, J. Am. Chem. Soc., **52**, 1919 (1930).

the y axis, we obtain

$$m_x = m_2 \sin \theta \qquad m_y = m_1 + m_2 \cos \theta \qquad m_z = 0$$

and
$$\mu = (m_2{}^2 \sin^2 \theta + m_1{}^2 + 2m_1 m_2 \cos \theta + m_2{}^2 \cos^2 \theta)^{\frac{1}{2}}$$
$$= (m_1{}^2 + m_2{}^2 + 2m_1 m_2 \cos \theta)^{\frac{1}{2}}$$
$$= 3.67$$

The agreement of this moment value 3.67 calculated for the gas with the observed value 3.69 is well within the accuracy of the values used.

The calculation of the moment of a molecule containing two or more dipoles which may change their directions relative to one another by rotation around bonds between atoms requires averaging over all possible positions around the bonds. A method of effecting this average was published as a general equation by Eyring[14] and as a number of special equations for individual molecules by Smyth and Walls.[15] An equation for the case of 1,2-disubstituted ethanes was published earlier by Williams,[16] and another special case was treated by Zahn.[17] The general equation[14] for the mean-square sum of n dipole moments, freedom of rotation about the bonds being assumed, is

$$\mu_a{}^2 = \sum_{j=1}^{n} m_j{}^2 + 2 \sum_{j=1}^{n} \sum_{s<j} \prod_{k=j}^{s+1} \cos \theta_k \, m_j m_s \qquad (2.3)$$

The meaning of the various quantities will be evident from the statement, sufficient in itself for the calculation, that for free rotation about connecting lines the mean-square sum of n vectors is equal to the sum of the squares of the lengths of the separate vectors, plus twice all the products of the lengths of two vectors multiplied by the product of the cosines of the angles θ_k made by the directed lines connecting the pair. θ_k is zero when the directed lines are continuations of each other. The product $m_j m_s$ of the lengths of the vectors, that is, the values of the dipole moments, is positive if they point in the same direction in passing along a chain and negative if they point in opposite directions. If a portion of a molecule is stiff, the dipoles existing in that portion may be resolved into a single resultant vector passing through the nearest point of rotation. If rotation around any bond is hindered, it must receive special consideration. The problem of restricted rotation is considered in Chap. XI.

The method may be illustrated by calculating the moment value in solution of β,β'-dichlorodiethyl ether,

[14] H. Eyring, *Phys. Rev.*, **39**, 746 (1932).
[15] C. P. Smyth and W. S. Walls, *J. Am. Chem. Soc.*, **54**, 2261 (1932).
[16] J. W. Williams, *Z. physik. Chem.*, **138A**, 75 (1928).
[17] C. T. Zahn, *Physik. Z.*, **33**, 400 (1932).

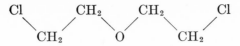

The carbon valence angle is 110° and the oxygen valence angle may, without serious error, be taken as 110°. All the angles between the directed lines are consequently $\theta_k = 180° - 110° = 70°$. The molecule may be treated as containing four dipoles, two acting along the lines of the two C—Cl bonds and having each a moment $m_1 = 1.7$ (the solution value for methyl chloride) and two along the lines of the two C—O bonds having each a moment m_2. m_2 may be calculated from the moment of dimethyl ether, which is the resultant of two such dipole moments: $2m_2 \cos 55° = 1.30$. Although the value $m_2 = 1.13$ thus obtained is for the gas and not for the solution, the possible error resulting from its use is no greater than the uncertainty in the m_1 value. The mean-square moment obtained by application of the rule stated above is

$$\mu^2 = 2m_1^2 + 2m_2^2 - 4m_1m_2 \cos^2 70° + 4m_1m_2 \cos^3 70° - 2m_2^2 \cos 70° - 2m_1^2 \cos^5 70° = 2.58$$

as compared to the value 2.57 found for the molecule in benzene solution.[15] The excellence of the agreement between the calculated and the observed value is somewhat fortuitous, as one might almost equally well use $m_1 = 1.8$, which would give a calculated moment 2.71. The difference 0.14 between the two calculated values is of the order of magnitude of the probable error due to group moment errors and inductive effects. Much greater differences between calculated and observed moment values are indicative of restriction of rotation around one or more bonds.

3. Inductive Effects. The inductive effects previously mentioned are the shifts of charge induced in a molecule by electric fields and are roughly calculable by the laws of electrostatics. A crude calculation was made of the shift of electrons in the hydrogen chloride molecule induced by the attractive force exerted by the proton,[1] and some discussion of the distortion of the hydrogen halide molecules by induction was given later.[2] The moment induced by a point charge e in a particle or element of volume of polarizability α_0 and at a distance r from e is

$$m = \frac{e\alpha_0}{r^2} \tag{3.1}$$

α_0 can be obtained for an atom or molecule as

$$\alpha_0 = \frac{3R}{4\pi N} \tag{3.2}$$

[1] C. P. Smyth, *Phil. Mag.*, **47**, 530 (1924).
[2] C. P. Smyth, "Dielectric Constant and Molecular Structure," Chemical Catalog, New York, 1931, chap. IV.

where R is the atomic or molecular refraction and N the Avogadro number. For accuracy, R should be extrapolated to infinite wavelength, but, for calculations such as these, the refraction for any wavelength in the visible region is sufficient.

Smallwood and Herzfeld[3] calculated the inductive effects of the two principal dipoles in disubstituted benzenes upon the rest of the molecule and, by locating the dipoles somewhat arbitrarily at the hypothetical circumferences of the carbon atoms, were able to account satisfactorily for the lowering of the observed moment values below those calculated for plane hexagonal models with undistorted structures. If the dipoles were assumed to be at the centers of the substituent groups, the inductive effects were found to be negligible, while, if they were assumed to be at the centers of the carbon atoms, the correction was far too large.

An approach to the problem of inductive effect may be illustrated by the discussion of the moments of some halogenated methanes.[4] The polarizability α of a portion of a molecule may, as a rough approximation, be treated as if the polarization occurred at one point. The moment induced at this point by a permanent moment m elsewhere in the molecule can then be calculated.[3] If the dipole m exerting the force E is located at the origin of a set of plane polar coordinates, the horizontal and vertical components of E at the point r, where the polarizability acts, are given by

$$
\begin{aligned}
E_x &= \frac{m_x(3\cos^2\theta - 1)}{r^3} + \frac{3m_y\sin\theta\cos\theta}{r^3} \\
E_y &= \frac{3m_x\sin\theta\cos\theta}{r^3} + \frac{m_y(3\sin^2\theta - 1)}{r^3}
\end{aligned}
\tag{3.3}
$$

where m_x and m_y are the components of m, which lies in the xy plane. The moment induced by m at the point r has the components

$$
m_{ix} = E_x\alpha \qquad \text{and} \qquad m_{iy} = E_y\alpha
\tag{3.4}
$$

The treatment of the effect of a system of charges as that of a single dipole located at a point within the system becomes an extremely rough approximation when the effect is considered at distances as small as those involved in the halogenated methanes. Although it is certainly justifiable to treat the principal dipole of CH_3Cl as lying in the C—Cl line, its size and its location in this line are uncertain. Consideration of the locations of the centers of gravity of the charges assignable to the C—Cl portion of the molecule places the principal dipole roughly $7/8$ of the distance, 1.76 A., from the carbon nucleus to the chlorine nucleus.[5] A

[3] H. M. Smallwood and K. F. Herzfeld, *J. Am. Chem. Soc.*, **52**, 1919 (1930).

[4] C. P. Smyth and K. B. McAlpine, *J. Chem. Phys.*, **1**, 190 (1933).

[5] L. Meyer, *Z. physik. Chem.* **8B**, 27 (1930).

moment m located at this point would induce a moment in each of the three C—H bonds, which is calculated in terms of m by using Eqs. (3.3) and (3.4), the arbitrary assumption being made that a polarizability[3,6] $\alpha = 0.66 \times 10^{-24}$ acts at the midpoint of the C—H bond, 0.53 A. from the carbon nucleus. However, in view of our uncertainty as to the moment of the C—H bond arising from inherent electrical asymmetry and of other uncertainties which cannot be eliminated from the treatment, it appears rational, in cases where at least one hydrogen is attached to the carbon, to assign the entire moment of the methyl halide to the carbon-halogen bond. The results of such treatment will not differ greatly from those to be obtained by using a smaller carbon-halogen bond moment and adding the effects of the C—H bonds.

In the methylene chloride molecule two moments of about 1.85×10^{-18} each in the C—Cl lines at an angle of $110°$ to one another would have a resultant 2.13×10^{-18}, as compared to the observed value 1.58×10^{-18}. With the dipoles located $\frac{7}{8}$ of the distance from the carbon to the chlorine nucleus, that is, 1.54 A. from the carbon nucleus, and with polarizabilities[3,6] $\alpha = 2.51 \times 10^{-24}$ assumed to be acting at the same points—a reasonable assumption—application of our equations shows that the inductive effect of one moment of 1.85 lowers the moment in the other C—Cl line to 1.36. The resultant of two such moments happens to be identical with the observed moment of methylene chloride. However, the moment of 1.36 would have a smaller inductive effect, and the lowering calculated for the other C—Cl moment would not be as great. This, in turn, would have a smaller inductive effect upon the first moment. Successive calculations lead to a value 1.49 for the moment of a C—Cl bond when a second chlorine is attached to the same carbon. This would give a moment of 1.71 for methylene chloride if the two C—Cl moments acted at an angle of $110°$ to each other, but the induced moments do not lie in the C—Cl lines, so that the resultant C—Cl moments make a slightly smaller angle with each other and have a resultant of 1.79, which is 0.22 higher than the observed value for methylene chloride.

Since one C—Cl dipole lowers the moment of another from 1.85 to 1.49, one might, as a very rough approximation, assume that two C—Cl dipoles would produce a lowering of 2×0.36 in a third C—Cl moment. In chloroform, which has a moment $3(\text{C—Cl}) \cos 70° = (\text{C—Cl})$, the moment would therefore be 1.13 as compared to an observed value 1.05. Similar calculations show that because of its much smaller polarizability ($\alpha = 0.626 \times 10^{-24}$), the C—F moment is less reduced by the inductive effect of an adjacent C—Cl than is a C—Cl moment, and, because of the smaller C—F distance, 1.41 A., the C—F moment reduces an adjacent C—Cl moment more than another C—Cl moment does. Table 3.1 gives

[6] C. P. Smyth, *Phil. Mag.*, **50**, 361 (1925).

the lowering of one carbon-halogen bond moment by the inductive effect of another on the same carbon.

The system of charges constituting a carbon-halogen group cannot be isolated from the rest of the molecule, and, unless we could determine exactly a point in the system where its moment could be regarded as acting and, similarly, a location for its polarizability, nothing would be gained by this process of isolation. A bond moment is merely a measure of the electrical asymmetry of a certain section of a molecule and is affected by the environment of the section. For example, we may think

TABLE 3.1. LOWERING OF CARBON-HALOGEN MOMENT ($\times 10^{18}$)

C—Cl by C—Cl	0.36	C—F by C—Cl	0.11
C—Cl by C—F	0.56	C—F by C—F	0.21

of the carbon tetrachloride molecule as resolved into four equal C—Cl moments, which, because of the symmetry of the molecule, cancel one another to give zero resultant moment. Each C—Cl moment consists of the moment due to an inherent asymmetry in the distribution of charge plus the moments induced by each of the three other C—Cl moments. In methyl chloride, the C—Cl moment contains the components in the C—Cl line of the moments induced by the H—C moments, which consist of a possible permanent moment plus the moment induced by the C—Cl moment. As only the roughest kind of separation of these effects can be made, it is as well to treat the entire moment of the molecule as the C—Cl moment. Attachment of more carbons to the methyl carbon gives molecules of somewhat increased moment because of induction,[7] but the effect is noticeable through only two carbons of a chain. Little error will arise from treating the moment of the —CH$_2$Cl group as a C—Cl moment equal to that of methyl chloride. In chlorobenzene, the C—Cl bond is different from that in an alkyl chloride and the moment is somewhat different. If two C—Cl's are separated from one another as in p- or m-dichlorobenzene, the moment of chlorobenzene may, with little error, be used as a C—Cl bond moment to calculate the resultant moment of the disubstituted molecule. However, in o-dichlorobenzene, each C—Cl bond moment is affected by the proximity of the other, not only through direct inductive effects of one C—Cl upon the other, but also through the effects upon the other adjacent parts of the molecule. The very approximate calculation by Smallwood and Herzfeld of the alteration in moment produced by these effects was possible because it was not large. From a practical point of view, the most useful procedure is to assign to one bond the moment of an entire simple molecule containing but one polar group, but it must be borne in mind that, when

[7] C. P. Smyth, *J. Am. Chem. Soc.*, **63**, 57 (1941).

the immediate environment of a bond moment changes, the moment may change.

Groves and Sugden[8] have made more detailed calculations of inductive effects, which, however, contain the unavoidable large uncertainties caused by uncertainty in the dipole locations.   The calculations of electrostatic inductive effects appear to have value in the interpretation of molecular moments, but the effects of induction may be obscured by other influences.

4. Bond Moments.   In Secs. 2 and 3, dipole moments have been treated as vector quantities acting in the direction of the bonds between atoms.   A natural development of this point of view was the assignment of a moment value to each bond between atoms.   The bond moment was thus a vector quantity acting in the line of the bond.   The moment of a diatomic molecule is equal to the one bond moment of the molecule, and the moment of a polyatomic molecule is the resultant of all the bond moments in the molecule.   A small but useful table of bond moment values was calculated[1] on the tacit but unwarranted assumption that the H—C bond on the benzene ring was zero.   Sidgwick[2] made a careful estimation of the best obtainable values for the moments associated with a considerable number of different bonds, and J. G. Malone[3] and M. G. Malone and A. L. Ferguson[4] added to the number of bond moment values and used the values to construct an electronegativity scale of the elements involved, which was compared to a similar scale prepared by Pauling[5] on the basis of thermal data.   Williams[6] had previously considered the possibility of determining the relative electronegativities of radicals by comparing the moments of analogous compounds containing the different radicals and also by measuring the moments of molecules in which any two groups to be compared were placed para to each other on a benzene ring.

In so simple a molecule as that of hydrogen chloride (Sec. 1), the moment depends not only upon the positions of the proton, the chlorine nucleus, and the electrons of the bond, but also upon those of the chlorine electrons not involved in the bond.[7]   The so-called moment of the C—Cl bond in a molecule involves shifts of the chlorine electrons as the result of attraction toward the carbon and of the forces exerted by the rest of

[8] L. G. Groves and S. Sugden, *J. Chem. Soc.*, 158 (1937).

[1] A. Eucken and L. Meyer, *Physik. Z.*, **30**, 397 (1929).

[2] N. V. Sidgwick, "The Covalent Link in Chemistry," Cornell University Press, Ithaca, N.Y., 1933, p. 146.

[3] J. G. Malone, *J. Chem. Phys.*, **1**, 197 (1933).

[4] M. G. Malone and A. L. Ferguson, *J. Chem. Phys.*, **2**, 99 (1934).

[5] L. Pauling, *J. Am. Chem. Soc.*, **54**, 3570 (1932).

[6] J. W. Williams, *Physik. Z.*, **29**, 683 (1928).

[7] C. P. Smyth, *Trans. Faraday Soc.*, **30**, 752 (1934).

the molecule upon these electrons. There is, in addition, the effect of the chlorine upon the rest of the molecule. This emphasizes the conclusion in Sec. 3 that a bond moment is merely a measure of the electrical asymmetry of a certain section of a molecule and is affected by the environment of the section. If the immediate environment of the section in molecules of different compounds is the same, the bond moment remains constant; if it is different, the electrical asymmetry of the section and its moment change more or less. In terms of resonance the rest of the molecule may be such as to alter the relative amounts of the contributions of the different structures or introduce new contributing structures, thus altering the bond moment.

Difficulties often encountered in the calculation of a bond moment value are illustrated by the case of the methyl chloride molecule, which has a dipole moment 1.87 measured in the vapor state, the resultant of three H—C bond moments and one C—Cl. The resultant dipole must lie in the axis of symmetry of the molecule, which is the line of the C—Cl bond. Since the molecule is approximately tetrahedral[8] with angles between the bonds of approximately 110°, each of the three H—C bond moments has a component $m_{H-C} \cos 70°$ in the C—Cl line and a component $m_{H-C} \sin 70°$ perpendicular to the direction of the C—Cl line. Since these three latter components make angles of 120° with one another in a plane perpendicular to the symmetry axis, their resultant is zero, and, since $\cos 70° = \frac{1}{3}$, the resultant of the three components in the axis of symmetry is m_{H-C}. The sum $m_{H-C} + m_{C-Cl} = 1.87$. If one of the two bond moments were known, the other could be calculated. However, the H—C bond moment cannot be determined by dielectric-constant measurements on hydrocarbons, for, according to the calculation just made, a hydrogen in the symmetrical tetrahedral methane molecule, which has zero moment, can be replaced by a methyl group without change in moment, and it should thus be possible to build up the paraffin series without change in the resultant zero moment of the molecule. The approximate correctness of this calculation is confirmed by the zero or very small moment values found for all of the paraffins thus far investigated (Sec. IX.1), which also prove the C—C bond moment to be zero, as would be expected.

A number of very approximate calculations[1,9,11-14], some using bond

[8] S. L. Miller, L. C. Aamodt, G. Dousmanis, and C. H. Townes, *J. Chem. Phys.*, **20**, 1112 (1952).

[9] L. E. Sutton, *Proc. Roy. Soc. (London)*, **133A**, 668 (1931).

[10] P. W. Allen and L. E. Sutton, *Acta Cryst.*, **3**, 46 (1950).

[11] H. G. Trieschmann, *Z. physik. Chem.*, **32B**, 22 (1936).

[12] H. M. Smallwood, *Z. physik. Chem.*, **19B**, 242 (1932).

[13] C. P. Smyth, *J. Phys. Chem.*, **41**, 209 (1937).

[14] B. Timm and R. Mecke, *Z. Physik*, **98**, 363 (1935).

moments and valence angles,[10] gave rough estimates between 0.2 and 0.6 for the H—C bond moment, with some uncertainty as to the sign.   The calculation of the H—C bond moment by Eucken and Meyer[1] attributed the moment of the toluene molecule, 0.4, entirely to the three H—C bonds of the methyl group, which, as has been shown, have a resultant moment equal to one H—C moment.   The value 0.4 thus obtained for the H—C bond would be sound only if the aromatic H—C bond para to the methyl group had zero moment, of which there was no evidence, and if no unsymmetrical distribution of charge were produced in the ring by the methyl group.   The electronegativities calculated by Pauling[5] from bond energies gave a difference 0.55 between hydrogen and carbon which was later[15] revised to 0.4.

Coulson[16] concluded that the inclusion of an atomic dipole term would change the bond moment previously calculated[13] from 0.3 for an H^+—C^- bond to 0.4 for an H^-—C^+ bond.   On the basis of both electron-pair and molecular orbital approximations, he concluded the moment to be about 0.4 and, with a few uncommon exceptions, practically independent of whether the carbon atom was aliphatic, aromatic, ethylenic, or acetylenic.   The placing of the negative end of the dipole toward the hydrogen was in agreement with the similar conclusion of Fuchs and Wolf[17] based on an obsolete theory of valence, which attributed the chemical bond to mutual polarization.

From measurements of the infrared dispersion of methane, Rollefson and Havens[18] calculated a moment value 0.307 for the H—C bond, and Thorndike's measurements[19] of the intensities of infrared absorption bands gave 0.31 for the H—C bond moment in methane and 0.26 to 0.35 from the ν_8 and ν_9 bending vibration bands for ethane, but only 0.104 or 0.094 from the ν_6 bending band.   Similar measurements by Thorndike, Wells, and Wilson[20] gave 0.77 from the ν_{11} out-of-plane bending, 0.52 from the ν_7 in-plane bending, and 0.37 from the ν_5 in-plane bending. They also calculated 0.57 for the H—C bond in hydrogen cyanide from the measurements of Foley.[21]   Thorndike assumed the positive end of the dipole to be toward hydrogen and gave 0.4 as the average value for its moment.

[15] L. Pauling, "The Nature of the Chemical Bond," 2d ed., Cornell University Press, Ithaca, N.Y., 1940, chap. II.

[16] C. A. Coulson, *Trans. Faraday Soc.*, **38**, 433 (1942).

[17] O. Fuchs and K. L. Wolf, Dielektrische Polarisation, "Hand- und Jahrbuch der chemischen Physik." A. Eucken and K. L. Wolf, Akademische Verlagsgesellschaft m.b.H., Leipzig, 1935, vol. 6, p. 356.

[18] R. Rollefson and R. Havens, *Phys. Rev.*, **57**, 710 (1940).

[19] A. M. Thorndike, *J. Chem. Phys.*, **15**, 868 (1947).

[20] A. M. Thorndike, A. J. Wells, and E. B. Wilson, Jr., *J. Chem. Phys.*, **15**, 157 (1947).

[21] H. M. Foley, *Phys. Rev.*, **69**, 628 (1946).

Cole and Thompson[22] revised and extended earlier measurements[23] of the intensities of some vibrational absorption bands of different classes of substituted benzenes and used the results to calculate values of the H—C bond moment. The values varied over a wide range, giving a mean of 0.57 for the moment of the dipole concluded to be H^+—^-C, with a possibility of small differences between molecules of different compounds. Walsh[24] argued that a polarity C^+—H^- should cause similarity in the properties of this bond to those of the carbon-halogen bonds and showed, by means of force-constant, thermochemical, and bond-length data, the existence of such a similarity. Gent,[25] in a critical survey of the problem, concluded that in methane and aliphatic compounds, when not subjected to complicating influences, the bond was C^+—^-H with a moment about 0.40. Under the influence of strongly polar groups, the bond moment was considered to be somewhat smaller. When other valences of the carbon atom were involved in an ethylenic or acetylenic bond, the hydrogen atom was more positive than in methane, the polarity being H^+—^-C in acetylene and approaching zero in ethylene. Mueller and Eyring,[26] considering the carbon-hydrogen bond as an isolated unit and including the effect of the interelectronic repulsions, concluded that the bond dipole was C^+—H^- with a moment about 0.30, while hybridization or replacement of hydrogen in a hydrocarbon by a highly electronegative substituent tended to reverse the direction of the moment. In later work Coulson[27] adhered to his earlier conclusion[16] that the carbon-hydrogen bond is C^+—^-H in aliphatic compounds, but changed to the conclusion that, for aromatic, ethylenic, and acetylenic carbon, the polarity was probably H^+—^-C.

A good deal of space has been devoted to the consideration of the moment of the H—C bond because most of the applications of bond moments to problems of molecular structure deal with organic molecules and, without an absolute value for the H—C bond, only relative values are obtainable for most of the other bond moments. The H—C bond moment thus plays a role somewhat analogous to that of the potential of the hydrogen or the calomel electrode in determining electrode potentials. It is certain from the facts which have been enumerated that the value of the H—C bond moment is small, almost certain that it lies between 0 and 0.6, and probable that it most frequently lies between

[22] A. R. H. Cole and H. W. Thompson, *Trans. Faraday Soc.*, **46**, 103 (1950).

[23] R. P. Bell, H. W. Thompson, and E. E. Vago, *Proc. Roy. Soc. (London)*, **192A**, 498 (1948).

[24] A. D. Walsh, *J. Chem. Soc.*, 400 (1948); *Discussions Faraday Soc.*, **2**, 18 (1947); *Trans. Faraday Soc.*, **43**, 68 (1947).

[25] W. L. G. Gent, *Quart. Rev. Chem. Soc.*, II, 383 (1948).

[26] C. R. Mueller and H. Eyring, *J. Chem. Phys.*, **19**, 193 (1951).

[27] C. A. Coulson, "Valence," Oxford, London, 1952, p. 208.

0.3 and 0.4, but may vary somewhat.   The value 0.3 previously used[13]
by the writer in calculating a list of moment values is probably as close
to a correct average value as any, but, since 0.4 has been more generally
used, a dipole H^+—^-C of moment 0.4 will be assumed when needed for
use in calculating other bond moment values.   This is evidently a very
approximate assumption since the moment may vary from one compound
to another and may have the direction C^+—^-H.

In polyatomic molecules where only one kind of bond occurs, as, for
example, in phosphorus trichloride, the bond moment may be calculated
from the molecular dipole moment and the valence angle, usually obtained
from electron-diffraction measurements or estimated from knowledge of
the normal atomic valence angles.   In general, the bond moment is calculated by equating the vector sum of all the bond moments in a molecule
to the measured molecular dipole moment and solving for the desired
bond moment, all the other moments and all the valence angles being
known.

In the discussion up to the present point in this section, the location
of the dipole along the bond has been immaterial.   If, however, there is
a question of the force exerted by the dipole upon its environment, the
exact location of the dipole, as well as its size and direction, becomes
important.   The dipole is sometimes treated as having a length equal to
that of the bond and a charge at each end such that the product of the
charge times the bond length is equal to the dipole moment.   The field
due to each charge is then calculated separately, an approximation which
abandons the essential definition of the dipole.   The alternative is to
treat the dipole as acting at a point somewhere along the bond and estimate the location of this point by considering the atomic radii and the
electronic and nuclear charges.   The location thus determined is necessarily extremely approximate, but may be used in the rough calculation
of inductive effects.   It would appear that neither of these approximations can give a wholly adequate representation of the charge distribution.   It is obvious that the value of a bond moment will vary with
its environment, and, even in a particular molecule, may be subject to a
considerable error in calculation.   For use in the consideration of the
geometrical structures of molecules, the moment of a group rather than
of a bond is commonly preferable, but, for fundamental considerations
of the structures of bonds and for some investigations of geometrical
structure, bond moments are useful.   Consequently, bond moment values
taken from the literature, recalculated from literature values with the
H—C value taken as 0.4, or newly calculated from recently available
data are given in Table 4.1, together with the differences between the
electronegativities X_A and X_B of the bonded atoms, which will be discussed later.   Many bond moments cannot be calculated from the avail-

TABLE 4.1. BOND MOMENTS ($\times 10^{18}$) AND ELECTRONEGATIVITY DIFFERENCES $X_A - X_B$

Bond	Moment	$X_A - X_B$	Bond	Moment	$X_A - A_B$
COVALENT SINGLE BONDS					
H—Sb	-0.08^r	-0.3	C—I	1.19^a	-0.1
H—As	-0.10^a	-0.1	C—Br	1.38^a	0.3
H—P	0.36^a	0.0	C—F	1.41^a	1.5
H—I	0.38^a	0.3	C—Cl	1.46^a	0.5
H—C	0.4	0.4	N—O	$(0.3)^b$	0.5
H—S	0.68^a	0.4	N—F	0.17^m	1.0
H—Br	0.78^a	0.7	P—I	0^a	0.3
H—Cl	1.08^c	0.9	P—Br	0.36^a	0.7
D—Cl	1.09^c		P—Cl	0.81^a	0.9
H—N	1.31^a	0.9	As—I	0.78^a	0.4
D—N	$1.30^{a,c}$		As—Br	1.27^a	0.8
H—O	1.51^a	1.4	As—Cl	1.64^a	1.0
D—O	1.52^g		As—F	2.03^a	2.0
H—F	1.94^h	1.9	Sb—I	0.8^a	0.8
C—C	0^a	0	Sb—Br	1.9^a	1.0
C—N	0.22^b	0.5	Sb—Cl	2.6^a	1.2
C—Te	0.6^b	-0.4	S—Cl	$0.7^{b,s}$	0.5
C—O	0.74^b	1.0	Cl—O	0.7^b	0.5
C—Se	0.8^b	-0.1	I—Br	1.2^s	0.4
C—S	0.9^b	0	I—Cl	1^s	0.6
			Br—Cl	0.57^s	0.2
			Br—F	1.3^s	1.2
			Cl—F	0.88^s	1.0
BONDS IN ORGANOMETALLIC COMPOUNDS AND SALTS					
Ge—Br	$>2.1^d$	1.1			
Ge—Cl	$>1.9^d$	1.3			
Sn—Cl	$>3.0^d$	1.3	K—Cl	$10.6^{p,i}$	2.2
Pb—I	$>3.3^d$		K—F	7.3^p	3.2
Pb—Br	$>3.9^d$		Cs—Cl	10.5^p	2.3
Pb—Cl	$>4.0^d$		Cs—F	$7.9^{k,p}$	3.3
Hg—Br	$>3.5^e$				
Hg—Cl	$>3.2^d$				
Au—Br	$>4^d$				
Li—C	1.4^q	1.5			

TABLE 4.1. BOND MOMENTS ($\times 10^{18}$) AND ELECTRONEGATIVITY DIFFERENCES $X_A - X_B$ (*Continued*)

Bond	Moment	Bond	Moment
COORDINATE SINGLE BONDS			
N $\rightarrow$ O	4.3[i,l]	Se $\rightarrow$ O	3.1[f,l]
P $\rightarrow$ O	2.7[f,l,n]	Te $\rightarrow$ O	2.3[f,l]
P $\rightarrow$ S	3.1[f,l,n]	N $\rightarrow$ B	3.9[l]
P $\rightarrow$ Se	3.2[f,l]	P $\rightarrow$ B	4.4[l]
As $\rightarrow$ O	4.2[f,l]	O $\rightarrow$ B	3.6[l]
Sb $\rightarrow$ S	4.5[f,l]	S $\rightarrow$ B	3.8[l]
S $\rightarrow$ O	2.8[f,l]	S $\rightarrow$ C	(5.0)[l]
DOUBLE AND TRIPLE BONDS			
C$=$C	0.0	N$=$O	2.0[b]
C$=$N	(0.9)[b]	C$\equiv$C	0.0
C$=$O	2.3[b]	C$\equiv$N	3.5[b]
C$=$S	2.6[b]	N$\equiv$C	3.0[b]

[a] C. P. Smyth, *J. Phys. Chem.*, **41**, 209 (1937).

[b] C. P. Smyth, *J. Am. Chem. Soc.*, **60**, 183 (1938).

[c] R. P. Bell and I. E. Coop, *Trans. Faraday Soc.*, **34**, 1209 (1938).

[d] C. P. Smyth, *J. Org. Chem.*, **6**, 421 (1941).

[e] C. Curran, *J. Am. Chem. Soc.*, **64**, 830 (1942).

[f] K. A. Jensen, *Z. anorg. allgem. Chem.*, **250**, 268 (1943).

[g] F. H. Müller, *Physik. Z.*, **35**, 1009 (1934); P. Abadie and G. Champetier, *Compt. rend.*, **200**, 1590 (1935); L. G. Groves and S. Sugden, *J. Chem. Soc.*, 971 (1935).

[h] N. B. Hannay and C. P. Smyth, *J. Am. Chem. Soc.*, **68**, 171 (1946); R. A. Oriani and C. P. Smyth, *J. Am. Chem. Soc.*, **70**, 125 (1948); *J. Chem. Phys.*, **16**, 1167 (1948); recalculated and corrected.

[i] E. P. Linton, *J. Am. Chem. Soc.*, **62**, 1945 (1940).

[j] For older and less accurate values for alkali halides, see H. Scheffers, *Physik. Z.*, **35**, 425 (1934); W. H. Rodebush, L. A. Murray, Jr., and M. E. Bixler, *J. Chem. Phys.*, **4**, 372 (1936).

[k] K. H. Hughes, *Phys. Rev.*, **70**, 570 (1946).

[l] G. M. Phillips, J. S. Hunter, and L. E. Sutton, *J. Chem. Soc.*, 146 (1945).

[m] H. E. Watson, G. P. Kane, and K. L. Ramaswamy, *Proc. Roy. Soc. (London)*, **156A**, 137 (1936).

[n] G. L. Lewis and C. P. Smyth, *J. Am. Chem. Soc.*, **62**, 1529 (1940).

[p] J. W. Trischka, *J. Chem. Phys.*, **20**, 1811 (1952).

[q] M. T. Rogers and A. Young, *J. Am. Chem. Soc.*, **68**, 2748 (1946).

[r] C. C. Loomis, M.I.T. *Quart. Rept.*, April 15, 1950, p. 29.

[s] See Sec. XII.9.

able dipole moment values because of the occurrence of two or more unknown bond moments in the same molecule. The assumption of a rough limit for one bond moment may be used to calculate a rough limiting value for another. The lower limits given for bonds in organometallic compounds are calculated on the assumption that the metal-carbon bond has the positive end of its dipole toward the metal. The actual moment of the bond listed would be the sum of the value given and the metal-carbon moment. The lower limit given is obtained by setting the metal-carbon moment equal to zero. The values given for the $N \rightarrow O$, $P \rightarrow O$, and $P \rightarrow S$ bond are quite different from those previously estimated,[28] having been calculated from more recent moment values, which should be less dependent on resonance and inductive effects than the old values. Indeed, correction for mesomeric effect has been made by Phillips, Hunter, and Sutton[29] in several of the values quoted. Nearly all the values in this group are subject to large errors. Group moments are tabulated and considered in a later section. The dash shown between the bonded atoms is not intended to imply anything as to the nature of the bond. The arrow representing the coordinate bond indicates that the atom at the left has supplied both the electrons of the covalent bond, so that the first atom has acquired a positive charge and the second a negative. This is, at best, only an approximate description for most of these bonds. The double and triple bonds between atoms of different elements usually contain contributions from polar structures.

Pauling[15] has concluded that the energy of a normal covalent bond A—B should be the geometric mean $[D(A-A)D(B-B)]^{1/2}$ of the bond energies $D(A-A)$ and $D(B-B)$ of the molecules A—A and B—B, which for most bonds differs little from the arithmetic mean $\frac{1}{2}[D(A-A) + D(B-B)]$, and he has used the excess of the observed bond energy $D(A-B)$ over this geometric or arithmetic mean as a measure of the difference in electronegativity between A and B. This excess, Δ' over the geometric mean, or Δ over the arithmetic mean, was converted into a convenient figure by converting the energies from kilogram calories to electron volts and taking the square root. The resulting quantity $(\Delta/23.06)^{1/2}$ was found to be additive, so that

$$\left(\frac{\Delta}{23.06}\right)^{1/2} = X_A - X_B \qquad (4.1)$$

where $X_A - X_B$ was called the electronegativity difference of the atoms A and B. No absolute values were found for X, only the differences being significant. For convenience, X for hydrogen was originally taken as zero in order to make possible the construction of an electronegativity

[28] C. P. Smyth, *J. Am. Chem. Soc.*, **60**, 183 (1938).
[29] G. M. Phillips, J. S. Hunter, and L. E. Sutton, *J. Chem. Soc.*, 146 (1945).

scale paralleling the electromotive series of the elements. It is these differences that are given in Table 4.1.

Mulliken[30] pointed out that the average of the first ionization energy and the electron affinity of an atom should be a measure of its electronegativity. Pauling found that by empirical manipulation these quantities could be made to give almost equal values for the monatomic elements, that is, the sums of the ionization energy and the electron affinity expressed in kilogram calories and divided by 130 were almost identical with the original values of X increased by 2.1, making $X_H = 2.1$ instead of 0.

As previously mentioned, similarity was observed[3,4] between several bond moment values and the electronegativity differences $X_A - X_B$ for the bonded elements. The writer[13,31] showed the closeness of the bond moment value to the electronegativity differences between hydrogen and several other atoms and between carbon and oxygen, nitrogen, and fluorine, and a tendency toward increasing discrepancy in other bonds as the bonded atoms increased in size (see Table 4.1). Examination of the bond moment in terms of an equation based upon the relations developed by Mulliken[30] indicated that close coincidence of bond moment values and electronegativity differences must be accidental, although the generally observed parallelism should occur. The discussion in Sec. 1 indicates even less theoretical basis for a connection between the two.

Pauling[15] used amounts of ionic character calculated from the moments of the hydrogen halides (cf. Sec. 1) to construct a curve relating the amount of ionic character of a bond A—B to the difference in electronegativity $X_A - X_B$ of the atoms. This curve was represented by an empirical equation:

$$\text{Amount of ionic character} = 1 - e^{-0.25(X_A - X_B)^2} \qquad (4.2)$$

However, the subsequently measured moment value[32,33] of hydrogen fluoride gave a point which, with the points for the other hydrogen halides, fell on a curve represented by the empirical equation[32]

$$\text{Amount of ionic character} = 0.16(X_A - X_B) + 0.035(X_A - X_B)^2 \qquad (4.3)$$

This equation was obviously not to be applied at the extreme limits of the electronegativity difference, where the approximate character of the underlying theory rendered meaningless the calculation of a very small amount of covalent character or a very small amount of ionic character.

[30] R. S. Mulliken, *J. Chem. Phys.*, **2**, 782 (1934); *ibid.*, **3**, 573 (1935).
[31] C. P. Smyth, *J. Am. Chem. Soc.*, **60**, 183 (1938).
[32] N. B. Hannay and C. P. Smyth, *J. Am. Chem. Soc.*, **68**, 171 (1946).
[33] R. A. Oriani and C. P. Smyth, *J. Am. Chem. Soc.*, **70**, 125 (1948).

Equation (4.3) has been concluded[34] to be the most satisfactory relation between the amount of ionic character and the electronegativity difference, but, in view of the fact (Sec. 1) that a purely covalent structure may have a considerable moment and that induced shifts of nonbonding electrons may alter the apparent bond moment value, it may well be questioned whether one should attempt to do more than indicate a rough proportionality for the relationship.

The effects of induced shifts of charge are very pronounced in the moments of the alkali metal halide molecules in the vapor state (Table 4.1). In terms of the resonance picture of these molecules, the lowering of the moment below that calculated for the undistorted ionic structure was attributed to partial covalent character of the bond.[15] However, from a consideration of quadrupole coupling data, Townes and Dailey[35] have assigned a maximum of 4 per cent covalent character to the bond in the sodium chloride molecule and 3 per cent to that in sodium bromide and have concluded that the alkali halides should be considered as almost purely ionic with a large amount of polarization reducing the moment. Rittner[36] has calculated the moments of alkali halide molecules by means of the equation

$$\mu = ea - \frac{a^4 e(\alpha_1 + \alpha_2) + 4ae\alpha_1\alpha_2}{a^6 - 4\alpha_1\alpha_2} \tag{4.4}$$

in which e is the electronic charge; a, the equilibrium separation of the ion centers; α_1 and α_2, the polarizabilities of the two ions; and the second term on the right is the total induced moment opposing the moment ea of the undistorted ionic structure. The calculated moment values differ from the observed by an average amount ± 6.5 per cent, no greater than the considerable uncertainties of the latter. It would appear, therefore, that the alkali halide molecules are almost pure ionic structures with their moments reduced about 20 to 50 per cent by mutual induction.

Bearing in mind the rough approximation involved in estimating the amount of ionic character from the bond moment, certain qualitative statements may be made concerning the values in Table 4.1. The bonds which are commonly regarded as normal, single covalent bonds usually have less than 20 per cent apparent ionic character. The bonds in arsenic trifluoride and antimony trichloride, low-melting and low-boiling compounds normally regarded as covalent, show 23 per cent ionic character, a value consistent with the amphoteric character of arsenic and antimony and the strong electronegative character of the two halogens. The lower limits of the amounts of ionic character calculated for the Ge—Cl and Ge—Br bonds, 18 and 19 per cent, are lower than the highest values for

[34] C. A. Coulson, "Valence," Oxford, London, 1952, p. 134.

[35] C. H. Townes and B. P. Dailey, *J. Chem. Phys.*, **17**, 782 (1949).

[36] E. S. Rittner, *J. Chem. Phys.*, **19**, 1030 (1951).

the typically covalent bonds, which is not surprising in view of the some-what amphoteric character of germanium. The lower limits for the bonds in these organometallic compounds increase from those for the germanium bonds through that for Sn—Cl to the Pb—X bonds. The few available values for the bonds in the organometallic compounds indicate their location in the logical position between the bonds of typical covalent compounds and those of salt molecules, but, if actual values instead of lower limits were available, they might overlap the salt molecules. If the positive end of the H—C bond moment were toward the carbon, the lower limits of the bond moments would be raised by 0.8 with correspond-ing increase in the amount of ionic character.

Double- and triple-bond moments usually have resonance contributions from semipolar bond structures, such as A^+—^-B or A^+=B^-, which seem to depend little upon the electronegativities of the bonded atoms. Sidgwick[37] called attention to the fact that the moments of double and triple bonds between atoms of different elements were more than two and three times the values for the single bonds. This is apparent in Table 4.1, where the cyanide moment is ten times that of the single carbon-nitrogen bond and the double bonds between carbon and oxygen and carbon and sulfur have moments about three times those of the single bonds. Although the C≡N bond is primarily C:::N, contribu-tion from a form $^+$C::N$^-$ would raise the moment, presumably being responsible for the high value observed. It is a semipolar bond acting in the opposite direction in the isocyanide N⇌C which gives it a large moment opposite in direction to that of the C=N bond[38] (see Secs. IX.3 and IX.4). These two triple-bond moments, one with the carbon positive and the nitrogen negative and the other with the carbon negative and the nitrogen positive, show that, although electronegativity may be a factor in determining the multiple-bond moments, it need not be the controlling factor.

The bond moments for the so-called coordinate single bonds are for-mally represented by a single structure, A^+—B^-, without resonance con-tributions from other polar structures. In accordance with the conven-tional view of this bond, Phillips, Hunter, and Sutton[29] have pointed out that, if the electron pair were symmetrically shared between the donor atom A and the acceptor B, the bond moment would be $4.80l$, where l is the bond length. If the observed moment is $4.80ly$, it may be supposed that the centroid of the bonding electrons is only a fraction $y/2$ of the bond length distant from the donor atom. The values of y calculated by using the observed bond lengths or values calculated from bond radii

[37] N. V. Sidgwick, "The Covalent Link in Chemistry," Cornell University Press, Ithaca, N.Y., 1933, p. 153.

[38] N. V. Sidgwick, *Chem. Revs.*, **9**, 77 (1931).

are: for NO, 0.65; PO, 0.36; PS, 0.33; SO, 0.4; NB, 0.52; PB, 0.47; OB, 0.49; SB, 0.42; and SC, 0.6. When a coordinate bond has no moment and y is accordingly zero, there is no bond.[29] One might suppose, therefore, that the smaller y is, the weaker is the coordinate link. The PO, PS, and SO bonds, if coordinate bonds, should then be weaker than the others, but they are shown by calculation of their energies to be actually stronger. Phillips, Hunter, and Sutton conclude that the lengths, strengths, and moments of the PO and SO bonds show that they are not coordinate bonds and that the available evidence favors a similar conclusion for the PS, PSe, SeO, and TeO bonds. They then revert to an earlier theory[39] of the nature of these bonds, according to which they are primarily double with d orbitals of the central atom involved. The double bonds themselves are presumed to be polar and largely responsible for the dipole moments, which may receive minor contributions from coordinate bond structure.

Although there seems to be good evidence in favor of the double-bond character of these bonds, it is clear that the NO bond, which is observed in the amine oxides, cannot be double since all of the available orbitals are used in forming the single bonds. In the bonds involving boron, which are observed in addition compounds with boron trifluoride and boron trichloride, there can also be no double-bond character since the $2s$ and $2p$ orbitals of the boron are completely filled in the formation of single bonds and, as in the nitrogen and oxygen atoms, no d orbitals are available. The values of y tell us that the NO bond moment is about $\frac{2}{3}$ what it should be if the bond were a pure, undistorted, single coordinate bond, the boron bonds are about $\frac{1}{2}$ what they should be, and the PO and PS bonds about $\frac{1}{3}$ what they should be. There is no sharp break between the bonds that cannot be double and those that can. Indeed, the necessarily single SB bond has only 0.42 the moment that it should have if it were a pure, undistorted coordinate bond, while the SO bond, thought by Phillips, Hunter, and Sutton to be double, has 0.40 the moment that it should have if it were a pure, undistorted coordinate bond.

It is interesting to examine these bonds by the classical method originally applied to the hydrogen halide moments as described in Sec. 1. The HF moment is 0.44 the value calculated for a pure, undistorted ionic bond, the HCl moment 0.18, the HBr moment 0.13, and the HI moment 0.05. Calculation of the inductive distortion of the outermost shell of electrons by the attractive force exerted by the proton showed that this

[39] L. Pauling and L. O. Brockway, *J. Am. Chem. Soc.*, **59**, 13 (1937); G. C. Hampson and A. J. Stosick, *J. Am. Chem. Soc.*, **60**, 1814 (1938); L. O. Brockway and J. Y. Beach, *J. Am. Chem. Soc.*, **60**, 1836 (1938); J. Y. Beach and D. P. Stevenson, *J. Chem. Phys.*, **6**, 75 (1938).

was sufficient to account for the progressive lowering of the moment below that of the undistorted ionic structure.   The electron shift which shortens the effective resultant dipole of the molecule increases as increasing size of the halogen reduces the binding forces on the outer electrons, increasing the atomic polarizability as measured by refraction.   The increase in polarizability with increasing size of the halogen more than compensates for the increase in internuclear distance in the hydrogen halide molecules.   In a structure A^+—B^-, the induced shift of charge should lower the moment below that calculated for the undistorted structure.   The lowering should be less, the smaller and, consequently, the less polarizable the bonded atoms.   The lowering is least for the bond between the small and difficultly polarizable nitrogen and oxygen atoms and greatest for the bond between the larger and more polarizable phosphorus and sulfur atoms.   Next after the NO bond, the bonds between the small nitrogen and boron and oxygen and boron atoms are least lowered.   However, the difference between the PB and OB bond lowerings is negligibly small, as is also that between the PO and PS lowerings. The general trend of these so-called coordinate-bond moments is consistent with a structure A^+—B^-, in which distortion lowers the moment, but the relative amounts of the lowering are not explained by the atomic polarizabilities alone.   Neither the coordinate bond nor the double bond alone provides a generally satisfactory description of all these bonds.   It is natural to suggest a certain amount of resonance between the two structures where this is possible, but it is clearly impossible for the bonds between two atoms of the first short period of the periodic system.   Since these bonds are commonly referred to as coordinate bonds, this nomenclature will be continued in the present work.

Although calculation (Sec. 1) shows that the bond moment value obtained from experimental data does not depend only on the electronegativity difference between the bonded atoms and although irregularities are evident in Table 4.1, it may be concluded that the polarities of single bonds increase roughly as a function of the electronegativity difference between the bonded atoms, the polarities of typically covalent bonds being low and those of what might be regarded as typically ionic bonds being high but not so high as would be expected of pure ionic structures.   The lowering of moment below that of the pure, undistorted ionic structure may involve resonance with a covalent structure, but is largely due to inductive distortion of the electronic shells.   Bonds between metallic and acidic elements in organometallic molecules may have polarities roughly intermediate between those of typically covalent and those of typically ionic bonds, but overlapping both.   The more polar bonds in certain organometallic compounds are at least as polar as those in some salt molecules.   It should be noted that the polarities found for bonds in salt molecules are for the molecules in the vapor state and not for the bonds between ions in crystals, where the so-called ionic character of the bonding should be greater. The polarities of coordinate bonds and of double and triple bonds involving contributions from structures with coordinate bonds are high. The polarities of the coordinate bonds are, however, not so high as would be expected of undistorted structures, and the polarities are largely independent of the electronegativity differences between the atoms, often being opposite in direction to the electronegativity difference.

5. Group Moments. To calculate what moment a given molecular structure might be expected to have, the moment associated with a group is more useful than that associated with merely one bond. Although greater uniformity of environment is obtained by using a group moment, it is obvious that the effective moment of a group may be altered by resonance or inductive effects. For this reason, the group moment is given in Table 5.1 as the molecular moment produced when the group shown in the first column is attached to the groups shown at the tops of the succeeding columns. The moment when the group is attached to the benzene ring contains the contributions through resonance of those polar structures postulated as arising through charge shifts around the ring. Although these contributions may be altered by the presence of other groups, the values given may be regarded as good first approximations to the resultant vectors produced by the groups in aromatic molecules. The moments under C_2H_5— should differ from those under CH_3— principally in the small inductive effects arising from the presence of the added CH_2 group in the ethyl compounds. The differences between the two sets of values should be a rough measure of the magnitudes of these effects. As the additional induced moments in the ethyl compounds commonly act at an angle with the bond between the ethyl and the attached group, a small error in the value of the angle in the last column results from the neglect of this angle, but the error is too small to be serious in comparison to the other uncertainties involved. The angle given in the last column is the angle which the plus-to-minus direction of the group moment makes with the direction of the bond of the carbon atom to the group in question. Two values are listed for each moment, one (Gas), the true value measured in the vapor state, and the other (Sol.), the value obtained from solution measurements, usually affected by mutual inductive effects between solvent and solute molecules. The solution values are the ones to be used for the calculation of moments measured in solution, as similar errors are then contained in both the observed and the calculated values, although, of course, differences in solvent effect may destroy the significance of small differences between observed and calculated moment values. The solution values are frequently given to only one decimal place because the experimental determinations often vary by as much as 0.1 among different investigators and different nonpolar solvents, benzene being the most generally used solvent. Other less-common group moments may be obtained from the moment values tabulated in Chaps. IX and X.

TABLE 5.1.[1] GROUP MOMENTS ($\times 10^{18}$)

Group, X	C_6H_5—		CH_3—		C_2H_5—		Moment angle $C \underset{\angle}{\longrightarrow} X$
	Gas	Sol.	Gas	Sol.	Gas	Sol.	
—CH₃	0.37	0.4	0	....	0	....	180°
—OCH₃	1.35	1.25	1.30	....	1.22	....	55°
—SCH₃	....	1.27	....	1.40	....	....	57°
—NH₂	1.48	1.53	1.23	....	1.2	1.38	100° (aliph.) 142° (arom.)
—I	1.7	1.30	1.64	1.5	1.87	1.8	0°
—Br	1.73	1.54	1.80	1.8	2.01	1.9	0°
—Cl	1.70	1.58	1.87	1.7	2.05	1.8	0°
—F	1.59	1.46	1.81	....	1.92	....	0°
—OH	1.4	1.6	1.69	1.66	1.69	1.7	62°
—COOH	....	1.64	1.73	1.63	1.73	1.68	74°
—COOCH₃	....	1.83	1.67	1.75	1.76	1.9	70°
—CHO	(3.1)	2.76	2.72	2.5	2.73	2.5	55°
—COCH₃	3.00	2.89	2.84	2.74	2.78	....	57°
—NO₂	4.21	3.98	3.50	3.1	3.68	3.3	0°
—CN	4.39	4.0	3.94	3.4	4.00	3.57	0°

The use of these group moments and the deviations to be expected may be illustrated by using the gas values in calculations on substituted benzenes as was done in Sec. 2 with solution values for the molecules. The moment given for C_6H_5—Cl is that of chlorobenzene and includes the small moment of the H—C bond and the resonance effects previously mentioned. The moment of p-chloronitrobenzene should, in the absence of mutual effects of the two substituents, be $4.21 - 1.70 = 2.51$. The observed[2] value, 2.78, is higher by a small amount, which can be regarded as a measure of the increase in resonance resulting from the mutual effects of the two substituents.[3] The moment of o-dichlorobenzene should be $2 \times 1.70 \cos 30° = 2.94$. The observed[4] value, 2.51, is lower by an

[1] C. P. Smyth, "Physical Methods of Organic Chemistry" (A. Weissberger editor), Interscience, New York, 2d ed., 1949, vol. I, pt. II, chap. XXIV.
[2] L. G. Groves and S. Sugden, J. Chem. Soc., 1782 (1937).
[3] C. P. Smyth and G. L. Lewis, J. Am. Chem. Soc., 62, 721 (1940).
[4] E. C. Hurdis and C. P. Smyth, J. Am. Chem. Soc., 64, 2212 (1942).

amount which is primarily a measure of the mutual inductive effects of the two C—Cl dipoles. The observed values for m-dichlorobenzene and m-chloronitrobenzene, in which mutual effects of resonance and of dipole-dipole induction can play little part, are in excellent agreement with the calculated value. If, on the other hand, similar calculations were made with, for example, the —COOCH$_3$ group moment, absurd results would be obtained, for its dipole does not lie in the direction of the group bond and rotation around this bond will affect the resultant moment. The method of calculation for the resultant of movable dipoles (Sec. 2 and Chap. XI) must be employed. Any considerable differences between observed and calculated results may be taken as evidence of restriction of rotation and may be used as a means of calculating the extent of the restriction[5] (Chap. XI). Obviously, group moments lying in the direction of the group bond should be used as far as possible for structural investigations.

6. Resonance and Molecular Moment. Until the development of the theory of resonance, considerable differences between the dipole moments of analogous aliphatic and aromatic compounds were not understood. Because of the polarizabilities of the two molecules in the vicinity of the C—Cl bonds, t-butyl chloride and chlorobenzene might be expected to have approximately equal dipole moments, but the vapor-state value for the former is 2.13 and that for the latter 1.70. In terms of the Kekulé formula, one can write two structures for chlorobenzene,

I   II

each of which should have a moment of about 2.13, residing largely in the C—Cl bond with a positive charge on the carbon and a negative on the chlorine but with small H—C bond moments and small secondary moments in the ring. Implicit in each of these structures is resonance in the carbon-chlorine bond which is to be regarded as the resultant of contributions from the structures C—Cl and C$^+$Cl$^-$. In terms of the resonance theory, Sutton[1] showed that one might write, in addition, three less-stable structures capable of making small but appreciable contributions to the structure of the molecule:

[5] R. A. Oriani and C. P. Smyth, *J. Chem. Phys.*, **17**, 1174 (1949).
[1] L. E. Sutton, *Proc. Roy. Soc. (London)*, **133A**, 668 (1931); *Trans. Faraday Soc.*, **30**, 789 (1934).

These structures arise through the shift of an unshared pair of electrons from the chlorine atom to the C—Cl bond leaving a positive charge on the chlorine and causing an electron shift within the ring to put a negative charge on an ortho or para carbon.   As these three structures would have large dipole moments more or less opposite in direction to those of the two Kekulé structures, their contributions should lower the moment of the molecule below that expected for the Kekulé structures.   The amount of the lowering, 0.43, may be used[2] to estimate the amount of the contribution of these three structures with the carbon-chlorine double bond to the structure of chlorobenzene in much the same way that the amount of ionic character in the H—Cl bond was calculated.   If the total contribution of the three polar structures III, IV, and V is X, that of the two structures I and II is $1 - X$.   If structures III, IV, and V contribute equally, the resultant moment of the molecule may be written

$$\mu = (1 - X)m_{\mathrm{I}} + 0.67\ Xm_{\mathrm{III}} + 0.33\ Xm_{\mathrm{V}} \tag{6.1}$$

where m_{I}, the moment of structure I, identical with that of structure II, is taken as equal to that of t-butyl chloride, 2.13, and acting in the direction of the C—Cl bond; and $m_{\mathrm{III}} = m_{\mathrm{IV}}$, the components in the C—Cl direction of the moments of structures III and IV, and m_{V} are calculated from the products of the electronic charge, 4.80×10^{-10}, times the interatomic distances of the charged atoms, these distances being calculated by simple geometry from the interatomic distances given by electron diffraction.[3]   With 1.39 A. for the C—C distance (the edge of the plane hexagon of the benzene ring) and with 1.69 as the C—Cl distance, the distance from the Cl to the ortho carbon comes out 2.67 A. and, from the Cl to the para carbon, 4.47 A.   Use of values for the C=Cl double-bond distance and the C—C single-bond distance instead would not appreciably alter the result.   The moments of structures III and IV are, therefore, $4.80 \times 10^{-10} \times 2.67 \times 10^{-8} = 12.8 \times 10^{-18}$, and the moment of structure V is $4.80 \times 10^{-10} \times 4.47 \times 10^{-8} = 21.5 \times 10^{-18}$.   Since the components of the moments of III and IV perpendicular to the C—Cl direction cancel one another, we need to consider only

[2] C. P. Smyth, *J. Am. Chem. Soc.*, **63**, 57 (1941).
[3] L. O. Brockway and K. J. Palmer, *J. Am. Chem. Soc.*, **59**, 2181 (1937).

$$m_{III} = m_{IV} = 12.8 \left(\frac{2.39}{2.67}\right) \times 10^{-18} = 11.5 \times 10^{-18}$$

where $2.39/2.67$ is the cosine of the angle between the direction of the moment of structure III or IV and the direction of the Cl—C bond. If in Eq. (6.1) we set $\mu = 1.70$, $m_I = 2.13$, $m_{III} = -11.5$, and $m_V = -21.5$, the minus sign being used because the moments of these polar structures are in the opposite direction to μ and m_I, we obtain $X = 0.024$. If the higher energy of the structure V resulting from its greater charge separation lowers its stability to such a point as to render its contribution negligible, the numerical coefficients in Eq. (6.1) change from 0.67 to 1 and from 0.33 to 0, and $X = 0.030$. These values for X are slightly lower than those previously calculated[2] and much lower than the value 0.15 ± 0.05 calculated from Pauling's empirical relation for the dependence of the amount of double-bond character upon bond length. In general, it was found[2] that the amount of resonance calculated from dipole moment was lower than that calculated from bond length by an amount appreciably greater than the sum of the probable errors of the two methods. The reasons for this discrepancy are not clear but probably lie in the approximations inherent in both methods of calculation.

Hugill, Coop, and Sutton[4] have made similar calculations, but have assumed that the moments of the contributing polar structures are reduced by induction and have used for their values 0.6 of the algebraic sum of the moment of the undistorted structure and the primary moment, for which the t-butyl halide moment has been used in these calculations. This reduction in the moments assigned to the polar structures increases the calculated amount of double-bond character by an amount too small to alter materially the large discrepancies found for the halogenated benzenes. These investigators have, however, greatly reduced, but not eliminated, the discrepancies by using the smaller moment values obtained by Groves and Sugden[5] by correcting for induction. They have further found that the use of the polar-structure moments arbitrarily corrected for induction by the factor 0.6 gives amounts of double-bond character for the carbon-halogen bonds in vinyl chloride, bromide, and iodide and in chloro- and bromoacetylene which are in quite satisfactory agreement with the values calculated from bond lengths. The basis for the use of this factor 0.6 is the attribution to inductive distortion of the difference between the observed moments of the alkali metal halide molecules and those calculated for the pure, undistorted ionic structures and a somewhat similar difference between the moment value observed for trimethyl-

[4] J. A. C. Hugill, I. E. Coop, and L. E. Sutton, *Trans. Faraday Soc.*, **34**, 1518 (1938).
[5] L. G. Groves and S. Sugden, *J. Chem. Soc.*, 1992 (1937).

amine oxide in very dilute solution and the value calculated on the basis of a pure ionic bond between the nitrogen and the oxygen. In these structures on which the value of the factor 0.6 is based, the ionic charges are on immediately adjacent atoms in contrast to the structures of the halogenated benzenes, where they are on atoms separated from each other by one other atom in the ortho structures and by three atoms in the para structures. It is evident, however, that the assignment to the postulated polar structures of moment values reduced by inductive distortion would reduce the discrepancies between the amounts of resonance contributions calculated from bond lengths and those calculated from dipole moments. A similar procedure would also raise the amounts of ionic character calculated for the bonds in salt molecules to values consistent with the conventional view of these highly polar structures. It would be consistent with the observed reduction of coordinate-bond moments below those calculated for undistorted structures, but would also result in considerably increased values for the amounts of ionic character calculated for traditionally covalent bonds.

Examples of the effects of other somewhat similar types of resonance upon dipole moment will be considered at this point as illustrations of the methods of approach. Many more will be discussed in the subsequent chapters.

In nitrobenzene, resonance elevates the moment above those of the nitroparaffins instead of lowering it. For this molecule, two Kekulé structures can be written with one oxygen of the nitro group negative and two structures with the other oxygen negative:

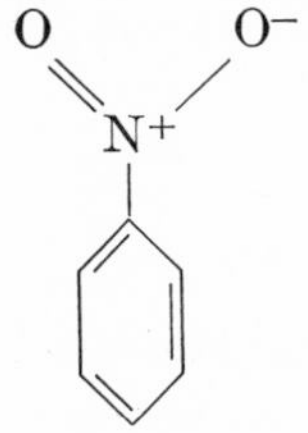

These structures should have a moment close to that of 2-nitro-2-methylpropane, 3.71, while the observed value is 4.21, both values being measured in the vapor state.[6-8] As in the case of chlorobenzene, structures can be written with a double bond between the ring and the attached group, but now the second electron pair comes from the ring.

[6] R. H. Wiswall and C. P. Smyth, *J. Chem. Phys.*, **9**, 356 (1941).
[7] E. C. Hurdis and C. P. Smyth, *J. Am. Chem. Soc.*, **64**, 2212 (1942).
[8] K. B. McAlpine and C. P. Smyth, *J. Chem. Phys.*, **3**, 55 (1935).

These structures would have large moments acting in the same general direction as those of the Kekulé model, so that small contributions from them are sufficient to give the large elevation of the moment 0.50 above that of 2-nitro-2-methylpropane, which differs by no more than 0.01 or 0.02 from the values for nitroethane, 1-nitropropane, and 2-nitropropane.[6] The resonance effect is more pronounced in p-nitrodimethylaniline,[9] which has a moment value 6.87 measured in solution, while the solution values of dimethylaniline and nitrobenzene are 1.58 and 3.98, respectively. In the absence of additional resonance, the moment of $C_6H_5N(CH_3)_2$ would not act in exactly the same direction as that of $C_6H_5NO_2$, but even if it did the sum of the two moments would be 1.31 below the observed. However, contribution from the structure

can easily account for the large increase in moment. In this structure, the unshared electron pair of the nitrogen is drawn into the double bond as are the unshared halogen electron pairs in the molecules just discussed (see Sec. X.3 for further discussion).

The lowering of moment when a double bond is adjacent to a halogen is greater than that in the halogenated benzenes, and the lowering when a triple bond is adjacent to a halogen is much greater still. The moment of vinyl chloride[4] is 1.44 as compared to 2.05 for ethyl chloride,[10] while the moment of chloroacetylene is only 0.44 and that of bromoacetylene[11]

---

[9] R. J. B. Marsden and L. E. Sutton, *J. Chem. Soc.*, 599 (1936).

[10] L. G. Groves and S. Sugden, *J. Chem. Soc.*, 158 (1937).

[11] L. O. Brockway and I. E. Coop, *Trans. Faraday Soc.*, **34**, 1429 (1938).

is 0. As in the halogenated benzenes, a structure may be written in which an unshared electron pair of the halogen moves into its bond with the carbon to form a double bond:

$$
\begin{array}{cc}
\underset{|}{\overset{H}{C}} \quad \underset{|}{\overset{H}{C}} \\
H-\underset{..}{C^-}-C=Cl^+ \qquad\qquad H-\overset{..}{C}=C=Cl^+
\end{array}
$$

Contributions from these structures would oppose the normal dipole moments such as are found in the alkyl halides and reduce the molecular moment. Shortening of the carbon-halogen bond length[11,12] found by electron diffraction gives evidence of considerable amounts of double-bond character in these bonds.

The molecular orbital method gives a quantitative treatment of charge distribution, from which dipole moments may be obtained.[13,14] The moment values thus calculated are often too large, as in the case of those estimated roughly from resonance contributions, and the charge distribution may be markedly different from that deduced from resonance considerations alone. The principles of resonance have been so generally used in the interpretation of dipole moments that they are extensively employed in the ensuing chapters. In many cases, the resonating polar structures provide not so much a theoretical explanation as an empirical description, which serves to correlate molecular behavior. The results of the application of the molecular orbital method to various molecules will also be discussed in the following chapters.

[12] L. O. Brockway, J. Y. Beach, and L. Pauling, *J. Am. Chem. Soc.*, **57**, 2693 (1935).

[13] C. A. Coulson, "Valence," Oxford, London, 1952.

[14] B. Pullman and A. Pullman, "Les Théories Électroniques de la Chimie Organique," Masson et Cie, Paris, 1952, chap. VII.

CHAPTER IX

DIPOLE MOMENTS AND STRUCTURES OF ALIPHATIC AND ALICYCLIC MOLECULES

The division of the discussion of structural phenomena according to classes of compounds cannot but be arbitrary and, at times, unsatisfactory. The general principles underlying the phenomena have been treated in Chap. VIII. In this and in subsequent similar chapters similar compounds will be grouped together and discussed in detail. For each compound, what is believed to be the best moment value or the average of the best values is tabulated. Where dependable gas values are available, they are used in preference to the results of liquid measurements. Moment values are rounded off to the first decimal place when the second place is clearly without significance. Many values measured in solution, usually in benzene, may have some significance relative to one another in the second decimal place. In case of doubt, the second decimal place is used in the following tables. Solution values are generally given in addition to gas values for comparison with the solution values of substances for which vapor values are not available.

Individual moment values in the literature up to early 1948 are given in the comprehensive tabulation "Tables of Electric Dipole Moments," L. G. Wesson, The Technology Press, Cambridge, Mass., 1948, which has been used without further reference for many of the data used in compiling the tables in this and the following chapters. More recent moment values are obtained from the lists in the annual "Digest of Literature on Dielectrics," National Academy of Sciences, National Research Council, Washington, D.C.

1. Hydrocarbons. In view of present-day certainty of the tetrahedral structure of methane, its zero moment may seem too obvious to discuss, but it should be remembered that this zero moment provided evidence against unsymmetrical structures which were at one time considered seriously. The symmetry of the methyl group has been discussed (Sec. VIII.4). If the methane molecule is a regular tetrahedron, each H—C bond lies in an axis of symmetry and the angles between these axes of symmetry are 109° 28', a value which in subsequent discussion will be taken as 110° without introducing any detectable error. The moment along any one of these four axes is then the moment ($m_{\text{H–C}}$) of the bond in this axis plus the sum of the components along this axis of each of the other three H—C bond moments, that is,

$$\mu = m_{\text{H–C}} + 3m_{\text{H–C}} \cos 110° = 0$$

The three components $m_{\text{H–C}} \sin 110°$ perpendicular to this axis of symmetry make angles of 120° with one another and, therefore, have zero resultant moment in this plane. The fact that cos 110° = $-\frac{1}{3}$, or, if we prefer, cos 70° = $\frac{1}{3}$, evidently makes a methyl group equivalent to an H—C in moment. The expected symmetry of the C—C bond is established by the zero moment of the ethane molecule.

TABLE 1.1. MOMENTS ($\times 10^{18}$) OF PARAFFINS

	GAS	
Methane	CH_4	0
Ethane	C_2H_6	0
Propane	C_3H_8	0
n-Butane	n-C_4H_{10}	0
Isobutane	$(CH_3)_3CH$	0
n-Hexane	n-C_6H_{14}	0
n-Heptane	n-C_7H_{16}	0
	LIQUID	
Pentane–dodecane	C_nH_{2n+2} (n = 5–12)	0
Hexadecane	$C_{16}H_{34}$	0
Branched-chain heptanes	C_7H_{16}	0
2,2,4-Trimethylpentane	$(CH_3)_3C{-}CH_2{-}CH(CH_3)_2$	0

The propane molecule is unsymmetrical along the line bisecting the C—C—C angle and would be expected to have a moment were it not for the equivalence of the H_3C moment to that of H—C. The small differences in energy between bonds on a secondary carbon and those on a primary carbon may give rise to some small lack of electrical symmetry, but it is evidently very small, probably less than 0.1 $\times 10^{-18}$ in moment.

As the energy of an H—C bond on a tertiary carbon atom may differ considerably from that of an H—C bond on a primary carbon atom,[1] and as a rough relation between bond energy differences and dipole moments has been indicated (Sec. VIII.4),[2,3] it has seemed possible that

[1] H. S. Taylor and J. O. Smith, Jr., *J. Chem. Phys.*, **8**, 543 (1940).

[2] L. Pauling, "The Nature of the Chemical Bond," Cornell University Press, Ithaca, N.Y., 2d ed., 1940, p. 236.

[3] C. P. Smyth, *J. Phys. Chem.*, **41**, 209 (1937).

isobutane might have a dipole moment of the order of 0.2×10^{-18} because of a difference in moment between the H—C bond on the tertiary carbon atoms and the other H—C bonds, which are all on primary carbon atoms. It will be shown in Sec. 2 that both n-perfluoropentane, $n\text{-}C_5F_{12}$, and isoperfluoropentane, $(CF_3)_2CFC_2F_5$, have moments indistinguishable from zero, indicating that, even with the much larger dipole of the C—F bond, the relations developed for the H—C bond hold and no measurable difference results from the attachment of the dipole to a secondary or tertiary carbon atom. The fact that Groves and Baker[4] have found zero moment for isopropylcyclohexane, which has one H—C bond on a tertiary carbon, as also for methyl, ethyl, and t-butylcyclohexane (Table 1.2), indicates that any difference in the moment of this H—C bond must be extremely small. The zero moments found for many branched-chain hydrocarbons could be cited in support of this conclusion, but their evidence is somewhat less conclusive because of their measurement in the liquid state. It is quite possible that the apparent difference in energy of the H—C bond on a tertiary carbon atom from that of the H—C bond on a primary carbon may arise from steric effects involving no detectable charge shift.

TABLE 1.2. MOMENTS $(\times 10^{18})$ OF SATURATED CYCLIC HYDROCARBONS

GAS		LIQUID	
Methylcyclohexane	0	Ethylcyclopropane	0
Ethylcyclohexane	0	n-Propylcyclopropane	(0.7)
i-Propylcyclohexane	0	Ethylcyclobutane	0
t-Butylcyclohexane	0	Cyclopentane	0
		Methylcyclopentane	0
		Cyclohexane	0
		Decahydronaphthalene cis	0
		Decahydronaphthalene trans	0

The zero moments for all but one of the cyclic molecules in Table 1.2 are consistent with the factors leading to zero moment for the paraffins. The not inconsiderable value reported in an isolated investigation is tabulated here in parentheses as doubtful because of its inconsistency with the zero value reported for ethylcyclopropane and ethylcyclobutane.

The zero moment of the ethylene molecule corresponds to the symmetrical planar structure generally ascribed to it and shows that there is no polarity inherent in the C=C bond. Although propane and n-butane have no moments, propylene and 1-butene have small moments, indistinguishable from each other in size. Evidently, a small electronic shift has occurred in these molecules, which the moments of unsaturated halides discussed in the next section show to be in the direction from the alkyl group toward the double bond. The shift may be described in

[4] L. G. Groves and J. W. Baker, *J. Chem. Soc.*, 1144 (1939).

TABLE 1.3. MOMENTS ($\times 10^{18}$) OF MOLECULES CONTAINING ONE OR TWO
DOUBLE BONDS IN THE VAPOR STATE

Molecule	Formula	Moment
Ethylene	$CH_2{=}CH_2$	0
Propylene	$CH_3CH{=}CH_2$	0.35
1-Butene	$C_2H_5CH{=}CH_2$	0.37
trans-2-Butene	$CH_3CH{=}CHCH_3$	0
Isobutylene	$(CH_3)_2C{=}CH_2$	(0)
Cyclohexene	$CH_2(CH_2)_3CH{=}CH$	0.6
Allene	$CH_2{=}C{=}CH_2$	(0.2)
1,3-Butadiene	$CH_2{=}CHCH{=}CH_2$	0
trans-1-Methyl-1,3-butadiene	$CH_3CH{=}CHCH{=}CH_2$	0.68
2-Methyl-1,3-butadiene	$CH_2{=}C(CH_3)CH{=}CH_2$	0.38
2-Ethyl-1,3-butadiene	$CH_2{=}C(C_2H_5)CH{=}CH_2$	0.45
1,2-Dimethyl-1,3-butadiene	$CH_3CH{=}C(CH_3)CH{=}CH_2$	0.63
1,3-Dimethyl-1,3-butadiene	$CH_3CH{=}CHC(CH_3){=}CH_2$	0.65
2,3-Dimethyl-1,3-butadiene	$CH_2{=}C(CH_3)C(CH_3){=}CH_2$	0.52
1,3-Cyclopentadiene	$CH_2CH{=}CHCH{=}CH$	0.53

terms of the theory of hyperconjugation[5] by writing for the propylene
molecule, for example, in addition to the normal structure

$$CH_3CH{=}CH_2$$

three structures such as

$$H^+CH_2{=}CH{-}{^-}\overset{..}{C}H_2$$

in each of which one of the three methyl hydrogens is ionic and a pair
of electrons has shifted to the carbon at the opposite end of the chain.
Only a very small resonance contribution from each of these structures
is needed to account for the observed dipole moment.   The symmetry
of the trans-2-butene molecule results in the observed zero dipole moment.
Since the isobutylene molecule would be expected to have a moment at
least as large as and probably larger than that of propylene, the zero
value in Table 1.3 is put in parentheses as being doubtful.   As a negative
value for the atomic polarization was given by the measurements on
cyclohexene,[6] the value 0.6 for its moment may be too high.   Kubo
drew no conclusions as to its molecular structure.   Since a moment value
as small as 0.2 is rarely distinguishable experimentally from zero, the
moment value of allene is placed in parentheses.   A zero moment is to
be expected for the linear structure indicated by electron diffraction.[7]

[5] R. S. Mulliken, C. A. Rieke, and W. G. Brown, *J. Am. Chem. Soc.*, **63**, 41 (1941).

[6] M. Kubo, *Sci. Papers Inst. Phys. Chem. Research (Tokyo)*, **32**, 26 (1937).

[7] P. W. Allen and L. E. Sutton, *Acta Cryst.*, **3**, 46 (1950).

The zero or extremely small moment value found for butadiene does not throw much light upon the question as to its existence in a cis form or a trans form with respect to the central C—C bond or a mixture of the two with the trans predominating. The trans form should have zero moment while the cis form should have a small moment, which, however, might easily be too small for detection even if the cis form made up a considerable fraction of a mixture of cis and trans forms. The more probable resonating forms may be written

$$H_2C\!\!=\!\!CH\!\!-\!\!CH\!\!=\!\!CH_2 \qquad H_2C^+\!\!-\!\!CH\!\!=\!\!CH\!\!-\!\!\overset{..}{C}H_2{}^-$$

$$H_2\overset{..}{C}{}^-\!\!-\!\!CH\!\!=\!\!CH\!\!-\!\!C^+H_2$$

The polarity arising from one polar structure just cancels that from the other, no matter whether the molecular form is cis or trans with respect to the central bond.

$$
\begin{array}{ccc}
\overset{\displaystyle H_2C^+}{\diagdown} \quad \overset{\displaystyle {}^-\overset{..}{C}H_2}{\diagup} & \text{or} & \overset{\displaystyle H_2C^+}{\diagdown} \\
CH\!\!=\!\!CH & & CH\!\!=\!\!CH \\
& & \diagdown \\
& & \overset{..}{C}{}^-H_2
\end{array}
$$

The shortening of the carbon-carbon single bond by about 0.07 A. as indicated by electron diffraction[7] gives evidence of the double-bond character in this bond corresponding to these two polar structures. The possible additional contributions from less-stable polar structures may have an almost undetectable effect.[8]

In 1-methylbutadiene, polarity should arise from polar structures analogous to those which have been proposed for propylene, but here the negative charge, instead of being displaced three carbon atoms away from the methyl hydrogens, is displaced five carbons away to give

$$H^+CH_2\!\!=\!\!CH\!\!-\!\!CH\!\!=\!\!CH\!\!-\!\!{}^-\overset{..}{C}H_2$$

and the moment should be correspondingly larger, as observed.[8]

Analogous structures for isoprene, or 2-methylbutadiene

$$
\begin{array}{c}
H^+CH_2 \\
\| \\
{}^-\!:\!CH_2\!\!-\!\!C\!\!-\!\!CH\!\!=\!\!CH_2
\end{array}
$$

should give rise to a moment like that of propylene. The amount of the contribution of structures of this type should be somewhat less than that in the case of propylene, as the amount of double-bond character of the central butadiene bond should reduce that of the bond to the methyl car-

[8] N. B. Hannay and C. P. Smyth, *J. Am. Chem. Soc.*, **65**, 1931 (1943).

bon. Although the observed moment value 0.38 for 2-methylbutadiene in Table 1.3 may be somewhat high, the fact that it is indistinguishable from that of propylene indicates that the polarities of the other possible types of contributing polar structures approximately cancel one another. This would occur if the molecule were trans in form or if the hyperconjugated structures with H^+ such as those written for butadiene make such small contributions as to cause a negligibly small moment in the cis form. This reasoning strengthens the conclusion that the unsubstituted butadiene molecule has a moment indistinguishable from zero, a conclusion consistent with the indications of electron diffraction that butadiene molecules must be essentially coplanar and trans[9] and with the conclusion of Mulliken[10] that the trans arrangement is the actual or at least the predominant form in butadiene.

The moment found for 2-ethylbutadiene is 0.07 higher than that of the corresponding methyl compound, a difference in the direction commonly observed between methyl and ethyl compounds and variously explained in terms of induction, contributions from hyperconjugated forms, or merely the greater strength of the ethyl group as an electron source. The difference is greater than the difference 0.02 found between 1-butene and propylene, but, in view of the unavoidable uncertainties in the absolute values of these small butadiene moments, they can be regarded as in qualitative agreement.

In addition to the nonpolar structure of 1,2-dimethylbutadiene

I $CH_3CH{=}C(CH_3){-}CH{=}CH_2$

and two compensating polar structures like those written for butadiene, one can write[11] three polar structures such as II and three such as III below

II $H^+CH_2{=}CH{-}C(CH_3){=}CH{-}\overset{..}{}\!\bar{C}H_2$
and

III $CH_3{-}\bar{\overset{..}{C}}H{-}\overset{\displaystyle H^+CH_2}{\overset{\|}{C}}{-}CH{=}CH_2$

Structure II should have a moment identical with that of the polar structures written for 1-methylbutadiene, and structure III with that written for propylene or 2-methylbutadiene. If structures II and III contributed independently to the 1,2-dimethylbutadiene structure, its moment should be the resultant of the moments of 1-methylbutadiene, 0.68, and 2-methylbutadiene, 0.38, or propylene, 0.35, due account being taken of the angle

[9] V. Schomaker and L. Pauling, *J. Am. Chem. Soc.*, **61**, 1769 (1939).
[10] R. S. Mulliken, *Revs. Mod. Phys.*, **14**, 265 (1942).
[11] N. B. Hannay and C. P. Smyth, *J. Am. Chem. Soc.*, **68**, 244 (1946).

between the dipoles of the two structures. The variety of forms made possible by cis-trans isomerism renders impossible any exact vector addition of the dipole moments resulting from II and III, but, as all probable forms give an angle considerably greater than 90° between the two vectors 0.68 and 0.38, a resultant close to the experimentally observed value 0.63 should be obtained.

In 1,3-dimethylbutadiene,[11] structures analogous to those for 1,2-dimethylbutadiene contribute. In addition to the nonpolar structure

I $CH_3CH{=}CHC(CH_3){=}CH_2$

and the compensating polar structures like those of butadiene, there are three contributing polar structures such as II and three such as III below

II $H^+CH_2{=}CH{-}CH{=}C(CH_3){-}^-\ddot{C}H_2$
and

$$H^+CH_2$$
$$\shortparallel$$
III $CH_3{\cdot}CH{=}CH{\cdot}C{-}{-}^-\ddot{C}H_2$

As before, the contribution of II should give rise to a moment 0.68 and that of III to a moment 0.38. Of the three most probable forms capable of arising from cis-trans isomerism, space models show two to have the two dipoles pointing approximately at right angles to one another and one to have them largely opposing. The observed moment 0.65 is a perfectly reasonable value for the resultant of these vectors.

The trans form of 2,3-dimethylbutadiene[8] should obviously have zero moment, while consideration of the interatomic distances and the valence angles leads to the conclusion that in the cis form the dipoles in the two halves of the molecule, each approximately equal to that in the 2-methylbutadiene molecule, should point nearly in the same direction and give a resultant moment approximately twice that of 2-methylbutadiene. The moment value 0.52 for 2,3-dimethylbutadiene in Table 1.3 is less than twice that of 2-methylbutadiene but is so large as to show that the cis structure must predominate largely over the trans. If the 2-methylbutadiene moment value 0.38 is high by as much as 0.10, which is not impossible, the observed 2,3-dimethylbutadiene moment would agree within its experimental error with the value calculated for the cis form. This establishment of the large predominance of the cis form agrees with the conclusions of Mulliken[10] that spectroscopic results look almost as if 2,3-dimethylbutadiene were pure cis. Cyclopentadiene[11] is a 1-substituted butadiene, but the ring structure necessarily makes the molecule cis with respect to the central double bond produced in resonance of the compensating butadiene type. The moment has been shown[11] to be consistent with the resonating structures which can be written for the molecule.

TABLE 1.4. MOMENTS ($\times 10^{18}$) OF FULVENES AND AZULENE IN SOLUTION[12]

Dimethylfulvene	1.48	Phenylbenzofulvene	1.3
Diethylfulvene	1.44	Diphenylbenzofulvene	1.3
Methylisobutylfulvene	1.4	Phenyldibenzofulvene	0.8
Diphenylfulvene	1.34	Diphenyldibenzofulvene	1.2
Bis-(p-chlorophenyl)fulvene	0.7	Azulene	1.0

Although various highly polar resonating structures can be written for the fulvenes and azulene, one would not necessarily predict on the basis of resonance the considerable polarities which are evidenced by Table 1.4. On the basis of the molecular orbital calculations of Coulson and Longuet-Higgins, fulvene (I) should have a moment of about 4.7 and azulene (II)

I   II

a moment of about 6, with the negative end of the dipole on the side of the five-membered ring in each case.[13]   Refinements in the calculations by Wheland and Mann[13] reduce the moment predicted for fulvene to about 1.5 to 2.0.   The different calculations of Wheland and Mann[13] give the various values 4.7, 3.1, 2.6, 1.1, 1.8, 0.7, and 1.9 for the moment of fulvene, while, from their observed values for substituted fulvenes (Table 1.4), they estimate 1.2 as a reasonable gas value for the moment.   The predicted direction of the fulvene moment is confirmed by the low moment of the bis-(p-chlorophenyl)fulvene molecule in which the two C—Cl moments evidently oppose the fulvene moment.   The trend of the moments of the benzofulvenes is qualitatively consistent with the approximate charge distributions calculated.[12]   The various calculated values,[12] 6.9, 5.25, and 3.8, for azulene are much higher than the observed value 1.0, showing the necessarily approximate character of the calculation.

TABLE 1.5. MOMENTS ($\times 10^{18}$) OF ALKYL ACETYLENES IN THE VAPOR STATE

Molecule	Formula	Moment
Acetylene	$HC{\equiv}CH$	0
Methylacetylene	$CH_3C{\equiv}CH$	0.74
Ethylacetylene	$C_2H_5C{\equiv}CH$	0.80
n-Propylacetylene	$n\text{-}C_3H_7C{\equiv}CH$	0.85
n-Butylacetylene	$n\text{-}C_4H_9C{\equiv}CH$	0.88
n-Amylacetylene	$n\text{-}C_5H_{11}C{\equiv}CH$	0.86
Di-n-amylacetylene (liquid)	$C_5H_{11}C{\equiv}CC_5H_{11}$	0

[12] See B. Pullman and A. Pullman, "Les Théories électroniques de la chimie organique," Masson et Cie, 1952, chap. VII.

[13] G. W. Wheland and D. E. Mann, *J. Chem. Phys.*, **17**, 264 (1949).

The zero moment of the acetylene molecule corresponds to the linear structure ascribed to it and shows that, as in the cases of the C—C and C=C bonds, there is no polarity inherent in the C≡C bond. The moment of methylacetylene is approximately twice that of propylene. In Sec. 2 it will be shown that the substitution of a halogen for a hydrogen adjacent to a C=C bond produces a moment smaller than that resulting from similar substitution adjacent to a C—C bond, while substitution adjacent to a C≡C bond produces a still smaller moment. The shortening of the length of the C—C bond in methylacetylene by 0.08 A. below that of the normal C—C bond may be described[14,15] as due, at least in part, to contributions from three structures, such as H^+CH_2=C=$^-\ddot{C}H$, which can account for the not inconsiderable moment of the molecule. Pullman and Pullman[12] attribute the moment to great electronegativity of the carbon atoms in a state of sp hybridization, resulting in an inductive shift of the electrons of the σ and π bonds. The small increases in moment from methyl to ethyl and ethyl to n-propylacetylene are little larger than the probable experimental error but qualitatively resemble similar increases in the alkyl halides, which may be attributed to inductive effects. Differences among the longer members of the acetylene series are well within the experimental errors. The zero moment for liquid di-n-amylacetylene is to be expected from the symmetry of the molecule.

2. Halogenated Hydrocarbons. Variations in the moments of the straight-chain chlorides and bromides longer than propyl are within the experimental error. The values for twelve pure straight-chain alkyl bromides in Table 16.2, Chap. I, calculated by means of the Onsager equation from the constants of the pure liquids, differ from 1.81 by no more than ± 0.03, but the changes in the gas values from the ethyl to the n-butyl halides appear significant, as do, to some extent, the small variations among the isomeric butyl chlorides. These latter variations appear much larger when measured in solution, but this has been shown to be due to the lowering of the apparent moment value by solvent effect (Sec. I.18) as the molecular shape departs from that of a sphere.[1] Discussion of the many solution measurements on alkyl halides available in the literature is evidently unprofitable.

The molecular moment of CH_3Cl may be treated as the resultant of the bond moments:

$$3(\text{H—C}) \cos 70° + (\text{C—Cl}) = (\text{H—C}) + (\text{C—Cl})$$

[14] L. Pauling, H. D. Springall, and K. J. Palmer, *J. Am. Chem. Soc.*, **61**, 927 (1939).

[15] L. Pauling, "The Nature of the Chemical Bond," Cornell University Press, Ithaca, N.Y., 1940, p. 162.

[1] R. H. Wiswall, Jr., and C. P. Smyth, *J. Chem. Phys.*, **9**, 356 (1941).

The structure of the bond may be described in terms of resonance as the resultant of the contributions of two structures, in the case of C—Cl,

$$C—Cl \qquad C^+Cl^-$$

Although it is customary to write only the covalent structure, the presence of a contribution from the ionic structure is implied in a bond written between atoms of two different elements. The moment of the C—Cl bond is so much greater than that of the H—C that, as an approximation, the entire molecular moment is commonly treated as lying in the C—Cl bond.

TABLE 2.1. MOMENTS ($\times 10^{18}$) OF ALKYL HALIDES IN THE VAPOR STATE

Molecule	F	Cl	Br	I
CH_3	1.81	1.87	1.80	1.64
C_2H_5	1.92	2.05	2.01	1.87
$n\text{-}C_3H_7$		2.10	2.13	2.01
$n\text{-}C_4H_9$		2.10	2.15	2.08
$n\text{-}C_5H_{11}$		2.12	2.19	
$n\text{-}C_7H_{15}$			2.15	
$i\text{-}C_3H_7$		2.15	2.19	
$i\text{-}C_4H_9$		2.04		
$s\text{-}C_4H_9$		2.12		
$t\text{-}C_4H_9$	2.05	2.13		

The increases in moment of the alkyl halides on going from the methyl to the ethyl compound and of the values for the butyl halide moments on going from primary to secondary to tertiary have been attributed to dipoles induced by the carbon-halogen dipole in the groups immediately attached to the primary carbon.[2] As is evident in Table 2.1, the methyl-ethyl moment difference increases for each change from fluorine to chlorine to bromine to iodine. The smaller increase from the ethyl to the n-propyl halides also increases by about the same amount on the change from chlorine to bromine, which is about the same as that from bromine to iodine. Any increase in moment on going from the n-propyl to the n-butyl halides is too small to be evident except in the case of the iodide. The long n-heptyl bromide molecule has the same moment as the n-butyl and n-propyl bromide molecules. Groves and Sugden[3] explained qualitatively the change in the increase of moment for the different halides in terms of the size of the halogen atom and an effect of the hydrocarbon chain upon the field of the primary dipole, but no quantitative expla-

[2] C. P. Smyth, "Dielectric Constant and Molecular Structure," Chemical Catalog, New York, 1931, pp. 75 and 102.
[3] L. G. Groves and S. Sugden, *J. Chem. Soc.*, 158 (1937).

nation has been advanced. Their calculation[4] of inductive effects gives a moment increase from methyl to ethyl chloride of 0.11×10^{-18} as compared to 0.18 observed; for the bromides, an increase of 0.11 calculated as compared to 0.21 observed; and, for the iodides, 0.10 as compared to 0.23 observed. Their calculated increase from ethyl chloride to i-propyl chloride, which is caused by increase in the amount of polarizable matter within the effective range of the C—Cl dipole, is 0.07 as compared to an observed 0.10, and, for the bromides, the calculated increase is 0.06 as compared to 0.18 observed. The increase in moment from normal to secondary butyl chloride should be approximately the same as that from n-propyl to i-propyl. The value observed in the present investigation is 0.03 as compared to 0.05 for the change from n-propyl to i-propyl chloride and for the change from normal to secondary butyl bromide observed by Groves and Sugden. The further increase observed from secondary to tertiary butyl chloride is only 0.01, an amount too small to establish the existence of the increase which is to be expected because of the further increase in the amount of polarizable matter within the effective range of the C—Cl dipole. The increase from ethyl to i-propyl chloride calculated by Groves and Sugden is approximately $\frac{2}{3}$ of that calculated for the methyl to ethyl increase, while the observed increases, though larger, are in the same ratio as the calculated. The moment induced in each methyl group added to the primary carbon has a considerable component perpendicular to the direction of the axis of the C—Cl dipole. When two methyl groups are present as in s-butyl chloride, these two components, making a wide angle with each other, have a resultant about equal to the contribution of the one component in ethyl chloride. In t-butyl chloride, these three components perpendicular to the C—Cl direction cancel one another so that the increases from the primary to the secondary compound should be less than that from methyl to ethyl and the increase from the secondary to the tertiary compound should be less than that from the primary to the secondary.

The branching of the chain in the i-butyl group is so far from the C—Cl dipole that one would, at first glance, expect it to have very little effect upon the moment of the molecule, the change, if any, being a slight increase due to the added amount of polarizable material near the limit of the effective inductive action of the C—Cl dipole. The small but appreciable decrease observed in the i-butyl chloride moment as compared to that of n-butyl chloride is, however, not inconsistent with the appearance of the molecular model, for, of the different positions possible for the two methyl groups through rotation around the carbon-carbon bonds of the molecule, a large fraction places these groups in the neighborhood of the C—Cl dipole where they would make such angles with the

[4] L. G. Groves and S. Sugden, *J. Chem. Soc.*, 1992 (1937).

axis of the dipole that the moments induced in them would oppose that of the inducing dipole and thus tend to reduce the observed molecular moment.

TABLE 2.2. MOMENTS ($\times 10^{18}$) OF POLYHALOGENATED PARAFFINS
(See Tables 3.1 and 4.1, Chap. XI, for temperature-dependent moments)

Molecule	Gas	Solution
CHF_3	1.61	
CF_4	0	
CH_2Cl_2	1.58	1.55
CH_2Br_2	1.43	1.4
CH_2I_2		1.1
$CHCl_3$	1.02	1.2
$CHBr_3$		1.0
CHI_3		0.9
CCl_4	0	0
CHF_2Cl	1.40	
$CHFCl_2$	1.29	
CF_2Cl_2	0.51	
CF_2Br_2	0.66	
$CFCl_3$	0.45	
CF_3Cl	0.46	
CF_3Br	0.65	
CF_3I	0.92	
CH_3CHF_2	2.24	
CH_3CHCl_2	2.07	1.9
$(CH_3)_2CCl_2$	2.25	2.1
CH_3CF_3	2.35	
CH_3CF_2Cl	2.14	
CH_3CCl_3	1.78	1.6
$CHCl_2CCl_3$	0.92	
CF_3CHF_2	1.54	
CF_3CF_2Cl	0.52	
CH_3CHBr_2		2.1
CH_3CHI_2		2.3
$CH_3CH_2CHCl_2$		2.1
$CCl_3CCl_2CHCl_2$		1.0
$CCl_3CCl_2CCl_3$		0
$CF_3(CF_2)_3CF_3$	0	
$(CF_3)_2CFCF_2CF_3$	0	

These substituted methanes can be used to illustrate the use of group and bond moments in the analysis of molecular structure.[5] In the following equations, the formula of a molecule or of a bond enclosed in parentheses will represent its moment. The different bond moments are exposed to somewhat different inductive effects in the different molecules, but, as the total resultant moments of the molecules are not large, it is

[5] C. P. Smyth and K. B. McAlpine, *J. Chem. Phys.*, **1**, 190 (1933).

evident that the differences in inductive effects, which in most cases partially cancel one another, may commonly, as an approximation, be neglected. Since, however, the C—F bond in methyl fluoride is not exposed to the inductive action of other carbon-halogen bonds, one would expect the values calculated by Eqs. (2.8) and (2.10) to be lower than the moment of methyl fluoride. The moment of $CFCl_3$ lies in the C—F line and is given by

$$(CFCl_3) = (C—F) - 3(C—Cl) \cos 70°$$
$$= (C—F) - (C—Cl) = 0.45 \tag{2.1}$$

since $\cos 70° = \frac{1}{3}$. The moment of CF_2Cl_2 must lie in the line which bisects the F—C—F angle and also the Cl—C—Cl angle and is given by

$$(CF_2Cl_2) = 2(C—F) \cos 55° - 2(C—Cl) \cos 55°$$
$$= 1.15 [(C—F) - (C—Cl)] \tag{2.2}$$

Substituting for (C—F) − (C—Cl) its value given by Eq. (2.1),

$$(CF_2Cl_2) = 1.15 \times 0.45 = 0.52 \tag{2.3}$$

as compared to an observed value 0.51.

As an approximation, the moment of $CHFCl_2$ may be regarded as lying in the H—C line. Consequently,

$$(CHFCl_2) = (H—C) + \frac{1}{3}[(C—F) + 2(C—Cl)] \tag{2.4}$$

A similar approximation gives

$$(CF_2Cl_2) = (C—F) - \frac{1}{3}[(C—F) + 2(C—Cl)] \tag{2.5}$$

Adding (2.4) and (2.5),

$$(CHFCl_2) + (CF_2Cl_2) = (H—C) + (C—F) \tag{2.6}$$

but $\qquad (H—C) + (C—F) = (CH_3F) = 1.81 \text{ (obs.)} \tag{2.7}$

and $\quad (CHFCl_2) + (CF_2Cl_2) = 1.29 \text{ (obs.)} + 0.51 \text{ (obs.)} = 1.80 \tag{2.8}$

The excellence of the agreement between the values calculated by (2.7) and (2.8) is accidental, as is shown by a similar calculation involving chloroform.

$$(CHCl_3) = (H—C) + (C—Cl) = 1.05 \text{ (obs.)} \tag{2.9}$$

Adding (2.1) and (2.9),

$$(CFCl_3) + (CHCl_3) = (H—C) + (C—F) \tag{2.10}$$

or 0.45 (obs.) + 1.05 (obs.) = 1.50, while Eq. (2.7) gives

$$(H—C) + (C—F) = 1.81$$

Subtracting (2.9) from (2.4) and rearranging,

$$(CHFCl_2) = (CHCl_3) + \frac{1}{3}[(C—F) - (C—Cl)] \tag{2.11}$$

but $(CHCl_3) = 1.05$, and, from Eq. (2.1), $\frac{1}{3}[(C—F) - (C—Cl)] = 0.15$. Consequently,

$$(CHFCl_2) = 1.05 + 0.15 = 1.20 \tag{2.12}$$

as compared to the observed value 1.29.

As an approximation similar to that in (2.4)

$$(CHF_2Cl) = (H—C) + \frac{1}{3}[2(C—F) + (C—Cl)] \tag{2.13}$$

Subtracting (2.9) from (2.13) and rearranging,

$$(CHF_2Cl) = (CHCl_3) + \frac{2}{3}[(C—F) - (C—Cl)] \tag{2.14}$$

but $(CHCl_3) = 1.05$, and, from Eq. (2.1), $\frac{2}{3}[(C—F) - (C—Cl)] = 0.30$. Consequently,

$$(CHFCl_2) = 1.05 + 0.30 = 1.35 \tag{2.15}$$

as compared to the observed value 1.40.

Although the H—C moment cancels in the final calculations with all these equations, it has been left in the initial equations to make clearer the assumptions. It is evident that the variation of moment among these different fluorochloromethanes agrees extremely well with the predictions of theory.

The moment values of the other substituted methanes in Table 2.2 are at least qualitatively consistent with the ideas discussed in connection with the chloromethanes and fluorochloromethanes. The increase in moment[6] in the series CF_3Cl, CF_3Br, and CF_3I gives evidence of increasing electronic shift in the direction of the fluorines, which may be described in terms of increasing inductive distortion of the Cl, Br, and I with consequent decrease in the C—Cl, C—Br, and C—I moments and increase in the differences between them and the CF_3 moment.

The 1,1-dihalogenated ethanes and the 1,1,1-trihalogenated ethanes show larger increases in moment as compared to the corresponding methanes than do the monohalogenated ethanes in Table 2.1. The inductive effect should be greater as there are now two or three dipoles instead of one to act on the methyl group. A maximum inductive effect is taken care of by using the ethyl-compound moments in calculating the moments of the ethanes. When this is done[7] for 1,1-difluoroethane, the calculated value is $1.15 \times 1.92 = 2.21$, in fair agreement with the observed value in spite of the neglect of the lowering of the moment of each C—F dipole by the inductive effect of the other. On a similar basis, the moment of 1,1,1-trifluoroethane should be equal to that of ethyl fluoride, 1.92, but it is 0.43 higher, although mutual induction between the C—F dipoles would tend to make it lower. For 1,1-dichloro-

[6] A. Di Giacomo and C. P. Smyth, Unpublished measurements.

[7] J. H. Gibbs and C. P. Smyth, *J. Am. Chem. Soc.*, **73**, 5115 (1951).

ethane and 1,1,1-trichloroethane, the calculated moments are 0.28 and 0.27 higher than the observed because of the much larger polarizability of chlorine as compared to fluorine. On the basis of the apparent mutual inductive lowering in the methanes, the discrepancy between observed and calculated values should be larger. These facts seem to provide evidence of increased shifts of electronic charge in the direction of the negative ends of the molecular dipoles, which have been described in terms of hyperconjugation and resonance,[8] or changing availability of the electrons of the central atoms to the attached group.[9] In considerations of this sort, one must always bear in mind that the treatment as distinct entities of two or three dipoles attached to the same atom is arbitrary in the extreme, if not actually naïve.

The moments of 1,1,1,2,2,3,3-heptachloropropane and pentachloroethane are slightly lower than that of chloroform presumably, because of the greater opportunity for inductive lowering in their molecules. In pentafluoroethane, the lowering of moment is much less because of the small polarizability of the fluorines. The apparent zero moment of perchloropropane in solution and the clearly established zero moments of perfluoropentane and perfluoroisopentane in the vapor state, already referred to (Sec. 1), show that the geometrical relations developed for the H—C bond hold and that the moment difference resulting from the attachment of a carbon-halogen dipole to a secondary or tertiary carbon atom instead of to a primary is very small, as also evidenced by the butyl chlorides (Table 2.1).

TABLE 2.3. MOMENTS ($\times 10^{18}$) OF HALOGENATED CYCLIC MOLECULES IN SOLUTION

Chlorocyclopropane	1.76	1,2-Dichlorocyclohexane cis (gas)	3.11
1,1-Dichlorocyclopropane	2.04		3.13
1,2-Dichlorocyclopropane, dl-	1.18	1,2-Dichlorocyclohexane trans (gas)	2.31
Perfluorocyclobutane (gas)	0		2.66
Fluorocyclopentane	1.86	1,4-Dichlorocyclohexane trans	0
Chlorocyclopentane	2.08	1,4-Dibromocyclohexane trans	0
Bromocyclopentane	2.20	1,4-Diiodocyclohexane cis	2.4
Iodocyclopentane	2.06	1,4-Diiodocyclohexane trans	0
1,1-Dichlorocyclopentane	2.35	1,2,4,5-Tetrabromocyclohexane	2.2
Chlorocyclohexane	2.2	1,2,3,4,5,6-Hexachlorocyclohexane α	2.2
Bromocyclohexane	2.2	β	0
Iodocyclohexane	2.0	γ	2.9
		δ	2.2
		Perfluoroethylcyclohexane	(0.7)
		Perfluoro-1,3-dimethylcyclohexane	(0.6)
		Perfluoro-1,4-dimethylcyclohexane	(0.8)

[8] E. C. Hurdis and C. P. Smyth, J. Am. Chem. Soc., **64**, 2829 (1942).

[9] A. A. Maryott, M. E. Hobbs, and P. M. Gross, J. Am. Chem. Soc., **63**, 659 (1941).

The moments of the cyclopropanes have been carefully measured in benzene solution. Two independent determinations of the moment of chlorocyclopropane[10,11] agree exactly on the value in Table 2.3. For purposes of comparison, Rogers and Roberts[11] confine themselves to moments measured in benzene solution, pointing out that the moment of chlorocyclopropane is 0.3 lower than those of isopropyl chloride and chlorocyclopentane, while mere inductive effect should cause virtually no difference. They suggest that a 2 to 3 per cent contribution from a polar structure

$$\begin{array}{c} CH_2 \\ | \quad \diagdown \\ | \quad \quad CH{=}Cl^{+} \\ {-}{:}CH_2 \end{array}$$

would account for this lowering of moment. Since there is a strain energy of 25 kcal. in this three-membered ring, it would not be surprising if the carbon-chlorine bond were altered sufficiently to change the moment by 0.3. 1,1-Dichlorocyclopropane is similarly lower than 1,1-dichlorocyclopentane and 2,2-dichloropropane. As implied in these comparisons, the derivatives of cyclopentane, in which there is no appreciable ring strain, have moments close to those observed for the corresponding secondary alkyl halides, although Rogers and Roberts[11] point out that the larger amount of polarizable matter near the line of the principal dipole in the cyclopentyl compounds would tend to make the contribution from induced dipoles larger than in the secondary alkyl halides, an increase occasionally observed but probably not provable without vapor measurements.

The moments of the monohalogenated cyclohexanes, which have negligible ring strain, are close to those of the corresponding cyclopentyl and secondary alkyl halides. The values for cis-1,2-dichlorocyclohexane correspond closely to a 1e, 2p configuration, while those for the trans isomer show the substance to be an equilibrium mixture of 1e, 2e and 1p, 2p configurations.[12] In the trans 1,4-dihalides listed in Table 2.3, the zero moments show that the carbon-halogen bonds point in opposite directions. In the more highly substituted cyclohexanes, impurities and uncertainty as to the identity of the isomers have led to some uncertainty and confusion. Electron-diffraction determinations[13] of the somewhat complex structures of the hexaclorocyclohexanes and dipole moment measurements[14] have given values for the four isomers in Table 2.3 which

[10] B. I. Spinrad, J. Am. Chem. Soc., **68**, 617 (1946).
[11] M. T. Rogers and J. D. Roberts, J. Am. Chem. Soc., **68**, 843 (1946).
[12] A. Tulinskie, A. Di Giacomo, and C. P. Smyth, J. Am. Chem. Soc., **75**, 3552 (1953).
[13] O. Bastiansen, O. Ellefsen, and O. Hassel, Research (London), **2**, 248 (1949).
[14] E. Amble and O. Hassel, Research (London), **3**, 52 (1950).

are consistent with their geometrical structures. The moment values here are useful merely as confirming the results of electron diffraction. The small moment values in Table 2.3 for the three completely fluorinated cyclohexane derivatives are enclosed in parentheses because the zero moments found for the perfluoropentanes in Table 2.2 and the large values of their atomic polarizations indicate that these apparent moment values may arise merely from large atomic polarizations. The actual moments are probably zero and thus consistent with the zero moments of the saturated cyclic hydrocarbons in Table 1.2 and with those of the completely halogenated hydrocarbons in Table 2.2.

TABLE 2.4. MOMENTS ($\times 10^{18}$) OF MOLECULES CONTAINING DOUBLE BONDS

	Vapor	Sol.		Vapor	Sol.
$CH_2{=}CHCl$	1.44		$CF_2{=}CFCl$	0.40	
$CH_2{=}CHBr$	1.41		$CCl_3CCl{=}CCl_2$		0.4
$CH_2{=}CHI$	1.26		$CH_2{=}CHCH_2Cl$	1.98	
$CH_2{=}CCl_2$		1.30	$CH_2{=}CHCH_2Br$		1.79
$CHCl{=}CCl_2$		0.9	$CH_2{=}C(CH_3)CH_2Cl$	1.85	
$cis\text{-}CHCl{=}CHCl$	1.89	1.8	$CH_2{=}C{=}CHCH_2Cl$	2.02	
$trans\text{-}CHCl{=}CHCl$		0	$cis\text{-}CH_3CH{=}CHCl$	1.71	1.65
$cis\text{-}CHCl{=}CHBr$		1.55	$trans\text{-}CH_3CH{=}CHCl$	1.97	
$trans\text{-}CHCl{=}CHBr$		0	$(CH_3)_2C{=}CHCl$	1.99	
$cis\text{-}CHBr{=}CHBr$		1.3	$CH_3CCl{=}CH_2$	1.69	1.53
$trans\text{-}CHBr{=}CHBr$		0	$CH_3CBr{=}CH_2$		1.51
$cis\text{-}CHI{=}CHI$		0.7	$cis\text{-}CH_3CH{=}CHBr$		1.57
$trans\text{-}CHI{=}CHI$		0	$CH_3CH{=}CCl_2$		1.69
			$(CH_3)_2C{=}CCl_2$		1.73
			$cis\text{-}CH_3CCl{=}CClCH_3$		2.4
			$trans\text{-}CH_3CCl{=}CClCH_3$		0
			$CH_2{=}CClCH{=}CH_2$		1.4

Reference has already been made (Sec. VIII.6) to the resonance treatment by Hugill, Coop, and Sutton of the vinyl halides. The lowering 0.61 of the moment of vinyl chloride below that of ethyl chloride and the shortening of the C—Cl bond 0.07 A. below the normal single-bond length is attributed to the contribution of the polar structure

$$H_2\overset{..}{C}{}^-\!{-}CH{=}Cl^+$$

The analogous lowering of 0.60 for vinyl bromide and 0.38 for vinyl iodide may be attributed to similar contributions from analogous polar structures. If these resonating polar structures had any real relation to chemical behavior, one would expect the most stable polar structure to be

$$H_2\overset{..}{C}{}^-\!{-}CH{=}I^+$$

because iodine is the least negative of the halogens, but the relative lowering for vinyl iodide is less than for the other two halides, indicating lower stability for this polar structure.   A similar discrepancy will be apparent in the monohalogenated benzenes where the moment lowering of fluorobenzene indicates that the polar structure with positive fluorine is more stable than the analogous structures of the other monohalogenated benzenes, although fluorine is the most negative element. In chloroacetylene and bromoacetylene, to be discussed shortly, the polar structure with positive bromine seems to be more stable than that with positive chlorine, as might be expected from the less-negative character of bromine, but, in vinyl chloride and vinyl bromide, the stabilities of the two structures appear to be about the same.   From other considerations, Waters[15] concludes that the canonical structures used to represent a molecule may not explain its chemical reactivity.

The low moments of 1,1-dichloroethylene and 1,1,2-trichloroethylene give evidence of the lowering of moment by mutual induction like that in methylene chloride.   The cis and trans 1,2-dihalogenated ethylenes are the molecules first subjected to study by the use of dipole moments as vector quantities.[16]   The considerable moments of the cis forms and the zero moments of the trans confirmed the symmetrical planar structure ascribed to ethylene by the organic chemist.

Electron diffraction[17] gives the C—C—Cl angle in chloroethylenes as 123°, which gives an angle of 66° between the two C—Cl bond directions. If, as an approximation, we assume that the two principal dipoles act in the directions of the C—Cl bonds and have moments equal to that of vinyl chloride, the moment calculated for cis-1,2-dichloroethylene is $2 \times 1.44 \cos 33° = 2.42$.   The moment 1.89 for the molecule in Table 2.4 is considerably lower, presumably because of mutual induction between the two dipoles.   The lowering becomes greater in the chlorobromo compound, still greater in the dibromo, and greatest of all in the diiodoethylene, as the increasing polarizability of the halogens gives increased inductive lowering.

[15] W. A. Waters, "Physical Aspects of Organic Chemistry," Van Nostrand, New York, 4th ed., 1950, p. 73.

[16] J. Errera, *J. phys. radium*, (6)**6**, 390 (1925).

[17] P. W. Allen and L. E. Sutton, *Acta Cryst.*, **3**, 46 (1950).

The moment of hexachloropropene, within the large probable error existing in a small moment measured in solution, agrees with that of propylene, although one might expect a difference because of the great difference between hydrogen and chlorine. The moment of allyl chloride is 0.12 lower than that of the corresponding saturated compound propyl chloride. This lowering indicates contributions from two forms with propylenelike polarity, such as

$$\overset{H^+}{^-:CH_2-CH=CHCl}$$

The moment of methallyl chloride is also lowered by contributions from propylenelike structures.[18] The moment of 4-chlorobutadiene-1,2, $CH_2=C=CH-CH_2Cl$, is only 0.08 lower than the value for the corresponding saturated compound n-butyl chloride, a difference which is consistent with the resonating structures possible for the molecule.[18] The moments of the chloropropylenes may be similarly accounted for.[18] As an illustration, contributing polar structures may be written for the two isomers of 1-chloropropylene

If the contribution from structure II diminishes that from I, the lowering of the moment by I should be less than in vinyl chloride. That a diminution occurs in isocrotyl chloride is shown by the fact that electron-diffraction measurements[19] indicate a shortening of the carbon-chlorine bond less than that in vinyl chloride. In cis-1-chloropropylene, the moment contribution of structure II, assumed, as usual, to be the same as that of propylene, 0.35, makes an angle of about 99° with the carbon-chlorine dipole and, therefore, raises the moment by about 0.09. As might be expected, the observed moment 1.71 is close to that of 2-chloropropylene. In $trans$-1-chloropropylene, the moment of structure II acts

[18] N. B. Hannay and C. P. Smyth, *J. Am. Chem. Soc.*, **68**, 1005 (1946).
[19] J. Y. Beach and D. P. Stevenson, *J. Am. Chem. Soc.*, **61**, 2643 (1939).

so nearly in the direction of the carbon-chlorine dipole that it should raise the resultant moment by about 0.35, that is, 0.26 more than the increase produced by the contribution of the analogous structure for the cis compound. This difference, 0.26, is exactly that observed between the cis and trans moments in Table 2.4. The moment of isocrotyl chloride, $(CH_3)_2C=CHCl$, should show an increase over that of *trans*-1-chloropropylene by an amount slightly less than 0.09 as the result of the added cis methyl group. In view of the various factors involved, the observed value 1.99 is in satisfactory agreement with this prediction.

As the rather small moment differences produced by unsaturation may be at least partly obscured by solvent effects, it does not seem profitable to discuss the other moment values in Table 2.4. Their variations seem in general to be consistent with those of the vapor values. The two isomers of 2,3-dichloro-2-butene are to be compared with those of 1,2-dichloroethylene. The trans isomer has zero moment as required by its symmetry, while the moment of the cis isomer is 0.6 higher than that of *cis*-1,2-dichloroethylene because of the added presence of two propylene-like moments.

TABLE 2.5. MOMENTS ($\times 10^{18}$) IN SOLUTION OF MOLECULES CONTAINING TRIPLE BONDS

$CH \equiv CCl$	0.44 (gas)	$CH_3(CH_2)_3C \equiv CBr$	1.1
$CH \equiv CBr$	0 (gas)	$CH_3(CH_2)_4C \equiv CBr$	1.1
$IC \equiv CI$	(0.3)	$CH_3(CH_2)_3C \equiv CI$	0.8
$CH_3(CH_2)_3C \equiv CCl$	1.23	$CH_3(CH_2)_4C \equiv CI$	0.8
$CH_3(CH_2)_4C \equiv CCl$	1.27		

Just as the moments of the alkyl acetylenes are much higher than those of the alkyl ethylenes, presumably because of resonance, so the moments of chloroacetylene and bromoacetylene are lowered by resonance much more than are the moments of vinyl chloride and vinyl bromide. This implies that the structures $H\overset{..}{C}^- = C = Cl^+$ and $H\overset{..}{C}^- = C = Br^+$ are more stable than the corresponding vinyl halide structures with positive halogen. Brockway and Coop[20] have found that the amount of double-bond character calculated from the shortening of the carbon-halogen bond as measured by electron diffraction agrees with that calculated from the lowering of moment. The moment value for diiodoacetylene must be regarded as indistinguishable from zero, the value required by its linearity. The moment values of the alkyl halogenoacetylenes may be calculated roughly as the sums of the moments of the corresponding alkyl and halogenoacetylene:

$$0.88(n\text{-}C_4H_9C \equiv CH) + 0.44(CH \equiv CCl) = 1.32$$

as compared to 1.23 observed for $n\text{-}C_4H_9 \equiv CCl$. The difference is less

[20] L. O. Brockway and I. E. Coop, *Trans. Faraday Soc.*, **34**, 1429 (1937).

than the probable solvent effect, not to mention the experimental errors. The difference between observed and calculated values is only 0.03 for n-$C_5H_{11}C{\equiv}CCl$. For the corresponding bromine compounds, the difference is 0.2, which is about the magnitude of the probable error. The zero moment of bromoacetylene as compared to 0.44 for chloroacetylene, the lower moments of 1-bromohexyne-1 and 1-bromoheptyne-1 as compared to the corresponding chlorine compounds, and the lower moments of 1-iodohexyne-1 and 1-iodoheptyne-1 as compared to the corresponding bromine compounds suggest but do not establish the possibility that iodine is positive in iodoacetylene.

3. Cyanides. In view of the large moment found associated with the cyanide group, the zero moment of cyanogen shows it to be a linear molecule, $N{\equiv}C{-}C{\equiv}N$, which agrees with aromatic-compound moments (Sec. X.3) and spectroscopic and electron-diffraction measurements[1] in showing that the valence bond of the cyanide group acts in the direction of the axis of the group. For hydrogen cyanide, three structures may be written:

$$H{-}C{\equiv}N \qquad\qquad H{-}C^+{=}N:{^-} \qquad\qquad H^+\overset{..}{C}{=}N:{^-}$$

The contributions of the two polar structures are presumably responsible for the large moment of the molecule and the different character of the H—C bond from that in the hydrocarbons. The magnitude of the moment indicates a considerable stability for one or both of these polar structures. The cyanogen halides show similarity in charge shifts to the halogenoacetylenes (Sec. 2). If the C—Br bond in cyanogen bromide were normal, the moment should be approximately equal to the difference between the moments of hydrogen cyanide and methyl bromide or of acetonitrile and methyl bromide:

$$(HCN) - (CH_3Br) = 2.93 - 1.80 = 1.13$$
or $$(CH_3CN) - (CH_3Br) = 3.94 - 1.80 = 2.14$$

This takes the negative end of the HCN dipole as toward the nitrogen, as required by the polar structures written for it and as clearly indicated by the moments of the chloroacetonitriles in Table 3.1 as well as by those of cyanide-substituted benzenes (Chap. X). The fact that the observed solution moment is much larger than these calculated values and indistinguishable from the gas moment of hydrogen cyanide suggests that the C—Br bond is like that in bromoacetylene, which has zero moment. Resonating structures for the molecule may be written $Br{-}C{\equiv}N$, $Br{-}C^+{=}N:{^-}$, $Br^+{=}C{=}N:{^-}$. The shortening of the carbon-bromine bond below the length of the normal single bond gives further evidence of this type of charge distribution. The still larger moment of cyanogen

[1] P. W. Allen and L. E. Sutton, *Acta Cryst.*, **3**, 46 (1950).

iodide indicates an even larger contribution from a structure with positive halogen, so large, in fact, that the iodine atom is positive in the molecule, as suggested in the case of iodoacetylene.

TABLE 3.1. MOMENTS ($\times 10^{18}$) OF CYANOGEN, HYDROGEN CYANIDE, AND SUBSTITUTED CYANIDES

Molecule	Formula	Vapor	Sol.	Molecule	Formula	Sol.
Cyanogen	$(CN)_2$	0		Trichloroacetonitrile	CCl_3CN	2.0
Hydrogen cyanide	HCN	2.93		Dichloroacetonitrile	$CHCl_2CN$	2.2
Cyanogen chloride	ClCN	2.80		Chloroacetonitrile	CH_2ClCN	3.0
Cyanogen bromide	BrCn		3.0	Methylene dicyanide	$CH_2(CN)_2$	3.6
Cyanogen iodide	ICN		3.71			

The moment of trichloroacetonitrile may be calculated as the difference between the moments of hydrogen cyanide and chloroform:

$$(HCN) - (CHCl_3) = 2.93 - 1.02 = 1.91 \text{ (gas)}$$

or the difference between acetonitrile and methyl chloroform:

$$(CH_3CN) - (CH_3CCl_3) = 3.94 - 1.78 = 2.16 \text{ (gas)}$$
or
$$3.5 - 1.6 = 1.9 \text{ (sol.)}$$

The differences between the two values calculated from gas measurements are real, but the calculated values differ from the observed solution value by no more than the possible solvent effects involved. The moment of chloroacetonitrile may be calculated by resolving two vectors, the C—Cl moment taken as the CH_3Cl moment, 1.8, and the CH_3CN moment, 3.5, in solution, at an angle of 110°:

$$(CH_2ClCN) = 3.5^2 + 1.8^2 + 2 \times 3.5 \times 1.8 \cos 110° = 3.4$$

The observed moment is 0.4 lower than this calculated value, presumably because of lowering of the two adjacent moments by mutual inductive effects. The lowering is greater in dichloroacetonitrile, with three adjacent dipoles, just as it is in chloroform as compared to methylene chloride. The moment of methylene dicyanide should be calculable from that of acetonitrile as $2 \times 3.5 \cos 55° = 4.0$. The lowering is relatively less than in methylene chloride as the two dipoles are farther apart, lying effectively between the C and the N.

The increase from the moment of hydrogen cyanide, 2.93, to that of acetonitrile, 3.94, is, though larger, analogous to that from formaldehyde to acetaldehyde (Sec. 6) and, as in that case, presumably arises in part from induction and in part from contributions from analogous polar structures. Two structures analogous to the first two for hydrogen cyanide

TABLE 3.2. MOMENT ($\times 10^{18}$) OF ALKYL, CYCLIC, AND UNSATURATED CYANIDES

Molecule	Formula	Vapor	Sol.
Acetonitrile	CH_3CN	3.94	3.5
Propionitrile	C_2H_5CN	4.00	3.6
n-Butyronitrile	$n\text{-}C_3H_7CN$	4.05	3.6
i-Butyronitrile	$(CH_3)_2CHCN$		3.6
Valeronitrile	$n\text{-}C_4H_9CN$	4.09	
t-Butyl cyanide	$(CH_3)_3CCN$		3.7
Isoamylcyanide	$i\text{-}C_5H_{11}CN$		3.5
Acrylonitrile	$CH_2{=}CHCN$	3.88	
trans-Crotononitrile	$trans\text{-}CH_3CH{=}CHCN$	4.50	
4-Cyanobutadiene-1,3	$CH_2{=}CHCH{=}CHCN$	3.90	
Methacrylonitrile	$CH_2{=}C(CH_3)CN$	3.69	
n-Butylpropiolnitrile	$C_4H_9C{\equiv}CCN$		4.21
n-Amylpropiolnitrile	$C_5H_{11}C{\equiv}CCN$		4.22
Cyclopropyl cyanide	$\begin{matrix} CH_2 \\ \quad \diagdown \\ \qquad CHCN \\ \quad \diagup \\ CH_2 \end{matrix}$		3.75
Methylcyclopropyl cyanide	$(CH_3)CHCH_2CHCN$		3.78
Cyclopentyl cyanide	$CH_2(CH_2)_3CHCN$		3.71

may be written for acetonitrile, and, in addition, three highly polar structures of the type[2]

$$H^+CH_2{=}C{=}N:^-$$

Indication of the contributions from such structures is given by the shortening of the carbon-carbon bond by 0.05 A. shown by electron-diffraction measurements.[1] The small rise from the methyl to the ethyl compound may arise from induction, as may the slight rises from ethyl to n-propyl to n-butyl, but these latter are little, if any, larger than the errors in their determinations. Among the solution values for the alkyl cyanides, the higher value for t-butyl probably arises from reduction in the lowering by solvent effect because of the approach of the molecule toward spherical form, although increased opportunity for induction may contribute. The careful measurements[3] on the cyclic cyanides in benzene solution indicate slightly higher values for cyclopropyl and methylcyclopropyl cyanides, but the differences seem too small to warrant structural interpretation.

For acrylonitrile, one may write[2] structures analogous to those for acetonitrile and, in addition, structures characteristic of the conjugated

[2] E. C. Hurdis and C. P. Smyth, J. Am. Chem. Soc., **65**, 89 (1943).

[3] M. T. Rogers and J. D. Roberts, J. Am. Chem. Soc., **68**, 843 (1946).

system. The explanation of the moment in terms of these structures is plausible, but not wholly convincing. The replacement of an end hydrogen by a methyl group in going from acrylonitrile to crotononitrile produces a rise in moment, 0.6, indistinguishable from the moment value of 1-methylbutadiene (Table 1.3), indicating the comparative stability of highly polar structures such as

$$H^+CH_2\!\!=\!\!CH\!\!-\!\!CH\!\!=\!\!C\!\!=\!\!N:^-$$

Both acrylonitrile and crotononitrile show values of MR_D appreciably higher than those calculated from atomic refractivities, an exaltation due to conjugation of the carbon-carbon double bond with the carbon-nitrogen triple bond. It would appear that the exaltation for crotononitrile (0.82) is greater than that for acrylonitrile (0.31) because the added resonance in crotononitrile gives a considerable increase in the mobility of the resonance electrons. A similar effect is shown by acrolein (exaltation, 0.62) and crotonaldehyde (exaltation, 1.36). The value and the origin of the moment of 4-cyanobutadiene are similar to those of acrylonitrile. The moment of methacrylonitrile, 3.69, shows a drop of 0.19, or 5 per cent, from that of acrylonitrile, analogous to the drop from allyl to methallyl chloride (Sec. 2).

The moment values of the two acetylenic nitriles in benzene solution are probably appreciably lower than the gas values. These may be larger than the moments of *trans*-crotononitrile and evidence qualitatively the same type of charge shift, as would be expected from the moments of the acetylenic compounds considered in Secs. 1 and 2.

4. Isocyanides, Isocyanates, Thiocyanates, and Isothiocyanates. The solution moment of ethyl isocyanide is hardly distinguishable (0.1 lower) from that of propionitrile. Electron-diffraction and spectroscopic investigations, as well as dipole moment measurements,[1] show the atoms C—N—C to have a linear configuration.[2-4] Of the two structures

$$CH_3N\!\!=\!\!C \qquad\qquad\qquad CH_3N^+\!\!\equiv\!\!C^-$$

the first would be bent and would have as moment the resultant of the small C—N and the somewhat larger C=N moments (Sec. VIII.4). The second would be linear and would have as moment the sum of the small C—N and the large $N^+\!\!\equiv\!\!C^-$ moments. The moments of substituted aromatic isocyanides (Chap. X) show the + to − direction of the dipole to be that of C—$N^+\!\!\equiv\!\!C^-$. The importance of the contribution of the polar triple-bonded structure is, therefore, evident. Gordy and Pauling[3] con-

[1] R. G. A. New and L. E. Sutton, *J. Chem. Soc.*, 1415 (1932).

[2] L. Pauling, "The Nature of the Chemical Bond," Cornell University Press, Ithaca, N.Y., 1940, p. 199.

[3] W. Gordy and L. Pauling, *J. Am. Chem. Soc.*, **64**, 2593 (1942).

[4] P. W. Allen and L. E. Sutton, *Acta Cryst.*, **3**, 46 (1950).

clude that hyperconjugation of the methyl group and the triple bond is smaller for the isocyanide than for the cyanide because the corresponding structure

$$H^+CH_2{=}N^+{=}C{:}^-$$

has an unstable distribution of charge. A contribution from this third structure would, however, contribute to the linearity and large moment observed. It is evident that the negative element nitrogen can acquire a positive charge in these structures almost as easily as the considerably less-negative element carbon.

TABLE 4.1. MOMENTS ($\times 10^{18}$) IN SOLUTION OF ISOCYANIDES, ISOCYANATES, THIOCYANATES, AND ISOTHIOCYANATES

Ethyl isocyanide	C_2H_5NC	3.5	Methyl isothiocy-		
Ethyl isocyanate	C_2H_5NCO	2.8	anate	CH_3NCS	3.2
Methyl thiocyanate	CH_3SCN	3.6	Ethyl isothiocyanate	C_2H_5NCS	3.3
Ethyl thiocyanate	C_2H_5SCN	3.6	Allyl isothiocyanate	$CH_2{=}CHCH_2NCS$	3.3

For ethyl isocyanate, three resonating structures may be written like those proposed[5] for methyl isocyanate

$$\underset{R}{\overset{N=C=O}{\diagup}} \qquad \underset{R}{\overset{\ddot{N}^-\!\!-C{\equiv}O^+}{\diagup}} \qquad \underset{R}{\overset{N^+{\equiv}C{-}O{:}^-}{\diagup}}$$

I   II   III

On the basis of the interatomic distances found by means of electron diffraction, which showed the isocyanate group to be linear with an R—N—C angle of 125° ± 5°, Eyster, Gillette, and Brockway[5] estimated that the fractional contributions of these three structures to the methyl cyanate structure were about 0.36, 0.26, and 0.38, respectively. It is reasonable to assume that approximately the same situation exists in ethyl isocyanate. The moment due to the contribution of the highly polar structure III would thus exceed that due to the contribution of the equally polar structure II, and the much smaller moment resulting from structure I would act in nearly the same direction as that of III. The resultant moment of the molecule should be smaller than those of the cyanides and isocyanides, as observed.

Structures may be written for the thiocyanates analogous to those for the normal cyanates[5]

I $\underset{R}{\overset{S^+{=}C{=}N{:}^-}{\diagup}}$ II $\underset{R}{\overset{\ddot{S}{-}C{\equiv}N}{\diagup}}$

[5] E. H. Eyster, R. H. Gillette, and L. O. Brockway, *J. Am. Chem. Soc.*, **62**, 3236 (1940).

A third structure with doubly charged sulfur and nitrogen should be too unstable to be important. In the case of the isocyanates, structure II opposes the moments of the other two structures. In these thiocyanates, the moments of the two principal contributing structures act in about the same direction, and, therefore, produce a larger resultant moment.

The structures of the isothiocyanates should result from contributing structures analogous to the three written for the alkyl isocyanates. The excess, 0.4 to 0.5, of their moments over that of ethyl isocyanate corresponds to the excess of the $C=S$ moment over the $C=O$ moment (Sec. VIII.4), a difference pointed out by Cowley and Partington[6] as existing between the moments of thiobenzophenone and benzophenone, 0.42, and dianisylthioketone and dianisylketone, 0.54, and as causing this difference between isothiocyanates and isocyanates. Hunter and Partington[7] conclude that the closeness of the moment values for ethyl and allyl isothiocyanates indicates the absence of influence of the principal dipole upon a double bond in the β position. The precision of the gas measurements upon allyl chloride (Table 2.4) is sufficient to show that the influence may be small, but nonetheless detectable.

5. Nitroalkanes and Chloronitroalkanes, Alkyl Nitrites and Nitrates.

Early dipole moment measurements on nitrobenzenes (Chap. X) indicated that the nitro group was symmetrical with its resultant moment acting in the direction of the group valence bond.[1] The symmetry of the group under ordinary circumstances has been confirmed by electron-diffraction measurements.[2-5] The group may be represented[5] by two equally stable resonating structures

The large resultant dipole obviously lies in the axis of the group bond, which bisects the ONO angle.

Some of the apparent differences among the vapor moments of the molecules in Table 5.1 are due to discrepancies between measurements of different investigators. From the vapor values, it is evident that the

[6] E. G. Cowley and J. R. Partington, *J. Chem. Soc.*, 45 (1936).

[7] E. C. E. Hunter and J. R. Partington, *J. Chem. Soc.*, 2825 (1932).

[1] C. P. Smyth, "Dielectric Constant and Molecular Structure," Chemical Catalog, New York, 1931, p. 121.

[2] L. O. Brockway, J. Y. Beach, and L. Pauling, *J. Am. Chem. Soc.*, **57**, 2693 (1935).

[3] F. Rogowski, *Ber. deut. chem. Ges.*, **75B**, 244 (1942).

[4] P. W. Allen and L. E. Sutton, *Acta Cryst.*, **3**, 46 (1950).

[5] L. Pauling, "The Nature of the Chemical Bond," Cornell University Press, Ithaca, N.Y., 2d ed., 1940, p. 201.

TABLE 5.1. MOMENTS ($\times 10^{18}$) OF NITROALKANES AND CHLORONITROALKANES

Molecule	Formula	Vapor	Sol.
Nitromethane	CH_3NO_2	3.50	3.15
Nitroethane	$C_2H_5NO_2$	3.70	3.2
1-Nitropropane	$C_3H_7NO_2$	3.72	3.38
2-Nitropropane	$CH_3CHNO_2CH_3$	3.73	3.41
2-Methyl-2-nitropropane	$CH_3C(CH_3)NO_2CH_3$	3.71	3.48
1-Nitro-n-butane	$C_4H_9NO_2$	3.6	3.4
Tetranitromethane	$C(NO_2)_4$	0	0
Nitroform	$CH(NO_2)_3$		2.71
Chloropicrin	CCl_3NO_2	1.88	1.85
Chloronitromethane	CH_2ClNO_2	2.91	
1-Chloro-1-nitroethane	$CH_3CHClNO_2$	3.33	
1-Chloro-1-nitropropane	$C_2H_5CHClNO_2$	3.52	

inductive effect of the large nitro group is barely if at all detectable beyond the first two carbons in the chain.

The fact that $(CH_3)_2CHNO_2$ and $(CH_3)_3CNO_2$ have moments indistinguishable from $CH_3CH_2CH_2NO_2$ confirms the conclusion for the straight-chain compounds that the inductive effect of the dipoles of the nitro group is hardly detectable in the moments beyond the first two carbons of the chain. This is understandable since the carbon-nitrogen bond moment is small and the large nitrogen-oxygen bond moments are separated by the nitrogen from the carbon chain. The small size of the inductive effect calculated approximately by Groves and Sugden[6] conforms qualitatively to these facts, although the observed inductive effect is larger than the calculated.

The moment values of 1-nitropropane, 2-nitropropane, and 2-methyl-2-nitropropane carefully determined in benzene solution by Dr. P. F. Oesper in the writer's laboratory are significant in the second decimal place relative to one another. Although the three vapor values are indistinguishable from one another, the solution values increase as approach toward spherical form decreases the lowering of moment by solvent effect (Sec. I.18). A virtual absence of solvent effect is shown by the moment of chloropicrin, which is close to spherical in form.

Some discrepancies are evident among the data for tetranitromethane, but it appears reasonable to conclude that the molecular moment is zero and that the difference between total polarization and refraction is atomic polarization. Such an absence of moment corresponds to the tetrahedral structure of the molecule and the symmetry of the nitro group and is in accord with the results of electron diffraction.[7] If there were no induc-

[6] L. G. Groves and S. Sugden, J. Chem. Soc., 158 (1937).

[7] A. J. Stosick, J. Am. Chem. Soc., 61, 3067 (1939).

tive action between neighboring dipoles, the moments of nitromethane and nitroform should be equal, as required by their tetrahedral structures.[8] The lowering of the moment by induction is much less in nitroform than in chloroform, for not only is the ratio of the tri- to the monosubstituted compound much larger, but the absolute lowering is only 0.5 as compared to 0.85. The total polarizability of the nitro group is slightly greater than that of chlorine, as shown by its refraction of 6.7 as compared to 5.97, but its polarizability per atom and per displaceable electron is only a little more than a third of that of chlorine and that for the chlorine electrons. In some positions of the nitro groups as they rotate around the C—N bonds, an oxygen of one nitro group may come very close to that of another with a considerable resultant lowering of the N—O dipole moments, but if, as it was found necessary to assume in the electron-diffraction investigation of tetranitromethane[7] and as should be equally probable here, the nitro groups are undergoing rotatory oscillation about the C—N bonds in such a way as to keep the oxygen-oxygen repulsions minimized as far as possible, the oxygens are somewhat removed from neighboring dipoles and the inductive effects should be smaller than those in chloroform. The smaller reduction in dipole moment is thus accounted for.

The moment of chloropicrin may be calculated roughly as the difference between that of nitromethane and that of methyl chloroform,

$$(CH_3NO_2) - (CH_3CCl_3) = 3.50 - 1.78 = 1.72$$

or as

$$(C_2H_5NO_2) - (CH_3CCl_3) = 3.70 - 1.78 = 1.92$$

The agreement of the first calculated value with the observed is almost as good as can be expected, and the agreement of the second is rather better than can be expected.

Calculation[9] of the moment of chloronitromethane by vector addition of the moments of methyl chloride and nitromethane gives a resultant moment of 3.40×10^{-18}. The observed moment 2.91 may, for the time being, be taken to indicate that the lowering due to mutual induction between the chloro and nitro groups is 0.49. This is comparable in magnitude to the lowering observed in methylene chloride, where the moment calculated is 2.16 and the observed is 1.58, so that the apparent inductive lowering is 0.58. Since the inductive lowering observed for the dichloro compound is slightly larger than that for the chloronitro compound, while the moment of nitromethane is nearly twice that of methyl chloride, we have further evidence that the nitro group is considerably less susceptible to inductive lowering of its moment than the chlorine atom. The moment of 1-chloro-1-nitroethane calculated by vector addition of

[8] G. L. Lewis and C. P. Smyth, *J. Am. Chem. Soc.*, **61**, 3067 (1939).
[9] E. C. Hurdis and C. P. Smyth, *J. Am. Chem. Soc.*, **64**, 2829 (1942).

the moments of ethyl chloride and nitroethane is 3.60×10^{-18}. The observed moment 3.33 indicates that the apparent inductive lowering is 0.27 as compared with 0.49 for monochloronitromethane. The moment rise expected between monochloronitromethane and 1-chloro-1-nitroethane is $3.60 - 3.40 = 0.20$, while the observed rise is 0.42. For the moment of 1-chloro-1-nitropropane we have: moment calculated—3.62, moment observed—3.52, apparent inductive lowering—0.10; expected rise from 1-chloro-1-nitroethane—0.02, observed rise from 1-chloro-1-nitroethane—0.19. These seemingly low inductive lowerings are evidently further examples of the increased shifts of electronic charge noted in Sec. 2 for di- and trihalogenated ethanes.

TABLE 5.2. MOMENTS ($\times 10^{18}$) OF ALKYL NITRITES AND NITRATES IN SOLUTION

Ethyl nitrite	C_2H_5ONO	2.3	Ethyl nitrate	$C_2H_5ONO_2$	2.91
n-Propyl nitrite	C_3H_7ONO	2.3	n-Propyl nitrate	$C_3H_7ONO_2$	2.98
n-Amyl nitrite	$C_5H_{11}ONO$	2.3	n-Butyl nitrate	$C_4H_9ONO_2$	2.96
Methyl nitrate	CH_3ONO_2	2.85	Pentaerythritol tetranitrate	$C(CH_2ONO_2)_4$	2.0

The nitrite and nitrate group moments differ from that of the nitro group in that they do not act in the direction of the group bond. On the basis of the interatomic distances indicated by electron diffraction for methyl nitrite[3] and methyl nitrate,[10] one may write resonating structures for the nitrite

and for the nitrate

where R represents the alkyl group. For the nitrite, the polar structure is written to account for the considerable moment. Contribution from such a structure seems to be more or less implicit in the structure of a double bond between the atoms of different elements. Since both the nitrate structures are polar, their moments should be larger than that of the nitrite. As the N—O bond moment of R—O—N is opposite in direction to the resultant of the moments of the other two N—O bonds, the resultant moments of the nitrates are smaller than those of the nitroalkanes.

[10] L. Pauling and L. O. Brockway, J. Am. Chem. Soc., **59**, 13 (1937).

The molecule of pentaerythritol tetranitrate, in which four CH_2ONO_2 groups are tetrahedrally arranged around a central carbon atom, has a moment because the bond angles of the four tetrahedrally grouped carbons as well as the possibly pyramidal forms of the nitrates prevent compensation of the moments.

6. Aldehydes and Ketones. For convenience in reference, the aldehydes and ketones are listed in separate tables, but the moments of both depend primarily upon the large dipole in the carbonyl group.

TABLE 6.1. MOMENTS ($\times 10^{18}$) OF ALDEHYDES

Molecule	Formula	Vapor	Sol.
Formaldehyde	HCHO	2.27	
Acetaldehyde	CH_3CHO	2.72	2.49
Propionaldehyde	C_2H_5CHO	2.73	2.54
n-Butyraldehyde	C_3H_7CHO	2.72	2.57
i-Butyraldehyde	$(CH_3)_2CHCHO$		2.58
n-Valeraldehyde	C_4H_9CHO		2.6
i-Valeraldehyde	$(CH_3)_2CHCH_2CHO$		2.6
n-Heptaldehyde	$C_6H_{13}CHO$		2.6
α-Ethylcaproaldehyde	$C_4H_9CH(C_2H_5)CHO$		2.6
Acrolein	$CH_2=CHCHO$	3.04	2.9
trans-Crotonaldehyde	$CH_3CH=CHCHO$	3.67	
Methacrolein	$CH_2=C(CH_3)CHO$	2.68	2.7
Tiglaldehyde	$CH_3CH=C(CH_3)CHO$		3.4
n-Butylpropiolaldehyde	$C_4H_9\equiv CCHO$		3.2
n-Amylpropiolaldehyde	$C_5H_{11}C\equiv CCHO$		3.2
Trichloroacetaldehyde	CCl_3CHO		1.58
Tribromoacetaldehyde	CBr_3CHO		1.69

The moment of formaldehyde is 0.45 lower than that determined for acetaldehyde, while the moment of acetone is 0.13 higher. The rise produced by substituting the first methyl group in formaldehyde is markedly greater than that produced by the introduction of the second methyl group. A rough calculation[1] of the moment induced in the methyl group by the dipole in the carbon-oxygen bond gives a moment rise from formaldehyde to acetaldehyde close to that observed. In view of the extremely approximate character of any such calculation, which may easily give an absolute error of more than 50 per cent, it is, perhaps, more significant that the ratio of the calculated rise from formaldehyde to acetone to that from formaldehyde to acetaldehyde is close to the observed. The fact that the second methyl group affects the calculated rise much less than the first is due to the cancellation of the component of moment induced in one methyl group perpendicular to the direction of the carbonyl-group axis by the component in the other methyl group.

[1] E. C. Hurdis and C. P. Smyth, *J. Am. Chem. Soc.*, **65**, 89 (1943).

TABLE 6.2. MOMENTS ($\times 10^{18}$) OF KETONES IN SOLUTION

Molecule	Formula	Moment
Acetone	CH_3COCH_3	2.85 (gas)
		2.75
Methylethylketone	$C_2H_5COCH_3$	2.8
Diethylketone	$C_2H_5COC_2H_5$	2.7
Methylpropylketone	$C_3H_7COCH_3$	2.7
Methyl-n-butylketone	$C_4H_9COCH_3$	2.7
Methyl-t-butylketone	$(CH_3)_3CCOCH_3$	2.8
Di-n-propylketone	$C_3H_7COC_3H_7$	2.7
Di-i-propylketone	$(CH_3)_2CHCOCH(CH_3)_2$	2.7
Methylamylketone	$C_5H_{11}COCH_3$	2.6
Ethylbutylketone	$C_4H_9COC_2H_5$	2.8
Methylhexylketone	$C_6H_{13}COCH_3$	2.7
Hexamethylacetone	$(CH_3)_3CCOC(CH_3)_3$	2.8
Methylnonylketone	$C_9H_{19}COCH_3$	2.7
Dioctylketone	$C_8H_{17}COC_8H_{17}$	2.8
Cyclopropylmethyl-ketone	$\overline{CH_2CH_2CH}COCH_3$	2.8
Cyclopentanone	$\overline{CH_2(CH_2)_3CO}$	3.0
Cyclohexanone	$\overline{CH_2(CH_2)_4CO}$	2.75
1,4-Cyclohexanedione	$\overline{CH_2{-}CH_2{-}CO{-}CH_2{-}CH_2{-}CO}$	1.4
2,2,4,4-Tetramethylcy-clobutane-1,3-dione	$\overline{(CH_3)_2C{-}CO{-}C(CH_3)_2{-}CO}$	(0.7) (gas)
		(0.8)
3,3-Dimethylcyclo-hexanone	$\overline{CH_2{-}CH_2{-}CH_2{-}C(CH_3)_2{-}CH_2{-}CO}$	2.92
3,4-Dimethylcyclo-hexanone	$\overline{CH_2{-}CH_2{-}CH(CH_3){-}CH(CH_3){-}CH_2{-}CO}$	2.83
3,5-Dimethylcyclo-hexanone	$\overline{CH_2{-}CH(CH_3){-}CH_2{-}CH(CH_3){-}CH_2{-}CO}$	2.89
Carvone	$C_9H_{14}CO$	2.8
Camphor	$C_9H_{16}CO$	2.95
Fenchone	$C_9H_{16}CO$	2.91
Menthone	$C_9H_{18}CO$	2.80
Cycloheptatrienone	C_7H_6O	4.3
Tetraphenylcyclopenta-dienone	$(C_6H_5)_4C_5O$	3.5
2,5-Bis-(4'-chloro-phenyl)-3,4-diphenyl-cyclopentadienone	$(C_6H_4Cl)_2(C_6H_5)_2C_5O$	4.6
Tetrakis-(4-chloro-phenyl)-cyclopenta-dienone	$(C_6H_4Cl)_4C_5O$	2.26
Ketene	$CH_2{=}CO$	1.45 (gas)
Dimethylketene	$(CH_3)_2C{=}CO$	1.8
Diphenylketene	$(C_6H_5)_2C{=}CO$	1.9
Diketene	$CH_3COCHCO$	3.53 (gas)
		3.3
Methylvinylketone	$CH_3COCH{=}CH_2$	3.0
n-Butylacetylacetylene	$C_4H_9C{\equiv}CCOCH_3$	3.2
n-Amylacetylacetylene	$C_5H_{11}C{\equiv}CCOCH_3$	3.2

The moments of acetaldehyde, propionaldehyde, and n-butyraldehyde are identical within the experimental error.   This result differs from that of the solution measurements, which show an increase of 0.05 from the moment of acetaldehyde to that of propionaldehyde and a further increase of 0.03 from propionaldehyde to n-butyraldehyde.   The solvent-effect lowering is of about the expected magnitude.   The absence of moment increase shown by the gas values for lengthening of the carbon chain beyond the two carbons of acetaldehyde parallels a similar absence of appreciable increase in the solution values of the ketones and in the gas values of the nitroparaffins beyond nitroethane (Sec. 5).   If the large increase in moment from formaldehyde to acetaldehyde arose wholly from induction, one might expect so large an effect to produce a further increase from acetaldehyde to propionaldehyde.   The absence of this increase may be regarded as an indication that the increase from formaldehyde to acetaldehyde is not caused wholly by induction, but, in part, by resonance.   However, approximate compensation of inductive effects could occur,[1] as suggested in the case of the alcohols (Sec. 8), and be a factor in preventing increase of moment with increase in the number of carbon atoms beyond two.

The large moment of the carbonyl bond has been attributed to a large contribution from a polar structure.[1]   On this basis, the principal structures of formaldehyde would be

$$CH_2{=}O \qquad\qquad {}^+CH_2{-}O{:}^- \qquad\qquad {}^+H\ddot{C}H{-}O{:}^-$$

For acetaldehyde, in addition to three structures analogous to the three written for formaldehyde, three structures may be written of the type

$$H^+CH_2{=}CH{-}O{:}^-$$

Evidence of contributions from such structures is given by the shortening of the C—C bond by 0.04 below the length of the normal single C—C bond found by means of electron diffraction.[2]   The large increase of moment produced by the presence of the double bond in acrolein may be attributed to the ease of transfer of charge through a double bond.   While the replacement of a methyl hydrogen in acetaldehyde by a methyl group does not increase the moment of propionaldehyde, the conjugation of the acrolein molecule facilitates[1] the transmission of charge to the negative oxygen by means of contributions from structures such as

$$^+CH_2{-}CH{=}CH{-}O{:}^- \qquad\qquad H^+\ddot{C}H{-}CH{=}CH{-}O{:}^-$$

The effect of hyperconjugation is shown more strikingly in the surpris-

---

[2] D. P. Stevenson, H. D. Burnham, and V. Schomaker, *J. Am. Chem. Soc.*, **61,** 2922 (1939).

ingly large rise in moment, nearly 0.6, resulting from the replacement of an end hydrogen in acrolein by a methyl group to form *trans*-croton-aldehyde. In addition to polar structures analogous to those which have been proposed for acrolein, one can write[1] for crotonaldehyde three highly polar structures such as

$$H^+CH_2 = CH - CH = CH - O:^-$$

the apparent stability of which should tend to increase the moment, as observed.

In methacrolein,[3] which has a moment 2.68—lower by 0.36 than that of acrolein, the charge shift from the methyl group gives rise to a propylene-like moment which opposes instead of reinforcing the polarity due to the carbonyl group. A moment equal to that of propylene, 0.35, would so nearly oppose the carbonyl moment as to reduce it by about 0.33, pro-vided that the methyl group were in the cis position relative to the oxygen. Calculation shows that, in this position, induction between the carbonyl dipole and the methyl group should give a moment lowering of about 0.24. As the cis position is an extreme one, the actual moment lowering below that of acrolein should be less than the sum of these two effects and close to the observed 0.36. The rise in moment from methacrolein to tiglaldehyde, in which the methyl groups are cis to one another,[4] is practically the same as that from acrolein to *trans*-crotonaldehyde and may be attributed to contributions from three highly polar structures like that written for the latter. The moments of *n*-butyl and *n*-amyl-propiolaldehyde are raised by a contribution from the structure[5]

$$R - C^+ = C = CHO^-$$

The large rise in moment, 0.63, from acrolein to *trans*-crotonaldehyde, is practically identical with the rise, 0.62, from acrylonitrile to *trans*-crotononitrile (Sec. 3), and with the moment of *trans*-1-methylbutadiene, 0.68 (Sec. 1). As the two rises in moment and the entire moment in the third case are due to contributions from analogous structures of the type

$$H^+CH_2 = CH - CH = C = N:^- \qquad H^+CH_2 = CH - CH = C - O:^-$$
$$H^+CH_2 = CH - CH = CH - \overset{..}{\,}CH_2$$

it would appear that these structures possess approximately equal sta-bilities as compared to the stabilities of the other structures contributing to their respective molecules.

[3] N. B. Hannay and C. P. Smyth, *J. Am. Chem. Soc.*, **68**, 1357 (1946).

[4] M. T. Rogers, *J. Am. Chem. Soc.*, **69**, 1243 (1947).

[5] H. L. Goebel and H. H. Wenzke, *J. Am. Chem. Soc.*, **59**, 2301 (1937).

The moments of trichloro- and tribromoacetaldehyde are much lower than those of the unsubstituted aldehydes because of the presence of the CCl_3 and CBr_3 dipoles. Coomber and Partington[6] have taken the —CCl_3 moment as 1.57 (the solution value for CH_3CCl_3) and the aldehyde moment as 2.49 (acting in the direction of the carbonyl bond) and have calculated the angle between these two vectors as 142°. They point out that this is larger than the angle 125° to be expected between a single and a double bond and that the apparent discrepancy may be attributable to lowering of the moments by mutual induction, neglect of which results in too high a calculated value for the angle. The moment values of these two molecules are thus consistent with their presumed structures.

The dipole moment of the acetone molecule lies in the axis of symmetry, which bisects the C—C—C angle. In the longer ketones, it is, therefore, perpendicular to the axis of the zigzag carbon chain of the molecule when this is extended. The fact that the angle between the dipole axis and the direction of maximum polarizability in the molecule is not far from 90° accounts for the absence of increase in moment with chain length and the smallness of the solvent effects in aldehydes and ketones (Table 18.1, Chap. I). The cyclic ketones, in which the carbonyl group forms part of the ring, seem to have moments 0.05 to 0.2 higher than those of the aliphatic ketones, probably because the direction of maximum polarizability in the molecule is more nearly that of the carbonyl dipole axis, thus permitting a small increase of moment by inductive effect.

Two different values have been reported for the moment of 1,4-cyclohexanedione, 1.6[7] and 1.3.[8] Le Fèvre and Le Fèvre[8] treat the substance as an equilibrium mixture of cis and trans configurations. The trans form should have zero moment, while, for the cis form, Le Fèvre and Le Fèvre calculate the moment value 4.1. They then calculate that, if the moment observed for the mixture of two molecular species is 1.6, the amount of cis form is 15 per cent, while, if it is as low as 1.2, the amount is only 9 per cent. They further calculate that, if the difference in energy between the two forms is only that due to dipole-dipole interaction, the amount of cis form should be 19 per cent, a figure of the same order of magnitude as that calculated from the observed moment.

The relative proportions of the two species, of moments μ_1 and μ_2, may be calculated by the use of a mixture relationship like that in Sec. I.10. $N\mu^2$ in Eq. I(6.13) may be written

$$N\mu^2 = n_1\mu_1{}^2 + n_2\mu_2{}^2 \tag{6.1}$$

[6] D. I. Coomber and J. R. Partington, *J. Chem. Soc.*, 1444 (1938).

[7] O. Hassel and E. Naeshagen, *Tidsskr. Kjemiog Bergvesen*, **10**, 81 (1930).

[8] C. G. Le Fèvre and R. J. W. Le Fèvre, *J. Chem. Soc.*, 1696 (1935).

where $N = n_1 + n_2$.

Then
$$\mu^2 = \frac{n_1}{N}\mu_1{}^2 + \frac{n_2}{N}\mu_2{}^2$$
$$= c_1\mu_1{}^2 + c_2\mu_2{}^2 \tag{6.2}$$

Taking $\mu = 1.6$, $\mu_1 = 4.1$, $\mu_2 = 0$,

$$c_1 = \frac{1.6^2}{4.1^2} = 0.15 = 15\%$$

In spite of their aromatic character, it has seemed best to discuss cycloheptatrienone and three tetracyclones at this point in order to compare them with the other cyclic ketones in Table 6.2. The slight increases in moment of acetophenone and benzophenone (Sec. X.2) above the values for the aliphatic ketones might be described in terms of additional small contributions from highly polar structures with positive charge on the ortho or para carbons of the ring. However, since the cyclic ketones in Table 6.2 have equally large moments, it would seem that the small increases in moment are caused largely by electrostatic induction. For cycloheptatrienone, we may write[9] six structures with a positive charge on the ring, such as

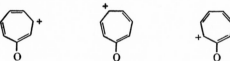

The large increase, about 1.4×10^{-18}, in moment of this molecule over those of the other cyclic ketones seems to indicate the considerable stability of these polar structures with resonance increased by the possible existence of six structures, probably differing little from one another in energy.

The moment value 3.5 of 2,3,4,5-tetraphenylcyclopentadienone or tetracyclone is less elevated than that of cycloheptatrienone, but still is about 0.6×10^{-18} larger than those of the previously discussed cyclic ketones. In addition to the normal structure I for the molecule, and the polar structure characteristic of all ketones with the carbonyl carbon positive and the oxygen negative, twelve polar structures such as II may be written,[9] with a positive charge on one of the four para or eight ortho carbons of the four benzene rings,

I   II

[9] A. Di Giacomo and C. P. Smyth, *J. Am. Chem. Soc.*, **74**, 4411 (1952).

As the moments of these structures are large, resonance involving very small contributions from each could cause the observed rise in moment. The stabilities of these structures must be greatly reduced by the steric repulsion between the phenyl groups, which prevents them from being coplanar. The moments of di- and tetrachlorotetracyclone may be calculated[9] on the basis of a model for the tetracyclone molecule as $3.5 + 2 \times 1.58 \cos 72° = 4.5$ for 2,5-bis-(4'-chlorophenyl)-3,4-diphenyl-cyclopentadienone and $3.5 + 2 \times 1.58 \cos 72° - 2 \times 1.58 \cos 36° = 1.8$ for tetrakis-(4-chlorophenyl)-cyclopentadienone. The dichlorotetracyclone moment thus calculated differs from the observed value by no more than the probable error, while the calculated value for the tetrachloro-tetracyclone is a little low, the discrepancy probably arising from the approximations made in the calculation.[9]

A qualitative description of the charge distribution in the cyclohepta-trienone and cyclopentadienone rings is given by Brown's calculation[10] of the number of π electrons per atom by the method of Coulson and Longuet-Higgins.[11] From the charge distribution and the dimensions of the tropolone ring given by X-ray analysis,[12] a dipole moment value 9.5×10^{-18} may be calculated for cycloheptatrienone.[9] A similar calculation gives 5.6×10^{-18} for the hypothetical cyclopentadienone, irrespective of whether the ring is taken as a symmetrical pentagon or as resembling that of cyclopentadiene. The calculated moments greatly exceed the observed, much as the values calculated for ionic structures tend to exceed such as may be observed,[13] but show that the molecular moments should be greater than those of ordinary aliphatic and aromatic ketones.

The small apparent moment values enclosed in parentheses for 2,2,4,4-tetramethylcyclobutane-1,3-dione, which should be symmetrical, are concluded not to be real, probably arising from atomic polarization.[14,15]

The moment of ketene, 1.45, is much lower than the value to be expected on the basis of the other moments in Table 6.2. Electron diffraction[16] indicates a shortening of 0.07 A. in the carbon-oxygen distance below that of the carbon-oxygen double bond, which was accounted for by supposing a 25 per cent contribution from the structure $^-:CH_2$—$C\equiv O^+$. A moment value not far from the observed can be calculated[17] from the contributions of this structure and others resembling ketone structures

[10] R. D. Brown, *J. Chem. Soc.*, 2670 (1951).

[11] C. A. Coulson and H. C. Longuet-Higgins, *Proc. Roy. Soc. (London)*, **191A**, 39 (1947).

[12] J. M. Robertson, *J. Chem. Soc.*, 1222 (1951).

[13] C. P. Smyth, *J. Am. Chem. Soc.*, **63**, 57 (1941).

[14] D. L. Hammick, G. C. Hampson, and G. I. Jenkins, *J. Chem. Soc.*, 1263 (1938).

[15] I. E. Coop and L. E. Sutton, *J. Chem. Soc.*, 1269 (1938).

[16] J. Y. Beach and D. P. Stevenson, *J. Chem. Phys.*, **6**, 75 (1938).

[17] N. B. Hannay and C. P. Smyth, *J. Am. Chem. Soc.*, **68**, 1357 (1946).

considered in this section.   If this calculation were correct, the oxygen atom would have only a very small negative charge, while the carbon to which it is linked would have a considerable positive charge and the other carbon a negative charge equal to the absolute difference between the other two charges.   Pullman and Pullman[18] consider it more logical to attribute the low moment value of ketene and also those of dimethyl-ketene and diphenylketene[19] to strong electronegativity of the central carbon resulting from its being in a state of hybridization like that of an acetylenic carbon (Sec. 1).

Angus, Leckie, Le Fèvre, Le Fèvre, and Wassermann[20] investigated the dipole moment, the heat of formation, and other physical properties of diketene and decided that the most probable of the three cyclic structures shown was II, for which

$$
\begin{array}{ccc}
\text{H}_2\text{C}\text{---}\text{C}\text{=}\text{O} & \text{H}_2\text{C}\text{---}\text{C}\text{=}\text{O} & \text{HC}\text{=}\text{C}\text{---}\text{OH} \\
|\quad\quad| & |\quad\quad| & |\quad\quad| \\
\text{O}\text{=}\text{C}\text{---}\text{CH}_2 & \text{HO}\text{---}\text{C}\text{=}\text{CH} & \text{HO}\text{---}\text{C}\text{=}\text{CH} \\
\text{I} & \text{II} & \text{III}
\end{array}
$$

they calculated a moment close to the observed value.   Their conclusion was that II represented the structure, with possible small amounts of I and III present.   From chemical behavior and parachor determination, Hurd and Williams[21] concluded the structure to be that of acetylketene IV or β-crotonolactone V.

$$
\begin{array}{ccc}
\text{CH}_3\text{---}\text{C}\text{---}\text{CH}\text{=}\text{C}\text{=}\text{O} & & \text{CH}_3\text{---}\text{C}\text{=}\text{C}\text{---}\text{H} \\
\text{IV}\quad\quad \|\quad\quad\quad\quad\quad\quad & \text{V} & |\quad\quad| \\
\text{O}\quad\quad\quad\quad\quad\quad & & \text{O}\text{---}\text{C}\text{=}\text{O}
\end{array}
$$

Hurd and Roe[22] indicated an equilibrium mixture of the two forms IV and V as probable, while Boese[23] adopted vinylaceto-β-lactone, VI, as a preferred structure:

$$
\begin{array}{c}
\text{CH}_2\text{=}\text{C}\text{---}\text{CH}_2 \\
\text{VI}\quad\quad\quad |\quad\quad| \\
\text{O}\text{---}\text{CO}
\end{array}
$$

From measurements of absorption spectra, Calvin, Magel, and Hurd[24] have concluded the β-crotonolactone formula, V, to be most probable,

[18] See footnote 12, Sec. 1.
[19] A. A. Hukins and R. J. W. Le Fèvre, *Nature*, **164,** 1050 (1949).
[20] W. R. Angus, A. H. Leckie, C. G. Le Fèvre, R. J. W. Le Fèvre, and A. Wassermann, *J. Chem. Soc.*, 1751 (1935).
[21] C. D. Hurd and J. W. Williams, *J. Am. Chem. Soc.*, **58,** 962 (1936).
[22] C. D. Hurd and A. S. Roe, *J. Am. Chem. Soc.*, **61,** 3355 (1939).
[23] A. B. Boese, Jr., *Ind. Eng. Chem.*, **32,** 16 (1940).
[24] M. Calvin, T. T. Magel, and C. D. Hurd, *J. Am. Chem. Soc.*, **63,** 2174 (1941).

together with the condition of extremely easy transformation into the isomeric acetylketene form, IV.   Unfortunately, the dipole moment does not provide a unique solution of the problem of these structures.   With free rotation around the single bonds and bond moments of 2.5 and 0.4 for C=O and H—C, respectively, the moment of structure IV is calculated[25] as 3.4, a value agreeing within the accuracy of the calculation with that observed for diketene.   For structures V and VI, the moment may be estimated[25] roughly as 3.4, in excellent agreement with the observed value.   It is thus evident that, although the dipole moment of the molecule eliminates structures I and III, it does not distinguish between the other four structures.   The results of electron diffraction[26] favor structures V or VI, but cannot distinguish between them.

The moment of methylvinylketone is raised by contribution from structures analogous to the polar structures written for acrolein, and the moments of n-butyl- and n-amylacetylacetylene are each raised by one from a polar structure analogous to that written for the propiolaldehydes.

7. Ethers and Alicyclic Oxides.   If the oxygen bonds in water, the alcohols, and the ethers used only p orbitals, the angle between the bonds[1] would be 90° in the absence of complicating effects.   The widening of the angle to 105° in the water molecule has been attributed to repulsion between the positive charges of the hydrogens and the widening in the ethers to steric repulsion between the two alkyl groups, dipole-dipole repulsion also contributing.   It has been suggested that the greater bulk of the ethyl groups causes greater repulsion and, hence, greater widening of the angle and greater reduction of moment in ethyl ether than in methyl.   Recent electron-diffraction measurements[2] give the C—O—C angle as 111° ± 3° in methyl ether and 108° ± 3° in ethyl ether, thus eliminating increased angle widening as the cause of the lower moment in ethyl ether.   If some bond hybridization occurs so that the bonds are not pure p bonds, the bond angle should be greater than 90°.   If the ether molecules form a zigzag chain, the oxygen valence angle being 110°, the molecule is rod-shaped and the molecular dipole is perpendicular to the rod axis, as in the ketones.   With this configuration for ethyl ether, the secondary dipoles induced in the terminal methyl groups should oppose the principal dipole and lower the moment below that of methyl ether.   The inductive effect should be negligible beyond the β-carbon, which is consistent with the identity of the moment of ethyl ether with those of the longer ethers.   The different disposition of the polarizable

[25] P. F. Oesper and C. P. Smyth, *J. Am. Chem. Soc.*, **64**, 768 (1942).

[26] P. W. Allen and L. E. Sutton, *Acta Cryst.*, **3**, 46 (1950).

[1] L. Pauling, "The Nature of the Chemical Bond," Cornell University Press, Ithaca, N.Y., 2d ed., 1940, p. 77.

[2] P. W. Allen and L. E. Sutton, *Acta Cryst.*, **3**, 46 (1950).

material in cyclohexyl methyl ether can account for its moment being slightly higher, like that of methyl ether. The solvent effect causes the solution values to be slightly higher than the gas values as calculated in Sec. I.18.

TABLE 7.1. MOMENTS ($\times 10^{18}$) OF ETHERS

Molecule	Formula	Vapor	Sol.
Methyl ether	$(CH_3)_2O$	1.29	
Ethyl ether	$(C_2H_5)_2O$	1.16	1.22
n-Propyl ether	$(C_3H_7)_2O$	1.18	1.2
Ethyl n-butyl ether	$C_2H_5OC_4H_9$		1.2
Ethyl isoamyl ether	$C_2H_5O(CH_2)_2CH(CH_3)_2$		1.2
n-Butyl ether	$(C_4H_9)_2O$	1.18	1.2
i-Amyl ether	$((CH_3)_2CH(CH_2)_2)O$		1.2
Cyclohexyl methyl ether	$C_6H_{11}OCH_3$	1.29	
Vinyl ether	$(CH_2{=}CH)_2O$		1.06
Vinyl n-butyl ether	$CH_2{=}CHOC_4H_9$		1.25
Vinyl isobutyl ether	$CH_2{=}CHOCH_2CH(CH_3)_2$		1.20
Ethoxyacetylene	$C_2H_5OC{\equiv}CH$		1.98
Butoxyacetylene	$C_4H_9OC{\equiv}CH$		2.03

The small lowering of the moment of vinyl ether below those of the alkyl ethers may be due to contributions from structures such as $CH_2{=}CH{-}\overset{..}{O}{}^+{=}CH{-}{}^-CH_2$, but, in the two monovinyl ethers in Table 7.1, the effect is too small to be detected. The high moments of ethoxyacetylene and butoxyacetylene are qualitatively consistent with the shift of electronic charge toward the acetylenic carbons in the substituted acetylenes (Sec. 1) and with the lowering of the moment of ketene below that of the normal ketones (Sec. 6). A possible resonating structure to indicate such charge shift would be $R{-}\overset{..}{O}{}^+{=}C{=}{}^-CH$.

If the bond moments are unaltered by ring formation and the H—C moments are lumped with the C—O moments, the moment of ethylene oxide should be calculable from the moment of methyl ether and the oxygen valence angle[2] as $1.29 \cos 30.5°/\cos 55.5° = 1.96$, which is surprisingly close to the vapor value 1.88. The propylene oxide moment should be about the same, as observed, and the value for 3,4-epoxybutene is nearly the same. The moment value, 2.0, reported for trimethylene oxide is inconsistent with the larger oxygen valence angle, $94.5° \pm 3°$, indicated for it by electron diffraction. The drop in moment to tetrahydrofuran, or tetramethylene oxide, is consistent with the increase in oxygen valence angle[2] to $111° \pm 2°$, but the moment of tetrahydrofuran is 0.4 higher than that of methyl ether with the same oxygen valence angle, a difference seemingly too high to be attributable wholly to inductive effect. Tetrahydropyran, or pentamethylene oxide, which should

TABLE 7.2. MOMENTS ($\times 10^{18}$) OF ALICYCLIC OXIDES IN SOLUTION

Molecule	Formula	Moment
Ethylene oxide	CH_2—CH_2O	1.88 (gas)
Propylene oxide	CH_3—CH—CH_2—O	1.98
3,4-Epoxybutene-1	CH_2=CH—CH—CH_2—O	1.92
Trimethylene oxide	CH_2—CH_2—CH_2—O	2.0
Tetrahydrofuran	$CH_2(CH_2)_2CH_2$—O	1.70
Tetrahydropyran	$CH_2(CH_2)_3CH_2$—O	1.9
Furan	CH=CH—CH=CH—O	0.69
2,5-Dihydrofuran	CH_2—CH=CH—CH_2—O	1.53
1,3-Dioxolane ring		
2-Methyl-1,3-dioxolane		1.21
2,4-Dimethyl-1,3-dioxolane		1.32
2,4,4,5,5-Pentamethyl-1,3-dioxolane		1.29
2,2-Dimethyl-1,3-dioxolane		1.12
2-Bromomethyl-1,3-dioxolane		2.28
1,3-Dioxane ring		
2-Methyl-1,3-dioxane		1.89
2-Methyl-2-amyl-1,3-dioxane		1.90
2-Bromomethyl-1,3-dioxane		2.89
1,4-Dioxane		0.3 (gas) 0.4
2,6-Dioxa-4-spiroheptane		0.8
1,3,5-Trioxane		2.18
Paraldehyde		2.03

have about the same oxygen valence angle as tetrahydrofuran, has a moment 0.2 higher. Although it is possible that the errors in some of the dipole moments and oxygen bond angles may be larger than they appear to be, it also appears likely that the large changes in the bond angle alter the charge distribution and, hence, the individual bond moments. Rogers[3] accounts for a change in charge distribution by writing polar structures such as $^+HCH_2=CH-CH_2$ for propylene oxide.

$$-O^{/}$$

Furan is included in Table 7.2 in spite of its aromatic character, because its structure can be most conveniently discussed at this point. The smallness of the moment of furan is attributable to resonance contributions from structures with positive oxygen somewhat analogous to that written for vinyl ether. The lowering of moment is much greater than that in vinyl ether because the number of possible stable structures with positive oxygen is greater and the restriction by the ring of the directions of their moments gives a larger resultant moment opposing the resultant of the two normal carbon-oxygen moments. A greater lowering will be noted subsequently in the thiophene and selenophene molecules for similar reasons. The resonating polar structures which lower the moment so much in the furane molecule cannot contribute to the structure of 2,5-dihydrofurane, which, therefore, has a considerably higher moment.

In the 1,3-dioxolane and 1,3-dioxane rings, the two C—O—C group dipoles make such angles with each other that considerable moments result. The possible molecular structures have been very qualitatively discussed by Otto.[4] In 1,4-dioxane, the smallness of the apparent moment shows that most of the molecules are in the so-called "chair form," in which the C—O—C dipole moments cancel each other and give zero moment, but the persistence of a small moment indicates the presence of a small fraction of the molecules in the "boat form," which should have a considerable resultant moment. The small but appreciable moment reported for 2,6-dioxa-4-spiroheptane indicates that each of the two rings is not planar, since, otherwise, the moments in the two halves of the molecule should cancel each other. The molecule of 1,3,5-trioxane can possibly exist in a chair form, for which Maryott and Acree[5] calculate a moment of 2.3, and a boat form, for which they calculate 0.6. As their experimentally determined value is 2.1 in benzene solution, they conclude that the substance is largely in the chair form, possibly, in equilibrium with a small amount of the boat form. A similar conclusion may be drawn as to the structure of the analogous paraldehyde molecule.

[3] M. T. Rogers, *J. Am. Chem. Soc.*, **69**, 2544 (1947).

[4] M. M. Otto, *J. Am. Chem. Soc.*, **59**, 1590 (1937).

[5] A. A. Maryott and S. F. Acree, *J. Research Nat. Bur. Standards*, **33**, 71 (1944).

8. Alcohols.   The molecular association of the alcohols, which has been previously discussed (Sec. III.3), increases the errors in the dipole moment measurements in solution unless they are carried out with precision at unusually high dilutions.   For this reason, it has seemed unprofitable to include in Table 8.1 the solution moments of larger alcohol molecules, which agree with the smaller alcohol moments within the experimental error.   The measurements of Maryott[1] at mole fractions between 0.00013 and 0.013 in benzene at 30° appear to be as precise as the gas values. In contrast to previous data, they show no change of polarization with concentration in the more dilute region.   They indicate a slight lowering of moment in methyl alcohol by solvent effect, which has been calculated to be negligibly small (Table 18.1, Chap. I).   In the other alcohols, the solvent effects appear to be no larger than the errors of observation or calculation.

TABLE 8.1. MOMENTS ($\times 10^{18}$) OF ALCOHOLS

Molecule	Formula	Vapor	Sol.
Methyl alcohol	CH_3OH	1.69	1.62
Ethyl alcohol	C_2H_5OH	1.69	1.66
n-Propyl alcohol	C_3H_7OH	1.66	1.66
Isopropyl alcohol	$(CH_3)_2CHOH$	1.63	1.66
n-Butyl alcohol	C_4H_9OH	1.65	1.69
Isobutyl alcohol	$(CH_3)_2CHCH_2OH$	1.63	1.70
sec-Butyl alcohol	$C_2H_5(CH_3)CHOH$		1.65
t-Butyl alcohol	$(CH_3)_3COH$		1.66

In the water molecule, the molecular dipole moment may be treated as the resultant of two H—O moments acting at an angle of 105° with each other, and, in the alkyl ether molecules, it may be treated as the resultant of two C—O moments, or, better, two R—O moments, acting at an angle of about 110° with each other.   The alcohol moment may be treated as the resultant of an R—O moment and an H—O moment making an unknown angle with each other, probably not far from 110°. These two bond or group moments may be calculated from the water and ether moments and the bond angles mentioned in Sec. 7.

$$2(\text{H—O}) \cos 52.5° = 1.84 \qquad (\text{H—O}) = 1.51$$
$$2(\text{R—O}) \cos 55.5° = 1.29 \qquad (\text{R—O}) = 1.14$$

The moment of the alcohol molecule may then be calculated from the vector relationship

$$\mu = [(\text{H—O})^2 + (\text{R—O})^2 + 2(\text{H—O})(\text{R—O}) \cos \theta]^{1/2}$$

With $\theta = 110°$, the moment calculated for methyl alcohol is 1.55 and,

[1] A. A. Maryott, *J. Am. Chem. Soc.*, **63**, 3079 (1941).

with $\theta = 105°$, it is 1.61, as compared to the vapor value 1.69. With $\theta = 102°$, a reasonable value, exact agreement is obtained between the observed and the calculated moment values, but the possible interactions which may have changed the H—O and C—O moments make this angle value somewhat uncertain. The angle ϕ which the resultant molecular moment makes with the direction of the C—O bond may be calculated by fixing reference axes in the C—O—H plane with the x axis in the C—O line. The components of moment along these axes are

$$m_x = 1.14 + 1.51 \cos 102° = 0.83$$
$$m_y = 1.51 \sin 102° = 1.48$$

Then $\tan \phi = m_y/m_x = 1.78$ and $\phi = 61°$. With the oxygen valence angle taken as 110° instead of 102°, $\phi = 67°$.

The small C—O moment should induce small moments in the carbon chain, tending to increase the molecular moment with increasing chain length as in the alkyl halides, though to a smaller extent because of the smaller primary moment. If the larger H—O moment were located in a trans position relative to that of the methyl group in ethyl alcohol, it would exert little effect upon this group, but, if it were in a cis position, the not inconsiderable moment induced by it should oppose and tend to reduce that of the molecule as a whole. The average effect of the H—O moment should come close to compensating the effect of the C—O in increasing the moment of ethyl over that of methyl alcohol, leaving the two nearly if not quite the same, as observed. Branching or lengthening of the chain can bring additional polarizable matter within the range of the H—O dipole in its cis position, where it may decrease the total moment slightly as apparent in Table 8.1.

9. Sulfides and Mercaptans. As the solution values of the mercaptans in Table 9.1 are uncertain by ± 0.1, their apparent variations with chain length are without significance. Hunter and Partington[1] have explained the differences between the moments of corresponding oxygen and sulfur compounds largely in terms of the considerable difference in polarizability of oxygen and sulfur, as was done roughly for water and hydrogen sulfide.[2] A C—S moment inherently larger than the H—S and a C—O inherently smaller than the H—O can account for the differences in moment.[3]

The saturated cyclic sulfides in Table 9.1 show an increase in moment over the alkyl sulfides analogous to that of the cyclic oxides over the alkyl ethers. The lowering of the divinyl sulfide moment is attributable[4] to

[1] E. C. Hunter and J. R. Partington, *J. Chem. Soc.*, 2812, 2819 (1932).
[2] C. P. Smyth, *J. Am. Chem. Soc.*, **46**, 2151 (1924).
[3] W. S. Walls and C. P. Smyth, *J. Chem. Phys.*, **1**, 337 (1933).
[4] N. B. Hannay and C. P. Smyth, *J. Am. Chem. Soc.*, **68**, 1005 (1946).

TABLE 9.1. MOMENTS ($\times 10^{18}$) OF SULFIDES AND MERCAPTANS

Molecule	Formula	Vapor	Sol.
Methyl sulfide	$(CH_3)_2S$		1.40
Ethyl sulfide	$(C_2H_5)_2S$	1.51	1.60
Propyl sulfide	$(C_3H_7)_2S$		1.55
n-Butyl sulfide	$(C_4H_9)_2S$		1.57
n-Amyl sulfide	$(C_5H_{11})_2S$		1.58
Ethylene sulfide	$CH_2\!-\!CH_2\!-\!S$	1.84	
3,3-Dimethyl-1-thiocyclobutane	$CH_2\!-\!C(CH_3)_2\!-\!CH_2\!-\!S$		1.8
2,6-Dithia-4-spiroheptane	$CH_2\!-\!S\!-\!CH_2\!-\!C\!-\!CH_2\!-\!S\!-\!CH_2$		1.1
Vinyl sulfide	$(CH_2\!=\!CH)_2S$	1.20	
Thiophene	$\begin{array}{c} CH\!=\!CH \\ \diagdown \\ S \\ \diagup \\ CH\!=\!CH \end{array}$	0.58	0.54
Tetrahydrothiophene	$CH_2(CH_2)_2CH_2\!-\!S$		1.87
Methyl mercaptan	CH_3SH	1.26	
Ethyl mercaptan	C_2H_5SH	1.56	1.4
n-Propyl mercaptan	C_3H_7SH		1.3
n-Butyl mercaptan	C_4H_9SH		1.4
n-Amyl mercaptan	$C_5H_{11}SH$		1.5

contributions from two structures, such as $CH_2\!=\!CH\!-\!S^+\!=\!CH\!-\!\ddot{C}H_2$. The lowering of the thiophene moment below the value for tetrahydrothiophene is much greater than that of vinyl sulfide because in thiophene the number of possible stable structures[5] with positive sulfur is greater and the restriction by the ring of the directions of their moments gives a larger resultant moment opposing the resultant of the two carbon-sulfur moments. The effect is analogous to the lowering of moment from that of tetrahydrofuran to that of furan (Sec. 7).

10. Monocarboxylic Acids and Their Esters. Many apparent moment values for fatty acids are omitted from Table 10.1 because they have not been measured at concentrations sufficiently low to avoid the presence of molecules in the associated form. These omitted values arise wholly or partly from the polarizations of the dimeric molecules. The solution values included without special notation have been measured[1,2] very carefully at extremely high dilutions down to mole fractions as low as 0.00005 in benzene, which should give the moment of the monomeric molecule

[5] V. Schomaker and L. Pauling, *J. Am. Chem. Soc.*, **61**, 1769 (1939).

[1] H. A. Pohl, M. E. Hobbs, and P. M. Gross, *Proc. N.Y. Acad. Sci.*, **40**, 389 (1940).

[2] A. A. Maryott, M. E. Hobbs, and P. M. Gross, *J. Chem. Phys.*, **9**, 415 (1941); *J. Am. Chem. Soc.*, **71**, 1671 (1949).

RCOOH. From polarization values at less high dilutions, Pohl, Hobbs, and Gross have calculated apparent moments between 0.88 and 1.06 for the dimeric $(RCOOH)_2$ molecules but, from the symmetry of the dimer molecules, have concluded that the differences between the total polarization and the electronic polarization, 16 to 23 cc., which give rise to these apparent moments, are probably atomic polarization. Their curves for polarization against concentration show that, in the dilute benzene

TABLE 10.1. MOMENTS ($\times 10^{18}$) OF MONOCARBOXYLIC ACIDS AND THEIR ESTERS

Molecule	Formula	Vapor	Sol.
Formic	HCOOH	(1.5)	1.77
Acetic	CH_3COOH	1.73	1.68
Heavy Acetic	CH_3COOD		1.64
Propionic	C_2H_5COOH	1.74	1.68
n-Butyric	C_3H_7COOH		1.9
Trimethylacetic	$(CH_3)_3CCOOH$		1.9
Stearic	$C_{17}H_{35}COOH$		1.80
Crotonic (trans)	$CH_3CH{=}CHCOOH$		2.13
Chloroacetic	$CH_2ClCOOH$		2.29
Trifluoroacetic	CF_3COOH	2.3	
Ethyl formate	$HCOOC_2H_5$	1.92	1.94
Propyl formate	$HCOOC_3H_7$		1.89
Isobutyl formate	$HCOOCH_2CH(CH_3)_2$		1.88
n-Amyl formate	$HCOOC_5H_{11}$	1.90	
Methyl acetate	CH_3COOCH_3	1.67	1.74
Ethyl acetate	$CH_3COOC_2H_5$	1.76	1.86
n-Propyl acetate	$CH_3COOC_3H_7$		1.82
Isopropyl acetate	$CH_3COOCH(CH_3)_2$		1.85
n-Butyl acetate	$CH_3COOC_4H_9$		1.84
i-Butyl acetate	$CH_3COOCH_2CH(CH_3)_2$		1.86
t-Butyl acetate	$CH_3COOC(CH_3)_3$		1.91
Cyclohexyl acetate	$CH_3COOC_6H_{11}$		1.90
Methyl propionate	$C_2H_5COOCH_3$		1.69
Ethyl propionate	$C_2H_5COOC_2H_5$		1.81
n-Propyl propionate	$C_2H_5COOC_3H_7$		1.77
Methyl butyrate	$C_3H_7COOCH_3$		1.71
Ethyl butyrate	$C_3H_7COOC_2H_5$		1.74
Methyl n-valerate	$C_4H_9COOCH_3$		1.74
Ethyl n-undecylate	$C_{10}H_{21}COOC_2H_5$		1.89
Methyl myristate	$C_{13}H_{27}COOCH_3$		1.74
Ethyl palmitate	$C_{15}H_{31}COOC_2H_5$		1.87
Ethyl stearate	$C_{17}H_{35}COOC_2H_5$		1.88
Methyl chloroformate	$ClCOOCH_3$		2.2
Ethyl chloroacetate	$CH_2ClCOOC_2H_5$		2.64
Ethyl dichloroacetate	$CHCl_2COOC_2H_5$		2.61
Ethyl trichloroacetate	$CCl_3COOC_2H_5$		2.55

solutions, the acid molecules are principally dimeric down to mole fraction 0.004, while, in dilute solution in heptane, formic and acetic acids are principally dimeric down to mole fraction 0.001.

Coop, Davidson, and Sutton[3] measured formic acid vapor at temperatures and pressures at which monomeric and dimeric molecules coexisted and found that the polarization of the dimer was constant or subject to slight increase with temperature. They therefore concluded that a difference of 15.5 cc. between the total polarization and the electronic polarization was probably atomic polarization and that the dimer moment was zero, in contrast to the permanent moment attributed to it by Zahn.[4] An apparent rise in the polarization of the monomer with temperature was indicated by them as possibly due to a transition from a low-energy state in which the hydroxyl hydrogen was locked cis to the carbonyl oxygen because of resonance and hydrogen bonding to a high-energy state in which the hydrogen was fixed trans to the carbonyl oxygen or was free to rotate around the hydroxyl oxygen. However, a rise of polarization has not yet been definitely established for monomeric acid molecules in the absence of dimeric molecules, which introduce some uncertainty into conclusions concerning the monomeric. Differences among the moment values for the unsubstituted fatty acids are no greater than the unusually large experimental errors caused by association combined with the probably smaller solvent effects for the monomeric molecules. It would appear that the formate moments may be slightly larger than those of the other unsubstituted ester molecules, but the differences among the ester molecules are no greater than the combined effects of solvent and of the errors arising from neglect of or inadequate approximation of atomic polarizations.

The moments of the fatty acid molecules are the resultants of the moments of the C—O, C=O, and H—O bonds previously examined in the ethers, alcohols, and ketones, but how much these bond moments may be modified by resonance and inductive effects in the acid molecules remains to be examined. Rotation of the hydroxyl group around the C—OH bond would change the resultant moment of the molecule, but, since temperature dependence of the moment of the monomeric form has not been clearly established, the fatty acids are discussed here rather than in the chapter on molecules with movable dipoles (Chap. XI).

The values of the bond angles given by electron diffraction[5] for the monocarboxylic acid molecules are approximate, but consistent within their probable errors with the usual single-single and single-double bond angles used for the RCOOH molecule in Fig. 10.1. The values for the

[3] I. E. Coop, N. R. Davidson, and L. E. Sutton, *J. Chem. Phys.*, **6**, 905 (1938).

[4] C. T. Zahn, *Phys. Rev.*, **37**, 1516 (1931).

[5] P. W. Allen and L. E. Sutton, *Acta Cryst.*, **3**, 46 (1950).

C—O and H—O moments shown along the bonds in Fig. 10.1 are those obtained in the discussion of the ethers and alcohols. The C=O bond value is slightly higher than that estimated from aldehyde and ketone moments, thus taking some, though perhaps insufficient, account of additional polarity arising from contribution from the structure[6]

$$RC \overset{\displaystyle O:^-}{\underset{\displaystyle O^+ \!\!-\!\! H}{}}$$

That the polar structure written above does not give a great deal of double-bond character to the C—OH bond is shown by the carbon-

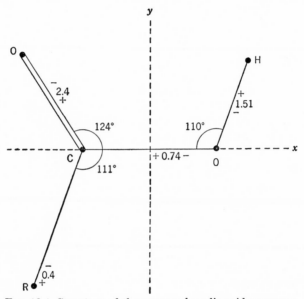

Fɪɢ. 10.1. Structure of the monocarboxylic acid monomer.

oxygen distances found by electron diffraction.[5] Much double-bond character would cause the molecule to exist in two isomeric forms with planar carboxyl groups. One form would have the hydroxyl hydrogen cis to the carbonyl oxygen as in Fig. 10.1, and the other would have it trans, a structure obtainable from that in Fig. 10.1 by rotating the O—H through an angle of 180° around the x axis. The moments of these structures may be calculated conveniently by choosing this axis as an x axis, a line perpendicular to it as the y axis as shown in Fig. 10.1, and a

[6] L. Pauling, "The Nature of the Chemical Bond," Cornell University Press, Ithaca, N.Y., 2d ed., 1940, p. 202.

z-axis, when needed, perpendicular to the plane of the paper. The calculations are shown in detail to illustrate the method.

cis Structure $m_x = 0.74 + 0.4 \cos 70° + 2.4 \cos 125°$
$$+ 1.51 \cos 110° = -1.02$$
$$m_y = 2.4 \sin 125° + 0.4 \sin 110° - 1.51 \sin 110° = 0.93$$
$$\mu = (m_x{}^2 + m_y{}^2)^{1/2} = 1.4$$
trans Structure $m_x = -1.02, \; m_y = 3.77, \; \mu = 3.9.$

As electron diffraction[5] indicates that the C—O—C plane is 30° ± 10° out of the cis planar configuration in methyl formate and 25° ± 8° out of it in methyl acetate, the moment of such a structure will be calculated for the acid molecule.

Nonplanar Structure $m_x = -1.02$
$$m_y = 2.4 \sin 125° + 0.4 \sin 110°$$
$$+ 1.51 \cos 110° \cos 30° = 1.12$$
$$m_z = 1.51 \cos 110° \sin 30° = -0.71$$
$$\mu = (m_x{}^2 + m_y{}^2 + m_z{}^2)^{1/2} = 1.7$$

The moment will also be calculated for the case of free rotation of the OH around the C—O line, or x axis. The only movable dipole moment is the H—O component $1.51 \sin 70°$, perpendicular to the x axis. m_x and m_y for the rest of the structure are then calculated to be $m_x = -1.02$, $m_y = 2.35$. Their resultant is 2.56 making an angle of 67° with the negative direction of the x axis. The rule for the resolution of movable dipoles (Sec. VIII.2) then gives the mean-square moment as

$$\mu^2 = 2.56^2 + 1.51^2 - 2 \times 2.56 \times 1.51 \cos 67° \cos 70° = 7.8$$
$$\mu = 2.8$$

Although the bond moment values are necessarily approximate, it is clear that the trans structure and that with free rotation of the hydroxyl have much too high moments to be possible alone. A mixture of isomeric cis and trans structures with the cis strongly predominant would give the observed moment. A considerable contribution from the polar structure with positive hydroxyl oxygen could raise the moment of the cis form to the observed value. Electrostatic attraction between the hydroxyl hydrogen and the strongly negative carbonyl oxygen should make the cis form much more stable than the trans and, if rotation occurred around the C—OH bond, should make the vicinity of the cis configuration the most stable region. An average departure of 30°, which gives a moment value indistinguishable from the observed, is thus very reasonable.

The moment of the ester molecules may be calculated by replacing the H—O moment in Fig. 10.1 by the R—O = H—C + C—O = 1.14.

With the C—O—C plane 30° out of the cis plane, the calculation gives a moment value 1.8, in satisfactory agreement with the observed values for the esters, which tend to be a little higher than the acid moments.

Brooks and Hobbs[7] and Hobbs and Weith[8] measured the dipole moments of benzoic acid, monohalogenated benzoic acids, and monohalogenated benzenes in dioxane solution and concluded from earlier measurements that the effects of solvent-solute interactions on the moment were not so serious as to invalidate the results obtained. They used the moments μ of the parahalogenated acid, m_1 of benzoic acid, and m_2 of the halogenated benzene to calculate θ, the supplement of the angle between the directions of m_1 and m_2 as given by

$$\mu^2 = m_1^2 + m_2^2 - 2m_1 m_2 \cos\theta$$

Since m_2 is in the line of the C—COOH bond, the result

$$\theta = 72 \text{ to } 76° = 74° \text{ (mean)}$$

is the angle between the moment of the carboxyl group and the direction of the valence bond holding it: ϕ ——C. In a qualitative treatment, these investigators took the carboxyl moment as acting in the plane of the ring, assumed an equal mixture of the cis and trans forms, and calculated moment values for the metasubstituted acids in good agreement with the observed values. They also pointed out that this was equivalent, as far as dipole calculations were concerned, to free rotation around the ϕ—C bond. Mutual induction apparently lowered the moments for the ortho compounds below the calculated values. The agreement between calculated and observed values for the meta compounds is evidently not to be regarded as quantitative evidence of the planarity of the carboxyl group.

The moment of crotonic acid is raised above those of the other unsubstituted acids in Table 10.1 just as the moments of acrolein and crotonaldehyde are raised above those of the other aldehydes (Sec. 6). The moment of chloroacetic acid is raised by the contribution of the C—Cl dipole, which, presumably, can rotate around the C—C axis. By combining vectorially the group moment 1.73 for the carboxyl group acting at the calculated angle 74° with the C—C bond with the moment 2.35 of 1,1,1-trifluoroethane (Sec. 2), the value 2.5 is obtained[9] for the trifluoroacetic moment in reasonably good agreement with the somewhat approximate value 2.3 in Table 10.1. It would appear from this that the presence of the three fluorines, which greatly increases the acidity of the

[7] C. S. Brooks and M. E. Hobbs, *J. Am. Chem. Soc.*, **62**, 2851 (1940).

[8] M. E. Hobbs and A. J. Weith, Jr., *J. Am. Chem. Soc.*, **65**, 967 (1943).

[9] See footnote 7, Sec. 2.

molecule, does not greatly alter the moment of the carboxyl group. In view of the evidence which has been mentioned or discussed, it appears that the hydroxyl hydrogens of the acids and the alkyl groups of the esters do not lie in the OCO plane and that the hydroxyl or alkoxy group may be undergoing a torsional oscillation or restricted rotation with the hydrogen or alkyl group well outside of this plane. However, the possibility of the existence of the molecules predominantly in isomeric planar forms is not completely excluded.

Spectroscopic and electron-diffraction evidence[5] indicates that the dimeric molecule of the acid is a symmetrical plane ring:

$$
\begin{array}{ccc}
& O\cdots H\!-\!O & \\
& /\!\!/ \qquad\quad \backslash & \\
R\!-\!C & & C\!-\!R \\
& \backslash \qquad\quad /\!\!/ & \\
& O\!-\!H\cdots O &
\end{array}
$$

This structure should have zero dipole moment but could well give rise to the previously indicated large atomic polarization by bending of the large dipoles out of the plane. Ritter and Simons[10] have concluded from vapor-density measurements that acetic acid vapor, within the range from 50 to 800 mm. pressure and from saturation temperature to about 170°, contains at least one polymer of order higher than the dimer and have proposed that this is a tetramer formed by the association of two dimer rings. Benzene solutions of acetic and butyric acids containing mole fractions from about 0.04 to 1.00 of acid showed[11] increase of both dielectric constant and polarization with concentration and temperature, the increase of polarization with concentration amounting to about 50 per cent for acetic acid and about 15 per cent for butyric acid. It is suggested that this unusual behavior may arise from the breaking of a hydrogen bond of a dimer ring and its reformation with the oxygen of another broken ring. Such hydrogen-bond dissociation and recombination should result in the presence of a few monomers, and more open-chain dimers and higher open-chain polymers, all capable of dipole orientation by orientation of the molecule either as a whole or in segments.

11. Amines. As the values in Table 11.1 for the three methylamines are carefully determined,[1] the differences between their gas values and those for the ethylamines may arise from errors in the latter. Since the axes of the molecular dipoles in the methylamines are not far from perpendicular to the directions of maximum polarizability in the molecules, the solvent effect causes the apparent moments in solution to be considerably higher than the gas values (Sec. I.18). Although gas values

[10] H. L. Ritter and J. H. Simons, *J. Am. Chem. Soc.*, **67**, 757 (1945).

[11] C. P. Smyth and H. E. Rogers, *J. Am. Chem. Soc.*, **52**, 1824 (1930).

[1] R. J. W. Le Fèvre and P. Russell, *Trans. Faraday Soc.*, **43**, 374 (1947).

are not available for s-butylamine, t-butylamine, and cyclohexylamine, it is probable that a considerable change in angle between the molecular dipole axis and the axis of maximum polarizability lowers the solvent effects and hence the apparent moment values for these molecules, which probably differ little in true moment from the methylamines, just as the higher alcohols differ little from methyl alcohol (Sec. 8).

TABLE 11.1. MOMENTS ($\times 10^{18}$) OF AMINES

Molecule	Formula	Vapor	Sol.
Methylamine	CH_3NH_2	1.28	1.46
Ethylamine	$C_2H_5NH_2$	1.0	1.38
n-Butylamine	$C_4H_9NH_2$		1.40
s-Butylamine	$C_2H_5(CH_3)CHNH_2$		1.28
t-Butylamine	$(CH_3)_3CNH_2$		1.29
Cyclohexylamine	$C_6H_{11}NH_2$		1.32
Dimethylamine	$(CH_3)_2NH$	1.02	1.17
Diethylamine	$(C_2H_5)_2NH$	0.9	1.13
Trimethylamine	$(CH_3)_3N$	0.64	0.86
Triethylamine	$(C_2H_5)_3N$	0.8	0.79

For the ammonia molecule, the moment value found[1] in benzene solution is 0.06 lower than the gas value 1.46, in accordance with the fact that the polarizability of the molecule is 2.42×10^{-24} in the direction of the symmetry axis, in which the molecular dipole lies, and 2.18×10^{-24} perpendicular to it.[2] The moment calculated[1] for pure liquid ammonia by means of the Onsager equation is 1.77, the elevation probably resulting from hydrogen bonding to form complexes of higher moment, which are presumably responsible for the abnormally high melting point and boiling point. Approximately equal moment elevations, 0.34 and 0.36, for pure liquid methylamine and dimethylamine suggest similar complex formation for these molecules, which should have less tendency to associate. For trimethylamine, which cannot form hydrogen bonds, the moment elevation in the pure liquid is only 0.10. Because of the approximate character of the Onsager equation, these indications of association are necessarily approximate.

The moments of ammonia, 1.46, and trimethylamine, 0.64, may be used to obtain H—N and R—N = (H—C) + (C—N) moments, just as the moments of water and methyl ether were used to obtain H—O and R—O moments (Sec. 8). The ammonia molecule may be treated as a tetrahedron with a single axis of symmetry passing through the nitrogen nucleus. The angles between this axis and the H—N bonds have been

[2] H. A. Stuart, "Molekülstruktur," Springer, Berlin, 1934, p. 221.

obtained spectroscopically[3] as 68°, which gives the H—N—H angles as 107°. Two values for the C—N—C angle in dimethylamine given by electron diffraction[4] are 108° ± 4° and 111° ± 3°. 110° would thus seem to be a satisfactory value to take for all the bond angles in the amines. It is convenient to establish a set of reference axes with the nitrogen at the origin and fix the x axis in the axis of symmetry of the ammonia and trimethylamine molecules. For methylamine, the xy plane is chosen to pass through the carbon nucleus, and, for dimethylamine, it is chosen to pass through the hydrogen. Moment components outside this plane of symmetry cancel one another. We may then write

$$3(\text{H—N}) \cos 68° = 1.46 \qquad (\text{H—N}) = 1.30$$
$$3(\text{R—N}) \cos 70° = 0.64 \qquad (\text{R—N}) = 0.62 \qquad (\text{C—N}) = 0.22$$

These values may then be tested by calculating from them the moments of methylamine and dimethylamine.

CH_3NH_2 (C in xy plane)

$$m_x = (\text{R—N}) \cos 70° + 2(\text{H—N}) \cos 70° = 1.10$$
$$m_y = -(\text{R—N}) \sin 70° + 2(\text{H—N}) \sin 70° \sin 30° = -0.64$$
$$\mu = (m_x^2 + m_y^2)^{1/2} = 1.27$$

$(CH_3)_2NH$ (H in xy plane)

$$m_x = (\text{H—N}) \cos 70° + 2(\text{R—N}) \cos 70° = 0.87$$
$$m_y = -(\text{H—N}) \sin 70° + 2(\text{R—N}) \sin 70° \sin 30° = -0.64$$
$$\mu = (m_x^2 + m_y^2)^{1/2} = 1.08$$

The agreement between these calculated values and the observed ones in Table 11.1 is fortuitously excellent for methylamine and within the errors of experiment and calculation for dimethylamine. For methylamine, $\tan \theta = m_y/m_x = -0.582$ gives the angle θ between the resultant molecular dipole and the x axis as 30°. Hence, the angle between the molecular dipole axis and the C—N bond direction is $30° + 70° = 100°$, that is, C———NH₂.

[3] G. Herzberg, "Infrared and Raman Spectra of Polyatomic Molecules," Van Nostrand, New York, 1945, p. 439.
[4] P. W. Allen and L. E. Sutton, *Acta Cryst.*, **3**, 46 (1950).

CHAPTER X

DIPOLE MOMENTS AND STRUCTURES OF AROMATIC MOLECULES

The origin of dipole moments, the structures of polar groups, and their interactions have been discussed in the two preceding chapters. The aim of the present chapter is to discuss those moment phenomena and effects which are characteristic of aromatic molecules. The differences between aliphatic and aromatic moments resulting from charge distribution in the ring have been illustrated by the discussion of the moments and structures of chlorobenzene, nitrobenzene, and p-nitrodimethylaniline (Sec. VIII.6). Some aromatic compounds, such as cycloheptatrienone (Sec. IX.6), tetracyclones (Sec. IX.6), furan (Sec. IX.7), and thiophene (Sec. IX.9), have been treated in the discussion of the related aliphatic compounds.

1. **Orientation of Substituents.** The reactions of aromatic compounds are, of course, closely related to the charge distribution in the ring, which is influenced by the substituents on the ring. Sutton[1] concluded that if we call positive the moments of the dipoles which have their positive end toward the substituent, and negative those in the opposite direction, then if the moment difference aryl − alkyl is positive, the substituent directs further substitution to the ortho and para positions, but, if this difference is negative, the direction is to the meta position. Sutton has tabulated a large number of aryl (Ar) − alkyl (Alk) moment differences which conform to this relationship for some substitution reactions.

Ri and Eyring,[2,3] on the basis of a number of reasonable postulates, have used the theory of absolute reaction rates to calculate the distribution of charges and, hence, the dipole moment from the ratio of the amounts of ortho, meta, and para products obtained in the nitration of monosubstituted benzenes. In the reverse calculation, they have used

[1] L. E. Sutton, *Proc. Roy. Soc. (London)*, **133**, 668 (1931).

[2] T. Ri and H. Eyring, *J. Chem. Phys.*, **8**, 433 (1940).

[3] S. Glasstone, K. J. Laidler, and H. Eyring, "The Theory of Rate Processes," McGraw-Hill, New York, 1941, p. 458.

the dipole moments of the monosubstituted benzenes to calculate the relative amounts of the ortho, meta, and para nitration products. The agreement between observed and calculated results is remarkably good, although it is a little disturbing to find excellent agreement between a moment value 1.02 thus calculated for the single benzoic acid molecule and an apparent observed value 1.00 which actually seems to arise from the atomic polarization of a nonpolar dimer. However approximate the theoretical treatment may be, it provides a plausible correlation of two totally different types of experimental data.

The difficulty of generalization in regard to orientation effects has been brought out in a discussion of chlorobenzene by Wheland,[4] who points out that in this molecule two different effects need to be considered separately. The strongly electronegative chlorine atom pulls electrons away from the carbon atom to which it is attached. If this charge displacement were the only factor, the orientation should be meta with deactivation for electrophilic reagents, and ortho, para with activation for radical or nucleophilic reagents. However, the displacement of electronic charge from the chlorine into or toward the ring represented by the contributions of structures III, IV, and V written for chlorobenzene in Sec. VIII.6 would tend to cause the orientation to be ortho, para with activation for an electrophilic reagent, indeterminate for a radical reagent, and meta with deactivation for a nucleophilic reagent. Wheland, therefore, concludes that it is impossible to predict with any assurance the orientation for any of the different types of reagent, and that each of the two opposing effects contributes to the result.

It is beyond the scope of this book to discuss organic reactivity, but the tabulation of the moments of monosubstituted benzenes and the differences between their values and those of the corresponding alkyl compounds may provide information of use in such discussions.

2. Monosubstituted Benzenes. The moment values for monosubstituted benzenes in Table 2.1 are listed without sign. In calculating the difference (ArX − AlkX) between the corresponding aryl and alkyl moments, it would be preferable to subtract the moment of $(CH_3)_3CX$ from that of the monosubstituted benzene, but too few values are available for t-butyl compounds to make it possible. As the difference between the t-butyl and n-butyl compound and, indeed, any n-alkyl above ethyl is usually small, the value for the n-butyl compound is used to obtain the difference when it is available. Since the aromatic moment values are listed noncommittally as positive, the moment differences do not have the same significance as those mentioned in Sec. 1. In view of solvent effects, the solution differences have a probable error of nearly 0.1, so that differences of 0.1 are hardly distinguishable from

[4] G. W. Wheland, "The Theory of Resonance," Wiley, New York, 1944, p. 267.

TABLE 2.1. MOMENTS ($\times 10^{18}$) OF MONOSUBSTITUTED BENZENES IN THE VAPOR STATE AND IN BENZENE SOLUTION

Substituent	Vapor	Sol.	Difference (Ar − Alk)	
			Vapor	Sol.
—	0	0	0	0
CH_3	0.37	0.4	0.37	0.4
C_2H_5	0.58	0.4	0.6	0.4
$(CH_3)_2CH$	0.65		0.65	
$(CH_3)_3C$	0.70	0.5	0.7	0.5
$CH{=}CH_2$	<0.2	(<0.4)	−0.2	(−0.2)
$C{\equiv}CH$		0.7		−0.2
F	1.59	1.46	−0.33	
Cl	1.70	1.58	−0.40	−0.4
Br	1.73	1.54	−0.42	−0.4
I	1.70	1.30	−0.38	−0.6
CH_2F	1.77			−0.1
CF_3	2.56			0.2
CH_2Cl		1.85		−0.1
$CHCl_2$		2.04		0.1
CCl_3		2.11		0.4
CH_2Br		1.86		−0.1
CN	4.39	3.90	0.30	0.3
NC		3.50		0
CH_2CN		3.50		−0.1
NCO		2.32		−0.5
SCN		3.59		0
NCS		2.9		−0.4
NO_2	4.21	3.98	0.49	0.6
NO		3.14		
CH_2NO_2		3.3		−0.1
CHO		2.76		0.2
$COCH_3$	3.00	2.89	0.15	0.2
$CO(C_6H_5)$		2.97		0.1
OCH_3	1.35	1.25	0.1	0
OC_6H_5	1.14	1.16	0	0
SCH_3		1.3		−0.2
SC_6H_5		1.51		0
OH	1.4	1.6	−0.3	−0.1
CH_2OH		1.68		0
SH		1.3		−0.1
COOH		1.64		0
$COOCH_3$		1.83		0
$N(CH_3)_2$	1.61	1.57	0.8	0.8
NH_2	1.48	1.53	0.2	0.2
$NH(C_6H_5)$	(1.3 mol. beam)			(0.4)
$N(C_6H_5)_2$		(0.3)		0.6
N_3		1.55		

zero. The possible error in the vapor differences is sometimes at least 0.1, but usually less.

Benzene. The use of the dipole moments of disubstituted benzenes to establish the plane hexagonal structure of the benzene ring has already been discussed (Sec. VIII.2). The symmetry of this plane hexagon, now established by X-ray and electron-diffraction measurements[1] also, necessitates the zero dipole moment observed directly.[2,3]

Alkylbenzenes. Although one alkyl group joined to another gives a paraffin molecule of zero or close to zero moment and one phenyl group joined to another gives the diphenyl molecule, which has zero moment, an alkyl group joined to a phenyl gives a molecule of small moment, which is shown by the moments of parasubstituted toluenes to have its negative end toward the ring. This moment may be described vaguely as produced by a shift of electrons in the direction from the alkyl group to the ring or precisely in terms of resonating polar structures. For the toluene molecule, in addition to the two Kekulé structures

CH_3 $\qquad\qquad\qquad$ CH_3

polar structures involving hyperconjugation[4] may be written as follows:

H^+CH_2 $\qquad\qquad$ H^+CH_2 $\qquad\qquad$ H^+CH_2

As each of the three hydrogens in each of these three structures may be the ionic one, nine such structures may be written. The moment could thus be the result of minute contributions from each of these nine highly polar structures. These structures are analogous to those written for propylene and the methylbutadienes (Sec. IX.1), and it is interesting that the moment of toluene is experimentally indistinguishable from those of propylene and 2-methylbutadiene. The increase in moment with increase in the size of the alkyl group parallels that in the alkyl halides, but is relatively larger. Although there is no reason to doubt the accu-

---

[1] P. W. Allen and L. E. Sutton, *Acta Cryst.*, **3**, 46 (1950).
[2] K. B. McAlpine and C. P. Smyth, *J. Am. Chem. Soc.*, **55**, 453 (1933).
[3] L. G. Groves and S. Sugden, *J. Chem. Soc.*, 1094 (1934).
[4] R. S. Mulliken, C. A. Rieke, and W. G. Brown, *J. Am. Chem. Soc.*, **63**, 41 (1941).

racy of the experimental values for the higher alkylbenzenes, it is to be hoped that they will be checked.

Molecular orbital methods of calculation have given two quite different charge distributions in the toluene molecule, both of which have moments close to the observed value. In terms of fraction of an electronic charge taken as -1, the charge per atom or atoms is as follows:

Molecule	I [5]	II [6]
Methyl H_3	$+0.042$	$+0.085$
Methyl C	$-.038$	$-.076$
1-C	$+.040$	$+.004$
2-C	$-.017$	$-.005$
3-C	$+.001$	$.000$
4-C	$-.011$	$-.004$

Column I is a charge distribution similar in most respects to that indicated qualitatively by the resonating structures, but column II locates the molecular dipole essentially in the methyl group.

The measurements made on styrene are insufficient to establish the absence of a very small moment in the molecule, but indicate that the moment is probably less than 0.2 and experimentally indistinguishable from zero. One may write polar structures for styrene analogous to those written for the butadienes. In one type, the ortho or para carbon or its attached hydrogen is positive and the terminal carbon negative, while, in the other, the terminal carbon or one of its attached hydrogens is positive and the ortho or para carbon negative.

$$ {}^+ \langle \bigcirc \rangle {=}CH{-}{}^-\ddot{C}H_2 \qquad\qquad {}^-{:}\langle \bigcirc \rangle {=}CH{-}{}^+CH_2 $$

Equal stabilities of the different structures would result in zero dipole moment. The absence of detectable moment shows that the two types of structure differ little in stability. This absence of detectable moment when a phenyl and a vinyl group are attached to each other is consistent with the fact that the attachment of a methyl group to a vinyl to form propylene gives practically the same moment as the attachment of a methyl group to phenyl to form toluene. It should be recalled, however, that the attachment of a group producing large charge displacement, such as cyanide or chlorine, to the phenyl or the vinyl group does not give the same moment in the two cases.

For phenylacetylene, one may write one type of resonating polar structure which would cause the positive end of the molecular dipole to be

[5] B. Pullman and A. Pullman, "Les Théories électroniques de la chimie organique," Masson et Cie, Paris, 1952, chap. VII.

[6] C. A. Coulson, "Valence," Oxford, London, 1952, chap. XII.

toward the ring and one which would cause the negative end to be toward the ring.   In the case of styrene, it has been seen that the two types of structure differ so little in stability that the resultant molecular moment is close to zero, if not actually zero.   For phenylacetylene, however, the moment is considerable and the moments of parasubstituted phenylacetylenes to be considered in the next section show that the negative end is toward the acetylene as in the alkylacetylenes.   The shift of charge may be attributed to the electronegativity of the acetylenic carbon, which is in a state of sp hybridization.[5]

Halides.   A detailed examination of the moment of chlorobenzene in terms of hypothetical polar structures with positive halogen doubly bonded to the ring has been given in Sec. VIII.6.   Calculation from the moment lowering by the method there described indicates a total contribution of 3 to 4 per cent from these polar structures for each of the four monohalogenated benzenes.[7]   The similarity of the moment lowerings in the four monohalogenated benzenes is shown by the values in Table 2.1.

Benzil, Benzal, and Benzo Compounds.   The benzil and benzal compounds in Table 2.1 do not differ from the corresponding alkyl compounds by more than the probable error in the difference.   This is analogous to the absence of any considerable effect of a double bond upon the moment of a chloride (Sec. IX.2) and of an isothiocyanate (Sec. IX.4) when it is separated by a C—C bond from the C—Cl or the C—NCS.   The greater though somewhat uncertain differences in the cases of benzotrichloride and benzotrifluoride suggest the possibility that the halogens may be drawing electronic charge away from the ring, that this tends to be compensated by the small charge shift in the opposite direction shown by the alkylbenzenes, but that the attraction exerted by three halogens more than compensates this opposite charge shift and causes the moment to be slightly higher than that of the corresponding alkyl compound.

Cyanide and Isocyanide.   The moment of benzonitrile or phenyl cyanide is increased by a charge shift somewhat like that in crotononitrile (Sec. IX.3).   The increase may be described in terms of small contributions from polar structures, such as III

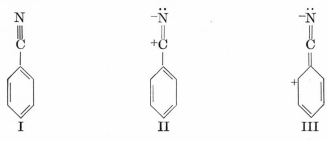

I   II   III

[7] C. P. Smyth, *J. Am. Chem. Soc.*, **63**, 57 (1941).

These contributions are, of course, in addition to those from the structures such as I and II.

For the isocyanide, two structures, I and II, may be written

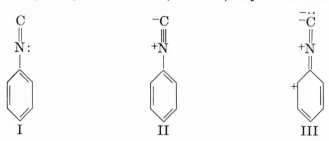

However, a shift of electrons from the ring as represented by a structure such as III gives two charges to the isocyanide carbon, the result being a lower stability than that of the singly charged structure. In these terms, the ring cannot contribute electronic charge to the isocyanide as readily as it can to the cyanide, and the moment of phenyl isocyanide is, therefore, close to that of the alkyl cyanide.

Isocyanate, Thiocyanate, and Isothiocyanate. Shift of the electronic charge from the nitrogen toward the ring as in the case of the halogenated benzenes could account for the decrease of moment from alkyl to aryl isocyanate and isothiocyanate. The main part of the moment in each case is accounted for by structures like those written for the corresponding alkyl compounds (Sec. IX.4). The moment of the thiocyanate is accounted for entirely by structures like those written for the alkyl thiocyanates (Sec. IX.4).

Nitrobenzene and Nitrosobenzene. The resonance and symmetry of the nitro group have been discussed under the nitroparaffins (Sec. IX.5), and the considerable increase in moment by displacement of electrons from the ring has been discussed as an example of resonance effects (Sec. VIII.6). The influence of the steric effect of substituents on this resonance will be examined in Sec. 3. The structure of nitrosobenzene may be reasonably described in terms of structures somewhat analogous to those written for nitrobenzene, such as

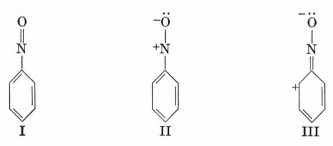

The CNO angle in I and III should be 125° and in II should be 110°, but resonance should widen it. That the angle is probably widened to 180° is indicated but not definitely established by the moments of the p-halogen and p-nitro-nitrosobenzenes (Sec. 3). The importance of the polar structures is shown by the large dipole moment of nitrosobenzene.

Aldehyde and Ketones. The small increase in these moments over those for the aliphatic compounds may be attributable to shift of electronic charge from the ring as in nitrobenzene and benzonitrile, a shift describable in terms of the contributions of polar structures analogous to those written for these two molecules. However, since the dimethylcyclohexanones and other cyclic ketones (Sec. IX.6) have equally large moments, it would seem that the charge shift is caused largely by electrostatic induction.

Ethers, Sulfides, Phenol, and Thiophenol. The moments of these compounds show no considerable effect of the ring except in the apparent lowering of the vapor value for phenol, which may arise from electronic charge shifts from the oxygen toward the ring, representable by structures[8] analogous to the three chlorobenzene structures with positive chlorine (Sec. VIII.6) and those to be written shortly for aniline. These could lower the R—O moment greatly and the H—O a little. If, as an extreme case, the R—O moment were reduced to zero and the H—O left unchanged, the resultant moment would be 1.5 (Sec. IX.8). If the usual expression for the resultant of two vectors is equated to the observed moment 1.4 and solved for R—O, H—O being taken as 1.5, no real solution can be obtained with the oxygen valence angle 110°. However, if the angle is widened to 115°, as a result of the contributions of the structures with double-bonded oxygen, a reasonable value, 0.99, is obtained for R—O.

Benzoic Acid and Methyl Benzoate. These molecules are like those of the benzil and benzal compounds in that their moments give no evidence of interaction between the polar group and the ring. The benzoic acid molecule tends to associate strongly like the fatty acid molecules (Sec. IX.10), and, like them, its dimer apparently has zero moment and a large atomic polarization.[9]

Amines. A shift of electronic charge like that discussed in detail for chlorobenzene and mentioned for phenol can account for the increase in moment of aniline over those of the monoalkylamines, the lower moment of diphenylamine, and the almost zero moment of triphenylamine.

Azides. The azide ion has been found by X-ray analysis to be linear and symmetrical, and its structure has been proposed[8] to be the resultant

[8] L. Pauling, "The Nature of the Chemical Bond," Cornell University Press, Ithaca, N.Y., 2d ed., 1940, chap. VI.

[9] H. A. Pohl, M. E. Hobbs, and P. M. Gross, *Proc. N.Y. Acad. Sci.*, **40**, 389 (1940).

of equal contributions from the three polar structures

$$-:N\!\!=\!\!^+N\!\!=\!\!N:^- \qquad\qquad -:\ddot{N}\!\!-\!\!^+N\!\!\equiv\!\!N \qquad\qquad N\!\!\equiv\!\!^+N\!\!-\!\!\ddot{N}:^-$$

Methyl azide has been shown by electron diffraction[8] to have a configuration which agrees well with equal resonance between two structures

$$CH_3\!\!-\!\!N\!\!=\!\!^+N\!\!=\!\!N:^- \qquad\qquad CH_3\!\!-\!\!^-\ddot{N}\!\!-\!\!^+N\!\!\equiv\!\!N$$

It is reasonable to suppose that two analogous structures contribute heavily to the structure of phenyl azide. Since the moment of this molecule is not inconsiderable, while the moment resulting from the two above structures would not be large, and since the moments of p-tolyl azide, p-chlorophenyl azide, and p-nitrophenyl azide (Sec. X.3) would indicate a much wider angle in the phenyl azides than the 120° angle indicated by electron diffraction for methyl azide, it is suggested that a considerable contribution may be made by a third structure

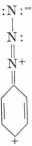

This would increase the dipole moment and widen the angle well beyond 120°.

3. Paradisubstituted Benzenes. Since the benzene ring has been shown to be a plane hexagon with its external valences coplanar, the moment resulting from the presence of the symmetrical methyl group must act in the direction of the bond between the methyl and the ring. The moments due to parasubstituted halogens must also act in this line and should, therefore, be the sum or difference of the solution moments of the monohalogenated benzene given in Table 2.1 and that of toluene, for which the gas value 0.37 is used, since it is more accurate, although experimentally indistinguishable from the solution value, 0.4. When the positive end of the toluene dipole is taken as lying toward the methyl group, such excellent agreement is obtained between the observed and calculated moments as clearly to establish the methyl-to-ring line as the plus-minus direction of the dipole. For the molecules which clearly have the two group dipoles in the same axis, the sum of the moment of toluene and that of the group-substituted benzene is given in the column headed

"Calc." Any appreciable excess of the observed moment over the calculated may be taken as evidence of an electronic shift in the direction from the methyl group toward the parasubstituent.

TABLE 3.1. MOMENTS ($\times 10^{18}$) IN SOLUTION OF p-SUBSTITUTED TOLUENES

Substituent	Obs.	Calc.	Substituent	Obs.
CH_3	0 (gas)	0 (gas)	NCS	3.3
CH_3	0	0	NO	3.79
C_2H_5	0	0	CHO	3.28
$CH(CH_3)_2$	0.1	0.3	OCH_3	1.20
$CH{=}CH_2$	0.6	<0.8	$OC_6H_4CH_3$	1.44 (gas)
$C{\equiv}CH$	1.0	1.1	$OC_6H_4CH_3$	1.44
F	2.01 (gas)	1.96 (gas)	OH	1.59
F	1.82	1.83	COOH	2.00
Cl	1.94	1.95	$COOCH_3$	2.05
Br	1.96	1.91	NH_2	1.29
I	1.71	1.67	$N(CH_3)_2$	1.29
NO_2	4.45	4.35	N_3	1.96
CN	4.37	4.27		
NC	3.97	3.87		

The moments of the hydrocarbons in Table 3.1 show that alkyl groups para to each other approximately cancel each other's moments, as expected; that, if styrene has any moment, which is doubtful, its positive end is probably toward the ring; and that the positive end of the phenylacetylene moment is clearly toward the ring. The moment resulting from the attachment of a methyl group to the ring is so small that its possible modification by interaction through the ring with a para substituent may well be less than the experimental error. However, except in molecules where the two dipoles are known to make an angle with each other, the larger observed moments are slightly higher than the calculated. It is evident from these toluene moments as well as from others that the principal resultant group dipoles are linear in p-nitrotoluene, p-tolunitrile, and p-toluisonitrile. The observed moment of each molecule is 0.1 higher than the calculated, a difference which could arise from atomic polarization (see Sec. XIV.4), or from a charge shift describable in terms of very small contributions from resonating polar structures, or from inductive effect since Marsden and Sutton[1] have calculated that the moment induced in a group of refractivity 6 to 9 cc., such as nitro or bromine, by a dipole of moment 1.5×10^{-18} in the para position would be 0.05 to 0.08×10^{18}, while that induced by a dipole of moment 4×10^{18} would be 0.13 to 0.21. There is similarly an apparent elevation of

[1] R. J. B. Marsden and L. E. Sutton, *J. Chem. Soc.*, 599 (1936).

moment in the molecules of the isothiocyanate, the aldehyde, and, particularly, of p-nitrosotoluene.

The moment values for p-cresol and p-cresyl methyl ether are indistinguishable from those for phenol and anisol. However, a moment calculation indicates the normality of the structures of these and the closely related compounds. The p-methyl group raises the moments of p-toluic acid and methyl p-toluate above those of benzoic acid and methyl benzoate, but the carboxyl moment angle prevents direct additivity. The lowering of the moment of p-toluidine and N-dimethyl-p-toluidine below the moments of aniline and N-dimethylaniline presumably arises largely from the angle between the component moments, which has been calculated[1] to be 38° or $CH_3 \cdots C \overset{142°}{\underset{+}{-\!\!\!\diagup\!\!\searrow\!\!\!\!-}} N(CH_3)_2$. The moment of p-tolyl azide is consistent with linearity of the azide group with its bond to the ring (cf. Sec. 2) or with the very wide angle indicated by the other p-substituted azides.

TABLE 3.2. MOMENTS ($\times 10^{18}$) IN SOLUTION OF HALOGENATED p-DISUBSTITUTED BENZENES

Substituents		Obs.	Calc.	Substituents		Obs.
F	Br (gas)	0.5	0.1	Br	CH_2Cl	1.72
	I (gas)	0.9	0.1		CH_2Br	1.73
Cl	Cl	0	0		CH_2NO_2	2.85
	Br	0	0	NO_2	CH_2Cl	3.59
	I	0.5	0.3		CH_2Br	3.57
Br	Br	0	0			
	I	0.5	0.2			

The zero moment values in Table 3.2 could be as large as 0.2 or 0.3 but are experimentally indistinguishable from zero and have been used in establishing the plane hexagonal structure of the benzene ring. The considerable differences between the observed values for p-fluorobromobenzene and p-fluoroiodobenzene and those calculated (column 3) for the plane hexagonal structures may arise from resonance effects but may be contributed to by atomic polarization and the possible presence of small amounts of the ortho compounds as impurities.[2] No moment values are calculated for the various benzyl derivatives, because they were originally used to establish the validity of the method of vector resolution in determining valence bond angles. The values, 114° to 119°, thus obtained for the C—C—X angle differed from the regular tetrahedral carbon valence angle 109° 28′ by no more than the errors in the method.[3]

[2] E. C. Hurdis and C. P. Smyth, J. Am. Chem. Soc., **64**, 2212 (1942).

[3] C. P. Smyth and W. S. Walls, J. Am. Chem. Soc., **54**, 1854 (1932).

TABLE 3.3. MOMENTS ($\times 10^{18}$) IN SOLUTION OF p-SUBSTITUTED CYANIDES, ISOCYANIDES, ISOCYANATES, THIOCYANATES, AND ISOTHIOCYANATES

Substituents		Obs.	Calc.	Substituents		Obs.	Calc.
CN	CN	0 (gas)	0	NC	NC	0	0
	Cl	2.56	2.32		Cl	2.08	1.92
	Br	2.64	2.36	NCO	Cl	0.8	0.74
	I	2.81	2.60	SCN	Cl	2.93	2.01
	NO₂	(0) (gas)	0.08	NCS	Cl	1.55	1.32
					Br	1.54	1.36

The zero moments of p-dicyano- and p-diisocyanobenzene show that the CCN and the CNC lines are straight. The small differences between the observed and calculated moments for the other cyanides and isocyanides are no larger than the possible effects of induction or atomic polarization.

It would be natural to interpret the parahalogenated isocyanate and isothiocyanate values as indicating that the C—Cl or C—Br and the C—NCO or C—NCS oppose each other in the same straight line, but the R—N—C angles indicated for the alkyl compounds (Sec. IX.4) seem to be less than 180°. Consequently, it is probable that angles less than 180° remain in the phenyl isocyanates and isothiocyanates. The presence of such an angle is clearly indicated by the large excess, 0.9, of the moment observed for p-chlorophenyl thiocyanate over the difference between the two component moments. It is evident that all the group dipoles in the molecules in Table 3.3 have their positive ends toward the ring.

TABLE 3.4. MOMENTS ($\times 10^{18}$) IN SOLUTION OF p-SUBSTITUTED NITROBENZENES, NITROSOBENZENES, AND AZIDES

Substituents		Obs.	Calc.
NO₂	NO₂	(0)	0
	F (gas)	2.87	2.62
	F	2.63	2.52
	Cl (gas)	2.78	2.51
	Cl	2.5	2.40
	Br	2.55	2.44
	I	2.8	2.68
NO	Cl	1.82	1.56
	Br	1.92	1.60
	I	2.16	1.84
	NO₂	0.84	0.84
N₃	Cl	0.4	0.81 (30°)
	NO₂	2.96	2.75 (30°)

The moment value for p-dinitrobenzene is experimentally indistinguishable from zero, which supports the symmetrical structure for the nitro group written as the resultant of equal contributions from

$$\begin{array}{cc} & O \\ & \parallel \\ -{}^+N & \\ & \diagdown \\ & O^- \end{array} \qquad\qquad \begin{array}{cc} & O^- \\ & \diagup \\ -{}^+N & \\ & \diagdown\!\!\diagdown \\ & O \end{array}$$

All the p-halogenated nitrobenzenes have dipole moments from 0.1 to 0.27 higher than the differences between the corresponding monosubstituted benzenes, suggesting the possibility of small resonance contributions from polar structures but readily accounted for by induction.

The excess of the observed moments of the p-halogenated nitrosobenzenes over the differences between the values for the corresponding monosubstituted benzenes is slightly larger than that in the case of the nitrobenzenes. It may arise from structures of the type

On the other hand, it could be due to a very obtuse but not 180° CNO angle (cf. Sec. 2). The agreement between the observed and calculated values for p-nitronitrosobenzene points to linearity of the group dipoles, so that the CNO angle in parasubstituted nitrosobenzenes may be taken as probably but not certainly 180°.

If the valence angle of the azide group were 120°, as indicated by electron diffraction for the methyl azide molecule (Sec. 2), the resultant moment for p-chlorophenyl azide would be 1.57 instead of the observed 0.4. Calculation of the angle from the observed moment gives an angle 165° in p-chlorophenyl azide, which is hardly distinguishable from 180°, because of the smallness of the moment, and a more dependable value 140° for the azide angle in p-nitrophenyl azide. A value of about 150°

or N_3 is consistent with these two moment values and with that of p-tolyl azide.

TABLE 3.5. MOMENTS ($\times 10^{18}$) IN SOLUTION OF p-SUBSTITUTED ALDEHYDES AND KETONES

Substituents		Moment	Substituents		Moment
CHO	CHO	2.35	COCH$_3$	Cl	2.29
	Cl	2.03		Br	2.29
	Br	2.20		I	2.23
	NO$_2$	2.41	COC$_6$H$_5$	Cl	2.71
COCH$_3$	COCH$_3$	2.71	COC$_6$H$_4$Cl	Cl	1.70
			COC$_6$H$_4$Br	Br	1.69

Evidence of the nonlinearity of the aldehyde and ketone dipoles with the C—C bonds is given by the large moments of the p-phthalic aldehyde and p-diacetylbenzene molecules. The angle θ between the aldehyde group moment and the C—C bond to the ring may be calculated by means of the equation

$$\mu = m_1 (2 - 2 \cos^2 \theta)^{1/2} \tag{3.1}$$

which is a special case of Eq. VIII(2.3) in which μ is taken as the moment of p-phthalic aldehyde and m_1 that of benzaldehyde, that is,

$$2.35 = 2.76 (2 - \cos^2 \theta)^{1/2} \qquad \theta = 130°$$

or

C —— $\underset{50°}{\angle}$ —— C=O

If the dipole moment is taken to lie in the direction of the C=O bond, the C—C=O bond angle is accordingly 130°. A similar calculation for p-diacetylbenzene gives $\theta = 125°$ and, hence, the angle between the C=O bond and the C—C bond to the ring is 125°. The use of this equation is based on the assumption of equal probability for all positions of rotation around the C—C bond to the ring. If this bond has sufficient double-bond character to limit the positions to the two in which the CHO or COCH$_3$ groups are coplanar with the ring, the equations give the same results, provided that the two positions are equally probable. By the ordinary resolution of vectors, the p-chlorobenzaldehyde moment gives $\theta = 133°$, the equation being

$$2.03^2 = 2.76^2 + 1.58^2 + 2 \times 2.76 \times 1.58 \cos \theta.$$

In view of the inductive effects and variations in solvent effect not taken into account in these calculations, variations of $\pm 5°$ in the calculated angles are not significant. Similarly, the moment of p-nitrobenzaldehyde gives $\theta = 144°$, which, however, is so much higher than the expected value 125° as to suggest that the contributions of the polar quinonoid structures are reduced by the simultaneous presence of the mutually opposing nitro and aldehyde groups and that the angle is, actually, not abnormally high. The values for the various ketones are consistent with those for the aldehydes, but, for p,p'-dichloro- and p,p'-dibromobenzophenone, the angle between the bonds to the carbonyl carbon comes out 132°, probably because of the steric repulsion between the two benzene rings. p,p'-Di-(dimethylamino)-benzophenone is considered in Sec. 10.

The dipole moments of the p-substituted diphenyl ethers and sulfides have been of interest principally as a means of investigating the oxygen and sulfur valence angles.[4-11] Values have been calculated for the valence angles in these molecules by the resolution of the component moments, as was done for the aldehydes and ketones in the preceding paragraphs. A wide spread is apparent among the angle values obtained from measurements on different compounds. After considering the various data, Sutton and Hampson[11] concluded the oxygen valence angle to be 128° ± 4° in diphenyl ether and the sulfur valence angle to be 113° ± 3° in diphenyl sulfide. The widening of the oxygen valence angle by about 16° over its value in dimethyl ether and chlorine monoxide is attributed to resonance involving structures with double-bonded oxygen, but one may also suspect steric repulsion between the two benzene rings as an important factor.

TABLE 3.6. MOMENTS ($\times 10^{18}$) IN SOLUTION OF p-SUBSTITUTED PHENOLS, ANILINES, AND N-DIMETHYLANILINES

Substituent	Phenols		Anisols		Substituent	Anilines		Dimethyl-anilines	
	Obs.	Calc.	Obs.	Calc.		Obs.	Calc.	Obs.	Calc.
OCH$_3$			1.72		N(CH$_3$)$_2$			1.23	
OH	1.4				NH$_2$	1.5			
F			2.09	2.09	F	2.75	2.74		
Cl	2.27	2.30	2.24	2.20	Cl	2.93	2.87	3.29	2.97
Br	2.18	2.27	2.20	2.17	Br	2.87	2.82	3.37	2.93
I			2.12	1.99	I	2.82	2.63	3.22	2.57
NO$_2$	5.04	4.34	4.76	4.41	CN	5.96	5.16	5.90	5.20
NO	4.72	(3.60)			NO$_2$	6.2	5.17	6.87	5.04
					NO			6.90	(4.49)

[4] E. Bergmann, L. Engel, and S. Sandor, Z. physik. Chem., 10B, 397 (1930).

[5] E. Bergmann and M. Tschudnowsky, Z. physik. Chem. 17B, 107 (1932).

[6] C. P. Smyth and W. S. Walls, J. Am. Chem. Soc., 54, 3230 (1932).

[7] G. C. Hampson and L. E. Sutton, Proc. Roy. Soc. (London), 140A, 562 (1933).

[8] G. C. Hampson, R. H. Farmer, and L. E. Sutton, Proc. Roy. Soc. (London), 143A, 147 (1933).

[9] G. M. Bennett and S. Glasstone, Proc. Roy. Soc. (London), 145A, 71 (1934).

[10] G. M. Bennett, Trans. Faraday Soc., 30, 853 (1934).

[11] L. E. Sutton and G. C. Hampson, Trans. Faraday Soc., 31, 945 (1935).

Since some of the moment values measured for the phenols, anilines, and N-dimethylanilines show marked differences for the same substance, it has seemed desirable to give in Table 3.6 the values collected or measured by Marsden and Sutton[1] and used by them to discuss the significance between observed and calculated values. In addition, the values for several other molecules are included. These values show for the anilines that resonance effects are not sufficient to make all the nitrogen valence bonds coplanar with the ring. Marsden and Sutton[1] have calculated the angle θ between the moment of dimethylaniline and the C—N bond to the ring by applying Eq. (3.1) to the moment of tetramethyl-p-phenylenediamine. The two solutions for θ are 33.5° and 146.5°. The lower value is close to the value 38° or C $\underset{142°}{\diagdown}$ N(CH₃)₂ calculated from the moment of N-methyl-p-toluidene, which they take to be the best angle value to use in the calculation of other substituted aniline moments. The moments of phenol, anisol, p-cresol, and p-cresyl methyl ether were used[12] to obtain the values of the angles employed in calculating the moments of the phenols and anisols in Table 3.6. Among the phenols, anisols, and anilines, the p-iodo to a small extent and the p-cyano, p-nitro, and p-nitroso to a large extent show excesses of the observed moment over the calculated by amounts greater than the previously mentioned effects of induction and atomic polarization. All the p-substituted dimethylanilines in Table 3.6 show excesses of observed over calculated moments larger than the inductive effects, the excesses being very large in the cases of the p-nitro and p-nitroso compounds. These excesses may be accounted for in terms of contributions from highly polar structures as shown in Sec. VIII.6. Although the writing of such structures may sometimes be regarded merely as a convenient method of describing the charge distribution in the molecule, the behavior of the substituted durenes[13] seems to give some reality to the description.

[12] L. E. Sutton, *Proc. Roy. Soc. (London)*, **133A**, 668 (1931).

[13] C. P. Smyth, "Chemical Architecture" (edited by R. E. Burk and O. Grummitt), Interscience, New York, 1948, p. 34.

The resonating structures which raise the moment of nitrobenzene 0.50 above that of 2-nitro-2-methylpropane impart so much double-bond character to the carbon-nitrogen bond that the two oxygens of the nitro group tend to lie in the plane of the ring. The moment value found in solution for nitrodurene, which is symmetrical as far as the two opposite pairs of methyl groups are concerned, is 3.39, in close agreement with the values found for the nitroparaffins (Sec. IX.5). The atomic dimensions are such that the adjacent methyl groups should repel the oxygen atoms when they are in the plane of the ring, although not definitely excluding them from this plane. It has been suggested[14,15] that this repulsion forces the oxygens out of the plane of the ring and thus eliminates or reduces the double-bond character of the C—N bond and the contributions of the polar structures, which are responsible for the elevation of the moment above those of the nitroparaffins. The potential energy of repulsion increases the energies of the polar, double-bonded structures, reducing their stabilities relative to the other structures and, consequently, the contributions which they make to the structure of the molecule. The steric effect is even more evident in the case of p-aminonitrodurene, the moment of which measured[14] in solution is 4.98 as compared to 6.2 observed and 5.17 calculated for p-nitroaniline (Table 3.6). Birtles and Hampson[14] found that the moment of nitroaminodurene, although lower than that of p-nitroaniline, was still greater than the sum of the moments of mononitrodurene and monoaminodurene indicating that the contribution of the highly polar quinonoid structure was not completely eliminated. Ingham and Hampson[15] found the behavior of the substituted mesitylenes to be similar to that of the durenes, the moments being lowered toward those of the corresponding aliphatic compounds. They concluded that the steric effect of the o-methyl groups on the relatively large oxygen atoms of the nitro group was more important than that on the hydrogen atoms of the amino group. Absence of this apparent effect of steric repulsion in bromonitrodurene and dinitroprehnitene will be noted later (Sec. 6).

Few and Smith[16] and Curran and Estok[17] investigated the possible stabilization of these polar structures by intermolecular hydrogen bonding in dioxane solution, finding an increase in polarity in the aromatic amines as shown in Table 3.7, in which the increases for ethyl p-aminobenzoate and p-aminoacetophenone are corrected for the moment angles involved. To this table have been added the approximate differences

[14] R. H. Birtles and G. C. Hampson, *J. Chem. Soc.*, 10 (1937).
[15] C. E. Ingham and G. C. Hampson, *J. Chem. Soc.*, 981 (1939).
[16] A. V. Few and J. W. Smith, *J. Chem. Soc.*, 753 and 2663 (1949).
[17] C. Curran and G. K. Estok, *J. Am. Chem. Soc.*, **72**, 4575 (1950).

observed between the measurements of different investigators on two nitronaphthylamines in benzene[18] and in dioxane solution.[19]

TABLE 3.7. INCREASES IN MOMENT FROM BENZENE TO DIOXANE SOLUTIONS

n-Butylamine	0	Ethyl p-aminobenzoate	0.44
tert-Butylamine	0	p-Aminoacetophenone	0.50
Aniline	0.24	p-Aminobenzonitrile	0.50
Methylaniline	0.19	p-Nitroaniline	0.57
Dimethylaniline	0.06	1-Nitro-4-naphthylamine	0.59
p-Chloroaniline	0.37	2-Nitro-6-naphthylamine	1.96
2,4,6-Tribromoaniline	0.28		
2,4,6-Tribromodimethylaniline	0		

Curran and Estok suppose that hydrogen bonding normally occurs between a dioxane oxygen and an amino group, but Few and Smith incline to the view that hydrogen bonding to the dioxane oxygens occurs only when it is facilitated by the possibility of resonance structures in the anilines. If hydrogen bonding occurs between dioxane and the butyl-amine, it does not affect the moments. However, it raises the moments of the anilines, which receive resonance contributions from highly polar structures. For dimethylaniline and 2,4,6-tribromodimethylaniline, in which the methyl groups give no opportunity for hydrogen bonding, the effect of dioxane upon the moment does not differ appreciably from that of benzene. For methylaniline, which can form a hydrogen bond, the dioxane raises the moment by 0.19, and for aniline, which has better opportunity for hydrogen bonding, dioxane raises the moment by 0.24. The increase in moment appears to be greater, the greater the contribution from the polar structure, which seems to be made more stable by the hydrogen bonding. The effect on the moment of 1-nitro-4-naph-thylamine is practically the same as that in p-nitroaniline, as would be expected from the structure of the former (Sec. 8). The increase is much greater for 2-nitro-6-naphthylamine, in which the charge separation in the polar structures is greater (Sec. 8).

In discussing fatty acids and their esters (Sec. IX.10), it was shown that the moment of the carboxyl group in p-halogenated benzoic acids can be treated as acting at an angle of about 74° with the direction of

the bond holding it to the ring, that is ϕ———COOH. Use of this angle and the moments of nitrobenzene and benzoic acid, 3.93 and 1.78, measured in dioxane solution gives a vector sum 3.85, differing by no more than the probable error from the value 4.02 measured for p-nitro-

[18] E. Hertel, Z. Elektrochem., 47, 813 (1941).
[19] W. Wassiliew and J. Syrkin, Acta Physicochim. U.R.S.S., 14, 414 (1941).

benzoic acid in dioxane solution.[20]   The benzene solution moment values of methyl p-bromobenzoate, 1.82, methyl benzoate, 1.83, and bromoben-

zene, 1.54, may be combined vectorially to obtain ϕ —— $\overset{+\diagup^{64°}}{}$ —— COOCH$_3$. This value is lower than that for the carboxyl group, as it should be, and has a considerably larger probable error, being lower than the approximate value 70° in Table 5.1, Chap. VIII.

4. Metadisubstituted Benzenes.   It has been shown (Sec. VIII.2) that the moment of m-dichlorobenzene gives evidence of the plane hexagonal structure of the benzene ring.   This structure gives an angle of 120° between the bonds from the ring to two meta groups so that when the group moments m_1 and m_2 act in the directions of the bonds, the resultant moment is

$$\mu = (m_1{}^2 + m_2{}^2 + 2m_1m_2 \cos 120°)^{\frac{1}{2}}$$

When $m_1 = m_2$, this gives $\mu = m_1 = m_2$, that is, the moment should be the same as that of the monosubstituted benzene.   The values of m_1 and m_2 are taken, as in the case of the p-substituted benzenes, from Table 2.1. In calculating the values for m-phenylenediamine and m-nitroaniline, Eq. VIII(2.3) has been used.

TABLE 4.1. MOMENTS ($\times 10^{18}$) IN BENZENE SOLUTION OF m-DISUBSTITUTED BENZENES

Substituents		Obs.	Calc.	Substituents		Obs.	Calc.
CH$_3$	CH$_3$	0.37	0.37	CH$_2$	I	1.58	1.52
F	F	1.58	1.59	CH$_2$	NO$_2$	4.14	4.18
Cl	Cl (gas)	1.67	1.70	Cl	NO$_2$ (gas)	3.69	3.67
Cl	Cl	1.48	1.58	Cl	NO$_2$	3.4	3.47
Br	Br	1.46	1.54	Br	NO$_2$	3.4	3.47
I	I	1.27	1.30	I	NO$_2$	3.3	3.52
NO$_2$	NO$_2$	3.89	3.98	NH$_2$	NO$_2$	4.94	4.79
CH$_3$	F (gas)	1.85	1.81	NH$_2$	NH$_2$ (gas)	1.70	1.74
CH$_3$	Cl	1.78	1.80	NH$_2$	NH$_2$	1.79	1.80
CH$_3$	Br	1.75	1.76				

For every substance in Table 4.1, the difference between the observed and the calculated moment value is no greater than the sum of the probable errors of the two values, which gives excellent confirmation, if such were needed, of the plane hexagonal structure of the benzene molecule.   Although the individual differences between observed and calculated moment values are too small to have any significance, their general trend is consistent with the small mutual inductive effects calcu-

[20] C. J. Wilson and H. H. Wenzke, *J. Am. Chem. Soc.*, **57**, 1265 (1935).

lated approximately by Smallwood and Herzfeld,* which would lower the calculated moment of m-xylene by only 0.01 and the calculated values from m-dichloro to m-dinitrobenzene by 0.07 to 0.13 and tend to raise most of the other calculated values very slightly.

The value of m-nitroaniline is included for comparison with that of p-nitroaniline, which was found (Sec. 3) to be raised to an extraordinary extent by a resonance contribution from a highly polar quinonoid structure with positive nitrogen. The fact that a similar structure cannot be written for the meta compound and that the observed moment agrees well with the value calculated in its absence is consistent with this resonance approach to structure.

5. Orthodisubstituted Benzenes. In contrast to the para and meta compounds, where, in the absence of complicating effects, the agreement is good between the observed moment values and those calculated on the basis of a plane, regular hexagon for the benzene ring, the moment values observed for the ortho compounds are consistently lower than the calculated, except when one dipole has its positive end toward the ring and the other its positive end away from the ring. This discrepancy, often called the ortho effect, is only about ⅓ as large in o-difluorobenzene with its small halogen atoms of low polarizability as it is in o-dichlorobenzene. With increasing size and polarizability of the halogen atoms, the ortho effect becomes relatively larger. It was tentatively attributed[1] to widening of the angle between the two dipole axes by steric repulsion between the two groups. However, the results of electron-diffraction measurements[2] subsequently indicated no measurable angle widening in o-dichlorobenzene and a widening of only about 10° in o-diiodobenzene,[3] while a widening of about 30° was necessary to account for the observed lowering. A more recent spectroscopic investigation is reported[2] as indicating that the chlorine in o-dichlorobenzene and the bromine in o-dibromobenzene are bent out of the plane of the ring by 18°, a steric distortion sufficient to account for the observed moment lowering. The previously mentioned (Sec. 4) work of Smallwood and Herzfeld showed that the ortho effect could be accounted for entirely by mutual inductive effects, but the calculation of these effects in the ortho compounds was necessarily subject to large error because of the uncertainty of the treatment, at so short a distance, of the charge distribution as equivalent to a dipole and then the uncertainty of the exact location of the dipole. A small difference in the location assumed for the dipole along the C—Cl bond, for

* H. M. Smallwood and K. F. Herzfeld, *J. Am. Chem. Soc.*, **52**, 1919 (1930).

[1] C. P. Smyth and S. O. Morgan, *J. Am. Chem. Soc.*, **49**, 1030 (1927).

[2] P. W. Allen and L. E. Sutton, *Acta Cryst.*, **3**, 46 (1950).

[3] S. B. Hendricks, L. R. Maxwell, V. L. Mosley, and M. E. Jefferson, *J. Chem. Phys.*, **1**, 549 (1933).

instance, would have an unimportant influence upon the dipole induced in a meta or para group, but a large effect upon that induced in an ortho group, because of its nearness. It may be concluded that both steric repulsion and mutual induction, which usually work in the same direction, are factors in the ortho effect, but that the effect of steric repulsion may often be negligibly small.

TABLE 5.1. MOMENTS ($\times 10^{18}$) IN BENZENE SOLUTION OF o-DISUBSTITUTED BENZENES

Substituents		Obs.	Calc.	Substituents		Obs.	Calc.
CH₃	CH₃	0.62 (gas) 0.58	0.64 .64	CH₃	F	1.35 (gas)	1.44
				CH₃	Cl	1.41	1.44
F	F	2.38	2.53	CH₃	Br	1.44	1.39
F	Cl	2.38	2.64	CH₃	I	1.21	1.16
F	Br	2.27	2.60	CH₃	NO₂	3.70	3.81
F	I	2.00	2.39	Cl	NO₂	4.59 (gas) 4.1	5.27 4.97
Cl	Cl	2.53 (gas) 2.27	2.94 2.74	Br	NO₂	4.1	4.93
Br	Br	2.1	2.67	I	NO₂	3.8	4.77
I	I	1.70	2.25	NH₂	CH₃	1.58	1.71
NO₂	NO₂	6.00	6.90	NH₂	NH₂	1.45	2.48
				NH₂	Cl	1.77	1.71
				NH₂	Br	1.77	1.69
				NH₂	NO₂	4.24	3.66

According to the calculations of Smallwood and Herzfeld, mutual induction should raise the moments of the orthohalogenated toluenes and of o-nitrotoluene by amounts of about 0.3 to 0.6, but Table 5.1 shows an increase of only 0.05 in o-bromo- and o-iodotoluene and a slight decrease in the other three compounds. The ortho effects here are apparently no larger than the experimental errors.

o-Phenylenediamine shows the largest ortho effect in Table 5.1. Tiganik,[4] by means of an equation identical with that used in obtaining the calculated values for this molecule and that of o-nitroaniline in Table 5.1, calculated 2.44 and 3.67 from slightly different constants and concluded that the two molecules represented the most extreme cases of hindered rotation and induction effect. There seems to be nothing

[4] L. Tiganik, Z. physik. Chem., 14B, 135 (1931).

abnormal in the inductive behavior of the amino group as shown by the moments of o-chloro- and o-bromoaniline, which are 0.06 and 0.08 higher than the calculated values[4] because the negative end of the resultant amino group dipole is toward the ring like that of the methyl group, while the halogen dipoles have their positive ends toward the ring, so that the mutual inductive effect increases the resultant moment of the two groups. When both group dipoles have their positive ends away from the ring, mutual induction lowers the moment, the observed value for o-toluidine being 0.13 below the calculated value.[4] The lowering by mutual induction should be greater than this in o-phenylenediamine because the second amino group moment is much larger than the methyl group moment, but not nearly great enough to explain the lowering of 1.03 indicated in Table 5.1. The effect implicit in Tiganik's "hindered rotation" is repulsion between the protons of the two amino groups, which should tend to cause the two groups to keep their protons as far apart as possible and thus bring about partial cancellation of the moment components perpendicular to the C—N bonds with consequent reduction in the resultant moment.

The ortho effect caused by mutual induction should be positive in o-nitroaniline but probably not large enough to account for the increase of 0.6 in the observed moment over the calculated value in Table 5.1. The resonance indicated for p-nitrodimethylaniline in Sec. 3 would give an analogous polar structure for the o-nitroaniline,

A small contribution from this structure would raise the resultant moment well above that calculated. As pointed out in Sec. 4, the moment of m-nitroaniline, which cannot have such a resonating polar structure, shows no such rise in moment. Here again, we have support for the resonance description of these molecular structures.

6. Polysubstituted Benzenes. Only four symmetrical, highly substituted benzenes are included in Table 6.1 since, like these, the others show moments indistinguishable from zero. The closeness to one another of the observed and the calculated values of the monohalogenated toluenes (Secs. 3 to 5) and the fact that the chloromesitylene, bromomesitylene, chlorodurene, and bromodurene moments differ from the moments of chlorobenzene and bromobenzene by no more than the probable experimental errors show the smallness of the mutual effects of the halogen and methyl groups.   The large effect of the methyl groups in nitrodurene in lowering the moment from that of a nitrobenzene to that of a nitroparaffin has already been discussed (Sec. 3).   However, the moment of bromonitrodurene gives little evidence of such lowering, since its value is 2.36 as compared to the differences $3.39 - 1.55 = 1.84$ between nitrodurene and bromodurene, $3.98 - 1.55 = 2.43$ between nitrobenzene and bromodurene,   and $3.98 - 1.54 = 2.44$ between   nitrobenzene   and bromobenzene.

TABLE 6.1. MOMENTS ($\times 10^{18}$) OF TRI-, TETRA-, PENTA, AND HEXASUBSTITUTED BENZENES IN BENZENE SOLUTION

Substituents	Moment	Substituents	Moment
1,2,3-Cl$_3$	2.31	1,3,5-(CH$_3$)$_3$, Cl	1.55
1,2,4-Cl$_3$	1.25	1,3,5-(CH$_3$)$_3$, Br	1.52
1,2,3,4-Cl$_4$	1.90	1,2,4,5-(CH$_3$)$_4$, Br	1.55
1,2,3,5-Cl$_4$	0.65	1,2,4,5-(CH$_3$)$_4$, (NO$_2$)	3.39
1,2,3,5-Br$_4$	0.7	1,2,4,5-(CH$_3$)$_4$, Br, (NO$_2$)	2.36
Cl$_5$	0.88	1-(CH$_3$), 2,4,6-Cl$_3$	0.54
Cl$_6$	(0)	1,2,5-(CH$_3$)$_3$, Cl$_3$	1.83
(CH$_3$)$_6$	(0)	1,2-(CH$_3$)$_2$, Cl$_4$	2.65
(CH$_3$)$_5$, Cl	1.85	1,2-(CH$_3$)$_2$, 4, 5-Cl$_2$	3.01
(CH$_3$), Cl$_5$	1.55	1,2-(CH$_3$)$_2$, 4,5-Br$_2$	2.86
(C$_2$H$_5$), Cl$_5$	1.50	1,2-(CH$_3$)$_2$, 3,4,5-Cl$_3$	2.46
1,3,5-(CH$_3$)$_3$, Cl$_3$	(0)	1,2,3,4-(CH$_3$)$_4$, Cl$_2$	2.93
1,2,4,5-(CH$_3$)$_4$, Cl$_2$	(0)	1,2,3,4-(CH$_3$)$_4$, (NO$_2$)$_2$	6.86

In pentamethylchlorobenzene, the moments due to the 2,3-methyl groups should cancel those due to the 5,6-methyl groups, leaving a moment equal to that of p-chlorotoluene.[1]   The observed value 1.85 is in satisfactory agreement with the observed value of p-chlorotoluene 1.94 (Table 3.1).   Similar treatment of pentachlorotoluene and pentachloroethylbenzene would have the moments due to the 2,3-chlorines canceling those due to the 5,6-chlorines, leaving moments equal to those of p-chlorotoluene and p-chloroethylbenzene, which should be almost identical in value.   The observed values are considerably lower than that of p-chlorotoluene, because of induction between the chlorines.   In the absence of induction, the moment of 1,2,3-trichlorobenzene should be 3.16, but a double ortho effect lowers it by 0.85.   In the absence of inductive effects, the moments due to the 1,4-chlorines in 1,2,4-trichlorobenzene should cancel each other, leaving a moment equal to that of chlorobenzene, 1.55, but the moment of o-dichlorobenzene (Table 5.1) is 2.27, about 15 per cent lower than the calculated value.   If the resultant of the 1,2-chlorine moments is taken equal to that of o-dichlorobenzene and acting in the line bisecting a 60° angle between the bonds of the 1,2-chlorines, and if the usual moment 1.58 is assigned to the 4-chlorine, the resultant moment

[1] C. P. Smyth and G. L. Lewis, J. Am. Chem. Soc., 62, 721 (1940).

of the molecule is calculated to be 1.23, in excellent agreement with the observed value 1.25.

The moment of 1,2,3,4-tetrachlorobenzene can be treated as made up of two vectors with a 120° angle between them and a value equal to that of o-dichlorobenzene, 2.27, which is reduced about 0.41 by the induction between the two chlorines. The resultant of the two vectors is, of course, 2.27, but their value will be reduced by the induction between the 2- and 3-chlorines. A reduction of 0.4 gives close agreement with the observed moment 1.90. The moment of 1,2,3,5-tetrachlorobenzene should be equal to the difference between the value for 1,2,3-trichlorobenzene and that for chlorobenzene, $2.31 - 1.58 = 0.73$. The difference between the observed and the calculated values is no more than the probable error. The moment of 1,2,3,5-tetrabromobenzene is about the same, for similar reasons. The moment of pentachlorobenzene should, in the absence of induction, be the same as that of chlorobenzene. The four ortho effects present in the molecule lower one another, so that the total lowering by induction is slightly less than that in 1,2,3-trichlorobenzene and 1,2,3,5-tetrachlorobenzene. As pentachlorobenzene differs from pentachloromethylbenzene and pentachloroethylbenzene only in lacking a methyl or ethyl group, one would expect the moments of these latter compounds to be about $0.88 + 0.37 = 1.25$, but they are about 0.3 higher.

In the molecule of 1,2,5-trimethyl-3,4,6-trichlorobenzene, absence of induction would leave a moment equal to that of p-chlorotoluene, 1.94. The observed value 1.83 is slightly lower than this, though not distinguishable from the moment of pentamethylchlorobenzene. One would expect the moment to be reduced more than 0.07 by the induction between the 3- and 4-chlorines. Indeed, if the resultant of these two chlorine moments is taken as equal to the moment of o-dichlorobenzene, 2.27, the moment calculated for the molecule is 1.54, 0.3 lower than that observed as in the cases of methyl- and ethylpentachlorobenzene.

The moment of tetrachloro-o-xylene should be equal to the sum of the moments of 1,2,3,4-tetrachlorobenzene and o-xylene, $1.90 + 0.62 = 2.52$, which is close to the observed value 2.64. The moment of 4,5-dichloro-o-xylene should similarly be equal to the sum of the moments of o-dichlorobenzene and o-xylene, $2.27 + 0.62 = 2.89$. The observed value is again higher by only 0.12. In other words, the tetrachloro-o-xylene and the 4,5-dichloro-o-xylene moments differ from each other by just the difference between the moments of 1,2,3,4-tetrachlorobenzene and o-dichlorobenzene, as they should, but both are slightly higher than the calculated values. Similarly, the moment of 4,5-dibromo-o-xylene, 2.86, is higher than the value calculated as the sum of the moments of o-dibromobenzene and o-xylene, $2.1 + 0.62 = 2.72$. In 3,4,5-trichloro-o-xylene, the moment due to the three chlorines may be taken as that of

1,2,3-trichlorobenzene, 2.31, and resolved at an angle of 30° with the moment of *o*-xylene, 0.62, to give 2.87, a value 0.41 higher than the observed. Dichloroprehnitene, or 1,2,3,4-tetramethyl-5,6-dichlorobenzene, should have the same moment as 4,5-dichloro-*o*-xylene. The observed value is 0.08 lower than this latter.

In the absence of complicating effects, the moment of dinitroprehnitene, or 1,2,3,4-tetramethyl-5,6-dinitrobenzene, should be equal to that of *o*-dinitrobenzene, 6.00, plus the moment 0.62 of *o*-xylene. The observed value 6.86 is slightly higher than this calculated value 6.62, although one might expect it to be slightly lower because of some reduction in the aromatic nitro moment by steric repulsion. The apparent effect of steric repulsion in lowering the moment of nitrodurene and *p*-aminonitrodurene (Sec. 3) is striking, but it is not evidenced in the moment of *p*-bromonitrodurene or dinitroprehnitene. Occasional excessive discrepancies in these moment values may arise from the presence of impurities rather than from inadequacy of the principles proposed.

7. Substituted Biphenyls. The zero moment values of biphenyl and the *p,p'*-dihalogenated biphenyls show clearly that the structure of the molecule is an extended one with the carbon-carbon bond connecting the rings lying in the plane of each ring. This structure is obvious in the light of present-day knowledge, but a bent structure had received some credence prior to the dipole moment measurements. Hampson and Weissberger[1] treated each of the monochlorobiphenyls as a chlorobenzene molecule to which a polarizable benzene ring was attached and calculated the moment from a value 1.55 for the moment of chlorobenzene and the polarizability of the benzene ring, obtaining the following moment values:

Molecule	Rings coplanar	Rings perpendicular	Free rotation
o-Chlorobiphenyl	1.31	1.40	1.36
m-Chlorobiphenyl	1.60	1.60	1.60
p-Chlorobiphenyl	1.64	1.64	1.64

For each of the three assumptions concerning relative ring positions, the agreement between observed and calculated values is as good as could be expected from the accuracy of the method of calculation and does not, therefore, decide between the different possible ring positions. The moments of the other monosubstituted biphenyls are similarly close to those of the corresponding monosubstituted benzenes. The moments of the three mononitrobiphenyls lie in the order required by their inductive effects, which should be analogous to those calculated for the monochloro-

[1] G. C. Hampson and A. Weissberger, *J. Am. Chem. Soc.*, **58**, 2111 (1936).

biphenyls, but the value for m-nitrobiphenyl should be closer to that of p-nitrobiphenyl. Probably, the discrepancy is within the experimental error, since the value for p-nitrobiphenyl in Table 7.1 is the mean of two values differing by 0.11.

TABLE 7.1. MOMENTS ($\times 10^{18}$) OF SUBSTITUTED BIPHENYLS IN BENZENE SOLUTION

Substituents	Moment	Substituents	Moment
o-F	1.50	p,p'-F$_2$	(0.35)
o-Cl	1.45	o,o'-Cl$_2$	1.91
m-Cl	1.64	m,m'-Cl$_2$	1.80
p-Cl	1.63	p,p'-Cl$_2$	0
p-Br	1.64	p,p'-Br$_2$	0
o-NO$_2$	3.80	o,o'-(NO$_2$)$_2$	5.19
m-NO$_2$	3.90	p,p'-(NO$_2$)$_2$	(1.0)
p-NO$_2$	4.22	p,p'-(CN)$_2$	(1.3)
p-NH$_2$	1.74	p,p'-(NO$_2$)NH$_2$	6.46

The effect of steric hindrance in giving rise to optical activity in o,o'-substituted biphenyls has been extensively investigated.[2] About 8 kcal. per mole of resonance energy in excess of the normal resonance energy in the two benzene rings[3] and a shortening of about 0.06 A. in the carbon-carbon bond between the two rings[4] indicate some double-bond character for the bond between the two rings, which would tend to make them coplanar. On the other hand, the atomic dimensions in the molecule are such as to cause some slight steric repulsion,[5] which might tend to turn the unsubstituted rings slightly out of the same plane. The effect is, of course, greatly increased when the ortho hydrogens are replaced by larger atoms or groups. If all positions of rotation about the bond between the two rings were equally probable, the mean moment (Sec. VIII.2) for both the ortho- and the metasubstituted biphenyls would be

$$\mu = m(2 - 2\cos^2 60°)^{\frac{1}{2}} = 1.41m \sin 60° = 1.22m \qquad (7.1)$$

where m is the moment of the monosubstituted biphenyl. This gives 1.77 for o,o'-dichlorobiphenyl, 2.00 for m,m'-dichlorobiphenyl, and 4.64 for o,o'-dinitrobiphenyl. If the amount of double-bond character in the bond between the two rings were sufficient to cause the rings to be coplanar and if the resulting cis and trans forms of the ortho- and meta-disubstituted biphenyls had equal energies, Eq. (7.1) would give the mean

---

[2] H. Gilman, "Organic Chemistry," Wiley, New York, 2d ed., 1943, vol. I, p. 347.

[3] L. Pauling, "The Nature of the Chemical Bond," Cornell University Press, Ithaca, N.Y., 2d ed., 1940, p. 137.

[4] P. W. Allen and L. E. Sutton, *Acta Cryst.*, **3**, 46 (1950).

[5] L. Pauling, *op. cit.*, p. 220.

moment for an equal distribution of the molecules between cis and trans forms and would thus fail to distinguish between the two extreme cases of free rotation and no rotation around the bond between the rings. Since the region of the planar cis position of maximum moment is excluded or made much less probable by steric repulsion in the ortho compounds, one would expect the observed moment to be lower than the value calculated by Eq. (7.1), instead of slightly higher as observed. Hampson and Weissberger[1] attributed the absence of lowering in the value of o,o'-dichlorobiphenyl to the effect of the dispersion forces between the chlorine atoms in drawing them toward, but not into, the cis position, which is made highly unstable, if not impossible, by the repulsion forces. The differences between the observed and calculated values for m,m'-dichlorobiphenyl are within the accuracy of the experiment and the approximations in the calculation. It is evident that the orthodisubstituted biphenyls cannot, as suggested by resonance considerations, consist of a mixture of cis and trans isomers, since the cis forms are largely excluded by repulsion and the trans forms would have zero moment. An equal probability of distribution around the bond between the two rings is excluded by the repulsion in the cis position. It is evident that some rotation or distribution of position around this bond occurs in the ortho forms, while, of course, less restriction should occur in the other forms.

The apparent moment values enclosed in parentheses for p,p'-dinitro- and p,p'-dicyanodiphenyl[6] are not to be taken as actual permanent moments but, probably, as the result of atomic polarization arising from slight bending of the long structure separating the two large opposed dipoles (Sec. XIV.4). Atomic polarization may also contribute somewhat to the large value found for p-nitro-p'-aminobiphenyl, which is slightly higher than the value 6.2 of p-nitroaniline and should arise in part from a contribution from a structure analogous to the highly polar structure contributing to that of p-nitroaniline.

8. Substituted Naphthalenes. The structure of the naphthalene molecule as two plane hexagons sharing an edge can be established by reasoning similar to that employed in determining the benzene structure (Sec. VIII.2). Comparison of the moments of 1-substituted naphthalenes in Table 8.1 with those for the monosubstituted benzenes (Sec. 2) shows a close parallelism. The slightly higher values of the 2-substituted naphthalenes are attributable to inductive effect (cf. Sec. 7), as will be shown shortly. The moments of the disubstituted naphthalenes are clearly the resultants of two dipoles acting at the corners of regular hexagons like that of the benzene ring. An ortho effect like that in o-disubstituted benzenes is evident. The zero moment of 2,6-dichloro-naphthalene shows that the two rings are coplanar.

[6] R. J. W. Le Fèvre and H. Vine, *J. Chem. Soc.*, 1878 (1938).

TABLE 8.1. MOMENTS ($\times 10^{18}$) IN BENZENE SOLUTION OF SUBSTITUTED
NAPHTHALENES

Moment
0

Substituents	Moment	Substituents	Moment
1-F	1.42	1,5-NO$_2$	0
2-F	1.52	1,8-NO$_2$	7.4
1-Cl	1.51	1-Br, 2-F	2.34
2-Cl	1.65	1-Br, 2-I	1.80
1-Br	1.53	1-Cl, 8-F	2.86
2-Br	1.70	1-Cl, 8-Br	2.64
1-I	1.43	1-Cl, 8-I	2.55
2-I	1.56	1-Br, 5-NO$_2$	2.49
1-NO$_2$	3.8	1-NO$_2$, 2-NH$_2$	4.55
2-NO$_2$	4.4	2-NO$_2$, 1-NH$_2$	4.90
1-NH$_2$	1.49	1-NO$_2$, 4-NH$_2$	6.4
2-NH$_2$	1.77	1-NO$_2$, 4-NH$_2$ (dioxane)	6.97
1,5-F$_2$	0	1-NO$_2$, 5-NH$_2$	5.1
1,2-Cl$_2$	2.47	2-NO$_2$, 6-NH$_2$	5.14
1,3-Cl$_2$	1.78	2-NO$_2$, 6-NH$_2$ (dioxane)	7.10
1,4-Cl$_2$	0.48	3-NO$_2$, 1-NH$_2$	5.14
1,5-Cl$_2$	0	4-NO$_2$, 2-NH$_2$	4.62
1,6-Cl$_2$	1.44	5-NO$_2$, 2-NH$_2$	5.03
1,7-Cl$_2$	2.55	8-NO$_2$, 1-NH$_2$	3.12
1,8-Cl$_2$	2.82	8-NO$_2$, 2-NH$_2$	4.47
2,3-Cl$_2$	2.55		
2,6-Cl$_2$	0		
2,7-Cl$_2$	1.53		

Hampson and Weissberger[1] have made an interesting empirical calculation on the chloronaphthalenes by establishing an a axis in the mutually shared side of the two rings and a b axis perpendicular to it in the plane of the rings. If the moment components along the a and b axes for the 1-substituted compound are x and y, respectively, and for the 2-substituted compound are p and q, respectively, equations may be written for moments as follows:

$$
\begin{aligned}
\text{1-chloronaphthalene} &= x^2 + y^2 = 1.51^2 \\
\text{2-chloronaphthalene} &= p^2 + q^2 = 1.65^2 \\
\text{2,7-dichloronaphthalene} &= 2p = 1.53 \\
\text{1,6-dichloronaphthalene} &= (x - p)^2 + (y - q)^2 = 1.44^2
\end{aligned}
$$

from which $x = 1.49$, $y = 0.22$, $p = 0.77$, and $q = 1.46$. These components give an angle of 8° between the moment of the 1-substituted compound and the a axis and an angle of 28° between the moment of

[1] G. C. Hampson and A. Weissberger, *J. Chem. Soc.*, 393 (1936).

the 2-substituted compound and the b axis.   These moment components were used by Hampson and Weissberger to calculate the moments of the other dichloronaphthalenes.   The two with zero moment are added to Table 8.2 for completeness.   The discrepancy between the observed and

TABLE 8.2. RATIOS OF OBSERVED TO CALCULATED MOMENTS OF
DICHLORONAPHTHALENES

1,7-Cl$_2$	0.99	2,3-Cl$_2$	0.87
1,3-Cl$_2$	0.97	1,4-Cl$_2$	0.92
1,8-Cl$_2$	0.94	1,5-Cl$_2$	1.00
1,2-Cl$_2$	0.87	2,6-Cl$_2$	1.00

the calculated value for the small moment of 1,4-dichloronaphthalene is much less than the probable experimental error.   The ratio μ_{obs}/μ_{calc} for 1,2- and 2,3-dichloronaphthalene, 0.87, is indistinguishable from the value 0.86 calculated by Hampson and Weissberger for o-dichlorobenzene, and the value of the ratio for 1,3-dichloronaphthalene agrees similarly with that for m-dichlorobenzene, 0.97.   The lowering of the observed moments below those calculated for the chloronaphthalenes is evidently due to the same effect as that in the benzenes, presumably mutual induction.   In 1,8-dichloronaphthalene, the dipoles are sufficiently close together to permit some lowering by induction.   The effect of halogen polarizability is evident in the moment of the other 1,8-dihalogenated naphthalenes in Table 8.1.   Only very slight lowering is evident in the moment of 1-chloro-8-fluoronaphthalene, while the moments of 1-chloro-8-bromo- and 1-chloro-8-iodonaphthalene show greater lowering than that in 1,8-dichloronaphthalene.   The moments of the other halogen and nitro-substituted naphthalenes are consistent with these evident relations.

Hampson and Weissberger have further calculated the moment induced in the four unshared C—H groups of one ring by the moment of the substituent of the other, which is taken equal to the moment of the monosubstituted benzene, the value 1.55 being used for chlorobenzene. The resultant moments thus obtained are 1.56 inclined at an angle of 8° with the a axis for 1-chloronaphthalene and 1.66 inclined at an angle of 28° with the b axis for 2-chloronaphthalene.   The excellent agreement with the observed moment values and the empirically calculated angles seems to provide clear evidence of the induction effect and the soundness of the treatment.

The moment of 1-nitro-2-naphthylamine is 0.3 higher than that of o-nitroaniline (Sec. 5), just as the moment of 2-naphthylamine is 0.3 higher than that of 1-naphthylamine, presumably because of the presence of the induced moment in the second ring.   The moment of 2-nitro-1-naphthylamine is higher by an additional 0.35 because of the greater inductive effect of the nitro group in the 2 position, as shown by the increase in the moment of 2-nitronaphthalene over that of 1-nitronaphthalene. The moment of 1-nitro-4-naphthylamine shows the same large increase by resonance as does that of p-nitroaniline (Sec. 2), from which it differs by only 0.2. On the other hand, in 1-nitro-5-naphthylamine, the moment is indistinguishable from the value 5.17 calculated for p-nitroaniline in the absence of interaction between the nitro and the amino groups (Table 3.6). Similarly, the moment of 2-nitro-6-naphthylamine, which should have the same value except for the small inductive increase previously noted, is 5.14. It is evident that the polar structure

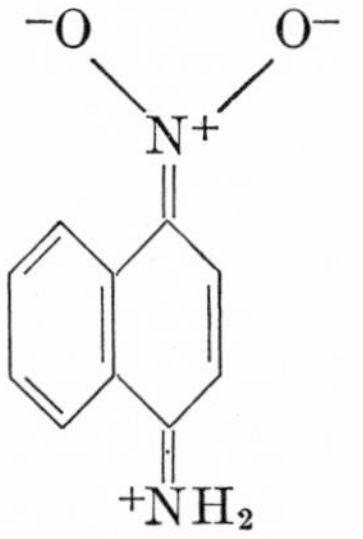

$$^-O \qquad O^-$$
$$\diagdown N^+ \diagup$$
$$+NH_2$$

possesses considerable stability when the molecule is in benzene solution and greater stability in dioxane (Table 3.7) as the result of hydrogen bonding. It appears that the structures

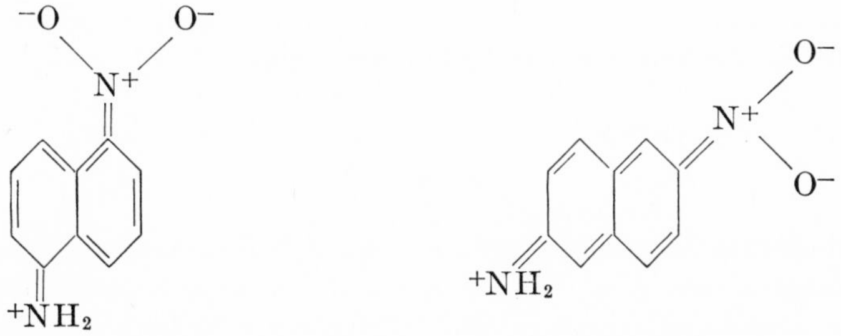

$$^-O \qquad O^-$$
$$\diagdown N^+ \diagup$$
$$+NH_2$$

$$O^-$$
$$N^+ \diagup$$
$$\diagdown O^-$$
$$+NH_2$$

make practically negligible contributions when the molecules are in benzene solution, but, in dioxane solution, the polar structure for 2-nitro-6-naphthylamine is apparently stabilized by hydrogen bonding (Table 3.7) to such an extent as to raise the moment by 1.96.

The moment of 3-nitro-1-naphthylamine shows an increase of 0.2 over that of m-nitroaniline, while that of 4-nitro-2-naphthylamine is slightly lower, the difference in both cases probably being due to inductive effects. The moment of 5-nitro-2-naphthylamine, which, like the two preceding molecules, cannot have the resonating polar structure, is slightly lower than that of 3-nitro-1-naphthylamine and close to that of m-nitroaniline (Table 4.1), as it should be. The moment calculated for 8-nitro-1-naphthylamine from the values for 1-nitronaphthalene and 1-naphthylamine, the amino angle being taken as 38°, is 2.78. The neglected inductive effect would raise the moment enough to account approximately for the discrepancy of 0.34.

It is evident that the numerous moment values for the substituted naphthalenes can be very successfully correlated with one another and with the moments of the substituted benzenes in terms of resonance and electrostatic induction.

9. Aromatic Heterocyclic Compounds. A few aromatic heterocyclic compounds have already been discussed in connection with alicyclic compounds. Others will be treated in this section to illustrate the relations between their dipole moments and structures. Table 9.1 gives the moments of a number of substituted pyridines and related compounds, together with the values calculated by the observers,[1-3] occasionally adjusted slightly to make them consistent with the group moment values used in this chapter.

The correctness of the plane hexagonal Kekulé model of the ring used in calculating the moments in Table 9.1 and of the assignment of the pyridine moment to the line bisecting the nitrogen valence angle is shown by the generally good agreement between the observed and calculated values. This receives further confirmation from the results of electron diffraction,[4] which indicate that pyridine has a structure analogous to that of benzene. The moment of pyridine is much larger than those of the alkyl amines and aniline, a fact which is explicable in terms of resonance contributions from the polar structures

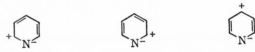

The moments of 4-chloropyridine and 3,5-dibromopyridine exceed the calculated values by amounts which could arise from the effects of induction or atomic polarization, while the value 4.36 for 4-aminopyridine in dioxane solution[2] is 0.57 higher than that in benzene solution, indicating, as previously observed (Sec. 3) for analogous structures, some stabilization of the polar structure by hydrogen bonding. The very large moment 6.0 found for 4-pyridol in dioxane solution is interpreted by Leis and Curran[2] as showing the existence of the compound largely as the 4-pyridone tautomer H—N⟨ ⟩=O, with a contribution from the polar structure H—$\overset{+}{\text{N}}$⟨ ⟩—O⁻, which is stabilized by Kekulé resonance. The

[1] C. A. Goethals, *Rec. trav. chim.*, **54**, 299 (1935).
[2] D. G. Leis and B. Columba Curran, *J. Am. Chem. Soc.*, **67**, 79 (1945).
[3] W. C. Schneider, *J. Am. Chem. Soc.*, **70**, 627 (1948).
[4] V. Schomaker and L. Pauling, *J. Am. Chem. Soc.*, **61**, 1769 (1939).

TABLE 9.1. MOMENTS ($\times 10^{18}$) IN BENZENE SOLUTION OF SUBSTITUTED PYRIDINES AND RELATED COMPOUNDS

Pyridines	Obs.	Calc.	Compound	Obs.	Calc.
Pyridine (dioxane)	2.23 / 2.22		Pyrazine	0	0
Substituents			Pyrazine (dioxane)	0.6	
4-CH₃	2.57	2.60	Pyridazine (dioxane)	3.94	4.03
2,6-(CH₃)₂	1.65	1.86			
4-Cl	0.84	0.65			
4-CN	1.61	1.67			
2-Br	2.98	3.23	Pyrimidine (dioxane)	2.42	2.23
3-Br	1.93	1.84			
3,5-Br₂	0.98	0.70			
2,6-Br₂	3.43	3.74			
2,4,6-Br₃	2.05	2.23			
2-NH₂	2.17	2.12			
3-NH₂	3.19	3.30	2,5-Dichloropyrimidine (dioxane)	2.72	2.23
4-NH₂	3.79	3.75	2-Methoxy-5-chloropyrimidine	(0)	
4-NH₂ (dioxane)	4.36	3.75	2-Mercapto-5-chloropyrimidine	(0)	
4-CH₃O	2.94	2.8	Pyrazole	1.57	
4-OH (dioxane)	6.0	3.5	1-Methylpyrazole	2.28	
			3-Methylpyrazole	1.43	
			Imidazole	3.84	
			1,2,3-Triazole	1.77	
			1,2,4-Triazole	3.17	
			1-Phenyl-1,2,4-triazole	2.88	
			4-Phenyl-1,2,4-triazole	5.63	
			Tetrazole	5.11	
			1-Methyltetrazole	5.38	
			5-Aminotetrazole	5.71	
			1-Phenyl-1,2,3-triazole	4.08	
			2-Phenyl-1,2,3-triazole	0.97	
			Benzimidazole (dioxane)	3.93	
			Benztriazole (dioxane)	4.07	
			2,2'-Dipyridyl	<0.68	0–3.8
			4,4'-Dipyridyl	(0.5)	0
			Quinoline	2.18	2.2
			Isoquinoline	2.53	2.5
			Pyrrole	1.80	
			Substituents 1-CH₃	1.94	
			Indole	2.11	
			Substituents 1-CH₃	2.16	
			2-CH₃	2.47	
			3-CH₃	2.08	

difference between the large moment of benzonitrile, 3.90, and that of pyridine, 2.23, exceeds the observed value for 4-cyanopyridine by only 0.06, a difference no greater than the probable experimental error.

The agreement between the observed and calculated values for pyrazine, pyridazine, and pyrimidine is within the probable errors. The absence of any considerable ortho effect in pyridazine is interesting. Schneider[3] attributes the zero moments of 2-methoxy-5-chloropyrimidine and 2-mercapto-5-chloropyrimidine to exact opposition of the moment of the ring to the resultant of the moment of the carbon-chlorine and methyl-oxygen or hydrogen-sulfur moments, resonance effects being involved. The moments of a large number of azoles have been measured and discussed by Jensen and Friediger.[5] Some of these are listed in Table 9.1 and some in Table 9.2. The small apparent moment value found for 4,4'-dipyridyl is just what would be expected to arise from atomic polarization and is indicative of an extended structure like that of diphenyl. The extremely small moment observed for 2,2'-dipyridyl is surprising in view of the considerable values for the 2,2'-substituted diphenyls (Sec. 7). It indicates a nearly or predominantly trans structure, probably stabilized by repulsion between the negative charges on the two nitrogens. The moment of quinoline is very close to that of pyridine, just as the moments of the 1-substituted naphthalenes are close to those of the corresponding substituted benzenes. The moment of isoquinoline agrees closely with the value calculated by adding to the moment of quinoline an inductive increase estimated from those observed from 1- to 2-substituted naphthalenes. The moment of pyrrole is considerably higher than those of secondary amines, probably because of resonance contributions from two structures with positive nitrogen.[6] The replacement of the hydrogen on the nitrogen by methyl apparently raises the moment very slightly. The moment of indole is 0.3 higher than that of pyrrole in contrast to the absence of appreciable difference between the moments of pyridine and quinoline. The replacement of the hydrogen on the nitrogen by methyl makes even less difference than in the case of pyrrole, and the effect on the moment of methyl in the 2 and the 3 position is like that in the case of benzene.

Furan (Sec. IX.7) and thiophene (Sec. IX.9) have been considered previously with somewhat similar aliphatic compounds. The moments of the halogen- and methyl-substituted thiophenes have been calculated[7] with fair success from the bond angles indicated by electron diffraction,[4] the moments of similarly substituted benzenes, and the moment of thio-

[5] K. A. Jensen and A. Friediger, *Kgl. Danske Videnskab. Selskab. Mat.-fys. Medd.*, XX, 20 (1943).

[6] E. G. Cowley and J. R. Partington, *J. Chem. Soc.*, 47 (1936).

[7] R. Keswani and H. Freiser, *J. Am. Chem. Soc.*, **71**, 218 and 1789 (1949).

TABLE 9.2. DIPOLE MOMENTS ($\times 10^{18}$) IN BENZENE SOLUTION OF SOME THIOPHENES, OXAZOLES, THIAZOLES, SYDNONES, AND RELATED COMPOUNDS

Thiophene	0.53	Isoxazole	2.81
Gas	0.58		
Substituents			
2-CH$_3$	0.67		
3-CH$_3$	0.82		
2,5-(CH$_3$)$_2$	0.51	2-Methyl-4,5-diphenyloxazole	1.7
2-Cl	1.60		
2-Br	1.37		
2-I	1.14		
2,5-Cl$_2$	1.12	Thiazole	1.64
2,3,4,5-Cl$_4$	0.93		
2,3,4,5-Br$_4$	0.73		
2-NO$_2$	4.18		
2,3,4,5-(C$_6$H$_5$)$_4$	0.60		
(C$_{10}$H$_6$)$_2$	0.8		
Benzo	0.62	Benzothiazole	1.45
Dibenzo	0.83	*Substituents*	
		2-SCH$_3$	1.42
		3-CH$_3$, 2-S	4.84
		2-SH	4.00
		4-CH$_3$, 2-SH	4.00
		6-CH$_3$, 2-SH	4.30

Sydnones

N-Phenyl	6.50	C-Chloro-N-phenyl	6.49
N-p-Tolyl	6.89	C-Bromo-N-phenyl	6.42
N-β-Naphthyl	6.9	N-Phenyl-C-methyl	6.57
N-p-Chlorophenyl	5.01	N-Cyclohexyl	6.7
N-p-Bromophenyl	5.13	N-Benzyl	6.27

2,3-Diphenyl-2,5-endothio-1,3,4-thiodiazoline	8.8
Diphenyl-methyl-endothio-triazoline (CHCl$_3$)	8.4
Triphenyl-endoanilo-triazoline	9.1
Diphenyl-methylmercapto-endoxy-triazoline (dioxane)	7.7
Methylmercapto-methyl-diphenyl-triazolinium iodide (CHCl$_3$)	11.0
Methylmercapto-diphenyl-thiodiazolinium iodide (CHCl$_3$)	13.1

phene itself. Some discrepancies are attributable to ortho effect. The treatment may be illustrated in detail by the discussion[8] of 2-nitrothiophene. Neglecting, for the time being, any effect of the nitro group upon resonance in the ring and assuming the thiophene moment to be 0.6

[8] P. F. Oesper, G. L. Lewis, and C. P. Smyth, *J. Am. Chem. Soc.*, **64**, 1130 (1942).

acting in the line bisecting the CSC angle, and the moment due to the nitro group to be equal to that of 2-nitropropane, the moment calculated for the molecule is 3.6 as compared to 4.18 observed. The nitro group moment used here includes the inductive effects in 2-nitropropane, which should differ little from the direct effects in 2-nitrothiophene. Evidently, polar structures analogous to those for nitrobenzene contribute to that of 2-nitrothiophene, such structures being

$$
\begin{array}{ccc}
HC{=\!=\!=}CH & & O^- \\
| \quad\quad\quad | & & \diagup \\
HC \quad\quad C{=\!}^+N & \\
\diagdown\!\diagdown \quad\quad \diagup & & \diagdown \\
S^+ \quad\quad O^- & & O^-
\end{array}
\qquad
\begin{array}{ccc}
HC{-\!-\!-}{^+}CH & & O^- \\
\| \quad\quad\quad | & & \diagup \\
HC \quad\quad C{=\!}^+N & \\
\diagdown \quad\quad \diagup & & \diagdown \\
S \quad\quad O^- & & O^-
\end{array}
$$

$$
\begin{array}{ccc}
HC{=\!=}CH & & O^- \\
| \quad\quad\quad | & & \diagup \\
HC^+ \quad\quad C{=\!}^+N & \\
\diagdown \quad\quad \diagup & & \diagdown \\
S \quad\quad\quad & & O^-
\end{array}
$$

Contributions from these structures will, obviously, raise the moment above that calculated with the moment for 2-nitropropane. If 4.0, the moment of nitrobenzene, is used instead of 3.4 for the moment due to the nitro group, the moment value calculated for 2-nitrothiophene is 4.2, in good agreement with the observed value. The small increases in moment of benzo-, dibenzo-, and dinaphthalenethiophene over the moment of thiophene suggest some resonance effects.[9]

The moment of isoxazole is but slightly larger than would be expected from the moments of furan and pyridine. The moment of 2-methyl-4,5-diphenyloxazole is much lower than that of isoxazole because of the much wider angle between the ring oxygen and nitrogen moments. The thiazole moment, as would be expected, is not very different, and the lowering of the moment from thiazole to benzothiazole suggests some additional resonance effects in the latter. The benzothiazoles have been discussed in detail elsewhere.[8] The isomer with the methyl group on the nitrogen has a moment more than three times as large as that of the molecule with the methyl on the mercapto sulfur, primarily because of the presence of the thiocarbonyl group. The moment calculated for this molecule is about 4.4. The moments of the mercaptobenzothiazoles should be close to that of 2-methylmercaptobenzothiazole, as the replacement of the mercaptan hydrogen by a methyl group should have only a small effect upon the moment. Evidently, these compounds exist largely in a lactam form, in which the migration of the hydrogen from the sulfur to the nitrogen leaves a structure like that of the thione with correspondingly large moment.

[9] R. G. Charles and H. Freiser, *J. Am. Chem. Soc.*, **72**, 2233 (1950).

The large moments of the sydnones[10,11] have been explained in terms of contributions from resonating polar structures,[10-12] and, indeed, the polarity is so great that the term "meso-ionic" has been suggested for compounds of this type.   Hill and Sutton[11] show that the observed moment of the sydnone ring is only about two-fifths of that calculated by the molecular orbital method, a discrepancy similar to that in the case of cycloheptatrienone (Sec. IX.6).   Jensen and Friediger,[13] who measured the last six compounds in Table 9.2, attribute the very large moments of the first four to the existence of the molecules as dipolar ions, such as

However, they consider that this is just one of several resonating dipolar structures.   The very large moments of the two iodides result from their existence as salts.

10. Resonance and Polarity in Polymethine Dyes and Related Molecules.   Table 10.1 gives the normal structures and the moments of twenty-five molecules which are of interest here, particularly because of the long displacements of charge permitted by their conjugated systems. Fourteen of these compounds have been discussed previously together with similar or related compounds because of the light which they throw upon the relations between color and constitution,[1-9] and many more dyes of more or less similar character have been discussed by Dr. L. G. S. Brooker and his colleagues with special reference to spectra, basicities,

[10] J. C. Earl, E. M. W. Leake, and R. J. W. LeFèvre, *J. Chem. Soc.*, 2269 (1948).

[11] R. A. W. Hill and L. E. Sutton, *J. Chem. Soc.*, 746 (1949).

[12] W. Baker, W. D. Ollis, and V. D. Poole, *J. Chem. Soc.*, 307 (1949).

[13] K. A. Jensen and A. Friediger, *Kgl. Danske Videnskab. Selskab. Mat.-fys. Medd.*, XX, 20 (1943).

[1] L. G. S. Brooker, R. H. Sprague, C. P. Smyth, and G. L. Lewis, *J. Am. Chem. Soc.*, **62**, 1116 (1940).

[2] L. G. S. Brooker, F. L. White, G. H. Keyes, C. P. Smyth, and P. F. Oesper, *J. Am. Chem. Soc.*, **63**, 3192 (1941).

[3] L. G. S. Brooker and R. H. Sprague, *J. Am. Chem. Soc.*, **63**, 3203, 3214 (1941).

[4] L. G. S. Brooker, G. H. Keyes, and W. W. Williams, *J. Am. Chem. Soc.*, **64**, 199 (1942).

[5] L. G. S. Brooker and R. H. Sprague, *J. Am. Chem. Soc.*, **67**, 1869 (1945).

[6] L. G. S. Brooker, A. L. Sklar, H. W. J. Cressman, G. H. Keyes, L. A. Smith, R. H. Sprague, E. Van Lare, G. Van Zandt, F. L. White, and W. W. Williams, *J. Am. Chem. Soc.*, **67**, 1875 (1945).

[7] L. G. S. Brooker, R. H. Sprague, and H. W. J. Cressman, *J. Am. Chem. Soc.*, **67**, 1889 (1945).

[8] L. G. S. Brooker et al., *J. Am. Chem. Soc.*, **73**, 1087, 1094, 5326, 5332, and 5356 (1951).

[9] W. T. Simpson, *J. Am. Chem. Soc.*, **73**, 5359 (1951).

TABLE 10.1. DIPOLE MOMENTS ($\times 10^{18}$) IN BENZENE SOLUTION OF POLYMETHINE DYES AND RELATED MOLECULES

(1)	p,p'-Di-(dimethylamino)-benzophenone $[(CH_3)_2NC_6H_4]_2CO$	5.37
(2)	Phenol blue	5.80
(3)	3-Ethyl-2-(γ-nitroallylidene)-benzothiazoline	9.23
(4)	3-Ethyl-2-anilinobenzothiazoline ($n = 0$)	2.37
(5)	($n = 1$)	4.17
(6)	($n = 2$)	5.32
(7)	2-(p-Dimethylaminostyryl)-benzothiazole	3.59
(8)	2-[2-(2-Benzothiazolyl) allylidene]-3-ethylbenzothiazoline	4.51
(9)	2-Acetonyl-1-ethyl-β-naphthothiazoline	5.23

TABLE 10.1. DIPOLE MOMENTS ($\times 10^{18}$) IN BENZENE SOLUTION OF POLYMETHINE DYES AND RELATED MOLECULES (*Continued*)

(10)	1-Ethyl-2-thioacetylmethylene-β-naphthothiazoline	6.64
(11)	2,7-Dibromo-9-[(3-ethyl-2(3)-benzothiazolylidene)-ethylidene] fluorene ($n = 1$)	5.21
(12)	($n = 2$)	6.9
(13)	3-[(3-Ethyl-2(3)benzothiazolylidene) ethylidene]-2-methylindolenine	7.68
(14)	1,2-Dimethyl-3-[β-(2-benzothiazolyl)vinyl]-indole	4.06
(15)	1,2-Dimethyl-3-[β-(4-quinolyl)vinyl]-indole	5.43

TABLE 10.1. DIPOLE MOMENTS ($\times 10^{18}$) IN BENZENE SOLUTION OF POLYMETHINE
DYES AND RELATED MOLECULES (*Continued*)

(16)	2-Methyl-3-[(1-methyl-4(1)-quinolylidene)ethylidene]-indolenine	
		10.6
(17)	2-*p*-Dimethylaminostyrylquinoline	
		3.12
(18)	5-*p*-Dialkylaminobenzylidene-3-methyl-1-phenyl-4-pyrazolone	
	(R = CH₃)	7.00
(19)	(R = C₂H₅)	6.51
(20)	5-*p*-Dialkylaminobenzylidene-3-ethylrhodanine	
	(R = CH₃)	5.92
(21)	(R = C₂H₅)	6.20
(22)	2-[(3-Ethyl-2(3)-benzothiazolidene)ethylidene]-3(2)-thianaphthenone	
		6.50

TABLE 10.1. DIPOLE MOMENTS ($\times 10^{18}$) IN BENZENE SOLUTION OF POLYMETHINE DYES AND RELATED MOLECULES (*Continued*)

(23)	3-Ethyl-5-[4-(1-ethyl-3,3-dimethyl-2(3)-indolylidene)-butenylidene]-rhodanine	6.91
(24)	1,3-Diethyl-5-[4-(1-ethyl-3,3-dimethyl-2(1)-indolylidene)-2-butenylidene]-2-thiobarbituric acid	9.70
(25)	1,3-Diethyl-5-[(1,3-diethyl-2(3)-benzimidazolylidene)-butenylidene]-barbituric acid	17.7 (dioxane)

and structures. The moment values for eleven more of these compounds, measured by Dr. G. L. Lewis or Dr. P. F. Oesper in the writer's laboratory, are published for the first time here. Because of the complexity of most of the compounds, it is convenient to number them in order in the table and refer to them by number in the text.

The moment of compound (1) is about 1.0 higher than the value calculated from the moments of dimethylaniline and benzophenone, indicating contributions from two polar structures analogous to that for *p*-nitroaniline, in which electrons move from the nitrogen and to the oxygen, the conjugated system providing the channel for the charge shift. The charge shift from nitrogen to oxygen or nitrogen to nitrogen is characteristic of many of the molecules in Table 10.1. It raises the moment of compound (2) from a roughly estimated 2.4 to an observed 5.8 and nearly doubles the moment of (3). The charge shift from one nitrogen to another is shown by compounds (4), (5), and (6). Polar structures may be written such as that for (5):

The bond moments in the normal structures of (4), (5), and (6) should be the same. The moment estimated for the normal structure of (4) is about 1.6 and those for (5) and (6) are about 2.0 with probable errors of about 0.5. The values estimated even more roughly for the polar structures are 20 to 30 $\times$ 10^{-18}. Uncertainty as to orientation of groups around single bonds, question as to cis or trans configuration at double bonds, and possible reduction of the moments of the polar structures by induced shifts of charge make these calculated moment values very uncertain. However, some contribution of the polar structure is indicated by the 0.8 excess of the observed moment of (4) over the calculated, and contributions from the polar structures are clearly indicated by the 2.2 excess for compound (5) and the 3.3 excess for compound (6). Since resonance gives some double-bond character to all the bonds of the central carbon chain, the chain tends to be extended. The increase in moment when n changes from 0 to 1 to 2 is not quantitatively proportional to the apparent increase in charge separation, but the observed moment increases greatly with increasing molecular length, as it should if increase in the length of the polar forms does not greatly decrease the stability. A similar increase in moment with increase in chain length is shown by (11) and (12), where the moment for the two molecules in the state represented by the formula should be about 1.6. Dr. L. G. S. Brooker has pointed out to the writer that a polar structure may be written which actually represents a large number of polar structures, each of which has a negative charge on one of the thirteen carbon atoms of the fluorene residue. The negative charge thus distributed over these atoms and the positive charge on the nitrogen are responsible for the three- to fourfold increase in moment of the molecule. The large effects of similar charge shifts are shown in the moments of compounds (13) to (22), none of which should exceed 2.8 in the absence of contributions from structures with widely separated positive and negative charges.

From the point of view of dipole moment, compounds (23), (24), and (25) are particularly interesting, (25) having a moment higher than any yet observed for a molecule other than that of a salt or a zwitterion, and, for this reason, they have been discussed in detail.[10] The moments of the nonpolar structures should differ somewhat from one another and cannot be calculated with exactness. None of them should exceed 2.5×10^{-18}, and little error will arise in our considerations from the assignment of a rough value $m_a = 2.0 \times 10^{-18}$ to the nonpolar structure of each of the three compounds. Compound (23) can have only one contributing polar structure, compound (24) has two identical polar structures, while compound (25) has four polar structures indistinguishable from one another as follows:

(23)

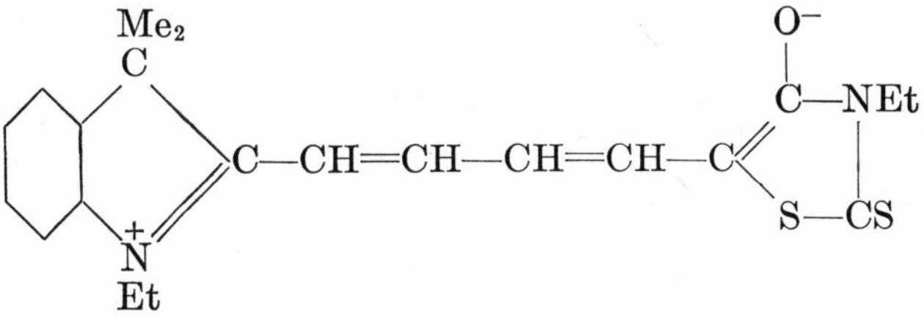

$$\text{Me}_2\text{C} \cdots \text{N}^+\text{Et} \quad \text{C—CH=CH—CH=CH—C} \quad \begin{array}{c} \text{O}^- \\ | \\ \text{C—NEt} \\ | \\ \text{S—CS} \end{array}$$

(1 structure)

(24)

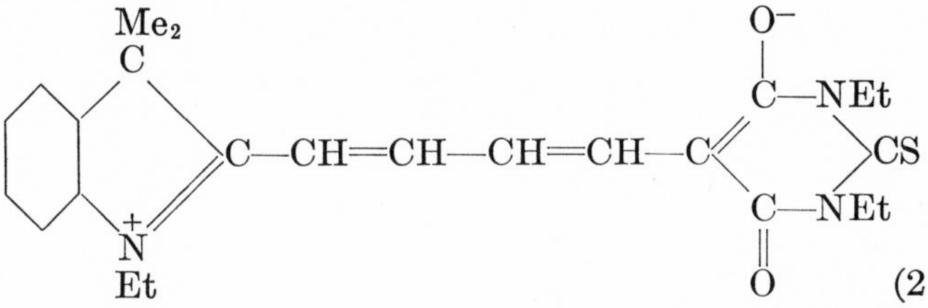

$$\text{Me}_2\text{C} \cdots \text{N}^+\text{Et} \quad \text{C—CH=CH—CH=CH—C} \quad \begin{array}{c} \text{O}^- \\ | \\ \text{C—NEt} \\ \\ \text{C—NEt} \\ || \\ \text{O} \end{array} \text{CS}$$

(2 structures)

(25)

$$\begin{array}{c}\text{Et}\\ \text{N}\end{array} \cdots \text{N}^+\text{Et} \quad \text{C—CH=CH—CH=CH—C} \quad \begin{array}{c} \text{O}^- \\ | \\ \text{C—NEt} \\ \\ \text{C—NEt} \\ || \\ \text{O} \end{array} \text{CO}$$

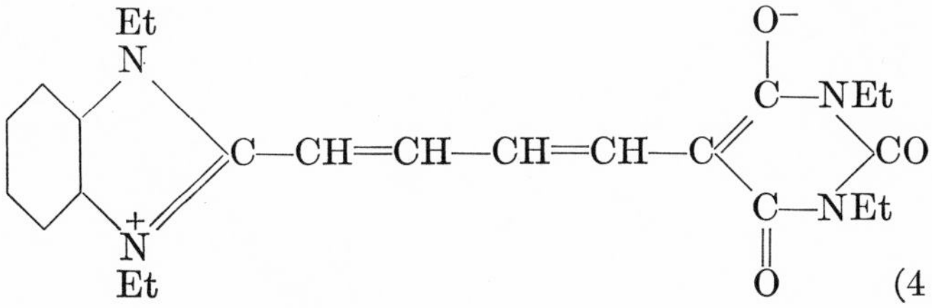

(4 structures)

[10] L. M. Kushner and C. P. Smyth, *J. Am. Chem. Soc.*, **71**, 1401 (1949).

The large values found for the dipole moments in Table 10.1, as compared to the relatively small values, about 2.0, calculated for the non-polar structures, show the considerable stability of the polar structure. The increase in moment from compound (23) to (24) to (25) corresponds qualitatively to the increase in the number of contributing polar structures from 1 to 2 to 4. The maximum value which the polar structure could have is the moment of the structure with an extended, planar, zig-zag chain, in which the charges are separated by a maximum distance. The value calculated approximately for this structure from the bond lengths and angles is 42×10^{-18}, while the value calculated from the mean square moment for all the possible orientations around the bonds of the chain is 30×10^{-18}. Even the lower of these two values is much higher than the value 21.4 estimated on the basis of reasonable values for the amounts of the contributions of the polar structures.[10] Conversely, the use of the moments calculated for the ionic structures without allowance for decrease of moment by an empirically introduced inductive distortion would give improbably low contributions from the polar structures (cf. Sec. VIII.6). In a quantum-mechanical calculation[10] of the relative energies of the structures, it was found that no solutions could be obtained when the moment of the polar structure was 21.4 or lower, which suggests that an intermediate value 30 for the moment of the polar structures may be the most reasonable.

The relation of the structures of some of these dye molecules to their light absorption has received further study by Kuhn.[11]

[11] H. Kuhn, *J. Chem. Phys.*, **17**, 1198 (1949).

CHAPTER XI

DIPOLE MOMENT AND INTRAMOLECULAR ROTATION

When a molecule contains two or more dipoles which may change their directions relative to one another as the result of rotation around bonds between atoms, the resultant molecular dipole moment cannot be calculated by means of the simple geometrical considerations generally employed in Chaps. IX and X. It has been shown in Eq. VIII(2.3) how the resultant molecular moment may be calculated as the mean square sum of the individual moments when all the positions around the intervening bonds are equally probable. Although the potential energies of all these positions are never identical, it may frequently happen that the variation of potential energy with rotation around the bond does not invalidate the use of the equation as a good approximation. In many cases, however, rotational positions which give high dipole moment are made improbable by high potential energies. The moment is then lower than that calculated by Eq. VIII(2.3) and commonly tends to increase with rising temperature. The departure of the observed moment from the calculated and its dependence upon temperature have given concrete evidence of the hindrance of rotation about the chemical bond.

1. **Internal Rotation Hindered by a Single Potential Barrier.** The 1,2-dichloroethane molecule has provided the most frequently investigated example of hindered dipole rotation. It was pointed out[1] that the molecules of the symmetrical di- and tetrahalogen-substituted products of ethane, such as ethylene chloride, might be regarded as consisting of two halves, each containing a dipole. One half might rotate about the bond into what may be called a trans position in which its moment would oppose and cancel that of the other half, or it might rotate into a cis position in which its moment would act as nearly as possible in the same direction and give maximum moment to the molecule. Intermediate positions would give intermediate moment values. All the positions were regarded as possible but not equally probable, and the moment observed for the substance was concluded to represent an average of values running

[1] C. P. Smyth, *J. Am. Chem. Soc.*, **46**, 2151 (1924).

from zero to a certain maximum value.[1]   Later, the average was calculated[2] by means of an equation which was a special case of the subsequently derived general equation VIII(2.3), all positions being treated as equally probable.

The effect of the potential energy due to the dipole-dipole interaction of the two halves of the molecule was taken into account[3] by the introduction into the Debye equation of a modifying factor which was a function of the reciprocal of the absolute temperature and contained several adjustable parameters capable of representing the observed increase in the ethylene chloride moment with increase in temperature.   For a temperature of 5000° or 6000°, the equation became equivalent to the special case of Eq. VIII(2.3) for ethylene chloride.   Introduction[4] of an H—C bond dipole moment in addition to the C—Cl moment gave two points of inflexion in addition to the maximum at the cis position and the minimum at the trans position in the curve for the potential energy as a function of the angle of rotation around the C—C bond.   As an approximation, the two points of inflexion were neglected and the curve for the dependence of the dipole-dipole interaction energy upon ϕ, the azimuthal angle, or angle between the projections of the two C—Cl bond directions upon the plane perpendicular to the C—C bond, was represented by

$$V(\phi) = \frac{V_0}{2} (1 + \cos \phi) \tag{1.1}$$

in which V_0 is the difference in energy between the cis position at the maximum and the trans position at the minimum of the potential energy curve.   The actual total dipole-dipole interaction energy is V_0 plus that for the trans position and is dependent upon the locations of the dipoles in the bonds.   It was concluded from this classical treatment that the dipole moment should vary in the observed manner because of the variation of energy with ϕ.   Use of these calculated energies in a wave mechanical treatment of the problem to calculate the energy levels and the molecular distribution among these levels led to a similar conclusion. So many factors had to be neglected that a quantitative calculation of the temperature variation of the moment seemed to be without significance.   These calculations using only dipole-dipole energies neglected the equally or more important van der Waals interaction energies but sufficed to give a rough qualitative representation of the observed behavior.[5]

[2] J. W. Williams, Z. physik. Chem., **138**, 75 (1928).

[3] L. Meyer, Z. physik. Chem., **8B**, 27 (1930).

[4] C. P. Smyth, R. W. Dornte, and E. B. Wilson, Jr., J. Am. Chem. Soc., **53**, 4242 (1931).

[5] See also J. M. Sturtevant, J. Am. Chem. Soc., **55**, 4478 (1933).

More rigorous calculations[6,7] led to essentially similar results, but the factors which had to be neglected seemed to render great rigor of treatment superfluous.

To find the average dipole moment of a molecule of the ethylene chloride type it is necessary to calculate the average value of the square of the moment, weighting each possible configuration of the molecule with a Boltzmann factor taken from the assumed potential function and averaging over all possible configurations. The square of the dipole moment as a function of the previously defined azimuthal angle ϕ is

$$\mu^2(\phi) = A + B \cos \phi \tag{1.2}$$

where $A = m_1^2 + m_2^2 - 2m_1 m_2 \cos \theta_1 \cos \theta_2$

and $B = 2m_1 m_2 \sin \theta_1 \sin \theta_2$

m_1 and m_2 are the group moments of the polar substituents on the two carbons and θ_1 and θ_2 are the angles between the dipole axes and the axis of rotation. The average value of the square of the dipole moment is given[8] by

$$\mu^2 = A + B\rho \tag{1.3}$$

where $$\rho = \frac{\displaystyle\int_0^\pi \cos \phi \exp\left[-V(\phi)/RT\right] d\phi}{\displaystyle\int_0^\pi \exp\left[-V(\phi)/RT\right] d\phi} \tag{1.4}$$

The potential function $V(\phi)$ may have various forms, of which the cosine potential function [Eq. (1.1)] is an example. The integrals arising when this cosine potential function is used have been evaluated,[9] since ρ may be written

$$\rho = \frac{iJ_1(iV_0/2RT)}{J_0(iV_0/2RT)} \tag{1.5}$$

where the numerator and denominator are Bessel functions, which have been tabulated. As $V_0/2RT$ approaches zero, ρ approaches zero and the moment approaches $A^{1/2}$, the value for free rotation, while, for very large $V_0/2RT$, ρ approaches -1 and the moment approaches $(A - B)^{1/2}$, the value for the trans position.

The use of the single minimum potential function represented by Eq. (1.1) was a justifiable approximation in the earlier investigations

[6] J. E. Lennard-Jones and H. H. M. Pike, *Trans. Faraday Soc.*, **30**, 830 (1934).

[7] W. Altar, *J. Chem. Phys.*, **3**, 460 (1935).

[8] J. Y. Beach and D. P. Stevenson, *J. Chem. Phys.*, **6**, 635 (1938).

[9] S. Mizushima and K. Higasi, *Proc. Imp. Acad. (Tokyo)*, **8**, 482 (1932); S. Mizushima, Y. Morino, and K. Higasi, *Sci. Papers Inst. Phys. Chem. Research (Tokyo)*, **25**, 159 (1934).

when little quantitative information on interatomic forces was available. Beach and Stevenson[8] obtained values of 4, 5, and 6 kcal. per mole for V_0 for ethylene chloride, chlorobromide, and bromide, respectively. The values varied irregularly by 0.1 to 0.3 kcal. with temperature, but the cosine potential function proved preferable to linear and parabolic functions. Subsequent calculations[10] with $m = 1.85 \times 10^{-18}$ for the —CH_2Cl and —CH_2Br group moments instead of the values 2.03 and 2.02 used by Beach and Stevenson gave values of 3.2, 3.9, and 5.1 kcal. per mole with less than ±3 per cent variation over a 239° temperature range for ethylene chloride and only ±1.5 per cent variation over a 97° range for the other two substances. Conversely, the value 3.2 for a single potential barrier in ethylene chloride represented fairly satisfactorily the variation observed[11] for its dipole moment with temperature in the vapor state, and a single barrier of 2.5 kcal. did almost equally well for 1,2-dichloropropane.[10]

Beach and Palmer[12] calculated an electron-diffraction curve for ethylene chloride by adding the intensity formulas for molecules having different values of ϕ weighted by the Boltzmann factor, exp $[-V(\phi)/RT]$, and obtained agreement with the experimental curve when V_0 was taken as 6.0 kcal. per mole, a value double that given by the calculation from dipole moment values, which was close to that calculated from the sum of the dipole-dipole interaction energy and the exchange repulsion energies between the atoms. A change to a somewhat arbitrary method of calculating the exchange repulsions raised the calculated energy barrier to about 6 kcal.

The succinonitrile, $(CH_2CN)_2$, molecule was investigated[13] in the belief that the large moments of the cyanide dipoles should make the use of a single potential barrier a less crude approximation. The total potential energy between the two halves of the molecule was calculated, without taking account of the effects of the two hydrogens in each half, as

$$U = U_s + U_d + U_i + U_m$$

where U_s = exchange energy giving rise to steric repulsion

U_d = van der Waals attraction energy

U_i = dipole induction energy

U_m = dipole-dipole repulsion energy

Each of these quantities is plotted against ϕ in Fig. 1.1, $\phi = 0°$ or 360° corresponding to the cis position, in which the projections of the

[10] R. A. Oriani and C. P. Smyth, *J. Chem. Phys.*, **17**, 1174 (1949).

[11] C. T. Zahn, *Phys. Rev.*, **38**, 521 (1931); *ibid.*, **40**, 291 (1932); E. W. Greene and J. W. Williams, *Phys. Rev.*, **42**, 119 (1932).

[12] J. Y. Beach and K. J. Palmer, *J. Chem. Phys.*, **6**, 639 (1938).

[13] G. L. Lewis and C. P. Smyth, *J. Chem. Phys.*, **7**, 1085 (1939).

C—C≡N moments in the plane perpendicular to the C—C axis of rotation coincide, and $\phi = 180°$ corresponding to the trans position, in which the projections point in opposite directions. The curves are approximate in the extreme but are sufficient to indicate the magnitudes and trends of the quantities involved and to show that the cosine function of Eq. (1.1) gives a not too bad representation of the variation of the energy with ϕ when the effects of the hydrogens are disregarded. With a constant value 3.44×10^{-18} used for the moment value of each half of the molecule, the height of the single restricting potential barrier V_0 was calculated to be 3.3 kcal., as shown in Fig. 1.1, but, when the lowering of each cyanide moment by the inductive action of the other, a factor generally neglected in such calculations, was taken into account, the total potential barrier was reduced to 1.6 kcal. The barrier height was calculated from dipole moment values measured in toluene solution from $-90°$ to $+90°$. Although the average of the values obtained by different methods of calculation was 1.5 kcal., it appeared that the most probable value

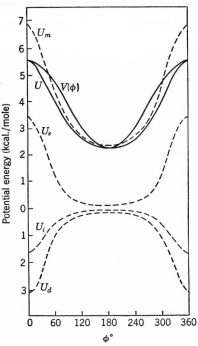

FIG. 1.1. Potential energies as functions of the azimuthal angle ϕ in succinonitrile. [G. L. Lewis and C. P. Smyth, J. Chem. Phys., **7**, 1085 (1939).]

was 1.2 ± 0.5 kcal., in satisfactory agreement with the value 1.6 calculated from the forces between the two halves of the molecule.

The uncertainty of calculations of this sort, which neglect possible lack of symmetry of the single bond around its axis, is shown by the calculation[14] of a hindering potential barrier of only 0.3 kcal. per mole around the C—C bond in ethane, in contrast to the value of 3 kcal. indicated by thermal measurements.[15-17] However, the use of a single potential barrier restricting rotation gives a parameter capable of the quantitative representation of the temperature variation of the dipole moments of some molecules. The height of the barrier calculated from

[14] H. Eyring, J. Am. Chem. Soc., **54**, 3191 (1932).

[15] G. B. Kistiakowsky and F. Nazmi, J. Chem. Phys., **6**, 18 (1938).

[16] G. B. Kistiakowsky, J. R. Lacher, and F. Stitt, J. Chem. Phys., **6**, 407 (1938).

[17] G. B. Kistiakowsky, J. R. Lacher, and W. W. Ransom, J. Chem. Phys., **6**, 900 (1938).

the dipole-moment lowering below the value calculated for unrestricted rotation is of the same magnitude as that obtained by other methods.

2. Rotational Isomerism. As a convenient approximation, the restriction of rotation around a single bond has been attributed in Sec. 1 primarily to the effect of a single potential barrier, the height of which was assumed to be sufficiently great to warrant the neglect of the effects of other smaller barriers. As a further approximation, the effect of the potential energy curve was represented by a cosine function, although the calculated form might differ appreciably from that of the cosine function. This latter approximation affected the result to some extent, but the effect was usually unimportant in comparison with those of other

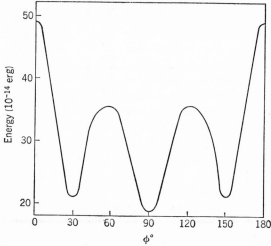

Fig. 2.1. Potential energy between the two halves of the 1,1,2,2-tetrachloroethane molecule. [*C. P. Smyth and K. B. McAlpine, J. Am. Chem. Soc.,* **57,** 979 (1935).]

factors. The low value, 1.36×10^{-18}, found[1] for the moment of 1,1,2,2-tetrachloroethane as compared to a value 1.8 calculated for free rotation, together with the absence of variation of the moment with temperature over a range of 35° (later found[2] to be at least 138°), showed the inadequacy of an explanation of the behavior of this molecule in terms of a single potential barrier. A very approximate potential energy curve (Fig. 2.1) showed three rather deep minima, two corresponding to staggered configurations of the chlorines being only 0.36 kcal. per mole higher than the trans configuration. The molecules were, therefore, treated as distributed among these three potential energy troughs, and their distribution was calculated by the Boltzmann equation, which gave a moment only 0.1×10^{-18} higher than the observed and indicated that

[1] C. P. Smyth and K. B. McAlpine, *J. Am. Chem. Soc.,* **57,** 979 (1935).
[2] J. R. Thomas and W. D. Gwinn, *J. Am. Chem. Soc.,* **71,** 2785 (1949).

any variation with temperature would be extremely small.   Thomas and Gwinn[2] used the absence of moment variation with temperature as evidence that the energy difference between the two configurations was 0 ± 0.2 kcal. per mole, a satisfactory confirmation of the much earlier and less accurate result.   Mizushima, Morino, and Kozima[3] determined the Raman spectrum and the dipole moment of 1,1,2,2-tetrachloroethane in solution in various solvents and adopted the molecular distribution in potential troughs employed by Smyth and McAlpine.[1]   Further measurements of Raman spectra led Mizushima and his coworkers[4-7] to conclude that the dihalogenated ethanes and somewhat analogous hydrocarbons existed as distributions of molecules among potential energy troughs, which could be described as giving rise to rotational isomers.

The intensities of the Raman lines and, as previously shown for 1,1,2,2-tetrachloroethane, the dipole moment depend upon the distribution of the molecules among the potential troughs, that is, upon the relative molecular concentrations of the rotational isomers.   As this distribution depends upon the differences between the minimum potential energy levels and not upon the heights of the potential barriers, the barrier height cannot be simply determined as in the case of the single-barrier curve discussed in Sec. 1.   No attempt can be made, therefore, to discuss the potential energy curves quantitatively, but the different molecular configurations corresponding to the maxima and minima around the axis of rotation can be conveniently represented by projecting the rotating atoms or groups to form conventionalized triangles upon a plane perpendicular to the axis of rotation.   The method of representation will be illustrated here by writing the configuration for 1,2-dichloroethane (Fig. 2.2). A in Fig. 2.2 is sometimes called an eclipsed structure because the projection of each atom on one side of the molecule covers that of the other, while B and C are called staggered structures.   It is evident that three eclipsed structures can be formed by making $\phi = 0°$, $120°$, or $240°$, while two equivalent skew, frequently called "gauche," structures can be formed by making $\phi = 60°$ or $300°$.   Some spectroscopic information has been interpreted as favoring the stability of the eclipsed structures, but, as a considerable number of Raman-spectra investigations[4-8] and

[3] S. Mizushima, Y. Morino, and K. Kozima, *Sci. Papers Inst. Phys. Chem. Research* (*Tokyo*), **29**, 111 (1936).

[4] S. Mizushima, Y. Morino, and M. Takeda, *Sci. Papers Inst. Phys. Chem. Research* (*Tokyo*), **38**, 437 (1941).

[5] S. Mizushima, Y. Morino, Y. Miyahara, M. Tomura, and Y. Okamoto, *Sci. Papers Inst. Phys. Chem. Research* (*Tokyo*), **39**, 387 (1942).

[6] Y. Morino, I. Watanabe, and S. Mizushima, *Sci. Papers Inst. Phys. Chem. Research* (*Tokyo*), **39**, 396 (1942).

[7] S. Mizushima and Y. Morino, *Bull. Chem. Soc. Japan*, **17**, 94 (1942).

[8] J. T. Neu and W. D. Gwinn, *J. Chem. Phys.*, **18**, 1642 (1950).

electron-diffraction measurements[9] indicate the existence of the staggered rather than the eclipsed forms and as the potential energy curves calculated from interatomic forces show the eclipsed forms to be at maxima and the staggered forms at minima, the eclipsed structures would normally seem to be too unstable to be considered as rotational isomers.

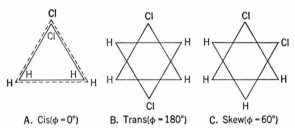

A. Cis($\phi = 0°$)   B. Trans($\phi = 180°$)   C. Skew($\phi = 60°$)

FIG. 2.2. Projection of configurations of 1,2-dichloroethane molecule upon plane perpendicular to the C—C bond.

The ratio of the number of molecules N_s in the skew configuration to the number N_t in the trans was calculated[10] from the equation for the mean square moment

$$\mu^2 = \frac{N_t m_t^2 + N_s m_s^2}{N_t + N_s} = \frac{m_t^2 + m_s^2 N_s/N_t}{1 + N_s/N_t} \tag{2.1}$$

in which m_t and m_s are the moments of the trans and the skew forms. The energy difference ΔE between the two configurations was obtained from the Boltzmann equation

$$\frac{N_s}{N_t} = \frac{2f_s}{f_t} e^{-\Delta E/kT} \tag{2.2}$$

in which f_s and f_t are the partition functions of the two configurations, ΔE is the energy difference between the trans and the skew troughs, and the factor 2 occurs because of the two equivalent skew configurations. With m_t and m_s estimated, N_s/N_t can be calculated from a single observed value of μ by means of Eq. (2.1), and ΔE can then be calculated by means of Eq. (2.2). In the absence of the data necessary for calculating f_s/f_t, this ratio can be approximated as 1. f_s/f_t was calculated by Mizushima and his coworkers as 0.95 at 298°K., 0.92 at 400°K., and 0.90 at 500°K. With $m_t = 0$, substitution of the values of μ observed for the vapor at different temperatures gave $\Delta E = 1.21$ kcal. per mole and $m_s = 2.55 \times 10^{-18}$ when $P_E + P_A$ was taken as 23.9 cc. to obtain μ,

[9] S. Yamaguchi, Y. Morino, I. Watanabe, and S. Mizushima, *Sci. Papers Inst. Phys. Chem. Research (Tokyo)*, **40**, 417 (1943).

[10] I. Watanabe, S. Mizushima, and Y. Morino, *Sci. Papers Inst. Phys. Chem. Research (Tokyo)*, **39**, 401 (1942).

and $\Delta E = 1.20$ kcal. per mole and $m_s = 2.67 \times 10^{-18}$ when $P_E + P_A$ was taken as 21.02 cc. With $m_t = 0.17 \times 10^{-18}$, a more accurate value than 0 because of oscillation in the potential trough, $\Delta E = 1.22$ kcal. per mole and $m_s = 2.54 \times 10^{-18}$ for $P_E + P_A = 23.9$ c.c. This value for m_s is in satisfactory agreement with the value 2.46 calculated from bond moments and mutual inductive effect. Insertion of the values of $\Delta E = 1.21$ and of f_s/f_t in Eq. (2.2) gave the value of the equilibrium ratio N_s/N_t of the two molecular species in the vapor at any temperature T. For the vapor at the boiling point the ratio was $N_s/N_t = 0.34$, that is, approximately one quarter of the molecules were in the polar skew configuration and three quarters in the nearly nonpolar trans configuration. With rising temperature, the proportion of polar molecules and, hence, the moment obviously must increase.

The mean moment for the molecules in the liquid state was calculated[10,11] by using the Onsager equation, I(14.25), and was then substituted in Eq. (2.1) to calculate the ratio N_s/N_t, which was then used[11] in Eq. (2.2) to calculate ΔE. N_s/N_t was also calculated from the intensity ratio of the Raman lines.[11] The results obtained by the two methods by Mizushima and his coworkers are tabulated in Table 2.1 for comparison.

TABLE 2.1. EQUILIBRIUM RATIO OF ROTATIONAL ISOMERS OF 1,2-DICHLOROETHANE

t, °C.	N_s/N_t (Moment)	t, °C.	N_s/N_t (Raman)
-10	1.5	-25	1.5
10	1.4	25	1.3
30	1.34	50	1.2
50	1.28	170 (vapor)	0.47
84 (vapor)	0.34		

The agreement between the ratio values obtained by the two methods is as good as could be expected. The value of ΔE calculated for the liquid is about 1 to 1.2 kcal. smaller than that for the vapor. If it were zero, the isomeric ratio should be 1.9 at 25°C. Mizushima and his coworkers[11-13] calculated a lowering of energy for the polar skew form in the liquid of about 1.0 kcal. per mole because of electrostatic interaction, an amount which was of the right order of magnitude to account for the change in ΔE. They showed,[14] moreover, that, on the liquefaction of n-pentane, the energy difference between the rotational isomers did not change as much as in the case of 1,2-dichloroethane, presumably

[11] I. Watanabe, S. Mizushima, and Y. Masiko, *Sci. Papers Inst. Phys. Chem. Research (Tokyo)*, **40**, 425 (1943).

[12] S. Mizushima, Y. Morino, I. Watanabe, T. Simanouti, and S. Yamaguchi, *J. Chem. Phys.*, **17**, 591 (1949).

[13] Y. Morino, S. Mizushima, K. Kuratani, and M. Katayama, *J. Chem. Phys.*, **18**, 754 (1950).

[14] S. Mizushima and H. Okazaki, *J. Am. Chem. Soc.*, **71**, 3411 (1949).

because of the lack of electrostatic interaction between the nonpolar n-pentane molecules in the liquid state. For 1,2-dibromoethane, they found ΔE in the vapor state 1.45 kcal. per mole from infrared measurements and 1.4 from dipole moment values, while in the liquid state the values were 0.65 from infrared, 0.75 from Raman effect, and 1.0 from dipole moment. The difference in ΔE in the vapor and liquid states was smaller than that in the case of 1,2-dichloroethane, corresponding to a calculated electrostatic interaction energy of 0.5 in the liquid as compared to 1.0 kcal. for 1,2-dichloroethane.

One would expect qualitatively a very considerable flattening of the potential energy curves of these polar molecules when the vapor is condensed and, consequently, a shift in the direction of a random distribution among the molecular configurations. This is shown by the higher moment values and lower temperature dependence of moments observed in solution.[15,16] A tendency toward increase in the effect of solvent with increase in the dielectric constant of some solvents was remarked upon by Mizushima and his coworkers,[16] but this effect is not evident in their tabulation of the moment values of 1,2-dichloroethane in different solvents, nor is it apparent in the measurements of Stearn and Smyth,[15] who concluded that solvent dielectric constant alone was not the determining factor. Benzene and toluene were found to exert an abnormally large effect, which, it was suggested, might result from the formation of an easily dissociated complex between solute and solvent, not subsequently observed in freezing-point measurements.[17] An abnormally large effect of the force field of the benzene molecule upon the critical wavelengths of benzene solutions has been observed in microwave measurements.[18] Raman-effect measurements[5] show that, when the 1,2-dihalogenated ethanes solidify, virtually all the molecules take up the trans configuration, presumably because of the closer packing thus obtained in the crystal lattice.

The discussion of rotational isomers has involved the energy differences between potential minima and has not given information concerning the heights of the maxima. Gwinn and Pitzer[19] have found a potential function

$$V(\phi) = \frac{V_1}{2} (1 - \cos \phi) + \frac{V_3}{2} (1 - \cos 3\phi) \qquad \text{cal./mole} \qquad (2.3)$$

[15] A. E. Stearn and C. P. Smyth, *J. Am. Chem. Soc.*, **56**, 1667 (1934).

[16] S. Mizushima, Y. Morino, and K. Higasi, *Sci. Papers Inst. Phys. Chem. Research (Tokyo)*, **25**, 159 (1934).

[17] H. Huettig, Jr., and C. P. Smyth, *J. Am. Chem. Soc.*, **57**, 1523 (1935).

[18] A. J. Curtis, P. L. McGeer, G. B. Rathmann, and C. P. Smyth, *J. Am. Chem. Soc.*, **74**, 644 (1952).

[19] W. D. Gwinn and K. S. Pitzer, *J. Chem. Phys.*, **16**, 303 (1948).

to be in agreement with all the data on heat capacity, entropy, and dipole moment of gaseous 1,2-dichloroethane when $V_1 = 1,830$ and $V_3 = 2,300$ for $0° < \phi \le 130°$ and $230° < \phi \le 360°$; $V(\phi) = \infty$ for $130° < \phi < 230°$. The assignment of ϕ values differs from that in Fig. 2.2 in that $\phi = 0°$ is the trans configuration and $\phi = 180°$ is the cis, which, with all positions within $50°$ of it, is excluded. This potential function gives an energy difference of 1.37 kcal. per mole between the skew and the trans potential minima, in fair agreement with the value 1.2 obtained by Mizushima and his coworkers. For 1,2-dibromoethane, Gwinn and Pitzer find it impossible to get satisfactory agreement between the calculated and the experimental values but conclude that the dipole moment requires that V_1 be within a few hundred calories of 2,100 cal. per mole, while to come close to the heat capacity or entropy requires that V_3 be $4,000 \pm 1,000$ cal.

Bloom and Sutton[20] have shown that the dipole moments of these molecules with two rotatable polar halves can be represented in terms of restricted rotation about a trans position by an equation like that which Sutton and his co-workers have used to calculate atomic polarization as arising from the vibrational bending of mutually opposed dipoles (Sec. XIV.4).

3. Dipole Moments and Structures of Polysubstituted Ethanes. The fundamental features of the problem of movable dipoles have been discussed in the two preceding sections, but it seems desirable to examine the magnitudes of the moments and their temperature dependence from the viewpoint of molecular composition. It is unfortunate that the instability of 1,2-difluoroethane has prevented its measurement. The smaller size of the fluorine atom as compared to the chlorine atom reduces the steric repulsion between the two in 1-fluoro-2-chloroethane, which reduces the heights of the maxima in the potential energy curve and the difference ΔE between the potential minima of the two skew configurations and that of the trans configuration. The proportion of the molecules in the skew configuration is increased thereby with consequent increase in mean moment and decrease in the dependence of moment upon temperature. Increasing size of the halogen atom increases ΔE, lowers the moment, and tends to increase the temperature dependence of the moment. The replacement of a hydrogen in 1,2-dichloroethane by a methyl group evidently lowers ΔE, causing a higher moment and lower temperature dependence,[1] and the double-bonded methylene group produces the same effect to a greater degree.[1] The electron-diffraction pattern obtained for 1,2-dichloropropane could be satisfactorily repre-

[20] G. I. M. Bloom and L. E. Sutton, *J. Chem. Soc.*, 727 (1941).
[1] R. A. Oriani and C. P. Smyth, *J. Chem. Phys.*, **17**, 1174 (1949).

sented[2] in terms of a single potential function or in terms of two rotational isomers, one having a trans configuration and the other a skew configuration in which the methyl group is trans to the chlorine in the other half of the molecule. The diffraction pattern was almost indifferently compatible with fractions of the skew isomer up to 0.5, but the dipole moment values[1] indicated[2] the fraction to be about 0.2 with an upper limit of about 0.3. The moment values gave[2,3] a value for ΔE of about 1 kcal. In order to obtain consistency between the indications of electron diffraction and dipole moment, Wood and Schomaker found it necessary to recalculate the moment values with an atomic polarization equal to $\frac{1}{10}$ of the electronic, the resulting moment values being 0.06×10^{-18} lower than those in Table 3.1.

TABLE 3.1. MOMENTS ($\times 10^{18}$) OF POLYSUBSTITUTED ETHANES IN THE VAPOR STATE

Molecule	Temp., °C.	Moment
FH_2C—CH_2Cl	36–233	1.84–1.97
ClH_2C—CH_2Cl	32–271	1.12–1.54
BrH_2C—CH_2Cl	66–163	1.09–1.28
BrH_2C—CH_2Br	66–163	0.94–1.10
ClH_2C—$C(CH_3)HCl$	71–235	1.46–1.68
ClH_2C—$C(=CH_2)Cl$	125–245	1.74–1.77
IH_2C—CH_2I (in hexane)	25–50	0.44–0.55
$(NC)H_2C$—$CH_2(CN)$ (in toluene)	−90–90	2.94–3.90
(gas)	170–240	3.45–3.57
Cl_2HC—CH_2Cl	91–242	1.41–1.48
F_2HC—$CHCl_2$	50–201	1.34–1.47
$FClHC$—$CHCl_2$	106–231	1.38–1.44
Cl_2HC—$CHCl_2$	89–228	1.32
$(ClHC=CH)HC$—CH_2Cl (104°)	124–205	1.79
$(ClHC=CH)HC$—CH_2Cl (112°)	122–230	1.81

Because of the solvent effect, the variation of moment in solution must be interpreted with care, but the extremely low moment of 1,2-diiodo-ethane shows the large steric effects of the iodine atoms. The ethylene cyanide moment, which has already been discussed (Sec. 1), was examined[4] in terms of a methyl cyanide moment measured in the same solvent and over the same temperature range. There is some doubt about the exact behavior of 1,1,2-trichloroethane, as Thomas and Gwinn[5] favor the use of a large atomic polarization to give a moment 1.25 to

[2] W. W. Wood and V. Schomaker, *J. Chem. Phys.*, **20**, 555 (1952).
[3] Y. Morino, I. Miyagawa, and T. Haga, *J. Chem. Phys.*, **19**, 791 (1951).
[4] G. L. Lewis and C. P. Smyth, *J. Chem. Phys.*, **7**, 1085 (1939).
[5] J. R. Thomas and W. D. Gwinn, *J. Am. Chem. Soc.*, **71**, 2785 (1949).

1.30×10^{-18} with very small or zero variation of moment with temperature, while the use of the molar refraction for the sodium D line for $P_E + P_A$ for the sake of consistency with the other results gives the small but appreciable variation with temperature[6] shown in Table 3.1. An apparent minimum tentatively indicated in the moment-temperature curve by the first measurements[7] was disproved by later measurements.[1,5,6]   In any event, the cis and two equivalent skew configurations

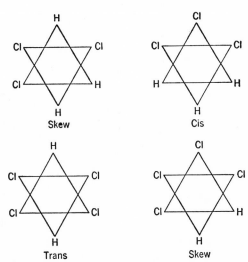

FIG. 3.1. Projection of configurations of 1,1,2-trichloroethane and 1,1,2,2-tetrachloro-ethane molecule upon plane perpendicular to the C—C bond.

correspond to minima in the potential energy curve, the cis having at least 4 kcal. per mole greater energy than the skew if the moment is 1.25×10^{-18} and virtually temperature independent, and about 2 kcal. greater energy if the moment is as shown in Table 3.1.   Potential energy curves consistent with these results have been calculated[1,8] and have been found to represent the results of electron-diffraction measurements.[8]

As described in Sec. 2, 1,1,2-trichloroethane appears to exist in two equivalent skew configurations and a trans (Fig. 3.1) with little energy difference between them.   The replacement of chlorine by fluorine lowers the steric repulsion and evidently lowers the total energy of the skew configuration more than it does that of the trans, since the moment increases when one and then two chlorines are replaced by fluorine.

The two isomeric 1,3-dichloropropenes are distinguished in Table 3.1

[6] A. Di Giacomo and C. P. Smyth, Unpublished measurements.
[7] R. A. Oriani and C. P. Smyth, *J. Chem. Phys.*, **16**, 930 (1948).
[8] A. Turkevich and J. Y. Beach, *J. Am. Chem. Soc.*, **61**, 3127 (1939).

by their boiling points since it is not certain which isomer is cis and which trans.   In the trans form the C—Cl moment adjacent to the double bond is parallel to the C—C axis of rotation so that the resultant dipole moment should be virtually independent of the azimuthal angle and hence of temperature, as observed.[9]   A value 1.92 calculated[9] for the moment agrees satisfactorily with the value observed for either form.   For the cis form, the variation in energy over a wide angle of rotation is so small that a moderate change of temperature should not greatly alter the molecular distribution.   The absence of an observed variation in moment is, therefore, not surprising, and the observed moment value is of the expected magnitude.

4. Molecules Containing More than One Axis of Dipole Rotation.

So many molecules contain more than one axis around which there is a possibility of dipole rotation with consequent change of moment that it will not be profitable to examine all in detail in this section.   However, the several molecular types and homologous series shown in Table 4.1 represent the variety of behavior that has been observed.   The preceding sections have shown that the molecules are distributed among a small number of potential energy troughs which occur as rotation takes place around each bond.   A state of completely free rotation would correspond to an equal distribution among an infinite number of such troughs.   The departure of the observed moment from the value calculated for such an equal distribution may often, but not always, give a rough idea of the restriction of rotation around the bond.   The moment value calculated for the hypothetical state of free rotation around each bond is, therefore, given for many of the molecules listed in Table 4.1.

A general equation, VIII(2.3), has already been given for the calculation of the molecular moment when freedom of rotation exists, that is, when all positions of rotation around the bonds are equally probable, and its use has been illustrated (Sec. VIII.2) by the calculation of the moment of β,β'-dichlorodiethyl ether.   The equations[1,2] for calculating many of the other moments in Table 4.1 are given below:

$$Br(CH_2)_nBr \qquad \mu = m_1[2 - 2(-\cos\theta)^n]^{1/2} \tag{4.1}$$
$$m_1 = C\text{—}Br \text{ moment} = 1.5 \ (n = 2), \ 1.7 \ (n = 3), \ 1.9 \ (n > 3)$$
$$\theta = \text{carbon valence angle} = 110°$$
$$CH_2BrCHBrCH_2Br \qquad \mu = m_1(3 + 4\cos^2\theta + 2\cos^3\theta)^{1/2} \tag{4.2}$$
$$m_1 = C\text{—}Br \text{ moment} = 1.5$$
$$\theta = \text{carbon valence angle} = 110°$$

[9] R. A. Oriani and C. P. Smyth, J. Chem. Phys., 17, 1174 (1949).
[1] C. P. Smyth and W. S. Walls, J. Am. Chem. Soc., 54, 2261 (1932).
[2] G. L. Lewis and C. P. Smyth, J. Am. Chem. Soc., 62, 1529 (1940).

$HO(CH_2)_2OH$

$$\mu = [2(m_2{}^2 + m_3{}^2 - m_2{}^2 \cos^2 \theta - m_3{}^2 \cos^2 \alpha \cos^2 \theta + 2m_2m_3 \cos \alpha \sin^2 \theta)]^{1/2} \quad (4.3)$$

$m_2 = $ C—O moment $= 0.7$
$m_3 = $ H—O moment $= 1.6$
$\theta = $ carbon valence angle $= 110°$
$\alpha = $ oxygen valence angle $= 110°$
$m_2 = 1.1$ and $m_3 = 1.5$; somewhat better values (Table 4.1, Chap. VIII) give virtually the same value of μ

$Cl(CH_2)_2OH$

$$\mu = (m_1{}^2 + m_2{}^2 + m_3{}^2 - 2m_1m_2 \cos^2 \theta + 2m_2m_3 \cos \alpha - 2m_1m_3 \cos \alpha \cos^2 \theta)^{1/2} \quad (4.4)$$

$m_1 = $ C—Cl moment $= 1.9$
$m_2 = $ C—O moment $= 0.7$
$m_3 = $ H—O moment $= 1.6$
$\theta = $ carbon valence angle $= 110°$
$\alpha = $ oxygen valence angle $= 110°$

$Br(CH_2)_3OH$

$$\mu = (m_1{}^2 + m_2{}^2 + m_3{}^2 + 2m_1m_2 \cos^3 \theta + 2m_2m_3 \cos \alpha + 2m_1m_3 \cos \alpha \cos^3 \theta)^{1/2} \quad (4.5)$$

$m_1 = $ C—Br moment $= 1.9$
$m_2 = $ C—O moment $= 0.7$
$m_3 = $ H—O moment $= 1.6$
$\theta = $ carbon valence angle $= 110°$
$\alpha = $ oxygen valence angle $= 110°$

$(C_6H_5O)_3P$

$$\mu = [3m_1{}^2(1 + 2 \cos^2 \alpha \cos \phi) + (3m_2{}^2 + 6m_1m_2 \cos \alpha)(1 + 2 \cos \phi)]^{1/2} \quad (4.6)$$

$m_1 = $ H—C + C—O moment $= 1.0$
$m_2 = $ P—O moment $= 1.2$
$\alpha = $ oxygen valence angle $= 110°$
$\phi = $ phosphorus valence angle $= 100°$

The use of increasing values for the carbon-halogen moment as the number of carbon atoms increases from two to three to four is a rough attempt to approximate the inductive effects. Much significance should not be attached to discrepancies as large as 0.2 or 0.3 between observed and calculated values. Since change of solvent effect commonly raises the apparent moment in solution by 0.01 or 0.02 for a 25° rise in temperature, the values over such a range are averaged in Table 4.1 unless the variation is more than 0.03.

In the polymethylene dibromides[1,3] and dicyanides,[4] the first members of the series have moments far below the values calculated for free rotation because of repulsion between the terminal groups, but nonamethylene and decamethylene dibromide and decamethylene dicyanide have

[3] C. P. Smyth and W. S. Walls, J. Chem. Phys., 1, 200 (1933).
[4] P. Trunel, Ann. chim. (Paris), (11)12, 93 (1939).

TABLE 4.1. MOMENTS ($\times 10^{18}$) OF MOLECULES CONTAINING MORE THAN
ONE AXIS OF DIPOLE ROTATION

Molecule	Solvent	Temp., °C.	Moment	
			Obs.	Free rotation
$Cl(CH_2)_3Cl$	Gas	101–201	2.07	2.36
$Cl(CH_2)_4Cl$	Gas	160–235	2.22	2.60
$Br(CH_2)_2Br$	Heptane	−30–50	0.75–0.97	1.99
	Benzene	20–50	1.19	
$Br(CH_2)_3Br$	Heptane	25–50	2.03	2.36
	Benzene	25–50	1.98	
$Br(CH_2)_4Br$	Heptane	25–50	1.96–2.01	2.67
	Benzene	25–50	2.02	
$Br(CH_2)_5Br$	Benzene	25–50	2.27	2.68
$Br(CH_2)_6Br$	Heptane	25–50	2.40	2.68
$Br(CH_2)_9Br$	Heptane	25–50	2.57	2.69
$Br(CH_2)_{10}Br$	Benzene	25–50	2.55	2.69
$BrH_2C—CHBr—CH_2Br$	Heptane	25–50	1.50	2.36
	Benzene	25–50	1.58	
$NC—(CH_2)_2—CN$	Toluene	−90–90	2.94–3.90	4.12–4.65
	Benzene	25–75	3.93	4.75
$NC—(CH_2)_3—CN$	Benzene	25–75	3.91–3.99	4.94
$NC—(CH_2)_4—CN$	Benzene	25–75	3.76–3.87	5.01
$NC—(CH_2)_5—CN$	Benzene	25–75	4.10–4.26	5.03
$NC—(CH_2)_7—CN$	Benzene	25–75	4.39–4.47	5.03
$NC—(CH_2)_8—CN$	Benzene	25–75	4.50–4.56	5.03
$NC—(CH_2)_{10}—CN$	Benzene	25–75	4.95–5.00	5.03
$NC—(CH_2)_{10}—Br$	Benzene	25–75	3.92–3.95	4.02
$H_2N—(CH_2)_2—NH_2$	Gas	82–156	1.94	1.88
	Benzene	25–75	1.92	
$H_2N—(CH_2)_3—NH_2$	Benzene	25–45	1.95	1.92
$H_2N—(CH_2)_4—NH_2$	Benzene	25–45	1.93	1.94
$H_2N—(CH_2)_5—NH_2$	Benzene	25–45	1.92	1.95
$H_2N—(CH_2)_6—NH_2$	Benzene	25–45	1.93	1.95
$H_2N—(CH_2)_8—NH_2$	Benzene	25–75	1.99	1.95
$Cl(CH_2)_2OH$	Gas	66–162	1.73	2.41
	Benzene	25–50	1.89	
	Dioxane	25–50	2.08	
$Cl(CH_2)_3OH$	Benzene	25–50	2.19–2.24	2.42
	Dioxane	25–50	2.30–2.35	
$Br(CH_2)_3OH$	Benzene	25–50	2.17–2.21	2.42
$HO(CH_2\ _2OH$	Gas	44–133	2.25	2.1
	Dioxane	25–50	2.29	
$HO(CH_3)HC—CH_2OH$	Dioxane	25–50	2.27	2.1
$HO(CH_2)_3OH$	Dioxane	25–50	2.51	2.1
$HO(CH_2)_6OH$	Dioxane	25–50	2.48	2.1
$HO(CH_2)_{10}OH$	Dioxane	25–50	2.53	2.1
$CH_3O—CH_2—OCH_3$	Gas	34–199	0.74–1.13	

TABLE 4.1. MOMENTS ($\times 10^{18}$) OF MOLECULES CONTAINING MORE THAN
ONE AXIS OF DIPOLE ROTATION (*Continued*)

Molecule	Solvent	Temp., °C.	Moment	
			Obs.	Free rotation
C_2H_5O—CH_2—OC_2H_5	Gas	56–203	1.22–1.26	
C_2H_5O—$CH(CH_3)$—OC_2H_5	Gas	55–203	1.07–1.21	
CH_3O—CH_2Cl	Gas	74–234	2.03	1.98
$Cl(CH_2)_2$—O—$(CH_2)_2Cl$	Benzene	25–50	2.57	2.94
$I(CH_2)_2$—O—$(CH_2)_2I$	Benzene	25–50	2.23	2.43
CH_3O—(CO)—OCH_3	Gas	55–206	0.86–1.01	
C_2H_5O—(CO)—OC_2H_5	Gas	80–204	1.06	
CH_3O—(CO)—Cl	Gas	35–207	2.38–1.68	
C_2H_5O—(CO)—Cl	Gas	35–207	2.56–1.43	
H_5C_2OOC—$COOC_2H_5$	Benzene	25–50	2.51	
H_5C_2OOC—CH_2—$COOC_2H_5$	Benzene	25–50	2.56	
H_5C_2OOC—$(CH_2)_2$—$COOC_2H_5$	Gas	157–246	2.30	2.7
	Kerosene	0–200	2.01–2.47	
	Benzene	25–50	2.14–2.21	
H_5C_2OOC—$(CH_2)_3$—$COOC_2H_5$	Benzene	25–50	2.42	
H_5C_2OOC—$(CH_2)_4$—$COOC_2H_5$	Benzene	25–50	2.42	
H_5C_2OOC—$(CH_2)_8$—$COOC_2H_5$	Benzene	25–50	2.50	
H_5C_2OOC—$(CH_2)_8$—$COOC_2H_5$	Benzene	25–50	2.49	
p-$C_6H_4(CH_2Cl)_2$	Benzene	25	2.20	2.0 or 2.46
p-$C_6H_4(CH_2Br)_2$	Benzene	22	2.04	2.0 or 2.46
o-$C_6H_4(CH_2Br)_2$	Benzene	25–50	2.02–2.08	2.54
	CCl_4	−15–45	1.79–1.92	
o-$C_6H_4(OCH_3)_2$	Benzene	10–40	1.18–1.32	1.93
m-$C_6H_4(OCH_3)_2$	Benzene	10–40	1.58	1.63
p-$C_6H_4(OCH_3)_2$	Benzene	10–40	1.70	1.46
o-$C_6H_4Cl(OCH_3)$	Benzene	10–50	2.47	2.27
	Heptane	−15–60	2.47	
$1,4$-$(t$-$C_4H_9)_2C_6H_2(OCH_3)$-$2,5$	Benzene	25	1.5	1.46
$(n$-$C_3H_7O)_3B$	Benzene	25	0.77	1.95
$(i$-$C_4H_9O)_3B$	Benzene	25	0.85	1.95
$(s$-$C_4H_9O)_3B$	Benzene	25	0.85	1.95
$(C_6H_5O)_3P$	Benzene	25	2.02	2.0
$(C_6H_5O)_3PO$	Benzene	25	2.81	(2.8)
$(C_6H_5O)_3PS$	Benzene	25	2.58	(2.6)

moments indistinguishable from the free-rotation values. This does not
mean that the long-chain molecules have complete freedom of rotation
around the carbon-carbon bonds, but that there are so many possible
configurations that the mean moment is indistinguishable from that for
free rotation, which, in turn, is indistinguishable from that for completely
random orientation of the two dipoles relative to each other:

$$\mu = 2^{1/2}m = 1.41 \times 1.9 = 2.69$$

for the dichloride. Indeed, Suzuki[5] has concluded that the greater stability of the trans configuration in the hydrocarbon chain lowers the moment below that calculated for free rotation, the lowering being appreciable even in decamethylene bromide but no greater than the uncertainty in the calculation of the free-rotation value in Table 4.1.

The polymethylene diamines[4] and glycols[1] contain the equivalent of four dipoles of smaller moment in each molecule, instead of two as in the bromides and cyanides, thus facilitating the approach toward a free-rotation value for molecules of shorter chain. The probability of compound formation with the solvent complicates the interpretation of the values for the glycols in dioxane solution, which, for the longer molecules, are so high as to suggest some stabilization of configurations of high moment.

The temperature dependence of the three glycol dialkyl ethers has been explained qualitatively by Kubo[6] in terms of the hindrance of rotation by intramolecular forces. The absence of temperature dependence for the moment of chloromethyl methyl ether and its agreement with the free-rotation value[7] are not to be regarded as proving free rotation, although the fact that one C—O dipole has its negative end toward the C—O axis of rotation and the C—Cl dipole has its positive end toward this axis reduces the forces between the two rotating groups.

Some difference is evident in the fairly normal behaviors[6,8] of dimethyl and diethyl carbonates because the ethyl group gives rise to greater steric repulsion than the methyl. However, the behavior of the two chloroformates is unique among the substances in Table 4.1 in that the moments decrease rapidly with rising temperature. The molecular moment calculated without regard for the effects of resonance and mutual induction has a maximum value 2.15 when the alkyl group rotates around the C—O axis so as to be cis to the chlorine atom and a minimum value 1.58 when it is trans to the chlorine atom.[8] It would appear that in the vicinity of room temperature the molecules are predominantly in a cis configuration, while at high temperatures they are predominantly in a trans configuration. Some stabilization of the cis and trans configuration would result from resonance. The diethyl esters of the dicarboxylic acids have six bond moments in each molecule with a variety of possible configurations even if rotation around the bonds is much hindered. It is, therefore, not surprising to find little variation of moment with temperature or with chain length, except in the solution values of diethyl succinate, to the variation of which solvent effect contributes a good deal. The mean

[5] K. Suzuki, *Bull. Chem. Soc. Japan*, **20**, 19 (1947).

[6] M. Kubo, *Sci. Papers Inst. Phys. Chem. Research (Tokyo)*, **30**, 169 (1936).

[7] J. H. Gibbs, Ph.D. Dissertation, Princeton University, 1950.

[8] S. Mizushima and M. Kubo, *Bull. Chem. Soc. Japan*, **13**, 174 (1938).

moment calculated for a completely random orientation in space of the two —$COOC_2H_5$ group moments, 1.9×10^{-18}, relative to one another is 2.69, only slightly higher than the values observed for the ester molecules.

For p-xylylene dichloride and dibromide, the moments calculated for free rotation are identical with those calculated for ethylene chloride and bromide, 2.0, if the same moment, 1.5, is used in the calculation. If the moment of the benzyl halide, 1.85, is used, the free-rotation value is 2.46 for both molecules. Probably, 2.0 is more nearly correct for the para compounds, in which the inductive effects cancel to a considerable extent. Exactly the same values would be calculated if cis and trans configurations coplanar with the ring were equally probable. It would appear that the —CH_2X groups are sufficiently far apart in the trans positions to be practically independent of one another, while, in the ortho positions, there is some slight lowering of moment by repulsion. A much more pronounced lowering is evident in o-dimethoxybenzene, while the groups seem to be independent of each other in the meta and para isomers.[9] In 1,4-di-t-butyl-2,5-dimethoxybenzene, the steric repulsion of the t-butyl groups should reduce the stability of configurations in which the methoxy groups approach coplanarity with the ring with their methyls cis to each other.[10] The observed moment is lower than that of p-dimethoxybenzene but closer to that calculated for free rotation, showing that the effect of steric repulsion upon the moment is small.

The free-rotation moments obtained for the trialkyl borates are calculated[2] by the same equation as that which has been given for triphenyl phosphite [Eq. (4.6)], the boron valence angle being taken as $120°$. It is evident that steric repulsion among the alkyl groups reduces the stabilities of the high-moment configurations. The larger size of the central atom in triphenyl phosphite evidently reduces the repulsion so that the moment is not lowered below that calculated for free rotation. The moments observed for triphenyl phosphate and thiophosphate are used[2] to calculate reasonable values for the PO and PS bonds, so that the free-rotation values in parentheses are without significance.

Debye and Bueche[11] have calculated the average dipole moment $\bar{\mu}$ of a polymer molecule in solution by the relation

$$\frac{\bar{\mu}^2}{3} = \left[P \sum_{m=1}^{N_0} \sum_{n=1}^{N_0} (\mu_n f)(\mu_m f) \right]_{av} \tag{4.7}$$

in which μ_n is the vector magnitude of the nth dipole of the chain, f is a

[9] S. Mizushima, Y. Morino, and H. Okazaki, *Sci. Papers Inst. Phys. Chem. Research (Tokyo)*, **34**, 1147 (1938).

[10] P. F. Oesper, C. P. Smyth, and M. S. Kharasch, *J. Am. Chem. Soc.*, **64**, 937 (1942).

[11] P. Debye and F. Bueche, *J. Chem. Phys.*, **19**, 589 (1951).

unit vector in the direction of the applied electric field, and P is the probability of occurrence of any particular chain configuration. The sums extend over all the N_0 dipoles on the chain, and the average is taken over all the possible chain configurations and orientations. For the molecule of polyparachlorostyrene, they obtain

$$\bar{\mu}^2 = 0.92 N_0 \mu^2 \tag{4.8}$$

if free rotation exists, but find experimentally that the factor is about 0.56 instead of 0.92, while for the similar compound polyvinylchloride[11,12] it is about 0.75.   Two possible models of the polyparachlorostyrene molecule with hindered rotation give the observed factor 0.56, but only one of them gives the molecular size determined by measurements of light scattering.   The model accordingly proposed[11] is a rather extended chain periodic in structure and repeating every four chain links, rotation around the carbon-carbon bonds being restricted to a free angle of about 65°.

[12] R. M. Fuoss, *J. Am. Chem. Soc.*, **63**, 2410 (1941).

CHAPTER XII

DIPOLE MOMENTS AND STRUCTURES OF
INORGANIC AND ORGANOMETALLIC MOLECULES

The relations between bond moment, bond character, and the electronegativity differences of the bonded atoms, which are fundamental in determining molecular dipole moments, have been considered in Chap. VIII. The relations between the moments and the geometrical configurations of molecules have been considered for organic compounds first because their great number and gradation in properties render them more suitable than inorganic for such a study. The order of the discussion of the inorganic molecules in this chapter will be based upon the periodic system.

1. Hydrogen, Deuterium, and Their Compounds. The hydrogen molecule, H_2, like the diatomic molecules of other elements, is symmetrical and, consequently, has zero moment.

The moments of the four hydrogen halides (cf. Sec. VIII.1) are remarkably close to the electronegativity differences between hydrogen and each halogen, the difference and the moment decreasing rapidly from the fluoride to the iodide. The use of the valence angles 105° for the water molecule and 92° for that of hydrogen sulfide gives bond moments of the same magnitudes as the hydrogen-oxygen and hydrogen-sulfur electronegativity differences. Similar consistency is evident in the moments of the tetrahedral molecules of ammonia, phosphine, and arsine. The structures of these molecules have been discussed by Coulson.[1] The decrease in moment with increase in size and polarizability of the negative atom is evident in all these values. The moment of stibine, 0.12, shows still further decrease with increasing size of the atom to which the hydrogens are attached. Hydrogen peroxide and hydrogen disulfide are considered in Sec. 8.

The zero moment of diborane, B_2H_6, evidences the molecular symmetry attributed to it in all the structures commonly proposed. The moment 2.13 of pentaborane, B_5H_5, and the value 3.52 for decaborane, $B_{10}H_{14}$,

---

[1] C. A. Coulson, "Valence," Oxford, London, 1952, chaps. IV and VII.

indicate that high polarity may be characteristic of asymmetric boron hydrides having a number of hydrogen bridge bonds.[2]

The moments of hydrogen chloride and deuterium chloride have been found[3] to be $\mu(HCl) = 1.085$ and $\mu(DCl) = 1.088$ if the slightly differing observed values $P_E + P_A = 6.84$ and 7.00 are used in the calculation. If a mean value $P_E + P_A = 6.92$ is used, the calculated moment values are $\mu(HCl) = 1.082$ and $\mu(DCl) = 1.089$. The difference between either pair of values differs by no more than its probable error from the difference 0.0049 calculated from the anharmonicity of the zero-point vibration and the effective charge derived from infrared data. Bell and Coop[3] have recalculated earlier measurements[4] on ammonia and deuteroammonia, taking account of the usually negligible effect of the moment of inertia [Eq. I(7.2)], as in the case of hydrogen and deuterium chlorides, and similarly averaging the values of $P_E + P_A$ observed for the two substances. The difference in moment 0.012 ($ND_3 > NH_3$) thus obtained agrees well with the predicted difference 0.009, which is chiefly attributable to the anharmonicity of the perpendicular vibration. A similar difference probably occurs between water and deuterium oxide but is smaller than the experimental errors in the measurements. The deuterium compound again has the higher moment in the case of the isocyanic acid molecules as given by microwave spectroscopy:[5]

$$\mu(HCNO) = 1.592 \pm 0.015$$

and $\mu(DCNO) = 1.619 \pm 0.015$.

2. The Inert Gas Elements. The monatomic molecules of helium, neon, argon, krypton, and xenon are found to have zero moments, as would be expected from the symmetry of the orbitals in their atoms and the pairing of the electrons in the orbitals.

3. Group I Elements. The moment value 0.97 reported[1] for the molecule of n-butyllithium in benzene solution, if, as usual, the H—C moment is taken as 0.4, gives an Li—C bond moment of 1.4, which is consistent with the electronegativity difference between the two bonded atoms.[1] The large moment of lithium perchlorate in dioxane solution,[2] 7.84, is close to the values for the alkali metal halide molecules in the vapor state, which have already been shown to be almost pure ionic structures polarized by mutual induction (Sec. VIII.4). As for all dependable values of polar bonds, the moment is lower than the value calculated for a pair of

[2] A. W. Laubengayer and R. Bottei, *J. Am. Chem. Soc.*, **74**, 1618 (1952).

[3] R. P. Bell and I. E. Coop, *Trans. Faraday Soc.*, **34**, 1209 (1938).

[4] J. M. A. de Bruyne and C. P. Smyth, *J. Am. Chem. Soc.*, **57**, 1203 (1935).

[5] J. N. Shoolery, R. G. Shulman, and D. M. Yost, *J. Chem. Phys.*, **19**, 250 (1951).

Footnotes for Sec. 3.

[1] M. T. Rogers and A. Young, *J. Am. Chem. Soc.*, **68**, 2748 (1946).

[2] M. G. Malone and A. L. Ferguson, *J. Chem. Phys.*, **2**, 99 (1934).

undistorted ions bonded only by the force between their charges. The moment values[3] of several alkali metal halide molecules dissolved in benzene as complexes with aluminum bromide, Al_2Br_6, molecules seem to be close to the values found for the unassociated molecules in the vapor state.

Tri- and tetraalkyl ammonium salts measured in very dilute benzene solution (Table 3.1)[4] may be compared with the alkali metal salts.

TABLE 3.1. DIPOLE MOMENTS ($\times 10^{18}$) AND CHARGE SEPARATIONS, r(A.), OF TRI- AND TETRAALKYLAMMONIUM SALTS IN BENZENE SOLUTION[4]

Molecule	μ	r
$[(n\text{-}C_4H_9)_4N][(C_6H_5)_3BOH]$	19.7	4.13
$[(i\text{-}C_5H_{11})_4N][(NO_2)_3C_6H_2O]$	18.3	3.82
$[(n\text{-}C_4H_9)_4N][(NO_2)_3C_6H_2O]$	17.8	3.73
$[(i\text{-}C_5H_{11})_4N]CNS$	15.4	3.23
$[(n\text{-}C_4H_9)_4N]ClO_4$	14.1	2.96
$[(i\text{-}C_5H_{11})_3HN][(NO_2)_3C_6H_2O]$	13.3	2.79
$[(n\text{-}C_4H_9)_3HN][(NO_2)_3C_6H_2O]$	13.1	2.74
$[(n\text{-}C_4H_9)_4N]Br$	11.6	2.43
$[(n\text{-}C_4H_9)_4N][C_2H_3O_2]$	11.2	2.35
$[(n\text{-}C_4H_9)_3HN]I$	8.09	1.69
$[(n\text{-}C_4H_9)_3HN]Br$	7.61	1.59
$[(n\text{-}C_4H_9)_3HN]Cl$	7.17	1.50

The largest moments in Table 3.1 are about twice the size of the largest alkali metal halide moments (Table 4.1, Chap. VIII) because of the very large sizes of the ions. The moment and apparent charge separation calculated as $r = \mu/4.80 \times 10^{-10}$ evidently decrease with decrease in ionic size. The moments of the trialkyl ammonium salts are considerably lower than those of the corresponding tetraalkyl ammonium salts, indicating that, as might be expected, the trialkyl ammonium ion is oriented with its single hydrogen toward the anion, thus shortening the molecular dipole. The increase in moment with increase in size of the halogen qualitatively parallels that from the fluoride to the chloride in the alkali metal salts, for which absence or uncertainty of data makes extension of the relationship uncertain. The logical increase in moment with increase in ionic radius is in contrast to the decrease with increasing internuclear distance in the molecules of the hydrides (Sec. 1), where covalent bonding predominates. The reduction of the moments by deformation of the ions is evidenced by the values of r, which for the halides are smaller than the radii of the halide ions:[5] I^-, 2.16; Br^-, 1.95; Cl^-, 1.81 A.

[3] I. A. Sheka, *Zhur. Fiz. Khim.*, **24**, 519 (1950).

[4] J. A. Geddes and C. A. Kraus, *Trans. Faraday Soc.*, **32**, 585 (1936).

[5] L. Pauling, "The Nature of the Chemical Bond," Cornell University Press, Ithaca, N.Y., 2d ed., 1940, p. 346.

The increase in moment from that of lithium perchlorate, 7.8, to that of silver perchlorate in benzene solution, 10.7, is qualitatively reasonable in view of the increase in size of the cation, but the possibility of compound formation with the solvent indicated by the abnormal solubility of the salt complicates the significance of the value. The moments of a few metal-organic compounds of copper and gold have been used, usually in conjunction with X-ray data, to determine molecular configurations. A fairly high polarity is shown for the Au—Br bond by its lower limit 4 given in Table 4.1, Chap. VIII.

4. Group II Elements. The zero moments of beryllium chloride and bromide in benzene solution indicate linear molecules, and those of the molecules of the coordination compounds, basic beryllium acetate, $(CH_3CO_2)_6Be_4O$, and beryllium acetylacetonate, $(C_5H_7O_2)_2Be$, evidence the symmetry of structure indicated by X-ray analysis and general structural considerations. The very large moments of the etherates of the beryllium halides, $BeCl_2 \cdot 2(C_2H_5)_2O$, 6.73, and $BeBr_2 \cdot 2(C_2H_5)_2O$, 7.55, are typical of the values found for molecular addition compounds. They are due principally to the resultant of two $O \rightarrow Be$ and two Be—X bonds.

The moment values reported[1,2] for a number of metal soaps show some discrepancies and a surprising dependence upon chain length, which suggest that some, at least, may depart from the true molecular moment because of strong intermolecular forces or even micelle formation. The apparent values run from 0.29 for zinc oleate to 5.49 for aluminum stearate. Zero moment could result from the symmetrical coordination of four oxygens around a bivalent metal or of six oxygens around a trivalent metal. The large moments, 4.3 to 4.8, of the calcium, cadmium, and lead soaps, like most of the other metal soap moments, are consistent with a lack of symmetry and the expected large metal-oxygen moments.

The apparent moments of diethyl- and diphenylmercury are so small as to indicate zero moment with some atomic polarization. The appreciable apparent moment values of the di-para-halogenated diphenylmercury molecules probably arise from large atomic polarization, the C—Hg—C group being linear with considerable flexibility.[3] The molecules in the vapor phase of the mercuric halides have been shown by electron diffraction[4] to be linear. The moments, 1.43, 1.53, and 1.67, measured in dioxane solution are, therefore, attributed to the formation of an addition compound with the solvent molecule.[5] Monoalkyl and monoaryl

[1] W. Ostwald and R. Riedel, *Kolloid-Z.*, **69**, 185 (1934).

[2] B. C. Banerjee and S. R. Palit, *J. Indian Chem. Soc.*, **27**, 385 (1951).

[3] N. V. Sidgwick, "The Chemical Elements and Their Compounds," Oxford, London, 1950, p. 309.

[4] P. W. Allen and L. E. Sutton, *Acta Cryst.*, **3**, 46 (1950).

[5] B. C. Curran, *J. Am. Chem. Soc.*, **63**, 1470 (1941).

mercuric halides show the large lower limits, 3.2 to 3.5, for the Hg—X bond moments given in Table 4.1, Chap. VIII.

5. Group III Elements. Three hydrides of boron have been mentioned in Sec. 1. The zero moments of the boron trihalides correspond to planar structures with the three halogens equidistant from the boron and located at the corners of an equilateral triangle. When, however, boron trichloride is dissolved in dioxane, a moment 4.86 results, apparently from the formation of a tetrahedral complex, $OC_4H_8O \cdot BCl_3$. From the moment 5.98 of the etherate of boron trichloride, $(C_2H_5)_2O \cdot BCl_3$, a moment of 5.2 has been calculated for this dioxanate[1] in fair agreement with the observed value. A considerable number of addition compounds involving boron trifluoride or trichloride have moments between 5 and 7.6. The compound $(CH_3)_3N \rightarrow BF_3$ has a moment 5.76 as compared to 4.95 for $(CH_3)_3N \rightarrow O$, the higher value probably being due to the B—F moments.

The moment 1.80 of borine carbonyl, H_3BCO, is much smaller than would be expected of a structure described[2] in terms of resonance between two structures

$$
\text{H} \qquad\qquad\qquad\qquad \text{H}
$$
$$
\text{H} : \ddot{\text{B}}^- : \text{C} : : : \text{O} : ^+ \qquad\qquad \text{H} : \ddot{\text{B}}^- : \text{C}^+ : : \ddot{\text{O}} :
$$
$$
\ddot{\text{H}} \qquad\qquad\qquad\qquad \ddot{\text{H}}
$$

each of which should give rise to a large moment. In the structure proposed by Coulson and Moffitt (Sec. 6) for carbon monoxide, which has almost no moment, the lone-pair electrons on the carbon atom are strongly directed away from the carbon-oxygen bond. If these electrons completed the boron octet without accompanying sizable charge displacement, the relatively small size of the moment would be accounted for, since in view of the nearly equal electronegativities, 2.0 and 2.1, of boron and hydrogen, the B—H moments should be very small.

In the borates, the three boron-oxygen bonds have symmetrical positions analogous to those of the halogens in the boron trihalides. The small moments of the trialkyl borates, 0.8, therefore, arise[3] from the distribution of the R—O moments around the B—O bond directions as described in Sec. XI.4.

The molecules of aluminum chloride, bromide, and iodide in the vapor state have been indicated by electron-diffraction measurements[4] to be symmetrical dimers, Al_2X_6, with the halogens at the corners of two tetrahedra, which share an edge. The approximately zero moments found

[1] T. J. Lane, P. A. McCusker, and C. Curran, *J. Am. Chem. Soc.*, **64**, 2076 (1942).

[2] L. Pauling, "The Nature of the Chemical Bond," Cornell University Press, Ithaca, N.Y., 2d ed., 1940, p. 264.

[3] G. L. Lewis and C. P. Smyth, *J. Am. Chem. Soc.*, **62**, 1529 (1940).

[4] K. J. Palmer and N. Elliott, *J. Am. Chem. Soc.*, **60**, 1852 (1938).

for the bromide and iodide in carbon disulfide solution show the symmetry of the molecule. In benzene, the moment 5.0 found for the bromide indicates dissociation into the monomer with the formation of an addition compound with the solvent. Like boron trifluoride and trichloride, aluminum chloride and bromide form a large number of addition compounds, which have moments from 6 to 9.7. The moment values of trimethylaluminum, dimethylaluminum chloride, and methylaluminum dichloride* are complicated by molecular association but tentatively indicate that the trimethylaluminum monomer has a pyramidal molecule with a moment of 1.7 ± 0.8.

Gallium chloride† resembles the aluminum halides in dimerizing, having little or no moment in solution in carbon disulfide and carbon tetrachloride and a large moment in benzene solution, and in the formation of addition compounds with moments from 6.8 to 9.2.

6. Group IV Elements. The surprisingly small size of the dipole moment of carbon monoxide, 0.1, hardly distinguishable from zero, has been attributed[1] to resonance among three almost equally stable structures, C^+—O^-, C=O, and C^-≡O^+, the contributions of the two polar structures to the molecular moment approximately canceling each other. The binding and the polarity or lack thereof are more satisfactorily represented[2,3] in terms of a σ bond formed by the oxygen $2p_x$ orbital and the carbon hybridized $s + p_x$ orbital, with polarity C^+O^-, two π bonds formed by two oxygen $2p$ and two carbon $2p$ orbitals, with polarity C^+O^-, and carbon $(s - p_x)^2$ lone-pair electrons. Approximate calculations[3] indicate that the moment of the electrons in the two π bonds is -1.9 and that of the other electrons is 2.1, giving a difference in good agreement with the small moment 0.1 observed for the molecule. The zero moment of carbon dioxide gave evidence of the now recognized linearity of the molecule,[4,5] the structure of which has been treated[3] like that of carbon monoxide. The moments of the two bonds cancel each other, but their polarities appear to be greater[6] than that of the carbon monoxide bond.

The carbon disulfide molecule resembles the carbon dioxide molecule in its linearity of structure[5] and zero moment. The moment of carbon oxysulfide, 0.72, is more than twice the difference between the C=O and

* R. H. Wiswall and C. P. Smyth, *J. Chem. Phys.*, **9**, 352 (1941).

† H. Ulich and G. Heyne, *Z. physik. Chem.*, **49B**, 284 (1941).

[1] L. Pauling, "The Nature of the Chemical Bond," Cornell University Press, Ithaca, N.Y., 2d ed., 1940, p. 135.

[2] C. A. Coulson, "Valence," Oxford, London, 1952, p. 212.

[3] W. E. Moffitt, *Proc. Roy. Soc. (London)*, **196**, 524 (1949).

[4] L. Pauling, *op. cit.*, p. 196.

[5] P. W. Allen and L. E. Sutton, *Acta Cryst.*, **3**, 46 (1950).

[6] C. A. Coulson, *op. cit.*, p. 186.

C=S bond moments in Table 4.1, Chap. VIII, but the bonds in the COS molecule probably differ somewhat from those in the ketones and thioketones, and their environments are certainly different. The moment of carbon oxyselenide, 0.75, hardly differs from that of the oxysulfide, the two structures presumably being closely similar. The moment of phosgene, 1.18, may be compared to the difference between the moments of acetone and 2,2-dichloropropane, $2.85 - 2.25 = 0.60$, and that between the moments of formaldehyde and methylene chloride, $2.27 - 1.58 = 0.69$. The larger value of the phosgene moment is readily explicable in terms of resonance contributions from two polar structures, such as

$$\begin{array}{c} Cl^+ \\ \diagdown \\ C-O^- \\ \diagup \\ Cl \end{array}$$

suggested by the shortening of the carbon-chlorine distance found by electron-diffraction measurements.[7] The much smaller moment of thiophosgene, 0.28, which has been discussed by Coop and Sutton,[8] is difficult to explain.

The zero moments of silane, disilane, silicon tetrafluoride, and silicon tetrachloride evidence the symmetry of the molecules, which resemble the analogous carbon compounds in structure. Chlorosilane and bromosilane have identical moments, 1.31, considerably lower than those of methyl chloride and methyl bromide, although the bond lengths and electronegativity differences of the silicon compounds are greater. The lowering can be accounted for in terms of a resonance contribution from a structure $H_3Si^-=Cl^+$, which would lower the resultant molecular moment with its positive end toward the Si and shorten the Si—Cl bond as observed by means of electron diffraction.[9] The moments of dichlorosilane, 0.85, and tribromosilane, 0.79, are lower than those of the monohalogenated compounds, just as are the moments of the analogous carbon compounds, and, presumably, from the same cause, inductive effects. The moment of fluorosilane, 1.27, is slightly lower than that of chlorosilane, just as the moment of methyl fluoride is lower than that of methyl chloride. This is consistent with the great shortening of the Si—F bond distance, which, in SiF_4, is even less than the sum of the double-bond radii.[10] The shortening of the bond to the halogen decreases[10] with increasing size and electropositive character of the central atom, and the

[7] L. O. Brockway, J. Y. Beach, and L. Pauling, *J. Am. Chem. Soc.*, **57**, 2693 (1935).

[8] I. E. Coop and L. E. Sutton, *Trans. Faraday Soc.*, **35**, 505 (1939).

[9] L. O. Brockway and I. E. Coop, *Trans. Faraday Soc.*, **34**, 1429 (1938).

[10] L. Pauling, *op. cit.*, chap. VII.

moment, 2.03, of monochlorogermane,[11] GeH_3Cl, is larger than that of methyl chloride. The moment of the M—X bond increases further from germanium to tin to lead until, in the trialkyl lead halides, the Pb—X bond is comparable in polarity to typical ionic bonds.[12-15] In the absence of mutual induction between the dipoles in the molecule, the tetrahedral angle 110° requires[11] a ratio 1.15 between the moment of MH_2Cl_2 and that of MH_3Cl. The observed ratios are: for CH_2Cl_2 and CH_3Cl, 0.85; SiH_2Cl_2 and SiH_3Cl, 0.91; GeH_2Cl_2 and GeH_3Cl, 1.15; $(C_2H_5)_2SnCl_2$ and $(C_2H_5)_3SnCl$, 1.12; and $(C_2H_5)_2PbCl_2$ and $(C_2H_5)_3PbCl$, approximately 1.07, as compared to 1.02 for $(CH_3)_2CCl_2$ and $(CH_3)_3CCl$. At least qualitatively, the lowering of moment of the dihalides by mutual induction shows the expected decrease with increasing dipole-dipole separation resulting from increasing size of the central atom.

The dipole moments of a series of linear polymethylpolysiloxanes, $(CH_3)_3Si[OSi(CH_3)_2]_qCH_3$, in which q has values 1,2,3,4, and 5, have been calculated from the dielectric constants[16] of the liquids by means of the Onsager equation and are found to be given by the empirical relationship $\mu = 0.70q^{1/2}$. For the cyclic compounds, $[(CH_3)_2SiO]_q$, in which q has the values 4,5,6,7, and 8, the moment values obtained in the same way approach the values predicted by this equation in the case of the larger rings.[16] The difference between the polarization of hexamethyldisiloxane measured in the vapor state[17] and the molar refraction would give a molecular dipole moment close to that calculated from the dielectric constant of the liquid, but the apparent constancy of the polarization over a temperature range of 200° indicates that the moment is rather small and that a large atomic polarization is responsible for part of the apparent moment value of the liquid. The apparent moment values of the other members of the polymethylpolysiloxane series should be similarly attributable, in part, to atomic polarization. Further work on the problem is in progress at the time of writing.[18]

The moment of triethylsilanol, $(C_2H_5)_3SiOH$, 1.50, is about 0.15 lower than that of t-butyl alcohol, just as the values for chlorosilane and bromosilane are lower than those for the analogous carbon compounds. The moments of the analogous tin and lead compounds increase to 1.91 and 2.4, a smaller increase than in the cases of the halides.

[11] C. P. Smyth, A. J. Grossman, and S. R. Ginsburg, *J. Am. Chem. Soc.*, **62**, 192 (1940).

[12] G. L. Lewis, P. F. Oesper, and C. P. Smyth, *J. Am. Chem. Soc.*, **62**, 3243 (1940).

[13] C. P. Smyth, *J. Am. Chem. Soc.*, **63**, 57 (1941).

[14] C. P. Smyth, *J. Org. Chem.*, **6**, 421 (1941).

[15] L. Malatesta and R. Pizzotti, *Gazz. chim. ital.*, **73**, 349 (1943).

[16] R. O. Sauer and D. J. Mead, *J. Am. Chem. Soc.*, **68**, 1794 (1946).

[17] A. Di Giacomo and C. P. Smyth, Unpublished measurements.

[18] See R. S. Holland and C. P. Smyth, *J. Am. Chem. Soc.*, **77**, 268 (1955).

Stannic chloride and titanium tetrachloride form addition compounds with organic molecules with moments of 6 to 8, arising largely from the presence of a coordinate bond.

7. Group V Elements. The zero moment of the diatomic nitrogen molecule is necessitated by its symmetry. The moment of nitric oxide is experimentally indistinguishable from zero. The structure of the molecule can be described in terms much like those used for carbon monoxide in Sec. 6, the structure :N≝O: corresponding[1] to resonance among three structures $^+$:N:O:$^-$, :N::O:, $^-$:N::O:$^+$, with, perhaps, some contribution from :N:O:. Approximately equal contributions from the two polar structures would then result in a nearly zero moment. In the molecular orbital description used by Coulson,[2] the cancellation of moment becomes understandable and leads to the belief that three-electron bonds are not highly polar.[2] For nitrous oxide, the very small moment, 0.16, of the linear molecule[3] can be explained[4] in terms of resonance between two almost equally stable structures, $^-$:N⚌$^+$N⚌O: and :N≡N$^+$—O:$^-$. The nitrogen dioxide molecule with a nitrogen valence angle[3] of 130° to 154° may be described[1] in terms of two structures,

In view of the almost, if not quite, zero moment of nitric oxide, a moment[5] of 0.31 is consistent with resonance between these structures. The seemingly carefully determined[5] moment value 0.37 of nitrogen tetroxide would, if correct, rule out a symmetrical structure[1] for the molecule and favor one[1] such as

$$^-:O \diagdown_{N^+-O} ^{N⚌O:} \diagup$$
$$:O$$

[1] L. Pauling, "The Nature of the Chemical Bond," Cornell University Press, Ithaca, N.Y., 2d ed., 1940, pp. 266–271.

[2] C. A. Coulson, "Valence," Oxford, London, 1952, pp. 152, 153, and 212.

[3] P. W. Allen and L. E. Sutton, *Acta Cryst.*, **3**, 46 (1950).

[4] L. Pauling, *op. cit.*, p. 126.

[5] R. W. Schulz, *Z. Physik*, **109**, 517 (1938).

in which some polarity on the right-hand side of the molecule would partially cancel the large moment on the left. The moment[6] 1.39 of nitrogen pentoxide results from the lack of symmetry introduced by the valence angle of the central oxygen in the molecule $O_2N—O—NO_2$, which is calculated[6] from the moment as roughly 145°.

If, as seems probable, no tautomeric shift occurs in the molecule of nitramide, a nitro group and an amino group are oriented relatively to each other as they are in p-nitroaniline, where the observed moment 6.2 is raised by additional resonance (Sec. X.3) above the value 5.2 calculated from the moments of nitrobenzene and aniline, which are themselves raised by resonance above the moments of the corresponding aliphatic compounds. The moment value 4.1 calculated for nitramide from the solution values for nitromethane and methylamine is but little higher than the observed value 3.75, which indicates that the normal structures, such as

$$H_2\ddot{N}—^+N \overset{\displaystyle \ddot{O}:}{\underset{\displaystyle \ddot{O}:^-}{\Big\backslash}}$$

are probably a fair representation of the molecule, since the moment would be raised by any considerable contribution from the structure

$$H_2N^+{=}^+N \overset{\displaystyle \ddot{O}:^-}{\underset{\displaystyle \ddot{O}:^-}{\Big\backslash}}$$

This structure is unstable because of the proximity of the positive charges on the two nitrogens, which are widely separated in p-nitroaniline.

The moments of the trihalides of the elements of the nitrogen family have been used to calculate the bond moment values discussed in Chap. VIII. These bond moments are, of course, subject to lowering by strong mutual inductive effects. The zero moments of phosphorus pentafluoride and pentachloride result from the symmetry of the trigonal bipyramids which the molecules form.[3] The moments found for nitrosyl chloride, 1.83, and nitrosyl bromide, 1.87, were estimated[7] to be too high for the purely homopolar structures such as $Cl—N{=}O$, and were, therefore, taken to be indicative of considerable contributions from ionic struc-

[6] G. L. Lewis and C. P. Smyth, *J. Am. Chem. Soc.*, **61**, 3067 (1939).
[7] J. A. A. Ketelaar, *Rec. trav. chim.*, **62**, 289 (1943).

tures, such as $Cl^-N{\equiv}O^+$, previously deduced from bond lengths.[8]   However, small nitrogen-halogen moments like that for N—F in Table 4.1, Chap. VIII, and an N=O moment close to the rough value 2.0 in Table 4.1, Chap. VIII, would account for these molecular moments.

The molecules of phosphorus oxychloride, $POCl_3$, and thiophosphoryl chloride, $PSCl_3$, are slightly distorted tetrahedra with the phosphorus near the center.[12]   The moment value 3.3 calculated for the P—O bond by adding the moment 0.9 of phosphorus trichloride to 2.40, the $POCl_3$ moment, is typical of the values found for coordinate bonds but is somewhat larger than the value 2.9 obtained as the difference between the moment of triphenylphosphine and that of its oxide,[9] $(C_6H_5)_3PO$.   A similar calculation from the moment 1.41 of thiophosphoryl chloride gives only 2.3 for the P—S, although the moment of triphenylphosphine sulfide[9] is 0.45 higher than that of the oxide.   The decrease in moment, 1.0, from $POCl_3$ to $PSCl_3$ is comparable to the decrease, 0.9, from $COCl_2$ to $CSCl_2$. Eight different resonating structures have been written to account for the bond lengths in the phosphoryl and thiophosphoryl halides.[10]   These can easily account for the observed moments.

Since the structure of tantalum chloride, $TaCl_5$, has been shown by electron diffraction to be a trigonal bipyramid, its small apparent moment value, 1.2, is probably the result of atomic polarization.   The moments of a number of molecules containing a coordinate bond between an atom of a member of the nitrogen family and one of oxygen or sulfur have been used to calculate[9,11] bond moment values in Chap. VIII.

8. Group VI Elements.   The zero moment of the symmetrical diatomic oxygen molecule is like that of other diatomic molecules of elements. The small moment, 0.6, of the ozone molecule is explicable[1] in terms of the resonating structures

of which the first two would be responsible for the moment, since the moments of the second two would cancel each other.   These structures are qualitatively consistent with an O—O—O angle of 127° indicated by electron diffraction[2] and a value[3] 117° indicated by microwave spectros-

[8] J. A. A. Ketelaar and K. J. Palmer, *J. Am. Chem. Soc.*, **59**, 2629 (1937).

[9] G. M. Phillips, J. S. Hunter, and L. E. Sutton, *J. Chem. Soc.*, 146 (1945).

[10] D. P. Stevenson and H. Russell, Jr., *J. Am. Chem. Soc.*, **61**, 3264 (1939).

[11] C. P. Smyth, *J. Am. Chem. Soc.*, **60**, 183 (1938).

[12] P. W. Allen and L. E. Sutton, *Acta Cryst.*, **3**, 46 (1950).

[1] G. L. Lewis and C. P. Smyth, *J. Am. Chem. Soc.*, **61**, 3063 (1939).

[2] W. Shand, Jr., and R. A. Spurr, *J. Am. Chem. Soc.*, **65**, 179 (1943).

[3] R. H. Hughes, *Phys. Rev.*, **85**, 717 (1952).

copy and inconsistent with a value 34° proposed[4] on the basis of infrared spectra and requiring a considerable coincidence in space of the terminal oxygens, which would thus be placed only 1.0 A. apart as compared to 1.21 A. in the O_2 molecule. The moment is smaller than might be expected from the polarities of the structures written for the molecule. This is explained by Phillips, Hunter, and Sutton[5] by replacing the third and fourth resonating structures by two structures

which are supposed to be more stable than the two structures responsible for the moment.

The moment of hydrogen peroxide[6] has been shown by Theilacker[7] to be in good agreement with a structure

which possesses rotational freedom, that is, equal probability of occurrence of the hydrogens in any position around the O—O bond, an oxygen valence angle 110°, and an H—O moment identical with that in water, so that

$$\mu_{H_2O_2} = \frac{2^{1/2}\mu_{H_2O} \sin 70°}{2 \cos 55°}$$

The value 2.20 thus calculated for dioxane solution is close to the observed 2.13, and the 1.98 calculated for ether solution is close to the observed 2.06. A rather widely accepted model,[8] which fits the observed moment, uses an oxygen valence angle of 100° and fixes the hydrogens so that an angle of 100° occurs between the H—O—O planes. This model with the angles 90° instead of 100° is indicated by an X-ray investigation[9] of liquid hydrogen peroxide. The moment 2.23 calculated for this model is also in satisfactory agreement with the observed value. If an exactly similar structure is assumed for hydrogen disulfide, H_2S_2, the calculated moment 0.96 is somewhat lower than the observed[10] value 1.17. If all positions of rotation around the S—S bond were equally probable, the same moment value would be obtained.[10] The discrepancy might arise from difference between the inductive effects in this molecule and those

[4] A. Adel and D. M. Dennison, *J. Chem. Phys.*, **14**, 379 (1946).

[5] G. M. Phillips, J. S. Hunter, and L. E. Sutton, *J. Chem. Soc.*, 146 (1945).

[6] E. P. Linton and O. Maass, *Can. J. Research*, **7**, 81 (1932).

[7] W. Theilacker, *Z. physik. Chem.*, **20B**, 142 (1933).

[8] W. G. Penney and G. B. B. M. Sutherland, *Trans. Faraday Soc.*, **30**, 398 (1934).

[9] J. T. Randall, *Proc. Roy. Soc. (London)*, **159**, 82 (1937).

[10] C. P. Smyth, G. L. Lewis, A. J. Grossmann, and F. B. Jennings, III, *J. Am. Chem. Soc.*, **62**, 1219 (1940).

in the H_2S molecule, from the moment of which the H—S bond moment 0.68 is calculated.

Although some early measurements upon pure sulfur indicated high polarity for the molecules, the seemingly dependable measurements show zero moment for the molecule in solution in carbon disulfide, where it is S_8, a molecule which in the vapor state is a symmetrical ring[11] and should be nonpolar. The dielectric constant of liquid sulfur up to 350° gives no evidence[12] of dipole moment in either the cyclic molecules or the long-chain polymers[13,14] which form as the temperature rises above 160°. However, the setting in of a small loss[12] at about 300° suggests the possibility of the formation of at least a small proportion of polar molecules as the temperature rises above this point.

The structure of the sulfur dioxide molecule may be described in terms of resonating structures analogous to the first two written for ozone and an additional structure containing two double bonds.[15] This is consistent with the O—S—O angle 119° indicated by electron diffraction, microwave spectroscopy,[11] and the dipole moment, 1.60. The moment is much larger than that of ozone, presumably because the electronegativity difference between the sulfur and oxygen atoms tends to stabilize the first two structures, which are responsible for the moment. The zero moment of the sulfur trioxide molecule shows the symmetry required by electron-diffraction measurements, according to which the sulfur lies at the center of an equilateral triangle with the oxygens at the corners.[11]

The zero moment of sulfur hexafluoride corresponds to the octahedral symmetry to be expected of the molecule and actually indicated by the results of electron diffraction.[11] The small moment, 0.6, roughly calculated for the sulfur dichloride, SCl_2, molecule corresponds exactly with the electronegativity difference between sulfur and chlorine and the Cl—S—Cl angle 102° indicated by electron diffraction.[11] The value 1.0 for sulfur monochloride, S_2Cl_2, for which electron diffraction[11] indicates an S—Cl distance the same as that in SCl_2, a Cl—S—S angle 104°, and an angle of about 92° between the S—S—Cl planes, gives an S—Cl bond moment value 0.7, which is not far from the electronegativity difference, 0.5, between sulfur and chlorine.

The moment[10] 2.1 of selenium monochloride, Se_2Cl_2, is higher than that of the corresponding sulfur compound, and the moment of selenium oxychloride, $SeOCl_2$, is 1.0 higher than that reported for thionyl chloride, $SOCl_2$. An increase in moment is to be expected from the more positive

[11] P. W. Allen and L. E. Sutton, *Acta Cryst.*, **3**, 46 (1950).

[12] H. J. Curtis, *J. Chem. Phys.*, **1**, 160 (1933).

[13] R. F. Bacon and R. Fanelli, *J. Am. Chem. Soc.*, **65**, 639 (1943).

[14] R. E. Powell and H. Eyring, *J. Am. Chem. Soc.*, **65**, 648 (1943).

[15] J. D. Dunitz and K. Hedberg, *J. Am. Chem. Soc.*, **72**, 3108 (1950).

character of selenium as compared to sulfur, but, as in the cases of other bonds involving atoms of considerable size, the increase is greater than would be anticipated from the difference 0.1 in the electronegativities of the two elements.

The molecules of thionyl chloride,[11,16] thionyl bromide,[11] sulfuryl chloride,[11] selenium oxychloride,[10] and chromyl chloride,[11,17] CrO_2Cl_2, have the forms of somewhat distorted tetrahedra. The moment values 1.44, 1.47, 1.80, 2.62, and 0.5 are consistent with the expected bond moment values,[10] some differences arising from differences in resonance, as in the phosphoryl and thiophosphoryl halides (Sec. 7). The Cr—Cl bond moment must be large,[17] like that of Sn—Cl, almost to cancel the presumably large Cr—O moment and give the small resultant molecular moment of CrO_2Cl_2. The large moment 2.54 of tellurium tetrachloride has been explained[17] as due to a structure consisting of a trigonal bipyramid with chlorines at four of the corners and an unshared electron pair at the fifth corner, probably one of the equatorial positions. This structure has been shown to be consistent with the results of electron diffraction.[18] The Se—Cl and Te—Cl bond moments necessary to produce the molecular moments which have been discussed would have to be much larger than the electronegativity differences between the elements.[10]

The observation by Smyth and Hannay in 1944 that the moment of the uranium hexafluoride molecule was indistinguishable from zero,[19] an observation confirmed by later measurements,[20,21] showed the untenability of a somewhat unsymmetrical structure proposed for the molecule on the basis of electron-diffraction measurements and indicated the probability of a symmetrical octahedral structure, which was not excluded by the electron-diffraction results.[19]

9. Group VII Elements. Although early measurements indicated some polarity in diatomic molecules of halogens, the data now available make it appear fairly certain that the Cl_2, Br_2, and I_2 molecules have zero moments, as would be expected from their symmetries. A moment 1.4 found[1] for iodine in benzene solution may be attributed to a molecular complex between iodine and benzene. Wide variations in the apparent moment of the iodine monochloride molecule were attributed to the effect

[16] I. E. Coop and L. E. Sutton, *Trans. Faraday Soc.*, **35**, 505 (1939).

[17] C. P. Smyth, A. J. Grossman, and S. R. Ginsburg, *J. Am. Chem. Soc.*, **62**, 192 (1940).

[18] D. P. Stevenson and V. Schomaker, *J. Am. Chem. Soc.*, **62**, 1267 (1940).

[19] J. J. Katz and E. Rabinowitch, "The Chemistry of Uranium," McGraw-Hill, New York, 1951, VIII-5, p. 438.

[20] C. B. Amphlett, L. W. Mullinger, and L. F. Thomas, *Trans. Faraday Soc.*, **44**, 927 (1948).

[21] D. W. Magnuson, *J. Chem. Phys.*, **19**, 1614 (1951).

[1] J. W. Williams and R. J. Allgeier, *J. Am. Chem. Soc.*, **49**, 2416 (1927).

of solvent, which has been interestingly discussed by Fairbrother, but it seems possible that such variations may result from experimental errors. The value reported for ICl vapor and those for BrF and ClF are close to the electronegativity differences for the elements, while the IBr and BrCl moments are considerably larger than the electronegativity differences, as is often the case. The moment of chlorine monoxide,[†] 0.8, when combined with the Cl—O—Cl angle 111° found by electron diffraction[‡] gives a Cl—O bond moment 0.7, but little higher than the electronegativity difference 0.5. Similar calculation of the chlorine-oxygen bond moment in chlorine dioxide from the molecular moment[†] 1.7 and the value 117° of the O—Cl—O angle[‡] gives 1.6, which is much higher than the electronegativity difference because of contributions from resonating polar structures:[‡]

The importance of the polar structures should be greater than it was thought to be by Dunitz and Hedberg because of confusion in the literature between the moment values of Cl_2O and ClO_2.

10. Group VIII Elements. The dimeric molecule of ferric chloride, Fe_2Cl_6, has been shown[1] to have a symmetrical bridge structure like that of aluminum chloride and should, therefore, have zero moment. The small moment value 1.27 observed[2] for it in dioxane solution may arise from monomer[2] or from coordination of a small percentage of ferric chloride molecules with dioxane[2] or from atomic polarization. The zero moments of nickel carbonyl, $Ni(CO)_4$, and osmium tetroxide, OsO_4, are consistent with the tetrahedral structures indicated for these molecules by electron diffraction.[3]

Many of the large number of Werner complexes or coordination compounds whose moments have been measured are platinum complexes, such as $(R_3P)_2PtX_2$ or $(R_2S)_2PtX_2$, in which dsp^2 hybridization of the platinum orbitals gives a square configuration[4] with the platinum at the center of the square and four valence bonds acting along the diagonals

* F. Fairbrother, *J. Chem. Soc.*, 847 (1936).

† D. Sundhoff and H. J. Schumacher, *Z. physik. Chem.*, **28B**, 17 (1935).

‡ J. D. Dunitz and K. Hedberg, *J. Am. Chem. Soc.*, **72**, 3108 (1950).

[1] O. Hassel and H. Viervoll, *Tidsskr. Kjemi Bergvesen. Met.*, **3**, 97 (1943).

[2] T. J. Lane, P. A. McCusker, and B. C. Curran, *J. Am. Chem. Soc.*, **64**, 2076 (1942).

[3] L. O. Brockway, *Revs. Mod. Phys.*, **8**, 231 (1936).

[4] L. Pauling, "The Nature of the Chemical Bond," Cornell University Press, Ithaca, N.Y., 2d ed., 1940, p. 98.

to the groups attached at the corners of the square. Jensen[5] has found that, for most of the α forms of the $(R_3P)_2PtX_2$ type of complex, the difference between the total polarization in benzene solution and the electronic polarization is 20 to 30 cc., while for the β forms it is 1300 to 4000 cc. By making the reasonable assumption that the 20 to 30 cc. difference for the α forms is atomic polarization, he obtains the moments of most of the α forms as approximately zero, thus showing them to have the trans configuration. The moment of β-$[(C_2H_5)_3P]_2PtCl_2$, for example, would be $\mu = 2[m_{(C_2H_5)_3P} + m_{P \to Pt} + m_{Pt-Cl}]$ cos $45° = 10.7$, which gives $m_{(C_2H_5)_3P} + m_{P \to Pt} + m_{Pt-Cl} = 7.6$. Since $m_{(C_2H_5)_3P}$ is presumably of the order of 1, $m_{P \to Pt}$ and m_{Pt-Cl} are probably not far from 3 each, that is, of about the usual magnitude of a coordinate single bond and of a metal-halogen bond (Table 4.1, Chap. VIII). The moment rises to 11.2 when the two covalently bonded chlorines in the molecule are replaced by bromines, but drops to 8.2 when they are replaced by iodines. This is in contrast to the steady continued increase in the moment of the salt $[(n\text{-}C_4H_9)_3HN]X$ when X changes from chloride to bromide to iodide (Table 3.1), giving increasing separation of the ionic charges. When phosphorus in β-$[(C_2H_5)_3P]_2PtCl_2$ is replaced successively by arsenic and antimony, the moment decreases from 10.7 to 10.5 to 9.2, perhaps because of increase in polarizability from phosphorus to arsenic to antimony.

In contrast to the zero moments found for the other α forms of these compounds, which are trans, α-$[(C_2H_5)_3P]_2Pt(NO_3)_2$ has a moment 2.75, which shows that the nitrate is covalently bonded to the platinum so that the Pt—O $\overset{\displaystyle NO_2}{\diagup}$ angle prevents cancellation of the nitrate moments by $\overset{\displaystyle NO_2}{\diagup}$ each other. Electron diffraction gives 105° for the covalent F—O bond angle in fluorine nitrate.[6] The moment of the α nitrite is zero, which shows[5] that it is not a nitrito compound, which would have an angle Pt—O $\overset{\displaystyle NO}{\diagup}$, but a nitro compound with the Pt—NO_2 moment in the direct line of the Pt—N bond. When alkyl sulfides, R_2S, instead of the phosphines, amines, and stibines, are coordinated with the platinum, the β forms, which are shown by their moments to be cis, have moments of the same large magnitude as those of the previously considered β forms. However, the α forms, instead of having zero moments as before for all the molecules except those of the nitrates, have moment values about 2.2,

[5] K. A. Jensen, Z. anorg. u. allgem. Chem., **225**, 97 (1935); ibid., **229**, 225 (1936).

[6] L. Pauling, op. cit., p. 209.

which are small enough to show them to be trans. The moment arises from the fact that the R_2S moment, 1.5, instead of acting in the direction of the bond to the platinum as does the R_3P moment, acts at an angle to it. Jensen[5] calculates the moment for free rotation of the two R_2S dipoles around the S—Pt—S axis as $\mu = 2^{1/2}\ 1.5 \sin 54° = 1.7$ and concludes that the higher observed value shows some preference for a cis orientation around the S—Pt—S axis. Change of valence angle or bond moment could, however, account for the small discrepancy, 0.5.

CHAPTER XIII

DIELECTRIC BEHAVIOR AND STRUCTURE OF AMINO ACIDS, PEPTIDES, AND PROTEINS

1. Introduction. The use of the dielectric increments and losses of solutions in the investigation of the structures of amino acids, peptides, and proteins has been well described by Edsall and Oncley.* The present chapter will, therefore, aim merely to summarize the subject, with the addition of more recent material, and correlate it with the earlier chapters of the present book. Because of the large polarities of the molecules of these substances, even those of lowest molecular weight have high melting points with decomposition and are virtually insoluble in nonpolar liquids. Dielectric investigations upon them are, therefore, confined largely to dilute aqueous and alcoholic solutions, principally the former.

2. Dielectric Increment, Dipole Moment, and Structure. The alkyl esters of the amino acids have the moderate-sized dipole moments[1] to be expected as the resultant of the polar groups which they contain (cf. Chaps. VIII and IX). Thus, the moment of glycine ethyl ester,[1] $H_2NCH_2COOC_2H_5$, is 2.1×10^{-18}. However, the molecules of the acids tend to form dipolar or zwitter ions, such as $H_3^+NCH_2COO^-$ from glycine. The very high polarities and consequent strong electric fields arising from these structures make approximate the calculation of their dipole moments from the dielectric constants of the aqueous solutions in which they usually have to be measured. For this reason, the dielectric increment δ is commonly used as a means of comparing the molecular polarities. δ is defined by the equation

$$\epsilon = \epsilon_1 + \delta c \qquad (2.1)$$

in which ϵ is the dielectric constant of the solution, ϵ_1 that of the pure solvent, and c the concentration of solute in moles per liter. For aqueous

---

* E. J. Cohn and J. T. Edsall, "Proteins, Amino Acids and Peptides," Reinhold, New York, 1943.

[1] J. Wyman, Jr., and T. L. McMeekin, *J. Am. Chem. Soc.*, **55**, 915 (1933).

solutions, it is sometimes defined[2] as the change of the dielectric constant of the solution per mole of solute per 1,000 g. of water. For the dilute solutions normally investigated, it makes very little difference whether the concentration of solute is expressed in moles per liter of solution or in moles per 1,000 g. or per liter of water. When the molecular weight of the solute is not known exactly, as in the case of the proteins, $\delta = \Delta\epsilon/c$ is replaced by a weight increment $\Delta\epsilon/g$, where g is the grams of solute per liter. $\Delta\epsilon/g = \delta/M$, where M is the molecular weight. The numerical values of the increments expressed in the two ways are quite different. For aqueous solutions of glycine at 25°, $\delta = \Delta\epsilon/c = 22.6$ and $\Delta\epsilon/g = 0.30$.

For the low concentrations, normally less than 0.01 mole fraction of solute, used in these measurements, δ has usually been found to be constant, that is, the dependence of ϵ upon concentration is linear, as it is up to somewhat higher concentrations in the solutions used for ordinary dipole moment determinations (see Chap. VII) and as are the values of ϵ' and ϵ'' measured at high frequencies.[3] With a few exceptions, such as solutions of urea, aqueous solutions of substances other than amino acids and proteins have negative values of δ, because water has so high a dielectric constant that replacement of part of it by a substance of lower dielectric constant naturally gives a lower dielectric constant to the mixture and, consequently, a negative value of δ. The dielectric increment for amino acids and proteins may vary considerably with hydrogen-ion concentration. Thus, Dunning and Shutt[4] found that δ for glycine was constant from pH = 4.5 to pH = 7.5, but fell sharply on both sides of this range, while Shutt[5] found that the weight increment for egg albumin went through two sharp minima, less than half of the maximum, in the range pH = 4.1 to 5.9.

Kirkwood[6] has used his equation (see Sec. I.15) to obtain an approximate relationship between the molecular dipole moment and the dielectric increment in the following manner. For a binary polar mixture,

$$\frac{\epsilon - 1}{3} v = \frac{3\epsilon}{2\epsilon + 1} (c_1 P_1 + c_2 P_2) \tag{2.2}$$

$$P_1 = \frac{4\pi N}{3} \left(\alpha_1 + \frac{\mu_1 \bar{\mu}_1}{3kT} \right) \tag{2.3}$$

$$P_2 = \frac{4\pi N}{3} \left(\alpha_2 + \frac{\mu_2 \bar{\mu}_2}{3kT} \right) \tag{2.4}$$

[2] W. P. Conner, R. P. Clarke, and C. P. Smyth, *J. Am. Chem. Soc.*, **64**, 1379 (1942).

[3] W. M. Heston, Jr., A. D. Franklin, E. J. Hennelly, and C. P. Smyth, *J. Am. Chem. Soc.*, **72**, 3443 (1950).

[4] W. J. Dunning and W. J. Shutt, *Trans. Faraday Soc.*, **34**, 479 (1938).

[5] W. J. Shutt, *Trans. Faraday Soc.*, **30**, 893 (1934).

[6] J. G. Kirkwood in E. J. Cohn and J. T. Edsall, "Proteins, Amino Acids and Peptides," Reinhold, New York, 1943, pp. 294–297.

where v is the mean molar volume, subscript 1 refers to the solvent, and subscript 2 to the solute. If ϵ is of the order of 100, as it is in aqueous solutions of amino acids, the factor $3\epsilon/(2\epsilon + 1)$ in Eq. (2.2) may be taken as approximately $\frac{3}{2}$. Equations (2.1) to (2.4) then give

$$\delta = \frac{9}{2{,}000}\left(P_2 - \frac{\phi_2 P_1}{v_1} + \frac{v}{v_1}\frac{P_1 - P_{01}}{c_2}\right) \qquad (2.5)$$

where v_1 is the molar volume and P_{01} the polarization of the pure solvent, and ϕ_2 is the apparent molar volume of the solute. At infinite dilution, Kirkwood writes

$$\delta_0 = \frac{9}{2{,}000}\left[P_{02} - \frac{\phi_{02}P_{01}}{v_1} + \left(\frac{\partial P_1}{\partial c_2}\right)_0\right] \qquad (2.6)$$

Setting $\tilde{\mu}_2 = (\mu_2 \bar{\mu}_2)^{\frac{1}{2}}$ and introducing numerical values, he obtains at 25° from the preceding equations

$$\tilde{\mu}_2 = 3.30\left\{\delta_0 + 0.0045\left[\frac{\phi_{02}P_{01}}{v_1} - \left(\frac{\partial P_1}{\partial c_2}\right)_0 - R_2\right]\right\}^{\frac{1}{2}} \qquad (2.7)$$

where R_2 is the molar refraction of the solute and $\tilde{\mu}_2$ is expressed in Debye units. Since the last three terms in the parentheses are not large, he writes, as a fair approximation,

$$\tilde{\mu} = 3.30\,\delta_0^{\frac{1}{2}} \qquad (2.8)$$

In view of the usual linear dependence of the dielectric constants of the very dilute solutions upon concentration, it is normally unnecessary to distinguish between δ_0 and δ.

From Eq. (2.8) and Wyman's value of δ_0 for glycine in water, 22.6, Kirkwood calculates $\tilde{\mu}_2 = 15.7$ and, from this and the value $\mu_2 = 15.0$ calculated from salting-in data, obtains $\bar{\mu}_2 = 16.4$. The difference 1.4 is the vector sum of all the moments resulting from the orientation of the adjacent water molecules by the two charges of the dipolar ion. Although this entire treatment is somewhat approximate, it is evident that $\tilde{\mu}_2$ is a fair approximation to the dipolar ion moment μ_2. The effective charge separation r, given by $\tilde{\mu}_2 = 4.80 \times 10^{-10}\,r$, is 3.27 A. in good agreement with the structural value 3.17 A. Kirkwood tabulates values of r calculated in this way for several dipolar ions and finds them to be very close to the mean distances between the NH_3^+ and COO^- groups calculated on the assumption of free rotation around the carbon-carbon bonds, the moment increasing with increase in the length of the chain between the two charged groups. Another example from Kirkwood's tabulation is ϵ-aminocaproic acid, the dipolar ion of which, $H_3^+N(CH_2)_5C\bar{O}O$, has $\tilde{\mu} = 29.0$ and $r = 6.04$ A. as compared to a separation 5.63 A. calculated on the basis of free rotation. This work gives an approximately quantitative justification for the earlier, more approximate conclusions of Wyman[7,8] along similar lines.

The satisfactory agreement of these somewhat roughly calculated dipole moments with the values estimated from the charge separations required by the geometrical structures contrasts with the discrepancies between the observed moment values and the much larger values calculated from the charge separations of the supposed resonating polar structures for many molecules (Sec. VIII.6).

The linear dependence of the dielectric increment of amino acids[9] upon the number of carbon atoms between the amino and carboxyl groups and of the peptides of glycine[2,9] upon the number of glycine units in the molecule follows from the proportionality $\delta \propto \mu^2 \propto r^2 \propto$ number of atoms in chain between charges (for free rotation). A detailed consideration[2] of the increments of the polypeptides indicates that their values are consistent with sufficient rotational freedom within the molecules to permit of an approximately random distribution of the orientations about the bonds. In the various di- and tripeptides investigated,[2] the principal effect of side chains upon the molecular moments appears to be the modification of the solvent effect.

Oncley[10] finds that, for many protein solutions, the linear dependence of $\Delta\epsilon$ upon g holds up to high concentrations, but, in some cases, especially when the increment is large, $\Delta\epsilon/g$ decreases somewhat with increasing concentration so that

$$\Delta\epsilon = Eg - Fg^2 \qquad (2.9)$$

where E and F are parameters characteristic of the individual proteins. Oncley lists[10] dipole moment values for sixteen protein molecules running from 170×10^{-18}, for myoglobin in water with $E = 0.15$ and a molecular weight of 17,000, to $1,400 \times 10^{-18}$ for edestin in 2 M glycine solution with $E = 0.7$ and a molecular weight of 310,000.

G. Jungner[11] used the ellipsoid method (Sec. VI.1) to measure very high increments for the polynucleotides and reported that the polyribose nucleotides showed considerably less polarity than the polyribodesose nucleotides, which had very large molar increments. I. Jungner[12] used the same apparatus in an improved form to measure aqueous solutions of sodium thymonucleate (DNA) produced by different methods and from different sources. A summary[12] of earlier investigations by other

[7] J. Wyman, Jr., and T. L. McMeekin, *J. Am. Chem. Soc.*, **55**, 908 (1933).

[8] J. Wyman, Jr., *J. Am. Chem. Soc.*, **56**, 536 (1934).

[9] J. Wyman, Jr., *Chem. Revs.*, **19**, 213 (1936).

[10] J. L. Oncley in E. J. Cohn and J. T. Edsall, "Proteins, Amino Acids and Peptides," Reinhold, New York, 1943, chap. 22.

[11] G. Jungner, *Acta Physiol. Scand.*, **10**, Suppl. 32 (1945).

[12] I. Jungner, *Acta Physiol. Scand.*, **20**, Suppl. 69 (1950).

methods indicated that the macromolecule of DNA was a thin, fairly rigid rod of polymerized mononucleotides with molecular weight varying from 200,000 to 3,000,000, a length varying from 2,000 A. for $M = 200,000$ to 5,230 A. for $M = 1,500,000$, a width lying within 13 to 22 A., and a ratio a/b of long to short axis of the particle, taken as an ellipsoid of revolution, increasing from 170 for $M = 430,000$ to 710 for $M = 3,000,000$. Jungner found the increment per gram per liter and, therefore, the dipole moment calculated from the molar increment to be proportional to the molecular weight, which could be varied by the use of different preparations and by depolymerization. At 20° the increment per gram was found to be about 40 for a molecular weight of 100,000, but it increased to about 235 at $M = 600,000$. For $M = 30,000$ the moment calculated according to Debye was 80, and, for $M = 600,000$, it was approximately $1,700 \times 10^{-18}$. However, the use of Eq. (2.8) to calculate the moment from these data gives the very high value $39,000 \times 10^{-18}$, instead of $1,700 \times 10^{-18}$. Allgén,[13] in a similar investigation of thymonucleohistone (DNHi), found linear dependence of the increment per gram and the dipole moment upon the degree of polymerization n, the number of mononucleotides in the molecule, which is, of course, proportional to the molecular weight. The specific dipole moment per mean mononucleotide, μ/n, varied for different specimens between 0.6 and 1.1×10^{-18}. The increment per gram amounts to about 80 for $n = 1,500$, which is smaller than that for DNA but much larger than those for most proteins, which usually do not exceed a maximum of 1.5 to 2.0. These investigators have used the Debye theory rather than the Onsager in their calculations and treat the dipole moment values as relative. As shown above, Eq. (2.8) would give much higher values for the moment.

In this discussion of dielectric increments the large values observed have been attributed to the partial orientation of large permanent dipoles in externally applied fields. However, Kirkwood and Shumaker[14] have proposed an alternative polarization mechanism for macromolecules containing loosely bound ions, such as protons, which, they suggest, may migrate within the molecule under the influence of the external field. Proteins containing a number of neutral and negatively charged basic sites, such as $-NH_2$ and $-COO^-$, to which protons may be bound, provide an opportunity for such a proton migration. Except in very acid solutions, the number of basic sites usually exceeds the average number of bound protons, giving opportunity for the existence of many possible configurations of the protons, differing little from one another in free energy. By a statistical method, Kirkwood and Shumaker show that fluctuations in charge and configuration of mobile protons in the mole-

[13] L. Allgén, *Acta Physiol. Scand.*, **22**, Suppl. 76 (1950).
[14] J. G. Kirkwood and J. B. Shumaker, *Proc. Nat. Acad. Sci., U.S.*, **38**, 855 (1952).

cule can give rise to a nonvanishing mean square dipole moment $\Delta\mu^2$, even if the mean permanent moment is zero. The results of their calculations for four protein molecules in aqueous solution are shown in Table 2.1 for comparison with the moment values calculated from the observed increments. $\Delta\mu$ is calculated for the case of a spherical molecule and for that of an ellipsoidal molecule. The effect of pH on the calculated $\Delta\mu$ of ovalbumin is shown by Kirkwood's calculation 449 for $\Delta\mu$ at a pH of 2 decreasing to 5 at a pH of 10. Table 2.1 shows that the

TABLE 2.1. DIPOLE MOMENT FLUCTUATIONS (WITHOUT ELECTROSTATIC INTERACTION)

Molecule	M	μ_{obs}	$\Delta\mu$	
			Sphere	Ellipsoid
β-Lactoglobulin	37,000	700	170	270
Ovalbumin	46,000	260	320	440
Horse hemoglobin	68,000	480	390	620
Human serum albumin	69,000	700 (380)	430	680

moments observed for three of the four protein molecules can be accounted for entirely in terms of proton migration. Only the moment of β-lactoglobulin exceeds the calculated $\Delta\mu$ by an amount large enough to require the existence of a permanent moment. Kirkwood and Shumaker conclude that the dipole moment fluctuation arising from the mobile proton distribution makes a contribution to the dielectric increment equivalent to that of a large permanent moment and that, while many protein molecules possess large permanent moments, the structural interpretation of the dielectric increments should be drastically revised.

On this basis, for example, one may well question the conclusion of Kurilenko and Tsiperovich[15] that dehydration of the egg albumin molecule caused by thermal denaturation reduces the dipole moment because of increased symmetry of the molecule.

3. Dielectric Loss and Molecular Size and Shape. Protein molecules are so large that the dispersion regions, which are characteristic of them in solution, occur at much lower frequencies than those of the solvents and can, therefore, be precisely established by a much larger number of points than is experimentally feasible at frequencies in and near the microwave region. Their behavior is represented by the dispersion equa-

[15] O. D. Kurilenko and A. S. Tsiperovich, *Ukrain. Khim. Zhur.*, **16**, 264 (1950); *Chem. Abst.*, **46**, 2098b (1952).

tions II(2.22) and (2.23), but Oncley[1,2] has found it convenient to use conductance instead of dielectric loss in describing the dispersion and in calculating molecular dimensions from the measured quantity. Equations (2.23), (2.30), (6.15), and (6.19) of Chap. II, with the replacement of k' by $k - k_0$ and of k_∞ by $k_\infty - k_0$, may be used to obtain

$$k = k_0 + \frac{(k_\infty - k_0)\omega^2\tau^2}{1 + \omega^2\tau^2} = k_\infty - \frac{k_\infty - k_0}{1 + (f/f_m)^2} = k_0 + \frac{(k_\infty - k_0)(f/f_m)^2}{1 + (f/f_m)^2}$$

$$(3.1)$$

in which k_0 is the low frequency or d.c. conductance and k is the observed specific conductance, equal to k_0 at low frequencies. For consistency with Chap. II, k, f, and f_m are used instead of Oncley's κ, ν, and ν_c. For each component of a homogeneous liquid mixture a conductance increment Δk corresponds to the change $k_\infty - k_0$ [Eq. (3.1)] in its dispersion region around f_m. For the mixture of components 1, 2, . . . , k may be written[1]

$$k = k_\infty - \frac{\Delta k_1}{1 + (f/f_1)^2} - \frac{\Delta k_2}{1 + (f/f_2)^2} - \cdots = k_0 + \frac{\Delta k_1(f/f_1)^2}{1 + (f/f_1)^2}$$
$$+ \frac{\Delta k_2(f/f_2)^2}{1 + (f/f_2)^2} + \cdots \quad (3.2)$$

where Δk_i and f_i are the conductance increment and critical frequency of the ith dispersion region. An analogous expression may be written for the dielectric constant

$$\epsilon' = \epsilon_\infty + \frac{\Delta \epsilon_1}{1 + (f/f_1)^2} + \frac{\Delta \epsilon_2}{1 + (f/f_2)^2} + \cdots \quad (3.3)$$

It follows from Eq. II(6.19) that

$$\Delta k_i = \frac{\Delta \epsilon_i f_i}{1.80} \quad (3.4)$$

where the conductance is expressed in ohms^{-1} cm.$^{-1}$ and the critical frequency in megacycles. The relaxation time corresponding to the ith dispersion region is, of course,

$$\tau_i = \frac{1}{2\pi f_i} \quad (3.5)$$

Equation II(5.1) has shown how the behavior of an ellipsoidal molecule may be represented in terms of three relaxation times. Oncley[1,2] has treated the protein molecules as ellipsoids of revolution having a relaxation time τ_a and a critical frequency f_a for orientation involving

---

[1] J. L. Oncley, in E. J. Cohn and J. T. Edsall, "Proteins, Amino Acids and Peptides," Reinhold, New York, 1943, Chap. 22.

[2] J. L. Oncley, J. D. Ferry, and J. Shack, *Ann. N.Y. Acad. Sci.*, **40**, 371 (1940).

rotation of the a axis around the b, and τ_b and f_b for orientation of the b axis around the a. From the equations of Perrin,[3] he has obtained τ_a and τ_b in terms of the ratio a/b of the semiaxes of the ellipsoid and the relaxation time τ_0 of a sphere of the same volume. The volume of the ellipsoid and of the sphere of equal volume is

$$V = \frac{4\pi ab^2}{3} \tag{3.6}$$

Equation II(2.49) then gives

$$V = \frac{RT\tau_0}{3\eta} = \frac{4\pi ab^2}{3} \tag{3.7}$$

and

$$f_0 = \frac{1}{2\pi\tau_0} = \frac{kT}{8\pi^2 ab^2 \eta} \tag{3.8}$$

Oncley takes $\Delta\epsilon_t$ as the sum of $\Delta\epsilon_a$ and $\Delta\epsilon_b$, expresses Eq. (3.3) in terms of a/b, f_0, $\Delta\epsilon_t$, and $\Delta\epsilon_a/\Delta\epsilon_b$, constructs a series of curves of $(\epsilon' - \epsilon_\infty)/\Delta\epsilon_t$ against f/f_0 for various values of asymmetry, a/b, and increment ratio, $\Delta\epsilon_a/\Delta\epsilon_b$, and, by comparison of the experimental curves with the calculated, evaluates a/b, $\Delta\epsilon_a/\Delta\epsilon_b$, and f_0.

The critical frequencies for the solutions of these large molecules tend to vary inversely as the viscosity of the medium, as required by Eq. (3.8). Thus, at 25°, solutions of insulin in 80, 90, and 100 per cent propylene glycol, with viscosities relative to water of 17.0, 28.0, and 48.0, show[1] critical frequencies of 0.59, 0.31, and 0.19 megacycles, in fairly close conformity with Eq. (3.8). Similarly, β-lactoglobulin in aqueous $M/2$ glycine solution of relative viscosity 1.08 at 25° shows the two critical frequencies 0.9 and 2.6 megacycles, while, at 0° with relative viscosity 2.12 and T lowered from 298° to 273°K., the critical frequencies are 0.44 and 1.25. a/b is calculated as 4 for this molecule.[1] In measurements on zein solutions Oncley, Jensen, and Gross[4] have followed the common practice of obtaining f_m as the "midpoint frequency," the frequency at which ϵ' has undergone half the total decrease involved in the dispersion region. They find that much more constant results are obtained if these values of f_m are multiplied by the relative viscosities of the solutions. This is further specific evidence of the approximate proportionality of the relaxation time to the viscosity, which is implicit in the adequacy of the agreement of the indications of the dielectric results for proteins with those of other methods of investigation.

In the investigations by G. Jungner, I. Jungner, and Allgén[5,6] discussed

[3] E. J. Cohn and J. T. Edsall, "Proteins, Amino Acids and Peptides," Reinhold, New York, 1943, chap. 21.

[4] J. L. Oncley, C. C. Jensen, and P. M. Gross, Jr., *J. Phys. & Colloid Chem.*, **53**, 162 (1949).

[5] See footnotes 11 to 13, Sec. 2.

[6] G. Jungner, I. Jungner, and L. G. Allgén, *Nature*, **163**, 849 (1949).

in Sec. 2, dispersion measurements indicated that the long, rodlike DNA molecule oriented by rotation only around its long axis and that this was probably true of the DNHi molecule also.   The approximate moments calculated were, therefore, the components perpendicular to the long axes. For both substances, the critical frequency increased with increasing concentration even at the very low concentrations employed, 0.0125 to 0.1 per cent and 0.1 to 0.4 per cent.   This was regarded[5] as connected with the formation in more concentrated solutions of a structure in which the larger aggregates were impeded in their orientation, the polarization becoming more dependent on smaller and more easily movable parts.

In general, the dielectric relaxation times found for the proteins are of just the order of magnitude to be expected from the values of molecular weight, asymmetry, and hydration determined by other methods.   The agreement between the various methods for determining axial ratio and hydration indicates that the protein molecules rotate as rigid units, which can be represented as ellipsoids of revolution.

An approximate idea of the electrical symmetry of the molecules can be gained by multiplying the value of the diameter R which the molecule would have if it were spherical by the charge E necessary to make $ER = \mu$.   The values of E thus obtained are much smaller than half of the total sum $2E_{max}$ of the cationic and anionic charges in the molecule, which would give $E_{max}R$ as the maximum possible moment for the value. E/E_{max} thus obtained for serum albumin is about 0.02, for hemoglobin 0.03, and for edestin 0.01.   The small values estimated for this ratio are taken by Oncley[1] as evidence of a fairly high electrical symmetry of the molecules.   According to the calculation of Kirkwood and Shumaker[7] of the large contribution made by proton migration to the apparent measured moment, the electrical symmetry is even higher in most molecules and virtually complete in some.

The determination of the relaxation time of an ellipsoidal molecule by the diffusion of mobile protons on its surface as well as by molecular rotation may change considerably the structural interpretation of dispersion data.   It would seem, offhand, a simple matter to distinguish between the two mechanisms.   However, Kirkwood and Shumaker[7] estimate that the process of distribution of protons possessing a translatory diffusion constant D on the surface of a sphere of radius b should have a relaxation time of the order of magnitude of b^2/D.   With $b = 30$ A., the radius of a sphere equal in volume to the serum albumin molecule, and with $D = 10^{-5}$ cm.² per sec., they obtain a relaxation time of the order of 10^{-8} sec., which is of the order observed for typical proteins.   Evidently, it is difficult to distinguish between the effects of fluctuations in proton configuration and rotational orientation of the entire molecule.

[7] J. G. Kirkwood and J. B. Shumaker, *Proc. Nat. Acad. Sci. U.S.*, **38**, 855 (1952).

Dielectric measurements[8,9] upon protein solutions at 1.26, 3.18, and 9.22 cm. wavelength give a single relaxation time very close to that of pure water. As would be expected, the frequencies are too high to permit dipole orientation of the protein molecules. Measurements upon solutions of horse methemoglobin, bovine-serum albumin, egg albumin, β-lactoglobulin, lysozyme, and gelatin are used[9] to estimate the amount of bound water (see Sec. III.6) carried through the solution with the protein as a function of axial ratio, the molecules being treated as spheroids. By combination of the hydration estimates with other data, it is concluded that the molecules of β-lactoglobulin and egg albumin approximate to prolate rather than oblate spheroids and that a large proportion of the charged groups in horse methemoglobin protrude from the surface of the molecule.

Oncley[1] has summarized the relaxation times of nineteen amino acids and peptides and compared them with values calculated by means of Eq. (3.7) for spheres having volumes equal to those of the molecules as given by their partial molal volumes corrected for electrostriction. The dielectric relaxation times for glycine and α-alanine are somewhat smaller than the values calculated from the volume by means of Eq. (3.7), but, as the molecules increase in size, the dielectric relaxation times become increasingly larger than the values calculated from molecular volume, but rarely exceed them by more than 50 per cent. The lower values of the dielectric relaxation times for glycine and alanine were attributed by Conner and Smyth[10] to the inner or microscopic viscosity being lower than the observed or macroscopic viscosity. (cf. Sec. IV. 4.) The larger dielectric relaxation times of the peptides were used by them to calculate the axial ratio a/b of the molecular ellipsoids of revolution, the values increasing from 1.1 for leucylglycine and 1.3 for diglycine to 2.1 for pentaglycine. The values of a/b for di-, tri-, tetra-, and pentaglycine showed an exact linear dependence upon the square root of n, the number of glycine residues, which is what one would observe if the molecules were rigid but randomly distributed in all possible configurations resulting from potential minima symmetrically distributed about the bonds of the backbone chain. The accuracy of the values is not sufficient to exclude the possibility of a linear increase with the first power of the chain length, but the approximately random distribution of the orientations around the bonds is also indicated by the dielectric-constant increments (Sec. 2). The values of a/b, 1.58, 1.57, and 1.57 for triglycine, alanyldiglycine, and leucyldiglycine, respectively, indicate[10] that these

[8] G. H. Haggis, T. J. Buchanan, and J. B. Hasted, *Nature*, **167**, 607 (1951).

[9] T. J. Buchanan, G. H. Haggis, J. B. Hasted, and B. G. Robinson, *Proc. Roy. Soc. (London)*, **213**, 379 (1952).

[10] W. P. Conner and C. P. Smyth, *J. Am. Chem. Soc.*, **64**, 1870 (1942).

three molecules have approximately the same shapes, but alanylleucyl-glycine, with $a/b = 1.33$, appears to be somewhat more nearly spherical since it has the large isobutyl group at the middle of the chain.

It is evident that the measurement of the dielectric constant and loss of protein solutions provides useful information concerning molecular size and shape, which can be used most effectively in conjunction with evidence obtained by other methods. It is not surprising that the dielectric relaxation times of the large protein molecules show approximately the theoretical proportionality to the viscosity when the macroscopic viscosity is used, because the solvent molecules surrounding them are so small in comparison as to give an approximation to the homogeneous fluid postulated in the theory. In view of the low values of the volumes calculated from the critical wavelengths of some twenty-seven organic halide molecules (see Sec. IV.4) and the almost complete breakdown of the relationship between the relaxation times of small molecules and the viscosity when the latter is high, it is somewhat surprising that the discrepancies in the relaxation times of the amino acids and peptides are so small.

CHAPTER XIV

ELECTRONIC AND ATOMIC POLARIZATION

1. Deformation Polarization. The previous chapters of this book have been concerned, for the most part, with the nature of the permanent electrical asymmetry of molecules and its relation to molecular structure and dielectric behavior. The present chapter is concerned primarily with the relations of the asymmetry induced by an electric field to the composition and structure of the molecules. (For additional material see the references.[1-3]) The experimental determination of refractive index, generally with a refractometer, has been described in many manuals of laboratory techniques. An authoritative account has been given by Bauer and Fajans.[2] The total polarization has been given in Eq. I(8.2) as

$$P = P_E + P_A + P_M$$

where $P_E + P_A$ is the so-called deformation or distortion polarization. An approximate plot of P against the logarithm of the frequency in Fig. 8.1, Chap. I, illustrates the fact that the distortion polarization is often small in comparison with the orientation polarization P_M, and the atomic polarization P_A is generally small in comparison with the electronic polarization P_E. Equations I(5.12) and I(9.2) show that

$$P_E + P_A = \frac{4\pi N}{3} \alpha_0 = \frac{n^2 - 1}{n^2 + 2} \frac{M}{d} = R \tag{1.1}$$

which is the Lorentz-Lorenz equation. It may be written

$$\frac{n^2 - 1}{n^2 + 2} = \frac{4\pi}{3} \sum_k N_k \alpha_k \tag{1.2}$$

[1] C. P. Smyth, "Dielectric Constant and Molecular Structure," Reinhold, New York, 1931, chap. VIII.

[2] N. Bauer and K. Fajans, "Refractometry," in "Physical Methods of Organic Chemistry" (A. Weissberger editor), Interscience, New York, 2d ed., 1949, vol. I, pt. II, chap. XX.

[3] C. J. F. Böttcher, "Theory of Electric Polarisation," Elsevier, Houston, 1952, chap. VIII.

where N_k is the number of molecules per cubic centimeter of polarizability α_k. For gases at ordinary pressures, n differs so little from 1 that Eq. (1.1) may be written

$$(n^2 - 1)\, \frac{M}{d} = 4\pi N \alpha_0 \tag{1.3}$$

and Eq. (1.2) may be written

$$n^2 - 1 = 4\pi \sum_k N_k \alpha_k \tag{1.4}$$

or

$$n - 1 = 2\pi \sum_k N_k \alpha_k \tag{1.5}$$

$(n^2 - 1)/d$ in Eq. (1.3) was used by Laplace[4] for the specific refraction, as was $(n - 1)/d$ by Gladstone and Dale.[5] Eykman[6] improved slightly on the constancy of the Lorentz-Lorenz expression by a purely empirical alteration to the denominator to make $(n^2 - 1)/(n^2 + 0.4)d$ the specific refraction. Since this is not completely constant and is without theoretical foundation, the Lorentz-Lorenz expression is generally employed.

The frequency dependence of the polarizability is given by classical dispersion theory[3,7] in terms of charged harmonic oscillators as

$$\alpha_0 = \frac{e^2}{4\pi^2 m} \sum_k \frac{f_k}{\nu_k^2 - \nu^2} \tag{1.6}$$

where e and m are the charge and mass of the oscillators, usually electrons, f_k is called[3] the strength of the oscillator, ν_k is its characteristic vibration frequency corresponding to an absorption wavelength, and ν is the frequency of the radiation. Substitution in Eq. (1.1) gives

$$R = \frac{Ne^2}{3\pi m} \sum_k \frac{f_k}{\nu_k^2 - \nu^2} \tag{1.7}$$

and in Eq. (1.4)

$$n^2 - 1 = \frac{N_1 e^2}{\pi m} \sum_k \frac{f_k}{\nu_k^2 - \nu^2} \tag{1.8}$$

These equations based on the model of elastically bound electrons represent qualitatively and sometimes quantitatively the experimentally

[4] P. S. Laplace, "Traité de mécanique céleste," t. IV, libr. X, p. 32, 1821.

[5] J. H. Gladstone and J. Dale, *Phil. Trans.*, **153**, 317 (1863).

[6] J. F. Eykman, *Rec. trav. chim.*, **14**, 185 (1895); "Recherches réfractométriques," Haarlem, 1919.

[7] J. H. Van Vleck, "Theory of Electric and Magnetic Susceptibilities," Oxford, London, 1932, chap. III.

observed dispersion curves.[3]   Equation (1.8) may be written

$$n^2 = 1 + \sum_k \frac{A_k}{\nu_k^2 - \nu^2} \tag{1.9}$$

where

$$A_k = \frac{N_1 e^2 f_k}{\pi m} \tag{1.10}$$

Since $\nu = c/\lambda$, Eq. (1.9) may be written

$$n^2 = 1 + \sum_k \frac{A_k \lambda_k^2}{c^2(1 - \lambda_k^2/\lambda^2)} \tag{1.11}$$

which may be developed in a series[3]

$$n^2 = 1 + \sum_k \frac{A_k \lambda_k^2}{c^2}\left(1 + \frac{\lambda_k^2}{\lambda^2} + \frac{\lambda_k^4}{\lambda^4} + \frac{\lambda_k^6}{\lambda^6} + \cdots\right) \tag{1.12}$$

leading to

$$n = a + \frac{b}{\lambda^2} + \frac{c}{\lambda^4} + \frac{d}{\lambda^6} + \cdots \tag{1.13}$$

where a, b, c, etc., are constants, c not being the velocity of light, which occurs in Eqs. (1.11) and (1.12).   This is the Cauchy dispersion equation.   At infinite wavelength ($\lambda = \infty$),

$$n = a = n_\infty$$

n_∞ may be calculated with fair accuracy by using only the first term with λ in Eq. (1.13), that is, by writing

$$n_\infty = n - \frac{b}{\lambda^2} \tag{1.14}$$

and using the values of n_1 at λ_1 and n_2 at λ_2, so that

$$n_\infty = \frac{\lambda_1^2 n_1 - \lambda_2^2 n_2}{\lambda_1^2 - \lambda_2^2} \tag{1.15}$$

Because the approximation made in obtaining Eq. (1.4) is justified only for gases, Eq. (1.15) is valid only for gases, but it has often been used for liquids and solids also.[3]

At frequencies remote from the electronic absorption frequencies ν_k, one characteristic frequency ν_0, or wavelength λ_0, may be introduced, so that Eq. (1.7) may be written

$$R = \frac{R_\infty}{1 - (\nu/\nu_0)^2} \tag{1.16}$$

This gives

$$R_\infty = R(1 - \lambda_0^2/\lambda^2) \tag{1.17}$$

which has been given as Eq. I(8.1).

This equation has been used[8] on many liquids, giving a value of R_∞ calculated from data at one pair of wavelengths rarely different by more than 0.1 per cent from the value calculated from data at another pair of wavelengths in the visible region.

A more accurate extrapolation is obtained by using an equation with three constants. For $\lambda = \infty$, that is, $\nu = 0$, Eq. (1.9) becomes

$$n_\infty{}^2 = 1 + \sum_k \frac{A_k}{\nu_k{}^2} \tag{1.18}$$

Combination of Eqs. (1.9) and (1.18) gives

$$n^2 = n_\infty{}^2 + \sum_k \frac{B_k}{\lambda^2 - \lambda_k{}^2} \tag{1.19}$$

where
$$B_k = \frac{A_k \lambda_k{}^4}{c^2} \tag{1.20}$$

Equation (1.19), which is generally called the Sellmeyer dispersion formula, and the Cauchy formula [Eq. (1.13)] with three terms have been found by Böttcher[9] to give deviations not larger than five units in the fifth decimal place from the observed refractive index for some substances and deviations of some units in the fourth place for other substances. With the three-constants formulas, the calculated values of n_∞ show differences in the fourth decimal place and, with the two-constants formulas, in the third place.[9] The two-constants formula is still quite adequate for use in consideration of dipole moment and atomic polarization.

2. Polarization of Ionic Solids and Electrolytes. The polarization of ionic solids, which consists of $P_E + P_A$, has been discussed in Sec. V.3, while that of electrolytes, which, for the most part, consists of P_E, has been discussed in some detail by Smyth[1] and Böttcher,[2] and by Fajans and his co-workers,[3] who have made important contributions to the subject. A table[1] of ionic refractions (Table 2.1) for the sodium D line calculated by approximate methods shows the decrease of the refraction of a given group of electrons with increasing nuclear charge and consequent increase in binding force, and the increase with increasing distance from the nucleus to be expected from Eq. I(4.4). As is to be expected, the trend of the refraction parallels that of the radius and volume.

[8] C. P. Smyth, *J. Am. Chem. Soc.*, **46**, 2151 (1924).

[9] Böttcher, *loc. cit.*

[1] C. P. Smyth, "Dielectric Constant and Molecular Structure," Reinhold, New York, 1931, chap. VIII.

[2] Böttcher, *loc. cit.*

[3] N. Bauer and K. Fajans, Refractometry, in "Physical Methods of Organic Chemistry" (A. Weissberger editor), Interscience, New York, 2d ed., 1949, vol. I, pt. II, chap. XX.

TABLE 2.1. IONIC REFRACTIONS, R_D (cc.)

		He 0.50	Li^+ 0.20	Be^{++} 0.09		B^{3+} 0.05	C^{4+} 0.03
$O^=$ 7	F^- 2.5	Ne 1.00	Na^+ 0.50	Mg^{++} 0.29		Al^{3+} 0.17	Si^{4+} 0.1
$S^=$ 15	Cl^- 8.7	A 4.20	K^+ 2.2	Ca^{++} 1.35	Zn^{++} 0.3	Sc^{3+} 1.0	Ti^{4+} 0.7
$Se^=$ 16.3	Br^- 12.2	Kr 6.37	Rb^+ 3.6	Sr^{++} 2.3	Cd^{++} 2.4	Y^{3+} 2.6	Zr^{4+} 2.0
$Te^=$ 24.4	I^- 18.5	Xe 10.42	Cs^+ 6.3	Ba^{++} 4.3	Hg 5.0	La^{3+} 4.0	Ce^{4+} 3.1

With the exception of the directly measured molar refractions for the rare gases, these values must be regarded as very approximate. Indeed, Böttcher[4] concluded that the apparent dependence of the ionic refractions upon concentration observed by Fajans and his coworkers was caused by the limited validity of the Lorentz-Lorenz expression and could be quantitatively explained by a corrected equation.

The two electrons of the helium atom give a refraction of 0.50, while the two electrons held by six positive charges in the C^{4+} ion give a refraction of only 0.03. The two inner electrons in the $O^=$ ion must contribute even less to the refraction of the ion which may, therefore, be regarded as due to the eight outer electrons. Similarly, the refraction of the Si^{4+} ion, 0.1, is so small that the contribution of this electron group to the refraction of the $S^=$ ion may be disregarded and the refraction attributed entirely to the outer eight electrons. Although, in the larger ions, the refraction of the inner electrons must evidently be larger than for those which have been considered, it must still be so small in comparison with that of the outer electrons that no serious error can arise from attributing the refraction wholly to the latter.

3. Refraction of Electron Groups. After the development of the Lorentz-Lorenz[1,2] expression, refraction was studied as a constitutive property in a largely empirical fashion.[3] The molar refraction of a compound was regarded as the sum of the refractions of the constituent atoms, a gram-atomic weight of an element in combination having associated with it a number called the atomic refraction, which was its con-

[4] C. J. F. Böttcher, Rec. trav. chim., 65, 39 (1946).

[1] H. A. Lorentz, Ann. Physik, 9, 641 (1880).

[2] L. V. Lorenz, Ann. Physik, 11, 70 (1880).

[3] For a summary of many of these studies, see F. Eisenlohr, "Spektrochemie Organischer Verbindungen," Ferd. Enke Verlag, Stuttgart, 1912.

tribution to the molar refraction of the compound. Double bonds and triple bonds had certain refractions assigned to them, and a conjugated system was recognized as giving rise to an increase, or "exaltation," of refraction. The atomic refractions of certain elements had values which depended upon the manner in which the element was bonded. Thus, different values were assigned to ethereal oxygen, carbonyl oxygen, and hydroxyl oxygen. However, once these differences were taken into account, the atomic refractions were surprisingly constant and could be used to calculate the molar refractions of most compounds with considerable accuracy.

Since the ionic refractions in Table 2.1 show that except in the case of large ions only the outermost electrons undergo sufficient displacement in the field of the electromagnetic wave to contribute appreciably to the polarization, it is possible to associate an observed refraction with certain small groups of electrons. The contributions of such electron groups to the refraction may be calculated[4] by means of simple equations like those used by von Steiger[5] to calculate bond refractions from atomic refractions, of which the following are given as examples:

$$(C\!-\!H) = \tfrac{1}{4}C + H \qquad (C\!-\!C) = \tfrac{1}{2}C$$
$$(C\!=\!C) = C + 1^= \qquad (C\!\equiv\!C) = \tfrac{3}{4}C + 1^{\equiv}$$

$$\overset{C}{\underset{H}{\diagdown}}\overset{..}{\underset{..}{O}}\diagup = \tfrac{1}{4}C + H + O' \qquad \overset{C}{\underset{C}{\diagdown}}\overset{..}{\underset{..}{O}}\diagup = \tfrac{1}{2}C + O< \qquad C\!=\!\overset{..}{\underset{..}{O}} = \tfrac{1}{2}C + O''$$

$$C\!-\!\overset{..}{\underset{..}{X}}: = \tfrac{1}{4}C + X \qquad Si\!-\!\overset{..}{\underset{..}{Cl}}: = \tfrac{1}{4}SiCl_4 \qquad S\!-\!\overset{..}{\underset{..}{F}}: = \tfrac{1}{6}SF_6$$

In these equations, each line joining the atoms represents a bonding electron pair, and each dot a displaceable electron which does not enter into a bond. The refraction in each case is supposed to arise only from the electrons thus indicated. H, C, O', O <, O'', X, $SiCl_4$, and SF_6 represent, respectively, the atomic or molecular refractions of hydrogen, carbon, hydroxyl oxygen, ethereal oxygen, carbonyl oxygen, a halogen, silicon tetrachloride, and sulfur hexafluoride, and $1^=$ and $1^{\equiv}$ are the refractions assigned to the double and the triple bond. The results calculated[4,6] in this manner are given in Table 3.1. A number of values in the original table[4] have been slightly revised, and several new values have been added, in particular, the refractions of several groups bonded to a silicon atom taken or calculated from the work of Warrick.[7]

[4] C. P. Smyth, *Phil. Mag.*, **50**, 361 (1925).
[5] A. L. von Steiger, *Ber. deut. chem. Ges.*, **54**, 1381 (1921).
[6] See footnote 1, Sec. 1.
[7] E. L. Warrick, *J. Am. Chem. Soc.*, **68**, 2455 (1946).

TABLE 3.1. REFRACTIONS OF ELECTRON GROUPS FOR D LINE (cc.)

H—H 2.08	Si—H 3.20	C—Zn 4.7	C—Hg 6.9
C—H 1.70	C—Si$_{al}$ 2.50	C—Sn 4.0	C—Pb 5.0
C—C 1.21	C—Si$_{ar}$ 2.56		
C=C 4.15	Si—Si 5.65		
C≡C 6.03			

$\overset{\text{H}}{\underset{\text{H}}{\diagdown}}$ H—N: 5.63

$\overset{\text{C}}{\underset{\text{H}}{\diagdown}}$ H—N: 5.13

$\overset{\text{C}}{\underset{\text{H}}{\diagdown}}$ C—N: 4.81

$\overset{\text{C}}{\underset{\text{H}}{\diagdown}}$ C—N: 4.65

$\overset{\text{H}}{\underset{\text{H}}{\diagdown}}$ Ö 3.76

$\overset{\text{C}}{\underset{\text{H}}{\diagdown}}$ Ö 3.23

$\overset{\text{C}}{\underset{\text{C}}{\diagdown}}$ Ö 2.85

$\overset{\text{B}}{\underset{\text{C}}{\diagdown}}$ Ö 3.39

C=Ö 3.42

$\overset{\text{Si}}{\underset{\text{H}}{\diagdown}}$ Ö 4

$\overset{\text{Si}}{\underset{\text{C}}{\diagdown}}$ Ö 3.26

$\overset{\text{Si}}{\underset{\text{Si}}{\diagdown}}$ Ö 3.50

$\overset{\text{H}}{\underset{\text{H}}{\diagdown}}$ H—P: 11.9

$\overset{\text{C}}{\underset{\text{C}}{\diagdown}}$ C—P: 11.28

$\overset{\text{H}}{\underset{\text{H}}{\diagdown}}$ S 9.57

$\overset{\text{C}}{\underset{\text{H}}{\diagdown}}$ S 9.40

$\overset{\text{C}}{\underset{\text{C}}{\diagdown}}$ S 9.18

$\overset{\text{Si}}{\underset{\text{Si}}{\diagdown}}$ S 12.50

C=S 10.61

$\overset{\text{C}}{\underset{\text{H}}{\diagdown}}$ Se 12.34

$\overset{\text{C}}{\underset{\text{C}}{\diagdown}}$ Se 11.96

$\overset{\text{C}}{\underset{\text{C}}{\diagdown}}$ Te 17.45

S—F: 1.95	Se—F: 2.23	Te—F: 2.47	
B—Cl: 6.99		B—Br: 9.98	
C—F: 1.83	C—Cl: 6.57	C—Br: 9.47	C—I: 14.51
Si—F: 1.50	Si—Cl: 7.18	Si—Br: 10.20	
	Ti—Cl: 9.5		
	Sn—Cl: 8.8		

When the refractions of these electron groups are used to calculate molar refractions, the discrepancies between observed and calculated values are of the order of 0.1 cc. As the group refractions are calculated, for the most part, from atomic refraction values, they give the same accuracy as the latter in calculating molar refractions.

Denbigh[8] calculated bond refraction values from individual molar refractions, obtaining values which, for the most part, differed only very slightly from the electron-group refractions in Table 3.1. Molar refractions calculated as the sum of these bond refractions differed from the observed usually by 0 to 1 per cent. However, the calculated value[8] of dipropargyl was 26.69 as compared to the observed value 25.75, a discrepancy of 3.7 per cent. The use of the electron group values in Table 3.1, in which the value for C≡C is 0.37 lower than Denbigh's value, gives 25.89, a discrepancy of only 0.5 per cent. Many of the values in Table 3.1 are for an electron-pair bond, but it would seem to be rather misleading, however convenient, to call an electron-group refraction, such as that of C—Cl:, a bond refraction, as has been done by some investigators.[8] In this case more than three quarters of the refraction arises from the nonbonding electrons.

The values in Table 3.1 show that the electrons binding two carbon atoms are more tightly held than those binding a carbon and a hydrogen atom, which, in turn, are more tightly held than the two electrons in the hydrogen molecule. It is apparent that the hydrogen exerts less binding force on the electrons of the C—H bond than does the carbon nucleus with its larger charge on those of the C—C bond. Although the silicon nucleus has a larger charge than the carbon, its greater distance from the electrons in the C—Si bond causes it to exert a smaller force upon them so that they are more loosely held than the electrons in the C—H bond. The looser binding of the π electrons in the double and triple bonds is evident. Denbigh[8] finds an almost linear increase in bond refraction with bond order for the carbon-carbon bonds.

The refraction for the electron pair of the C—Zn bond calculated from the refractions of zinc methyl and zinc ethyl probably contains a small contribution from the electrons underlying the bonding pairs, as Table 2.1 shows a refraction of 0.3 for the Zn^{++} ion, and the same is presumably true to a greater extent of the values for the C—Hg, C—Sn, and C—Pb bonds. The usual decrease in electron constraint with increase in atomic size is shown by these values. The values for the Ti—Cl: and Sn—Cl: groups presumably contain small contributions from the underlying electron shells in the titanium and tin atoms, but contributions of this character should be negligible in the other groups.

In the values for the nitrogen electron group, calculated from data on ammonia and the amines, it is apparent that an attached carbon atom causes greater electron constraint than a hydrogen, the constraint increas-

ing from the
$$\begin{matrix} H \\[-2pt] \diagdown \\[-6pt] H-N: \\[-6pt] \diagup \\[-2pt] H \end{matrix}$$
to the
$$\begin{matrix} C \\[-2pt] \diagdown \\[-6pt] C-N: \\[-6pt] \diagup \\[-2pt] C \end{matrix}$$
group. The difference in effect is less

marked in the larger phosphorus electron group. Similarly, the carbon atom produces stronger constraint than the hydrogen when attached to an electron group of the oxygen family, but the difference in effect decreases as the volume of the group increases, with accompanying decrease in the electron constraint. When a carbon atom attached to

the group
$$\begin{matrix} C \\[-2pt] \diagdown \\[-6pt] \ddot{O} \\[-6pt] \diagup \\[-2pt] C \end{matrix}$$
is replaced by the larger atom of silicon, the electron con-

straint is decreased, but it is interesting that the
$$\begin{matrix} Si \\[-2pt] \diagdown \\[-6pt] \ddot{O} \\[-6pt] \diagup \\[-2pt] Si \end{matrix}$$
refraction is still

only half the roughly estimated value 7 for the oxide ion in Table 2.1. It has been suggested that the silicon-oxygen bonds in the silicones may be ionic, but the oxygen refraction here is lower than in the orthophosphate ion, in which it is covalently bound to the central phosphorus atom.

The
$$\begin{matrix} Si \\[-2pt] \diagdown \\[-6pt] \ddot{S} \\[-6pt] \diagup \\[-2pt] Si \end{matrix}$$
refraction 12.50 is relatively closer to the value 15 estimated

for the sulfide ion in Table 2.1. When a carbon atom is replaced by a boron atom, with its smaller nuclear charge, a considerable decrease in the electron constraints is apparent, and the weaker forces exerted by the boron nucleus are evident again in the higher values for the refractions of the B—$\ddot{C}$l: and B—$\ddot{B}$r: groups as compared with those for the

C—$\ddot{C}$l: and C—$\ddot{B}$r: groups.

The refractions calculated for the electron groups in the hexafluorides of sulfur, selenium, and tellurium show an interesting progression. The value for S—$\ddot{F}$:, 1.95, is larger than the value for C—$\ddot{F}$:, 1.83, by no more than might be expected because of the larger size and consequent lower electron constraint in the sulfur atom, while that of the Te—$\ddot{F}$:

group is practically identical with that of the fluoride ion (Table 2.1), although the stability and low boiling point of tellurium hexafluoride are properties not ordinarily associated with substances whose molecules contain polar bonds. The value for Sn—C̤l̈: is only slightly lower than that given for the chloride ion in Table 2.1.

Fajans and Joos[9] calculated the refractions of various molecules and anions in which oxygen atoms or ions were held by a single central atom or ion. The structure was arbitrarily separated into a single central ion surrounded by $O^=$ ions, which might, perhaps, better be called oxygen octets. The refraction of the central ion was obtained from the values in Table 2.1 directly or calculated from them by extrapolation. Subtraction of this refraction from that of the entire ion or molecule left the contribution of the $O^=$ ions, which, when divided by the number of $O^=$ ions, gave the refraction per ion. The values thus obtained are given in Table 3.2 opposite the arbitrarily assumed central ion.

TABLE 3.2. REFRACTION (R_D) OF THE OXYGEN OCTET BOUND BY A CENTRAL ION

C^{4+}	4.08	N^{5+}	3.66				
Si^{4+}	4.42	P^{5+}	4.05	S^{6+}	3.65	Cl^{7+}	3.32
Ti^{4+}	6.3						

It is evident that the tightness of binding increases with increase in the ionic charge and decreases with increase in the size of the ion. The refraction of the oxygen octet when bound to Ti^{4+}, 6.3, is close to the value for the $O^=$ ion, 7, while the other values are not far from that of the octet linked to carbon, a linkage which is regarded as typically nonpolar. The virtually ionic value for the oxygen bound to the titanium is consistent with the looseness of the structure indicated by dielectric behavior (Sec. V.9).

In general, it is evident that, as would be expected, the effects of nuclear charge and of volume upon the refractions of electron groups in molecules are similar to their effects upon ions. Although the atomic, bond, and electron-group refraction values which have been obtained generally reproduce surprisingly well the observed molar refractions, variation in intramolecular forces produces some variation in the refractions, as evidenced, for example, by the difference between the refraction 34.61 found for 2,2-dimethylpentane and the value 34.25 for the isomeric 3-ethylpentane.[10] Bauer and Fajans[11] cite an atomic refraction of lead of 17.31 calculated from the molar refraction of tetramethyl lead as com-

[9] K. Fajans and G. Joos, Z. Physik, 23, 1 (1924).
[10] C. P. Smyth and W. N. Stoops, J. Am. Chem. Soc., 50, 1883 (1928).
[11] See footnote 2, Sec. 1.

pared to a value 20.05 from that of tetraisopropyl lead, and a variation in the atomic refraction of fluorine from 0.63 to 2.03. These variations are exceptional, but a very small alternation, about 0.03 cc., in the refraction of a CH_2 group along the chain of a paraffin molecule has been observed,[12] and an analogous alternation in values of the CH_2 increments in tetraalkyl compounds of group IV elements has also been observed.[11] In calculating the molar refraction of a substance by means of atomic, bond, or group refractions, the effect of the usually small variations in these values can be minimized by making the necessary additions to or subtractions from a dependable refraction value for a closely related substance.

The effects of intermolecular forces on refraction are very small. The approximate constancy found for the refractions of the components of a number of mixtures[13] seemed to indicate a negligible effect of the molecules upon one another. The refractions of binary mixtures of heptane with butyl chloride, butyl bromide, ethyl iodide, heptyl bromide, ethyl alcohol, and butyl alcohol were measured and compared[14] with the value of R_{12} calculated from an equation analogous to that used for the calculation of the total polarization P_{12} [Eq. I(10.6)]. The average difference between the observed and calculated values of R_{12} was of the same magnitude as the probable error in the measurements. In other words, R_1 and R_2 were constant as far as could be measured throughout the mixtures, which means that in these liquids the contribution to the polarization of the electronic shifts induced in a molecule is practically independent of the surrounding molecules. Evidently, any variation in the hydrogen bonding of the alcohols which may accompany change in concentration affects the refraction by amounts too small to be apparent. Small departures from the additivity implied in the calculation of the refraction of the mixtures have been reported for some mixtures of nonelectrolytes, and the fairly considerable departures caused by strong ionic fields have been discussed elsewhere (see footnotes 1 to 3 for Sec. 1). Increases of 0.005 to 0.015 per cent per degree[14] in the molar refractions of liquids with rise of temperature and of about 1 per cent with vaporization have been attributed by Fajans and his coworkers[11] to loosening of the electronic binding due to increase in intermolecular distance. Similar increases in the total polarization of nonpolar liquids have been observed and tentatively explained in the same way[12,15] (Sec. III.1).

[12] R. W. Dornte and C. P. Smyth, *J. Am. Chem. Soc.*, **52**, 3546 (1930).

[13] See S. Smiles, "The Relation between Chemical Constitution and Some Physical Properties," Longmans, London, 1910, p. 244.

[14] C. P. Smyth, E. W. Engel, and E. B. Wilson, Jr., *J. Am. Chem. Soc.*, **51**, 1736 (1929).

[15] C. P. Smyth and W. N. Stoops, *J. Am. Chem. Soc.*, **50**, 1883 (1928).

The polarizability of an anisotropic molecule, though averaging out to a constant value α_0, is actually different in different directions in the molecule, so that as an approximation

$$\alpha_0 = \frac{b_1 + b_2 + b_3}{3} \tag{3.1}$$

where b_1, b_2, and b_3 are the molecular polarizabilities along three mutually perpendicular axes.   The polarizability of the molecule may be described in terms of a polarization ellipsoid having semiaxes b_1, b_2, and b_3.   Not many values of b_1, b_2, and b_3 have been determined because of the difficulties involved in making the necessary accurate measurements.   Their determination from the combined use of refractive index, Kerr constant, and the degree of depolarization of light have been described by Stuart,[16] who has tabulated many of the values.

When a beam of light passes through a transparent dielectric material, a portion of it is coherently scattered by the periodically changing dipoles induced by its electric field.   The light coherently scattered by isotropic molecules is completely polarized, while that scattered by anisotropic molecules is only partially polarized.   The degree of depolarization Δ of the scattered light is the ratio of the intensity I_p of the light vibrating parallel to the direction of the incident beam to the intensity I_r of the light vibrating perpendicular to it:

$$\Delta = \frac{I_p}{I_r} \tag{3.2}$$

It may be shown[16] that

$$\frac{10\Delta}{6 - 7\Delta} = \frac{(b_1 - b_2)^2 + (b_2 - b_3)^2 + (b_3 - b_1)^2}{(b_1 + b_2 + b_3)^2} \tag{3.3}$$

The relative intensities I_p and I_r can be measured by means of an analyzer.

When anisotropic molecules are placed in an electric field E, enough orientation occurs to produce a very small difference between the refractive index n_p for light whose electric vector is parallel to the electric field and the index n_r for light with its electric vector perpendicular to the field.   The so-called Kerr constant is given by

$$K = \frac{n_p - n_r}{n}\frac{1}{E^2} \tag{3.4}$$

It can be shown that, for gases,

$$K = K_1 + K_2 \tag{3.5}$$

[16] H. A. Stuart, "Molekülstruktur," Springer, Berlin, 1934, chap. 6.

where $\quad K_1 = \dfrac{\pi N_1}{15kT} \dfrac{n_\infty - 1}{n - 1} [(b_1 - b_2)^2 + (b_2 - b_3)^2 + (b_3 - b_1)^2]$

$$= \frac{3}{2kT} \frac{(n_\infty - 1)(n - 1)\Delta}{\pi N_1(6 - 7\Delta)} \tag{3.6}$$

$$K_2 = \frac{\pi N_1}{15k^2 T'^2} [(m_1{}^2 - m_2{}^2)(b_1 - b_2) + (m_2{}^2 - m_3{}^2)(b_2 - b_3)$$

$$+ (m_3{}^2 - m_1{}^2)(b_3 - b_1)] \tag{3.7}$$

where m_1, m_2, and m_3 are the components of the permanent dipole moment of the molecule in the three axes of the polarization ellipsoid. These equations contain too many unknowns to be solved for a completely unsymmetrical molecule, but, for molecules possessing some symmetry, the number of unknowns may be sufficiently reduced to render them useful. In the early days of dipole-moment investigation, Kerr-effect measurements seemed to offer a promising, though somewhat difficult, method of obtaining additional information along similar lines, but the development of the electron-diffraction method provided a more attractive means of studying molecular asymmetry.

The values of a number of polarizabilities selected from a large table given by Stuart[16] and from a small revised table given by Denbigh[8] are tabulated below.

TABLE 3.3. POLARIZABILITIES ($\times 10^{25}$) OF MOLECULES

Molecule	b_1	b_2	b_3
N_2	24.3	14.3	14.3
O_2	24.3	11.9	11.9
N_2O	53.2	18.3	18.3
CO_2	41.0	19.3	19.3
CS_2	151.4	55.4	55.4
SO_2	54.9	27.2	34.9
CCl_4	105	105	105
$SnCl_4$	137.7	137.7	137.7
CH_3Cl	54.2	41.4	41.4
$CHCl_3$	66.8	90.1	90.1

In the absence of other information, these values would serve to establish the approximate isotropy of the CCl_4 and $SnCl_4$ molecules, the linearity of the N_2O, CO_2, and CS_2 molecules, the nonlinearity of the SO_2 molecule, and the symmetry of the CH_3Cl and the $CHCl_3$ molecules about an axis.

The largest polarizability tends to be in that direction in the molecule in which the largest number of highly polarizable atoms lie. The reason for this has been demonstrated by Silberstein in an approximate calculation.[16] In a molecule consisting of two atoms of polarizability α_1 and

α_2 with a distance r between their centers, the dipole moments induced in atoms 1 and 2 by an electric field E acting in the direction of r will be

$$m_1 = \alpha_1 \left(E + \frac{2m_2}{r^3} \right) \tag{3.8}$$

$$m_2 = \alpha_2 \left(E + \frac{2m_1}{r^3} \right) \tag{3.9}$$

$2\alpha_1 m_2/r^3$ is the dipole moment induced in atom 1 by the polarized atom 2, and $2\alpha_2 m_1/r^3$ is the moment induced in atom 2 by atom 1. If E acts in a direction perpendicular to r, the two induced moments are

$$m_1' = \alpha_1 \left(E - \frac{m_2'}{r^3} \right) \tag{3.10}$$

$$m_2' = \alpha_2 \left(E - \frac{m_1'}{r^3} \right) \tag{3.11}$$

Since
$$m_1 + m_2 = b_1 E \tag{3.12}$$
and
$$m_1' + m_2' = b_2 E = b_3 E \tag{3.13}$$

it is evident that b_1 must be larger than b_2 and b_3. Combination of Eqs. (3.8) to (3.13) gives equations for b_1 and b_2 in terms of α_1, α_2, and r. For a molecule of two like atoms, $\alpha_1 = \alpha_2$, and the equations simplify to

$$b_1 = \frac{2\alpha_1}{1 - 2\alpha_1/r^3} \tag{3.14}$$

$$b_2 = b_3 = \frac{2\alpha_1}{1 + \alpha_1/r^3} \tag{3.15}$$

For the H_2, N_2, O_2, and Cl_2 molecules, Eqs. (3.14) and (3.15) give values of r in fair agreement with the values calculated from viscosities and critical data.[16]

The excess of b_1 over b_2 and b_3 in the CS_2 molecule is unusually great because of the large polarizabilities of the sulfur atoms. b_2 and b_3 are larger than b_1 for the $CHCl_3$ molecule because they lie parallel to the plane of the very polarizable chlorine atoms.

Several investigators[17-20] have treated bonds as polarization ellipsoids. Denbigh[8] has concluded that in diatomic hydrides the longitudinal polarizability of the bond is proportional to r^3, while, for bonds not involving hydrogen, it is given approximately by $b \times 10^{25} = n^2 r^6 + 6.0$, where n is the bond order and r its length in angstroms.

4. Atomic Polarization. Sections 2 and 3 have considered the polarization arising from the movement of electrons relative to atomic nuclei,

[17] E. H. L. Meyer and G. Otterbein, *Physik. Z.*, **32**, 290 (1931); **35**, 249 (1934).
[18] G. Sachse, *Physik. Z.*, **36**, 357 (1935).
[19] C. H. D. Clark, *Nature*, **138**, 126 (1936).
[20] S. N. Wang, *J. Chem. Phys.*, **7**, 1012 (1939).

P_E. The present section will consider the polarization arising from the movement of atomic nuclei relative to one another. Changes in dipole moment result from such movements through changes in the lengths of bonds and of the angles between them and through the bending or twisting of polar groups relative to one another. For an independent one-dimensional oscillator, Coop and Sutton[1] obtain by classical methods [cf. Eqs. (1.6) and (1.7)]

$$P_A = \frac{N e_i^2}{9\pi m_i(\nu_i^2 - \nu^2)} \tag{4.1}$$

where ν_i is the natural vibration frequency of an effective mass m_i carrying an effective charge e_i and ν is the frequency of the deforming field. If the restoring forces are assumed to obey Hooke's law, the natural vibration frequency is

$$\nu_i = \frac{1}{2\pi}\left(\frac{f_i}{m_i}\right)^{1/2} \tag{4.2}$$

where f_i is the force constant. Equation (4.1) may, therefore, be written

$$P_A = \frac{4\pi N e_i^2 \nu_i^2}{9 f_i(\nu_i^2 - \nu^2)} \tag{4.3}$$

When ν is small in comparison with ν_i, as is the case in radio-frequency measurements, Eq. (4.3) reduces to

$$P_A = \frac{4\pi N e_i^2}{9 f_i} \tag{4.4}$$

For a vibration along a bond of length l, $e_i = d\mu/dl$. Calculations[2] from infrared intensity measurements show that, for HCl, HBr, CO, CO_2, NH_3, and CH_4, e_i is less than one-fifth of the charge of an electron, while f_i is so large that the calculated P_A is less than 0.1 cc. per bond. For changes in the angle between two dipoles of moment μ_i, Coop and Sutton[1,3,4] obtain

$$P_A = \frac{4\pi N \mu_i^2}{9 V_i} \tag{4.5}$$

where V_i is the force constant of bending. This equation reproduces in a roughly quantitative fashion a number of observed atomic polarizations,[1] some of which will receive comment after the values have been tabulated.

Atomic polarization values have been determined by various methods. For nonpolar substances, fairly accurate values are given by the differ-

[1] I. E. Coop and L. E. Sutton, *J. Chem. Soc.*, 1269 (1938).
[2] J. H. Van Vleck, *Phys. Rev.*, **30**, 43 (1927); see also footnote 7, Sec. 1.
[3] A. E. Finn, G. C. Hampson, and L. E. Sutton, *J. Chem. Soc.*, 1254 (1938).
[4] N. R. Davidson and L. E. Sutton, *J. Chem. Soc.*, 347 (1939).

ence between the total polarization P and the molar refraction extrapolated to infinite wavelength, $P_E = R_\infty$, given by Eq. (1.17). For polar substances, P_A has occasionally been estimated as the difference between the polarization of the solid, for which P_M is taken as zero, and P_E. Chapter V has shown that P_M is rather commonly not zero unless the measurement is made at a temperature far below the melting point. The difficulty of accurate density measurements on the solid and the possible errors in dielectric-constant measurement resulting from voids make extremely uncertain this determination of P_A as a usually small difference between two relatively large quantities, one of which is subject to a large probable error. The method most generally employed for P_A is to plot P against $1/T$ for a vapor, which, according to Eqs. I(9.1) and (9.2), gives a straight line with the intercept at $1/T = 0$ equal to $P_E + P_A$. Subtraction of P_E from the value of the intercept then gives a value of P_A which contains a large error resulting from the uncertainty of the long extrapolation to obtain the intercept. The better measurements on gases give a fair idea of the magnitude of P_A. The application of this method to dilute solutions gave much too high values for most substances because of the variation of solvent effect with temperature and was soon abandoned.[5] The absorption and reflection coefficients of a number of liquids have been measured[6] for radiation in the far infrared obtained by the method of Reststrahlen and have been used to calculate the refractive indices. The corresponding values of $P_E + P_A$ are of the same magnitude as those obtained by the polarization-temperature method for gases. Another possible method is to calculate P_M from the dipole moment value obtained by means of microwave spectroscopy and subtract it and P_E from P for the gas to get P_A. This method still involves the large error in a small difference between two large quantities. For example, if $P = 50 \pm 0.5$ cc. and $P_A = 2$ cc., the error in P_A would be 25 per cent even if P_E and P_M were without error, which the latter, particularly, certainly is not.

Table 4.1 gives values of atomic polarizations for nonpolar and for polar molecules, the latter giving little more than the orders of magnitude involved. The values for the nonpolar liquid hydrocarbons from pentane through dodecane are taken from the measurements of Smyth and Dornte[7] on the straight-chain hydrocarbons and from those of Smyth and Stoops[8] on the isomers of heptane. The values for the heptanes are selected as the lowest and the highest among those for the nine isomers. The values for these liquid hydrocarbons should be correct to ± 0.1 cc.,

[5] C. P. Smyth, *J. Chem. Phys.*, **1**, 247 (1933).

[6] C. H. Cartwright and J. Errera, *Proc. Roy. Soc. (London)*, **154A**, 138 (1936).

[7] R. W. Dornte and C. P. Smyth, *J. Am. Chem. Soc.*, **52**, 3546 (1930).

[8] C. P. Smyth and W. N. Stoops, *J. Am. Chem. Soc.*, **50**, 1883 (1928).

but relative to one another they should be somewhat better than this, good enough to warrant listing an approximate average increase of 0.07 per CH_2 group. Most of the other values are calculated from the values of the deformation or distortion polarization and the refraction tabulated for gases by Maryott and Buckley.[9] Values for several organic molecules containing fluorine are taken from the measurements of Gibbs, Di Giacomo, and Smyth.[10,11] When values of the refraction at infinite wavelength were not available for use as P_E, approximate values were estimated by subtracting from R a very rough empirical correction for the dispersion, amounting to 4 per cent of its value at or near the D line. This was done only when the values of P_A were so large as not to be seriously affected by the small resulting error in P_E. Many more values for polar molecules might have been included, but they would have been even more approximate than the listed values, which, for the polar molecules, show only the rough magnitudes. The few values listed as zero are not actually zero but merely indistinguishable from it by these dielectric measurements.

The very small atomic polarization values of the aliphatic hydrocarbons are consistent with the smallness of the moments associated with the H—C bonds, and their increase of about 0.07 cc. with the addition of a CH_2 group to the chain is qualitatively consistent with the increase which should accompany increase in the number of bonds available for bending and stretching by the external field. The values calculated from infrared-dispersion measurements on liquids by Cartwright and Errera,[6] for hexane, 0.26, benzene, 0.55, and carbon tetrachloride, 1.2, are somewhat smaller than those in Table 4.1, but their values for toluene, 0.9, carbon disulfide, 2.3, ethyl ether, 3.2, and propyl ether, 5.0, are consistent with those in Table 4.1. Their values for several alcohols, 1.9 to 4.6, are much larger than the negligibly small values found from dielectric measurements, which are, however, too inaccurate to be listed. Their value for water, 3.2, is much larger than the value 0.3 in Table 4.1, which, based on vapor measurements, is very approximate but certainly much smaller than 3.2. As the higher value is qualitatively consistent with the values of ϵ_∞ given by microwave measurements (Chap. IV), it would appear that the hydrogen bonding in the liquid may be a factor.

The atomic polarization values for the hydrides of boron, silicon, and phosphorus contain large probable errors, which may be responsible for their unexpectedly large values. The small values for the diatomic mole-

[9] A. A. Maryott and F. Buckley, Table of Dielectric Constants and Electric Dipole Moments of Substances in the Gaseous State, *Nat. Bur. Standards Circ.* 537, 1953.

[10] J. H. Gibbs and C. P. Smyth, *J. Am. Chem. Soc.*, **73**, 5115 (1951).

[11] A. Di Giacomo and C. P. Smyth, Unpublished measurements.

TABLE 4.1. ATOMIC POLARIZATIONS (cc.)

Nonpolar Molecules				Polar Molecules			
CH_4	0.1	Acetylaceto-nates		CO	0	NO	0.2
				COS	1.5	HCl	0.5
C_2H_6	0.1	$Be(C_5H_7O_2)_2$	28	CS_2	2	DCl	0.6
C_3H_8	0.3	$Al(C_5H_7O_2)_3$	43	$COCl_2$	2	HBr	0.2
C_4H_{10}	0.6	$Cr(C_5H_7O_2)_3$	44	CF_3Cl	4	HI	0.3
C_5H_{12}	0.61	$Fe(C_5H_7O_2)_3$	59	CF_3Br	3	H_2O	0.3 ± 0.3
C_6H_{14}	0.67	$Th(C_5H_7O_2)_4$	77	CF_3I	6	H_2S	0.6 ± 0.6
C_7H_{16}	0.77	Hg	0	CF_2Br_2	2	NH_3	0
$(C_2H_5)_3CH$	0.76	SiH_4	2	C_2F_5Cl	6	NF_3	2
$(CH_3)_2CHCH_2CH$	0.96	Si_2H_6	4	CHF_3	3	PH_3	2
$(CH_3)_2$		B_2H_6	1.5	$CHCl_3$	4		
C_8H_{18}	0.78	BF_3	2.3	CH_2Cl_2	4	SO_2	1
C_9H_{20}	0.78	BCl_3	4	CH_3F	3	$SOCl_2$	4
$C_{10}H_{22}$	0.96	$C(NO_2)_4$	4	CH_3Cl	2	SO_2Cl_2	5
$C_{11}H_{24}$	1.03	CF_4	2.7	CH_3Br	1		
$C_{12}H_{26}$	1.11	C_4F_8 (cyclic)	6	CH_3I	2		
$-CH_2-$	0.07	$n\text{-}C_5F_{12}$	8.5	C_2H_5F	2		
C_2H_2	1.3	$i\text{-}C_5F_{12}$	8.5	C_2H_5Br	3		
C_2H_4	0.4	CCl_4	2	$(C_2H_5)_2O$	3		
C_6H_6	1.5	SiF_4	5.4	$(C_4H_9)_2O$	4		
$p\text{-}C_6H_4(CH_3)_2$	(3)	$TiCl_4$	5	$C_6H_5CH_3$	1		
$p\text{-}C_6H_4Cl_2$	3.2	$GeCl_4$	8				
$p\text{-}C_6H_4(NO_2)_2$	9	$SnCl_4$	11				
$p\text{-}C_6H_4O_2$	9	$SnBr_4$	8				
$2,5\text{-}(CH_3)_2\text{-}1,4\text{-}C_6H_2O_2$	10	SnI_4	(7)				
$2,5\text{-}Cl_2\text{-}1,4\text{-}C_6H_2O_2$	9	PF_5	6.2				
Tetramethylcyclobu-tanedione	10	SF_6	5				
$p\text{-}C_6H_4(CN)_2$	13	SeF_6	5.5				
$(CN)_2$	8	TeF_6	8				
$p\text{-}NCC_6H_5NO_2$	9	$HgCl_2$	6				
		$HgBr_2$	7				
		HgI_2	7				
		SO_3	2				
		OsO_4	5				

cules are probably indistinguishable in these measurements from the very small values calculated from the bond stretching.[2] This approximate agreement removes what appeared to be a serious discrepancy between theory and experiment in the early work on atomic polarization. It also indicates that the principal source of atomic polarization is the bending rather than the stretching of the bonds, which is consistent with the generally much smaller force constant for bending than for stretching.

The values for the polar halogen-substituted methanes and ethanes are so approximate that they merely indicate P_A to be about 2 ± 1 when one C—X dipole is present and from 3 to 6 when three or more C—F and C—Cl dipoles are present. The planar triangular molecules of BF_3 and BCl_3 differ from CF_4 in P_A by no more than the considerable probable errors. For the four molecules carbon tetrafluoride, perfluorocyclo-butane, perfluoropentane, and isoperfluoropentane, the values of P_A are roughly proportional to the number of C—F bonds present, suggesting an approximate additivity like that in the hydrocarbons. The P_A values of the AX_4 and AX_6 molecules tend to increase with increasing size of the central atom A, which gives greater A—X bond moment and more space for the displacement of the X atoms. For the SnX_4 molecules, P_A decreases with increase in the size of X, which decreases the space for the displacement of the halogen atoms and may decrease the Sn—X bond moment slightly. The atomic polarization of tetranitromethane, 4, is smaller than would be expected from the large moment associated with the nitro group and the large P_A value 9 of p-dinitrobenzene, but this can be accounted for by hindrance of the displacement of the nitro groups by steric repulsion caused by their size and by the negative charges on the oxygens. For a tetrahedral molecule, AX_4, Coop and Sutton[1] write [cf. Eq. (4.5)]

$$P_A = \frac{16\pi N\mu^2}{9V} \tag{4.6}$$

where μ is the A—X bond moment and V is the force constant for the bending of any one bond relative to another. From P_A and estimated values of μ, they calculate reasonable values of V.

Coop and Sutton[1] treat the linear cyanogen molecule as containing two independent oscillators, each two-dimensional, and use Eq. (4.6) with $\mu = 3 \times 10^{-18}$ and $V = 2.93 \times 10^{-12}$ erg per radian² per molecule to calculate $P_A = 11.4$. They point out that, if the C≡N moments were reduced from 3 to 2.5 by mutual induction, the calculated P_A would be 8, as in Table 4.1, while the calculated value 11.4 is close to that for p-dicyanobenzene, where the C≡N moments are too far apart to be appreciably affected by mutual induction. Table 4.1 shows that when two large dipoles like those associated with the carbonyl, nitro, and cyanide groups point in opposite directions on opposite sides of a molecule, an atomic polarization not far from 10 cc. occurs.

The constancy with temperature of the polarizations P of the metal acetylacetonates in Table 4.1 shows that the molecular moments are zero. This means the mutual cancellation not only of the large metal-oxygen bond moments but also of the presumably smaller bond moments in the acetylacetonate group, the attachment of one of which to the central metallic ion is shown below:

$$CH_3C=O$$
$$CH \qquad M$$
$$CH_3C-O$$

The large number of polar bonds in these molecules gives opportunity for large atomic polarization by bending of the bonds, and it seems possible that an appreciable amount of polarization may arise by stretching of the bonds as in an ionic solid.

It is evident that atomic polarization depends upon the size and number of dipoles in the molecule, upon the bending of the bonds containing or attached to these dipoles, and, usually only to a very small extent, upon the stretching of the bonds. Although increase in the number of polar groups tends to increase the atomic polarization, the latter is not, in general, an additive quantity. When, however, the molecule is increased in size by the addition of groups similar to several of those already present, as in the hydrocarbon and fluorocarbon series, the atomic polarization may be a roughly additive quantity. As it has no direct relation to the electronic polarization, it cannot be a constant fraction of the latter as assumed in some empirical corrections used in the calculation of dipole moments. In view of the similarity in the atomic polarizations of compounds containing similar oscillating systems, the unknown atomic polarization of a molecule can be very roughly estimated from those for somewhat similar molecules.

NAME INDEX

SUBJECT INDEX

The only substances listed in the Subject Index are those discussed by name in the text. Many other substances are listed by name or formula in the tables of related substances and a few of these are mentioned only by formula in the text. They may be located easily by reference to the tables and the adjacent text.

Absorption coefficient, 60, 217
Absorption index (see Absorption coefficient)
Acetaldehyde, 289, 291
Acetamide, 87
Acetic acid, 85, 305, 309
Acetone, 103, 114, 133, 289, 293
Acetonitrile, 133, 281, 282
Acetophenone, 294
Acetylacetonates, 421, 422
Acetylene, 268
Acetylenes, 267
Acetylenic nitriles, 283
Acrolein, 283, 291, 292
Acrylonitrile, 282, 283, 292
Activation, entropy of, 63
    free energy of, 63, 119, 120
    heat of, 63, 119, 120
Air, 75
α-Alanine, 401
Alanylglycine, 401
Alanylleucylglycine, 402
Alcohols, 29, 89, 105–111, 113, 301, 302, 419
Aldehydes, 289–293, 319, 325
Alkali metal halides, 135, 136, 138, 248, 377
Alkyl bromides, 78, 115–121, 163, 268
Alkyl halides, 113, 269
Allene, 263
Allyl chloride, 278, 283
Allyl isothiocyanate, 285
Aluminum bromide, 377, 379, 380
Aluminum chloride, 379, 380
Aluminum iodide, 379
Aluminum stearate, 378
Amines, 309–311, 319
p-Aminoacetophenone, 328
ϵ-Aminocaproic acid, 394
p-Aminonitrodurene, 328

4-Aminopyridine, 342
Ammonia, 133, 155, 231, 310, 311, 375, 376
Ammonium bromide, 155, 156
Ammonium chloride, 155, 156
Ammonium dihydrogen arsenate, 195
Ammonium dihydrogen phosphate, 195
Ammonium iodide, 155, 156
Ammonium salts, 156
n-Amylacetylacetylene, 297
n-Amyl alcohol, 83, 105, 109
i-Amyl bromide, 177
t-Amyl chloride, 162
n-Amylpropiolaldehyde, 292
Aniline, 89, 112, 319, 329
Anilines, 326, 327
Anisol, 322
Anisotropy, 35, 136
Anomalous dispersion (see Dispersion)
Anthracene, 133
Antimony, 390
Antimony trichloride, 248
Aqueous solutions, of electrolytes, 90–95
    of nonelectrolytes, 89, 90
Arc plot, 104
    (See also Cole and Cole plot)
Arsenic, 390
Arsenic trifluoride, 248
Arsine, 155, 375
Association, molecular, 80, 108
Atomic polarization, 13–15, 136, 222, 416–422
Attenuation constant, 217
Azides, 319, 323
Azimuthal angle, 356
Azulene, 267

Bakelite, 188
Barium titanate, 195–198

431